TRACES OF THE TEMPLARS

Temple Manor, Strood, one summer morning.
On the way from London to Dover.

TRACES OF THE TEMPLARS

by

George F. Tull

The King's England Press

1999

Traces of The Templars
is typeset by Moose Manuscripts
in 12pt Garamond and published by
The King's England Press, Cambertown House,
Commercial Road, Goldthorpe, Rotherham, S63 9BL.

ISBN 978-1-872438-16-0

Digitally printed on demand by
The King's England Press
in association with Lulu.com

In memory of my old friends, Sir Frederick Bowman and the Revd. John A. Lloyd.

'Uniting in themselves the two most popular qualities of the age, devotion and valour, and exercising them in the most popular of all enterprises, the protection of the pilgrims and of the road to the Holy Sepulchre, they speedily acquired a vast reputation and a splendid renown'
- Charles G. Addison, *The History of the Knights Templars*, p. 3.

'The Templars found themselves heroes almost overnight and donations poured in ... Europe was thrilled by these holy warriors who guarded the throne of David. The brethren loved Outremer, the Holy Land, nearest to the kingdon of God.'
- Desmond Seward, *The Monks of War*, pp. 24 and 27.

Non nobis Domine, non nobis, sed Nomini Tuo da gloriam.
- The Templars' battle cry.

Temple Manor, Strood. Only the left-hand part of the building was known to the Templars. (See plan, p.48.)

Temple Manor, Strood. The Undercroft.

INTRODUCING THE TEMPLARS

It is a commonplace thought of hagiographers that God raised up certain saints at particular times to do a particular work (e.g. the founding of a religious order for the ransoming of captives from the Saracens). In similar fashion it may be said of the Knights Templar that they were founded at a crucial time in the history of western civilisation, which was exactly the right time for the work which they undertook. Few historians today would deny the truth of that, even if they preferred a more cautious approach to the subject. Had it not been for the Crusades and a renewed interest in the Holy Land, there might never have been an Order of the Temple.

St. Bernard of Clairvaux, in his usual rhetorical style, admitted that he did not know whether to call them monks or knights; the same question has puzzled writers since. It need not worry us however; we can see how they combined both roles, without ourselves having to pass value judgements.

Not long ago the word 'mediaeval' was used indiscriminately as a term of opprobrium, a synonym of backward and outdated, or worse. More sensible views prevail now that mediaeval studies enjoy a new popularity. If in our own day there is a resurgence of interest in the Templars, may it not spring from a deeply felt need of their virtues? There is certainly nothing outdated about their standards of self-discipline and chivalry, of service given nobly and willingly.

It is hoped that readers will not be irritated by the number of unproved speculations in this book. Where certainty is not possible, a reasonable theory seems better than a blank and more helpful to our understanding. The object of this book is simply to present in readable form as much information as can be found about the Templars in England. To claim more than that would be presumptuous.

To help form a clear picture of Templar England it has seemed desirable to sketch in some general background, which has necessitated going beyond our national boundaries. Without this, the result would be somewhat incomplete.

Before going further it must be admitted - to the lasting shame of our fellow-countrymen - that a determined effort was made to erase the name and memory of the Templars from our history, though they had served Christendom faithfully and well and died the death of honour. Even now it is not easy to find accurate information; many questions have to remain unanswered, though there has been a certain revival of interest among historians during the present century. Tracing the spread of the Templars in England is a journey from the known to the unknown. Unfamiliar places hesitantly reveal their lonely secrets, forgotten for six centuries and more. Few artefacts have been preserved; one may search in vain for such things in our museums.

Not all the sites have been excavated. Those which have, mostly from the 1890's onwards, have yielded a limited amount of data to add to our information from other sources, mainly on the size of the preceptories and their buildings. The fact that remains of buildings are extremely scanty has one advantage, namely a welcome lack of commercialism. Ultimately, it is not a matter of how much is left, but rather how much we can mentally reconstruct, without romancing or unintentionally falsifying the truth. The historian's task is difficult, but not impossible.

In distantly surveying what may be called 'the Templar period', we become aware of various human qualities. It was undeniably one of the most exciting periods of history, a time of idealism, high endeavour, generosity; but also, ultimately, of frustration and tragedy, all of which affected England and still affect us today.

No attempt has been made to construct a complete 'roll of honour'. Even if it was feasible, such a list of names would have little use or meaning for the reader. Of the English Preceptors, only a few names are known. A list of the Masters in England does exist and contains eighteen names (see Appendix 1) some of which feature in these pages.

In the author's opinion we have no reason to be critical of the Templars. For one thing, it is not possible for us to know all the facts concerning them; the interval of time between their lives and our own is too great. (Even the illustrations of the Templar habit are to some extent conjectural and drawn centuries later.) We cannot consider ourselves to be better than them or superior in our achievements, given our changed circumstances. Yet perhaps the gap is not so unbridgeable after all. They are our fellow-countrymen who have known many of the same experiences as ourselves. We can at least try to understand and be appreciative of their labours in field, fold and hall. Such an effort is not without its reward.

History is rather like solving a puzzle. Here we can endeavour to assemble the pieces, but without complete success, since we cannot replace what has been lost altogether. What has been spared of that great age of church and cathedral building is all the more precious as primary sources of our knowledge. Architecture and archaeology undoubtedly help.

When one climbs up the Western Heights at Dover, walks what seem like endless miles through Sussex lanes to Shipley, or comes almost unexpectedly on the great church at Temple Balsall, one is not conscious of romantic dream heroes imagined by some well-intentioned Victorian author: even less does one think of finding a mythical hoard of treasure buried by the Templars. The excitement of discovery is real enough, but the search is both practical and historical. In this quest there is no place for fiction. The authenticity of the known sites is not in doubt, nor the kind of men who inhabited them. There is scope for increased knowledge of the subject, otherwise the present book would not have been written.

To the serious student of Templar history there is no substitute for visiting as many of the relevant sites as possible. Most of all, it is worth making the journey to Templecombe in Somerset and obtaining the key of the village church, near the railway station, to gaze at an anonymous and venerable portrait of Christ. That is a pilgrimage unlike any other. Perhaps we are drawn into their company to appreciate more closely the spiritual ethos of the order which formed a bridge between monasticism and the knightly ideal: the poor soldiers of Christ.

It is worth mentioning that the Order began to exist about the same time that St. Thomas Becket was born in the City of London. The whole of the Templar era was a time when many notable Saints were active in building up Christendom: St. Francis, St. Dominic, St. Thomas Aquinas and those, like St. Felix of Valois, St. John of Matha and St. Peter Nolasco, whose special concern was the welfare and ransom of Christian captives. All this activity proceeded parallel to the work of the Temple. Christendom was in a state of creative ferment, developing doctrine and putting faith into action.

As a frontispiece it is appropriate to select a summer view of Temple Manor, Strood, since this was the first site I visited in connection with this study of Templar England.

Some six or seven years of research led to the production of this book. Travel, observation and photography have played a great part in its make-up. The author does not claim to have covered every aspect of so large a subject, nor does he wish to view the Templars through an academic microscope. No amount of scientific analysis would help our appreciation. Various disciplines are involved here: history, religion, ecclesiastical art and architecture, and so on, but ultimately it is a personal response.

THE START OF THE ORDER

The foundation can be dated 1118-19, the place was Jerusalem, the city known as the navel of the world, but from the first, the Templars were predominantly French. Hugh de Payens, a knight from Champagne, together with Godfrey de Saint Adhemar, a Fleming, and seven friends from northern France, decided to join forces and form a chivalrous brotherhood with the charitable aim of protecting pilgrims to the Holy Places from Saracen attacks. King Baldwin I of Jerusalem gave them for their headquarters part of the Royal Palace, the former al-Aqsa mosque in the Temple enclosure, the supposed site of the Temple of Solomon, from which they took their title.

Of course, the Order did not come to maturity, fully organised, overnight. It developed from that beginning: nine knights tested and proved, holding firm their vocation. In 1128 the Council of Troyes approved the Templar rule submitted to it by Hugh de Payens, the first Master of the Temple. In 1139 the Templars obtained a Papal Bull from Innocent II, confirming their rule and extending their privileges, which included exemption from paying tithes. Most importantly, they were placed directly under the Pope's own jurisdiction and were therefore independent of any bishop's control, thus occupying a strong position of advantage within the Church, an elite corps of 'fighting monks'.

With the blessing of St. Bernard of Clairvaux and the full approbation of the Church, the Order increased and spread rapidly. Its existence largely coincided with the twelfth-century Renaissance, a time of strong religious fervour and of course, the Crusades and the new ideal of Christian knighthood. Altogether the time was propitious. Much romantic nonsense has been written about chivalry: the bitter hardships and privations of service overseas must surely have outweighed the sense of adventure, although the idea of venturing for Christ in defence of Christendom was a strong motive and these were men of courage and enthusiasm.

Though technically not Crusaders, the Templars are known to have been involved as the right wing of crusading armies in the field. The upper half of their banner was black and the lower half white, indicatring that they were black and terrible to their enemies, but fair and favourable to the friends of Christ. This closely guarded banner was called Beauseant, (more correctly spelt Baucent) that is, 'the piebald standard'.

The dynamic Br. Hugh, the first Master (who, like his companions, was a veteran of the First Crusade), came to England in the summer of 1128 and here he was 'well received by all good men'. With ten years of experience, the Templars were still new enough to attract attention. Many consciences were aroused by first-hand news of the Holy Land. The time was ripe for action and everywhere men flocked to join the Order. In Stephen Howarth's opinion, 'the unique attraction of the Templars was their combination of war and worship, the two passions of the age'.[1] Thus the Order was planted here in fertile soil and began to develop quickly. When the Master returned to the Holy Land in 1129, it was at the head of a valiant band of Knights Templar, drawn principally from England and France. It is said that he took 300 new brothers with him.

What began as a distinctly French enterprise soon achieved an international (or supra-national) character and was as much at home in England as in other countries. The Norman invasion had prepared the way for such a movement, with a renewed sense of law and order, a genius for administration and military conquest, now harnessed to the ideals of crusading.

Two distinguished Templar chaplains of a later century, Pierre de Bologna and Renaud de Provins, left a written statement in 1310, that 'the Order of the Temple was created and founded in the charity and love of a true fraternity and that it is ... close to God the Father, a saintly and immaculate Order free of all taints and vices, in which there is and always will be in vigour a regular doctrine, a salutary observance, and that as such it is approved, confirmed and honoured by numerous privileges of the Holy See.'

Before proceeding to discover what we can of the Templars in England, it is reasonable to look in some detail at the organisation itself, to understand how it worked. The structure of the Order, unique in Christendom, its way of life, customs and ethos were determined by the Rule, which exists in Latin and French versions. To examine this at length would be tedious to the reader, but the Templars' Rule can be summarised readably. It is for the most part based on common sense, backed up with scriptural injunctions. The Rule, freely accepted by grown men, provided for every eventuality. Therein lay the strength of the Templars.

Theirs was a lifestyle alien to many Christians today.[2] The austere St Bernard, having had a direct hand in forming their constiutions, was understandably prejudiced in their favour. In his *Exhortatio ad Milites Templi*, he gave a vivid and moralistic picture of the early Templars as he saw them. His description is worth quoting at length.

'Their first rule of life is obedience. There is no superfluity in diet or dress; necessity only is consulted. They live a common life, in sobriety and pleasant conversation, without the distraction of wives and children. Like the early Christians, the whole company have one purse, one heart and one soul, and study nothing so much as to submit their individual wills to that of their superior. They neither sit idle nor wander for their pleasure, they earn their bread by mending their arms and clothes. No insolent, or immoderate laughter are heard among them. They abhor chess and dice; they neither hunt nor hawk. They detest actors, sorcerers, jongleurs, licentious songs and gay spectacles as vanities, falsehoods and follies. They cut their hair short, never adorn, seldom wash themselves; they pride themselves on neglected hair, soiled with dust and burnt by the sun and the hauberk ... wonderful and strange it is to see them at once as gentle as lambs and as bold as lions. I hardly know whether to call them monks or knights, wanting as they do neither the meekness of the monk nor the courage of the knight'.

St. Bernard died in 1153, by which time the Templars had been established in England about 25 years. Later, Jaques de Vitry, Bishop of Acre, a frequent companion of the Knights on their military expeditions, echoed St Bernard's words, describing them as 'lions in war, gentle lambs in the convent'. Templars stand among the least sentimental of men, with no illusions about 'other faiths', or who were the enemies of Christ. Without theological complexity, they professed their belief in 'one God, one faith, one baptism and one Catholic Church'. Here was 'a perpetual sacred soldiery' not numerically vast by modern standards, but a fully professional army sworn to fight only in the name of Christ.

It may be wondered how far the powerful influence of St. Bernard continued to direct their spirit and shape their attitudes. The young Burgundian knight who found his vocation at Citeaux was able to observe the first 35 years of the Temple's growth and he never lost his interest in it. Almost the last letters he wrote were on its behalf. Despite his constantly poor health, he had been the best recruiting agent of the Order, and, spurred on by his words, many knights enrolled in the new brotherhood. He emphasised that if they were faithful, the Poor Soldiers of Christ were sure to reap their reward. They could fight in the full assurance that, whether they lived or died, Christ had them in His safe keeping. So it was that St Bernard recommended the brethren to remind themselves of this on the battlefield by use of the ejaculation, 'Living or dead, Lord, we are Thine'. Their dedication was continually re-affirmed. Courage became habitual.

This new soldiery was ready to face up to any call of duty. Fulk, Count of Anjou, who became King of Jerusalem, was associated with this social community whom he described as 'the reverent knights, whose whole life is spent in combating for God, both in body and soul, and who, despising all worldly things, are daily prepared for martyrdom'. Though the Templars were never short of sufficient recruits, that first vigorous growth was their most glorious period, when their ideals were fresh and untarnished.

That Catholic faith for which they lived and died was the common heritage of Christendom, as yet undivided in the west. To improve our perspective it will be helpful to quote some fine words of G. K. Chesterton[3], which seem to go to the heart of the matter:

'Europe became Christendom ... Christianity did *not* conceive Christian virtues as tame, timid, and respectable things. It *did* conceive of these virtues as vast, defiant, and even destructive things, scorning the yoke of this world, dwelling in the desert, and seeking their meat from God.'

If this could apply to ordinary, less militant Christians, how much more so to the Knights of the Temple, venturing all for Christ. Those strong positive virtues, besides being signposts on the pilgrimage of life, were also spiritual weapons to be used in the redemption of the Holy Land. Idealism was in the air, perhaps more than at any other time in history, inspiring many deeds of charity and bravery and sometimes impetuous actions; the very stuff of true chivalry. Of no other age could it be asserted more truthfully that the Catholic faith was the dominating fact in the history of Europe.

As will be seen, the qualities of renunciation, poverty, endurance, disipline and courage, all blend and harmonise in the most perfectly natural way in the ideal that the Rule set before each Templar. Nothing could be more affecting or more Christian than the promise made in the name of the Order to the new brother on the day of his reception - a reward of bread and water, the habit, suffering and labour in plenty. The Order would offer no more than it could be certain to give. They were encouraged to expect a spiritual reward, that which Christ promised to all faithful disciples: 'Rejoice and be glad, for great is your reward in Heaven'. In the 'Directory' which St Bernard wrote for the Templars, *De Laude Novae Militiae, ad Milites Templi,* (The Praises of the New Knighthood) he stated explicitly that the Knight Templar who devotes his strength and his arms to the service of God can become a saint by being a good soldier.

They were to form a religious army of occupation - men whose vocation it was to patrol and defend the Holy Land and keep peace there, as far as humanly possible. The major part of St Bernard's little treatise 'is devoted to showing the Templars how they can make their residence in Palestine the occasion of a particularly deep life of prayer and meditation. It does not seem that they fully appreciated St Bernard's programme.'[4]

Although he had been willing to lead a new Crusade, he did not set foot in Christ's country and so had no personal knowledge of conditions there. His advice was somewhat theoretical. Templars were practical men, whose immediate actions would need to be based on military stratagem. At least there was no doubt of the ideals which they had chosen. Human nature did not always correspond with grace, as the theologians would say, but those first ideals did not fade from sight and continued to inspire new recruits to the Order. Indeed such powerful ideals were necessary if men were to undertake this unremitting service. St Bernard was exactly the right moral leader to proclaim them.

Confusion was rife in Christendom and beyond its borders. There was a great need for level headed men, who would hold such principles tenaciously in all circumstances. The New Knighthood did not fail in its response. Acceptance of the Rule brought its members together and made them a strong and well respected body.

It must be obvious that wherever a number of men are living together as a community, there must needs be a strong sense of obedience. The individuality of human nature, if not curbed, can soon lead to anarchy and the wreck of true community life. For the Templars, with their dedicated purpose, it was doubly important to present a united front at all times.

Templars were not the only men of their time with high standards. John of Salisbury (1115-80) Bishop of Chartres, summarisied the functions of knighthood in phrases which accord perfectly with Templar ideals: 'To protect the Church, to fight against treachery, to reverence the priesthood, to fend off injustice to the poor, to make peace in your own province, to shed your blood for your brethren and, if needs be, lay down your life.' If all secular knights had accepted some such principles of conduct, St Bernard would have found less to criticise. Those who joined the Temple certainly needed those qualities of chivalry though they did not always practise them.

No-one could say that, in this period, knighthood (properly understood) was an easy living. With the Templars, this was made clear right from the start, in the Rule and in the solemn ceremony in which the new Knight was initiated into a family of brothers, having left his own natural family and severed his claims to any inheritance. There was no romantic glamour, no trappings of finery; such things would be a hindrance to him. Even his mental image of Christ would have been that of the thorn-crowned Redeemer suffering in abject poverty, rather than of *Christus Rex* reigning eternally in glory.

Renunciation, unfashionable and distasteful to many Twentieth century minds, cannot be side-stepped in this connection. It is essential to our understanding of the Templars. To arrive at the truth about their character, we need to see that considerable sacrifice was demanded of every recruit before he could join the ranks of Christ's Poor Soldiers.

Although the spiritual life remained (as it always is) essentially private, the communal life of the Templars contained little else that could be regarded as private. All that could be renounced was renounced. The rights of the individual were subjected to the corporate whole. Putting off the old life, so as to put on a new life, was a familiar Christian concept signifying Baptism, the Resurrection, and also the entrance into the monastic life: hence the putting aside of fine worldly clothes, not for any dramatic effect, but in symbolic renunciation of worldly prospects. (One is reminded of the action of St. Francis of Assisi in 1207.)

The shields carried by Templars did not display any personal heraldry. All such family pride had been discarded, as part of that great act of renunciation on joining the Order. Henceforth they could only glory in the Cross, which was at the heart of their discipline, their devotion and their whole life. Likewise custody of the senses was an integral part of the Templars's spiritual formation and their system of discipline.

The element of renunciation was central to the ceremony of admission of a new Knight, held symbolically at night when all was quiet and only the altar candles dispelled the darkness. Three times the candidate was asked if he wished to enter the Order of the Temple, thrice he affirmed his wish and thrice begged humbly for bread and water. Three times he was warned solemnly;

'You must entirely renounce your own will -
And entirely submit to that of another -
you must fast when you are hungry -
Keep watch when you are weary -
Thirst when you would drink'

Such language seems to echo some of the New Testament warnings of the risks inherent in Christian discipleship and the paradox of losing one's life to find it.

Such total renunciation brought a spiritual reward 'sharing in the good works which have been done by the Order since its foundation and such as shall be done to the end.' Templars were relieved of the trivial side of knighthood, the pastimes of secular knights and all the fiction of 'courtly love.' The only material compensation promised them was 'bread and water, the poor mantle of the Order and much hardship and labour'. All starkly honest. In fact, daily life in the Preceptories was a good deal more pleasant, affording a much more palatable diet than the basic bread and water.

The 'poor mantle of the Order' was likewise a fundamental token of poverty, replacing the fine garments and rich display of a secular knight, which were so much castigated by St.Bernard. The mantle or cloak, to use a more familiar word, was similar in form to the priest's cloak, but white for professed Knights. As an outer garment it was a protection in severe weather and at night.The material was coarse, emphasising the hardship and their monastic simplicity and dependence on the Order for everything. We do not know whether the distinctive dress of the Templar Knights was derived from that first adopted by their founders in the Holy Land, or modelled on the Cistercian monks' habit. Tbe point is not of importance. Spiritually the all-embracing white cloak was to remind the wearers 'to commend themselves to their Creator by a pure life.' There was a constant emphasis on cultivation of the virtues. The integrity of the Templars was a significant factor in their developent. They were real monks, not only in name, and a pure life was as essential as personal poverty and obedience. Certainly the monastic life as they understood it was complete in itself, apart from the priesthood and different from it, a point which will be returned to later. The poor mantle, while losing none of its inherent symbolism, won its own prestige as the livery of Christ's soldiers.

Their white cloak remained plain without any cross until Pope Eugenius III in 1146 authorised the Templars to wear a red cross on the chest, as a symbol of the martydom to which they were constantly exposed, from the enemies of the Cross. There could be no mistaking the Knights Templar riding along in those austere cloaks. From their foundation there were within the Order three classes of Templar: Knights, the fully professed members, who bore the brunt of active service in the Holy Land and formed the main part of the Order (though not numerically the largest part); Squires[5] or Sergeants who, besides being warriors, acted as grooms and bailiffs; and Servitors - farm workers, etc. There were also Confreres (corresponding to tertiaries) who could be married. These Associates of the Temple were often wealthy noblemen.

From 1172 priests were admitted to serve within the Order as chaplains and clerks. Since priests were not allowed to bear arms, their work was religious, medical and non-military.

By 1250 it was an essential condition not only to be a knight, but 'a knight's son, or the descendant of a knight on his father's side', before a man was admitted as a professed Knight Templar. Thus the concept of an elite Christian chivalry was fostered.

The splendid phrase attributed to Pope St. Gregory VII, 'I would rather risk my life to deliver the Holy Places than govern the universe', could well be taken to epitomise the aspiration of every true Templar. Their motto, 'In hoc signo vinces' (In this Sign conquer) asserted their determination to triumph through the Cross.

It is said that, on account of the red cross on the habit, they came to be popularly known as Red Cross Knights or less accurately, Red Friars, but the latter is most likely a corruption from Red Cross Freres[6].

The first Templars were ministered to by Canons Regular. Later, as the Order increased, secular (i.e. diocesan, non-monastic) priests acted as chaplains. Those priests who joined the Templars would also have come from the secular clergy. Their status was something akin to that of an army chaplain.

The Chaplains accompanied the Knights in action, so that the two aspects of the Templar vocation were closely linked. The Guardian of the Chapel (*Custos Capellae*) had charge of the portable chapel and its contents, which were always carried by the Templars into the field. This portable chapel was a round tent, which was pitched in the centre of the camp; the quarters of the brethren were arranged round it, so that they might in the most convenient manner assist at Mass and the Divine Office and thus fulfil the religious duties of their profession wherever they were. The chapel was at the heart of the camp more exactly than at home in the Preceptories. There was also a military reason for this position, namely that the chapel might be better defended in case of a sudden attack on the camp.

The Chaplains of the Order took precisely the same vows as the rest of the brethren and enjoyed no privileges above their fellows[7]. They remained in complete subjection to the Knights, for they were not allowed to take part in the consultations of the chapter unless they had been enjoined to do so. This underlines the point that the Temple was primarily a lay Order and necessarily so, since the duties of Priesthood and Knighthood were incompatible. For its military role to be effective, the Knights had to be in the majority and not under the control of priests (except with regard to spiritual matters in a normal confessor/penitent relationship).

This lay control was not derogatory to the priestly ministry. In fact the Chaplains shared the hardships and the glory of their brethren in action equally. Priests also acted as almoners of the Preceptories (*Praeceptoria*). Br. Jacques de Molay, the last Grand Master (from 1295), who previously had been the Master in England, declared that 'no other Order had...priests who celebrated Mass with more dignity and devotion.' He was certainly in a position to know, after a lifetime in the Order.

Not being choir monks, the brothers would not have made a special study of the plainchant. They would have committed to memory the most frequently sung chants of the Mass. Polyphony had begun to develop in this period, but it would not have been possible for the small shifting populations of the English Preceptories, (who were probably unmusical anyway), to sing in two or more parts except perhaps on the rarest occasions. At Christmastide they would have sung together cheerfully to honour Christ's Nativity. Not all their waking hours were spent in church.

In England the non-combatant servitors formed the most numerous section of the Order. These men, who spent their lives cultivating the soil and the spiritual life, would have seemed very similar to other monks. Cistercian brothers provide the nearest parallel, except that they normally inhabited larger monasteries. Manual work was an essential part of their Rule. The servitors, even if they never set foot outside their native land, were none the less linked with the Knights campaigning in the Holy Land. The Preceptories depended on them for much of the daily maintenance, as well as work on the farms. This is not to say that they enjoyed hard manual work; they chose to do it for love of God, rather than working for a feudal lord. In the Order they enjoyed a steady life with few anxieties. They were less mobile than the Knights, since their function was different. As will be apparent from the variety of occupations needful to the Preceptories, the servitors had considerable responsibility. The Order could hardly have existed for long had its membership consisted solely of Knights (as at the beginning), since their means of support would have proved insufficient. Rural work was essential.

In humble obedience, the Templars all accepted the authority of the Church and of the Order as the basis of their profession. Without that there would have been no firm foundation.

An American scholar, Thomas W. Parker[8], has made a more precise classification of the Templars, breaking down membership of the Order into (at least) five distinct classes of brothers, which existed in England as elsewhere:

(1) The Knights (fratres milites, frères chevaliers), who alone wore the prestigious white mantle with a red cross;

(2) The sergeants or esquires (clientes, frères sergens), who were required to be of free birth. They wore black or brown mantles. Associated with them were the frères casaliers, who managed and protected the smaller Templar houses and farms;
(3) Chaplains (fratres capellani, frères chapelains);
(4) Manual labourers, artisans, domestic servants and farm workers (frères de métier), the most numerous as mentioned above;
(5) Associates (affiliés) and temporary members (fratres ad terminum, frères a términe), who might join the Order during the last years of their lives.

These reflect the varied and complex levels of the social scale. Such categories do not add much to our knowledge of the Templars.

The Order of the Temple was no more democratic than the Church itself. Under the Pope, to whom he promised perpetual obedience and fidelity, the authority of the Master of the Temple was absolute; he was 'Magnus Magister' and ranked as a sovereign prince ruling his subjects, though still styled 'Brother'. In practice his authority belonged more to the office than to the man. Some ruled for only a short while after election, in uncertain conditions, but continuity of command was maintained. It was possible to abdicate from the Mastership and to resign from the Order.

No one was compelled to join the Templars, quite the reverse; entrance to the Order was not made easy, they were discouraged, so that only those men whose vocations seemed strong and sure were accepted. Good physique and a beard were not sufficient qualifications!

A new brother undertook four vows, namely obedience, chastity, poverty and the continual support of the Holy Land, only the last being peculiar to the Temple. Knights were not tied to the particular house where they were admitted. Their dedication was to the Order itself. This ensured their mobility and solidarity, both necessary qualities.

One cannot imagine anything more independent than the Order of the Temple - and legitimately so, but too much so for its own good. Within the empire of the Church the Templars served as the well-trained front line soldiers, continually ready to guard its physical boundaries against the infidels.

CY

Enw / Name

Katherine

Rhif Cerdyn / Card Number

80313367

Dyddiad / Date

04/04/2022

Ffoniwyd, Ebostiwyd / Phoned, Emailed

Voicemail

SUR

The overall management of the Preceptories was regulated by chapters composed of senior Knights. The ordinary chapters were held once a year (up to 1295, thereafter more frequently) at the different Preceptories, which the Master visited in succession. At these chapters new members were admitted into the Order, business was transacted, lands were bought, sold and exchanged, and presentations were made by the Master to vacant benefices entrusted to the Order. Many such rights of patronage were acquired by the Templars. In this way they could appoint clergy whom they deemed worthy and who would be helpful to the Temple. These chapters seem to have developed in form from the chapters held (much more often) in abbeys, though on a wider scale and also having something of the character of a visitation, with the Master taking the place of the bishop.

For a side-light on the chapters we may consult Matthew Paris' *English History*. Referring to the Old Temple outside the city of Paris, he wrote what must have been common knowledge at that time: 'At certain periods and terms, all the Cismontane Templars' (i.e. those north of the Alps) 'assembled at that place at their general chapter and found ample accommodation there; and it is necessary for them all to lodge in one building, for at their chapter they discuss their matters of business during the night.' Somewhat similar arrangements must have been made in England for their deliberations. Presumably they would be less likely to be disturbed at night, after the day's work was done.

That the English and French provinces were closely connected is shown by the fact that in 1161 the French Master could preside over a General Chapter of the English province held in London. This does not seem surprising bearing in mind the French origin of the Order less than half a century before; Norman-French, the 'lingua franca', was generally used by chivalric and educated classes on both sides of the Channel.

Here in England, the Master (*Magister Templi in Anglia*, as he was officially called in documents) exercised general supervisory powers over the officials, members and property of the Order in his province. This required him to be itinerant, travelling around between the Preceptories with his staff and attendants, living off the proceeds of the Order's estates. At other times he would have been resident at the Temple in London, where his responsibilities were equally great.

It was inevitable that the Master would be *ex officio* a highly influential person, to whom those in authority could turn. Examples are numerous. Thomas Becket (who became the illustrious St. Thomas of Canterbury), from the time when he was Chancellor of England, enjoyed close relations with the Templars and had lodged at the Paris Temple more than once. Br. Richard de Hastings was a good and reliable friend of his. Another Master, Br. Aymeric de St. Maur, was a faithful adviser to King John for over a decade and it seems probable that other Masters gave similar service. The same 'Br. Aymeric Master of the knighthood of the Temple in England' is mentioned in the preamble of King John's Magna Carta (1215), following the list of Bishops, as having advised the King to grant the Charter. It has often been remarked how the most competent Templars were chosen for important service outside the Order. We shall probably never know the full extent of their confidential service to kings and bishops. Reference will be made later to the instance of the Bishop of Lincoln's almoner, as showing the high esteem felt for the Brothers. It would seem that unpopular kings like John needed men of high principles whom they could trust.

The international status conferred by Papal authority on the Templars, almost from the start, meant that they could be impartial and act in this way as advisers and agents, without becoming involved as statesmen. There can be no doubt that such a moral position brought its own temptations and dangers to the spiritual life. Their prudence was respected, but they were also envied for their power.

In 1241 the King's almoner was Br. John, a Templar; while for some time prior to 1253 Br. Roger was almoner, but under such a grasping and unworthy king as Henry III, it was a thankless office. Though he was capable of generosity and devotion, the King had an uncertain temper and respected no one who opposed his avarice. The fact that Templars were so employed during this reign and that of his father argues strongly for their trusted character.

In the opinion of some scholars the Templar Rule was nearer to the Augustinian model than to the less flexible Cistercian Rule. The Temple was always a separate, self-governing Order, never linked to the Cistercians or any other of the older Orders. When they acquired the partially completed buildings of a Benedictine priory and its lands at Denny, this was unique, being the only English property transferred directly from another Order.

As will be seen, the usual mode of acquisition from the first was by donation from noble landowners, presumably from pious motives or partially so. This in itself indicates good relationships, upon which the Templars built. Without such practical help the Order could not have increased so rapidly, or achieved so much. Admittedly the work in England was supportive of the main raison d'etre of the Order, acting as a firm foundation.

Most of what has been written of the Templars by earlier writers concerns the serving Knights, which is by no means the whole story. The present study focuses rather more on those men whose lives were spent mainly in baking or brewing, caring for the horses and farm stock, or other manual work so essential and yet so anonymous. Such occupations are a recurring theme. Certainly a homely earthiness is to be expected of those who worked in the rural Preceptories, sons of the English soil with no other ambition than to do their duty faithfully according to the Rule.

These lower ranks (if one may call them that) would have been of mixed ancestry, drawn from the local population, while many of the Knights derived from Norman French families who settled here after the Conquest. There were possibly also descendants of Viking invaders in the north. Despite such different origins, their allegiance was to the same cause. The same Rule bound Knights and servitors alike.

There was much that was not mentioned by St. Bernard, nor specified in the Rule, because such needful occupations were taken for granted. All Religious houses had perforce to be self-supporting if they were to continue. Their only subsidies were endowments from charitable donors. In this respect the Templars were more fortunate than most, for they were given ample estates ripe for cultivation. From documentary evidence we learn how widespread were their territories. It will be obvious from the multiplicity of crafts practised, (from cutting wood for building, stonemasonry, every form of agriculture, transport and repair of their equipment, to banking), that collectively the Templars had to be more versatile than most other monks.

Taking all things into account we can build up quite a lively picture of Templar activities in this country, without getting too deeply involved in feudal customs of land tenure and labour. The manorial system had by now become established, the backbone of our rural economy. All was not easy going in England and the Templars here needed patience and tenacity to advance their organisation. Yet the strenuous years from 1138-42 saw the growth of the Templars' power in London, the extension of their possessions in the southeast and and south of England and in the southern midlands and also the beginning of their great influence in Lincolnshire and the north. If the unquiet reign of King Stephen saw them rooting themselves firmly in the land, in the relatively peaceful times which followed, they developed and consolidated their estates throughout England. They were energetic and competent landlords, and in a good and helpful sense, progressive. In new settlements like Temple Bruer, local custom and tradition were respected, but adapted to the existing conditions, modified, ordered and regulated to meet the requirements of the time. we can say that the Templars were both benefactors and beneficiaries on a large scale, in England and elsewhere.

Having mentioned the manorial system in relation to the Templars, it needs to be stressed that manor houses were not necessarily enormous buildings[9]. Strood Manor in Kent is a case in point of a manageable-sized house. The grant of a manor usually carried with it the advowson of the church, so that the Lord of the Manor (the Templars in the present context) could decide who was to be the priest of the parish. They could not, of course, usurp the bishop's canonical authority over his clergy. They had no authority in diocesan affairs and did not function within that system.

Much of our factual information derives from the documented results of an inquest (that is, a formal enquiry) made in 1185 at the command of Br. Geoffrey, the Master in England; this was a sort of Domesday process, restricted to certain aspects of Templar property.

'The number of manors, farms, churches, advowsons, demesne lands, villages, hamlets, windmills and watermills, rents of assize, rights of common and free warren, and the amount of all kinds of property, possessed by the Templars in England at the period of the taking of this inquisition, are astonishing.' (C.G. Addison)[10]

1185 was an important year in the growth of the English Preceptories. During it the Latin Patriarch of Jerusalem, seeking support for the hard pressed Christians there, came to England, visited the New Temple in London and consecrated its round Church. In the same year the Templecombe property was acquired and the Dunwich Temple was established. The Order was both expanding and consolidating its resources, a continuing process. Such growth in their first half century here was remarkable enough: more was to be added at various times in the thirteenth century.

Locally, the fortunes of the Order often depended on the benevolence of rich and powerful families. In Sussex, for example, the de Braose family who held the Castle of Bramber and who were largely responsible for creating the port of New Shoreham, when the River Adur was silting up at Old Shoreham. Seemingly from the highest motives, members of such wealthy landowning families as Philip de Braose donated estates to the Templars, leading to the establishment of new Preceptories. They settled where they had obtained land. It would be fanciful to imagine that they planned a complete network of properties covering the whole of England. A glance at the map shows the uneven distribution of the Preceptories. Nevertheless it is convenient for us to think of them as nationally organised under an administrative head, the Master in England (with Yorkshire a separate province). This was how they came to develop following their rapid growth early in the twelfth century.

The name 'Temple' has its special significance. Its use, coupled with the geographical place-name for each of the Preceptories, implies an overall anonymity; each is a member of the whole body, a segment of the Temple in Jerusalem where it all began. The fact that they would all possess the same spiritual character does not imply uniformity, as can easily be appreciated without looking further than the English Preceptories. There are diversities of function, but the same Order. It cannot be denied that there was an amazing variety of talents.

In charge of each colony of Knights was the Preceptor, literally a teacher or instructor responsible for the correct observance of the precepts or Rule, ideally an experienced Knight, able to instruct younger members of the Order and generally to direct the working of the Preceptory. Sometimes however, the Preceptor was a Chaplain or a servitor, though this would only have been so when there was a shortage of Knights available. In 1308 the English houses totalled 135, which included only 6 Knights and 11 priests; clearly a state of decline, even though these figures are open to question. It has been suggested that there were never more than 150 Templars in England at one time, of whom not more than a tenth were Knights. Certainly the majority would have been overseas while the Latin Kingdoms were in existence. Wastage of manpower was never a Templar failing.

In some places, Keele for example, the Templars made their mark on the countryside as pioneers, working at clearing and colonizing densely wooded land which they were given, before a Preceptory could be established[11]. They were also engaged in reclaiming barren marshland and fens. Not all the estates given to them were prime agricultural land, but they accepted the challenge. English Templars were also active creators of markets and market towns, though not always successfully. Their initiative seems to have been boundless, especially in relation to fund-raising projects.

Life in the Preceptories here, as in Outremer, was governed by the code of Mediaeval chivalry, that amalgam of military, social and religious commandments, which required its knights to be pious, patriotic, brave and obedient. Of course the penalties for serious breaches of the Templar Rule were most severe, but to maintain total efficiency, discipline was essential. They chose to live in a world of masculine virtues. The Templars enjoyed unique prestige, but the luxury of soft living was not for those who were called to 'endure hardness as a good soldier of Jesus Christ'. Such was not a virtue for its own sake, but a means to an end. If in the defence of the Holy Land we see them mainly as the warriors of Christendom, it is in the Preceptories that we see them as monks at home and to some of us (perhaps even most of us), that is the more endearing aspect of their life. At home they seem closer to us in our more familiar rural landscapes. Their mode of life can be imagined without difficulty.

Each dawn brought the same tasks, to be done regardless of weather conditions; the same routine of work and prayer which formed an ordered life, the work depending on what kind of farm it was and what was needed. Nothing spectacular in the daily life of the Preceptories, certainly nothing that the contemporary chronicler would find of 'news value'. Life went on as it always has on farms and in monasteries, everyone doing his appointed task, his own share in the rural economy. Yet with the Templars it was not just a self-contained enterprise; not just a matter of producing better crops than previously, or increasing the herds grazing in their pastures. The work was always orientated towards Outremer.[12] The end result was always to give assistance to the Order in the Holy Land, through their labours here. This was true of every one of the rural Preceptories across the length and breadth of England (and other countries). Each had to be as self-supporting as possible, providing for the daily needs - and more, a surplus to be sold.

There were many elements of the day when ordinary monastic discipline took precedence over the ways of secular knights. To cite the most obvious: eating two austerely ample meals each day on plain wooden tables, without the entertainment of a minstrel and his harp, and without female company. Templars did not engage in tournaments for pride, or for the favour of a noble lady. Such would have been vain show and folly. Each night after Compline, the great silence was kept strictly. The day followed a carefully organised timetable, as in all monastic houses, to ensure efficiency with a minimum of fuss. The Pope's elite army had to be efficient at all times. The Knights could not afford to be careless or unready. For some, the friendly silences of their woodlands, of the wide fields of young green corn and the untroubled night were a remote preparation for the menacing silence of enemy occupied territories.

To readers unfamiliar with the subject it may come as a surprise that the majority of Templars in England, at any time, were to be found in country districts. Yet this is obviously so from the evidence we have. The barns at Cressing, the fishponds and the rich farming lands around many of the Templar sites remain as a reminder. Away from the towns and built-up areas, the real English countryside has changed surprisingly little, despite changes in farming methods.

The Templars did own houses in towns and cities, for example in the city of Lincoln where they had fifteen tenants, but the bulk of their property was in rural regions. There, year in, year out, the orderly cycle of the countryside continued relentlessly and the Templars were part of it. The continuing harvest of the earth and the harvest of the spirit never ran contrary.

Through green, leafy ways, past farm buildings, churches and an occasional wayside cross, the Knights rode on their strong horses, with a deep interior joy. Life was good and there was much to inspire them. Life here in the English countryside was based on a true economy of the land, regulated by the natural rhythm of the seasons; of seedtime and harvest, Rogations and Lammas, which would correspond well with the monastic system. The combination of the small numbers of people involved and the size of the farms and other properties owned by the Templars can only mean that they worked hard in the rural Preceptories and were well organised. The fact that their enterprises prospered is a testimony to their genius for hard work and the generosity of their benefactors. As individuals vowed to poverty, Templars owned nothing; while corporately they became substantial property owners - as also did other monastic Orders at this time.

The manors which they owned produced rent for the Templars either in money, corn, or cattle and the produce of the soil. By the custom in some of these manors, the tenants were annually to mow three days in harvest, one at the charge of the house; and to plough three days at the like charge; to reap one day, when they should have a ram provided from the house, 8 pence, 24 loaves and a cheese of the best in the house, together with a pailful of drink. There were various regulations binding upon the tenants concerning the farm stock, which are not of particular interest to us.

Sir Edward Coke (writing as a legal historian) observed that the Knights were 'cruce signati' (marked with the cross) and as the cross was the ensign of their profession and their tenants enjoyed great privileges, they erected crosses upon their houses, to identify them, so that those inhabiting them might be known as tenants of the Order and thereby be freed from many duties and services to which other tenants were subject; 'and many tenants of other lords, perceiving the state and greatness of the Knights of the said Order, and withall seeing the great privileges their tenants enjoyed, did set up crosses upon their houses, as their very tenants used to doe, to the prejudice of their lords.' We know that this happened in Bristol and caused some trouble. Perhaps such an abuse was inevitable and the Order should not be held to blame. So serious did the offence become that the law was invoked to deal with such fraudulent claims. A statute of Edward I in 1285 prohibited unauthorised use of the Templar Cross on penalty of forfeiture of land to the superior lord or to the King.

As Lords of the Manor the Templars possessed rights which we do not associate with members of Religious Orders, including the provision of local justice.

Of course we have no authentic likeness of the Templar brethren to stir our imagination. Portraits were not painted of them and if there had been, they would have been fairly stylized. From an enlargement of the early seal, showing two Knights riding the same horse, we can learn nothing further: use and age have worn down this impression to resemblance of an almost ghostly apparition. So it is that artists are free to interpret as they will the data that we have of armed Knights attired in their white cloaks with the single adornment of a red cross. That was sufficient identity.

The *minnesinger* Tannhauser, as illustrated in the great German manuscript known as the Codex Manesse, where he is dressed as a Teutonic Knight, has been mistakenly supposed to be a Templar. Yet he plainly wears a black cross instead of a red one. This is unfortunate for our present purpose, since it is a particularly fine illustration from the Templar period.

It will be found that certain related themes recur constantly throughout the Templar story: the Cross, the Holy Land, the likeness of Christ. Just as the heraldic device on a shield disclosed, to those who could 'read' it, the bearer's identity or allegiance, even more so the Cross made abundantly clear to all, friend and foe alike, that here was an avowed warrior of Christ. The Christian symbol could never be misunderstood. The Knights were expected to be at all times worthy Cross-bearers.

With regard to the likeness of Christ, as revered in the Order of the Temple, William Anderson[13] has made an interesting speculation: '...there could have been amongst the Templars a mystical teaching founded both on the teachings of St. Bernard and on the possession of the miraculously preserved features of Christ and a ritual associated with it that could have influenced Dante if he were affiliated to the Templars...'

It may be noted that seals used by the Master in England in the late twelfth century show the *Agnus Dei* symbol of Christ, which had become identified with the Temple. Thus there was now a threefold recalling of Christ - the Cross, the likeness of His Face and the mystic Lamb. These symbols would speak only of Jesus Christ, as surely as did the Holy Land. Nothing could emphasise more clearly the Christocentric character of the Order.

An example of a small circular Common Seal depicting the Holy Lamb (facing towards the right) with nimbus, Cross and banner, can still be seen. The impression is clear. It was affixed to a Grant of land and a building by the Chapel of St. Werburgh in London, by Br. Haimeric de St. Maur, Knight, minister (i.e. Master) of the Temple in London, with the assent of his Chapter held at Temple Cowley, *circa* 1200. Over four centuries later (in 1684) the seal was remembered and copied on the entrance to Middle Temple Lane from the Strand. Here however it was reversed, so that the Lamb faces to the left. The tiny title deed, finely scripted and only ten lines long, is now kept in the Public Record Office nearby. Parchments were precious and so legal documents were often small. The symbolism of the *Agnus Dei*, 'the Lamb as it had been slain', is expressive of sacrifice, redemption and resurrection, the central points of the Christian Faith. There is no hint of unorthodoxy: the iconography derives directly from John 1, 29. [14]

From its inception as a small group of like-minded men, the Order was guided by motives that were religious and charitable, duty to God and to neighbour. At that crucial time in western Christendom the instinct to go on pilgrimage, chiefly to the Holy Places intimately linked with the life of Christ, was strong. This and the dangers encountered by pilgrims was the catalyst which started a series of Crusades and the Knights Templar, as we have seen. Their special attachment to the Holy Land and the defence of pilgrims was impressed like a seal upon the Templar character.

One further word about the Cross: so far as we can ascertain, the Templars' stone crosses generally had arms of equal length, in the manner of Consecration crosses. There seems no special reason why they did not favour the Latin cross so beloved of the Cathedral builders of that era.

If we have no portrait of a Knight Templar, we have that valued painting of Christ; and to the perceptive mind that says all. We cannot be totally certain of its connection with the Templars - yet why else should it have been found in such an otherwise unimportant village as Templecombe?

Having considered the background and ethos of the Templars and their way of life as envisaged in the Rule, we can now see what can be learned from a closer survey of the English Preceptories.

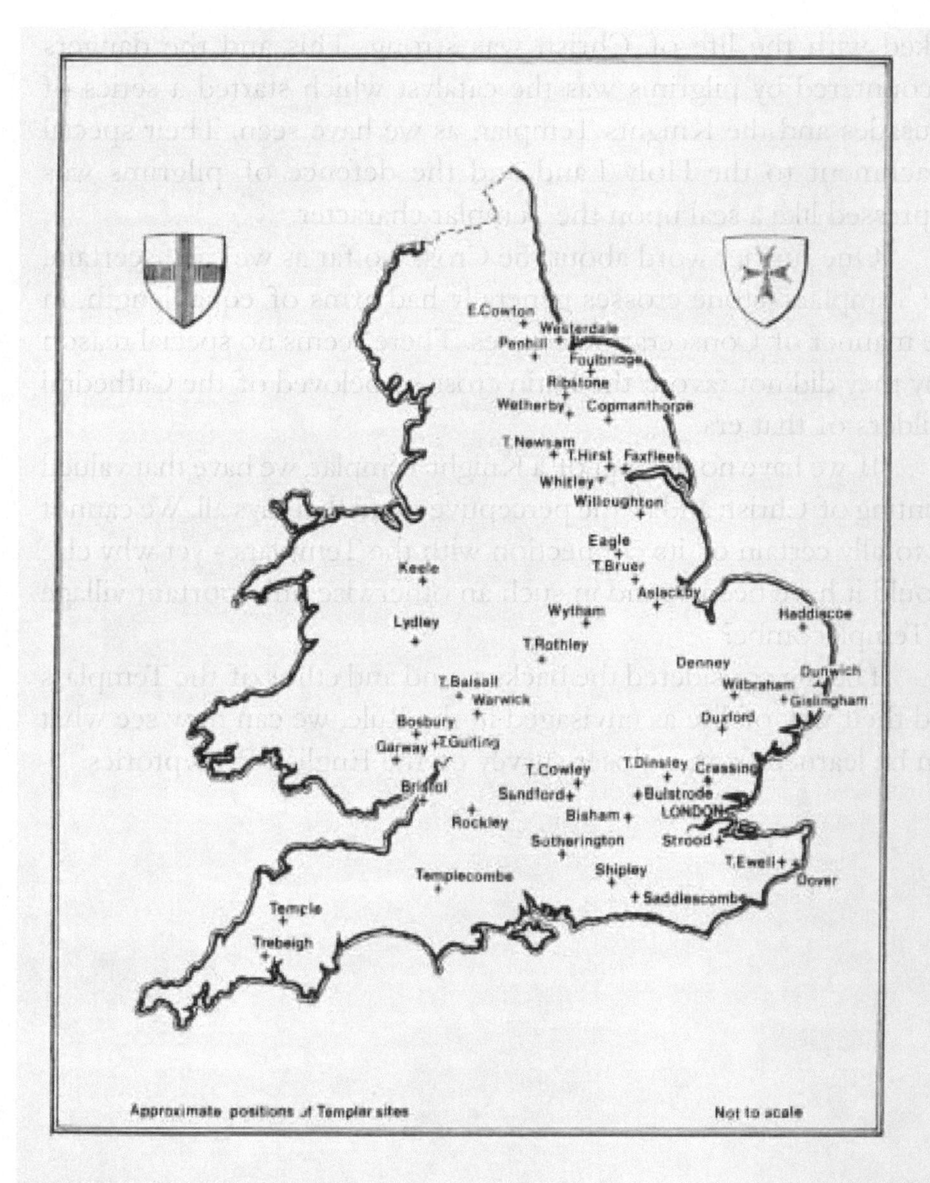

Plan to illustrate the distribution of sites throughout England.

THE ENGLISH PRECEPTORIES

The Knights Templar, although they perished tragically early in the fourteenth century, have left their name impregnated forever on the geography of England, and elsewhere. They owned a large number of farm properties and estates and were well endowed. Since they were officially known as the Order of the Temple, it is easy to identify the situation of many of their properties from the use of this name. Their corporate existence lasted only from 1118 to 1314.[15] After that their property changed hands any number of times, some of the buildings being greatly altered or even demolished, making it more difficult for us to trace their occupation.

They have no memorial, yet their memorial is everywhere, for throughout the counties of England they founded a well organised network of Preceptories. This tough body of men, which uniquely combined the high ideals of the monastic life and knighthood in a single Order, had to be mobile. By the nature of their calling, they were ready to move quickly to wherever they were needed. The Preceptories provided convenient staging-posts along the way. That is one way to look at it.

We are accustomed to think of the Templars as fearless crusaders, giving battle to the infidels, but this is not a properly balanced view; we need to consider also the peaceful aspect of the Templars. The rural Preceptories make us aware of the other side of their life: country pursuits and quiet meditation. Yet there is much more than that to be considered.

The Preceptories were established principally for managing the property of the Order. The community at each Preceptory consisted of some serving brethren, a chaplain to cater for their spiritual needs, and one or more Knights under the rule of the Preceptor exercising his command. After provision for their own maintenance and for hospitality, the surplus of revenue was sent to the Master, to be transmitted to the Holy Land. From the nature of their function as estate management centres, the Preceptories (outside London) were usually in fairly remote country districts, away from towns. Bristol, an obvious exception to this, due no doubt to its strategic position on the Avon, will be considered in some detail even though it may never have attained the status of a Preceptory.

From the map it appears that, apart from Dover and Dunwich which were established ports, the Templars avoided building their Preceptories anywhere near the sea coast of England; one assumes that this was with an eye to possible risks from invasion, piracy, or danger from storms. They knew the sea and its risks well enough.

It is not really surprising that the earliest rural foundations, Cowley and Cressing (both 1136) and Shipley (*circa* 1139), were all in the southern counties and within riding distance of London, the administrative centre. Of course we know more about London because of its importace. The Order would not have functioned nearly so efficiently in England without its headquarters in the capital, to consolidate its work. In a sense, the London centre was the mother-house, of which the other Preceptories were cells; all were based on the manorial system.

What is especially interesting about the Old Temple (*Vetus Templum*), off Chancery Lane in the parish of St. Andrew, Holborn, is that most likely it was founded during the visit of Br. Hugh de Payens to this country. Thus the London house had a direct link with the early days of the Order, when it was beginning to attract English recruits. When those original buildings became inadequate, they were sold in May 1161 (and confirmed by charter of Henry II) to Robert de Chesney, Bishop of Lincoln, to be the London Inn for himself and his episcopal successors, for one hundred marks and the payment of a small annual rent. It would seem from this that the Templars retained the freehold interest in the Old Temple after the erection of

Temple church: the Round, looking towards the west door. Some of the effigies can be seen in the foreground.

their *Novus Templum*. The point is of some historical interest since it is known that St. Hugh, Bishop of Lincoln, lay sick of a fever at the Old Temple, where he ultimately died on 16th November 1200, lying on a cross of blessed ashes spread on the ground and reciting the words of the *nunc dimittis*. One would like to think that he was attended by the Red Cross brethren. We do know that Br. Morinus, a Templar, had served as his almoner. St. Hugh's body was taken into the Old Temple Church for a Requiem.

Since they did not form part of any diocese, the English preceptories have been grouped according to counties, for convenience. Yorkshire, with its ten constituent preceptories, is a special case and is placed at the end.

The Templars had their own system of estate management, on feudal lines. The scattered manors and estates were grouped together into Bailiwicks, which were large administrative and fiscal units. The county of Kent was one, containing over a thousand acres of arable land, meadows, woodlands and market gardens. Another example was the Bailiwick of Warwick which extended from Shropshire to Northamptonshire, taking in part of Leicestershire, while the other part of that county came within the Bailiwick of Witham in Lincolnshire. It would be needlessly complicated for us to stick to this structure.

It is not so easy for us to realise how much the Templars were assisted by the natural resources then available in profusion. The proximity of running water led to its use as power for driving mills, as at Temple Guiting in the Cotswolds and in Yorkshire. Even the Fleet River, which in later centuries gained an unsavoury reputation, was of service to the Temple. Pasturage for cattle was plentiful and the virgin soil of newly cleared woodlands good for the cultivation of cereal crops, as at Keele.

We do not know where their stone quarries were. It seems that on their arrival in London, *(circa* 1128), they did not find any satisfactory quarry nearby, since the stone used at the Old Temple was brought over from France. Later, as they became established in different parts of the country, they would have utilised local stone where possible. There could have been no shortage of timber for the building of houses and barns. Most of what they needed was at hand, thanks to the generosity of wealthy donors of estates.

All of which seems to underline what was said by way of introduction, that the Order was founded at exactly the right time in history. The conditions were favourable, certainly so in England.

It was never inteded that the Preceptories should become vast monasteries where the same brothers would live permanently. In modern terms they had something of the character of transit camps, as far as the serving Knights were concerned. All that the order held out to its knights was an opportunity to flee from the sins of the world, to be the servants of God and the Order, to live in poverty and do penance. In this way the Preceptories could also be power houses of virtue. Life here was wholesome, but not cosy. Obviously we cannot generalise too much, as conditions were not static; they were certainly more spartan in the years when new foundations were being made and the Order's recources had still to be built up.

The houses of the English Province were variously situated, radiating out from the capital. It seems that the rural Preceptories at least were constructed and run on utilitarian lines, that is with a view to their use, rather than to impress visitors. 'Stately homes' belong to a much later period in history. The more remote Preceptories were separated by sizeable tracts of uninhabited country, much of it forest, the natural haunt of wild beasts, which the Templars were not allowed to hunt. But now, turning again to London: walk down Chancery Lane towards the River and you are in Templar country.

The New Temple, London.
Remaining fragments of the Knights' refectory

The New Temple, exterior of the Church,
showing the two stages of building.

LONDON

This Preceptory held a position of primacy in England, the Master of the London Temple acting as Provincial, governing 28 other Preceptories throughout the country. This unique position has already been commented on. Its history falls into two parts, which slightly overlap.

(1) THE OLD TEMPLE. The Poor Fellow-Soldiers of Christ and of the Temple of Solomon, to use their full name, (known in England as the Knights Templar), came to London *circa* 1128, settling first on a site outside Holborn Bars on land now covered by Southampton Buildings. Built as the headquarters of the province or *bailia* of England, the Preceptory had its garden and orchard, its boundary ditch and outbuildings, its cemetery and round Church built of imported Caen stone. The Old Temple had a short existence before becoming the Bishop of Lincoln's London Inn. There is some obscurity about the first half-century or so of the Templars' establishment here.

Stow, writing in 1598, stated that 'a great part of this Old Temple was pulled down in the year 1595'. Excavations were made *circa* 1905 and foundations thought to be of a circular church were discovered just south of Holborn. It was characteristic of the earlier Templars that they built circular churches (like chapter houses), to which a rectangular choir was added eastwards. Also discovered during this excavation was a cavity which may have been a pond or stew for keeping a supply of fish for the Knights in residence there. Seemingly nothing else was found.

Archbishop Theobald of Canterbury (d. 1161) granted an indulgence to persons visiting the Church of the Old Temple during Whitsuntide, when the Feast of Dedication was kept. (The year of the dedication is not known.) His successor, St. Thomas of Canterbury, confirmed this indulgence and transferred it to the New Temple, 'super Tamensem fluvium sita est' *circa* 1162.

(2) THE NEW TEMPLE. About that time, or before, the Templars, having been offered a large part of the property belonging to a crusader, Robert de Beaumont, Earl of Leicester, Justiciar and Steward of England, that lay between Fleet Street and the River at King's Reach, had moved from the Holborn premises to the site which we now know as the Temple, or more correctly, the New Temple, the larger and more convenient site on Thames-side. Now only the name, a fragment of the Refectory wall, usually unnoticed, and the Church (much restored) remain of this important establishment. Yet this is of great interest.

The Temple Church is the best known of the so-called Round Churches, built in imitation of the Holy Sepulchre of the Lord in Jerusalem. The Round, 58 feet in diameter, was consecrated in honour of the Blessed Virgin by Heraclius the Latin Patriarch of Jerusalem in March 1185[16]. This was possible because the Order was exempt from the jurisdiction of any diocesan bishop. The chancel, 82 feet long, was added in 1240, so what we see is as close as we can get to a complete Templar church of both styles - if we can forget the present furnishings. The architecture, combining rounded windows and simple pointed arches, and the modern stained glass (put in since World War II), evoke memories of the Knights. The Norman west doorway, despite some deterioration of the stonework, is very fine.

Cistercian churches have always been dedicated to Our Lady and since the Templars from their origin had much in common with the Cistercian brethren, it is not at all surprising that they shared this practice; nor was this in itself remarkable, for Marian dedications were already popular in England, the 'dowry of Mary'.

The Master lived at the London Temple, in addition to the Preceptor of London (also known as Procurator of the *Bailia* of London). The Preceptor was responsible for various properties in London parishes and Middlesex, besides a quay and mills on the

Fleet River close by. Of their tide mill we know that Henry II granted to the Temple 'a place in the Fleet, next to Castle Baynard, and all the course of water of the Fleet to make a mill'. This led to trouble and eventually in 1307 to litigation, since they put two gates in the mouth of the stream and began to reclaim the land, so that fewer ships could get in than formerly, owing to the altered levels of the water. To the west of the Fleet (that is on the opposite bank) was a wide strip of marshland known as London Fen, also belonging to the Templars, which they reclaimed.

The reclamation of otherwise marshy and unusable land and milling were necessary skills. Temple Mills on the border of Hackney Marsh, at Loughton on the Lea, was so called because the property belonged to the Templars who held a manor in Hackney. Temple Mills Lane and Mill Lane mark the site. Temple Mills Bridge, built by the Templars, crossed the River Lea. The material welfare of the Temple and its properties needed constant attention.

On the spiritual side was the Prior, whose duties were concerned with the Church and its services. Within the Church were Chapels of St. Nicholas and St. John, with a built-on Chapel of St. Anne (of which remains of the crypt survive, though inaccessible). The Temple was well provided with liturgical books, plate and vessels of silver, silver gilt, ivory and crystal, vestments, frontals and altar cloths. Among the relics kept there were two crosses containing fragments of the True Cross and a relic of the Holy Blood, as well as six pyxes and coffers containing other relics. It is said that one of the swords with which St. Thomas Becket was slain was preserved in this church. The Templars were well placed to obtain relics.

In 1231 Henry III endowed a chantry, to be served by three chaplains, with an income of eight pounds per annum. He, like several other monarchs, was favourably disposed towards the Temple and expressed a desire to be buried there 'with the brethren of the Chivalry of the Temple, expecting and hoping that, through our Lord and Saviour, it will greatly contribute to the salvation of our soul'. Queen Eleanor also provided for her burial here, but in neither case were their wishes followed.

William Marshall, Regent of England and Protector of the young King Henry III and a most famous knight, was associated with the Templars, being admitted on his deathbed in 1219. He was buried in the New Temple and his effigy, only slightly damaged, lies with those of other knights here in the Round, a tall man in armour[17]. Less honoured was Br. William de la More, the Martyr, who was the last Master of the Temple in England. He died a prisoner in the Tower of London in 1312 after much affliction.

Only six stone coffins are left in the stony, forlorn churchyard to the north of the Round, all that is now visible of the Temple burial ground. Since they are without legible inscriptions we cannot even be sure that these were Templar burials.

Returning to inside the Round - St. Bernard would no doubt have strongly disapproved of the series of 62 grotesque heads whose finely sculpted features display an astonishing variety of character, mostly anguished or doleful. Why they were placed there at all is puzzling. They could hardly have represented Knights Templar, living or departed. Perhaps we are given a preview of infidels unhappy at the Last Judgement? The question of their identity remains open.

In this part of London, outside the City itself but within the Bars, the Templar presence was very active, with much coming and going.[18] Not merely concerned with administrative duties, the Knights rode out from the Temple to their tilt yard in St. Clement Danes parish, for military exercises. A farrier worked conveniently close, shoeing the horses when required. In 1134 two forges, one in the parish of St. Brigide (Bride) and the other in the parish of St. Dunstan-in-the-West, were granted by Henry I to the Master and Brethren of the Temple. One forge, measuring 18 feet by 4 feet, was 'edified and sett' a little to the east of St. Dunstan's Church. The other, 15 feet by 9 feet, stood on the west side of that church. It has been suggested that, in addition to horseshoes, weapons for the Knights in Outremer may have been fashioned there. The grant of these forges ('Duarum Forgiarum in Fletestrete') was confirmed by Henry II at an increased rent in 1185. Thus the Templars' tenancy continued for upwards of half a century. It is thought possible that the Knights may have bought horses at Smithfield, the "smooth field" where there was weekly "a much frequented show of fine horses for sale", as noted by the chronicler William Fitzstephen (d. ?1190) in his *Description of the Most Noble City of London.* There was a constant need of horses for transport in so mobilean order.

Alongside the River extended a spacious pleasure ground for the recreation of the brethren, who were not permitted to go into the city without leave of the Master. This area, now the Temple Gardens, was also one of the places used for military exercises and training the horses. It is hard for us to imagine such a scene of brisk activity when we see these Gardens bright with daffodils in the Spring, oblivious of the heavy traffic rushing along the Embankment outside. There is still a sense of enclosure, of a place set apart.

Across the River was a large field of approximately 15 acres known as Fickettscroft, which may also have been used for military exercises. Associated with the London house, in addition to the mills already mentioned, were ponds, roads, gates and piers, all providing necessary services or revenue. According to the 1185 survey, the Templars held the advowsons of St. Clement Danes (from *circa* 1173) and the Chapel of the Holy Innocents, in the Strand (which later became St. Mary-le-Strand).

There are still some intangible links with the Temple north of the Thames not yet mentioned: it has been suggested, with some logic, that New Street, later known as Chancellor's Lane and now as Chancery Lane, was 'made by the Templars, possibly starting as no more than a trampled way through the fields, while the Templars were moving down from Holborn to their new quarters by the River.'[19] In 1313 this lane was called Newstrete of the Templars. Lincolns Inn Fields were marked on Mediaeval maps as Campus Templariorum (the field of the Templars).

Several times in the thirteenth century the Great Council (or Parliament) met at the New Temple, before Westminster became its regular meeting place. Sometimes the Master was summoned to attend the Great Council and take part in its deliberations, along with the Barons and Bishops of the realm. Simon de Montfort was a frequent visitor.

Mention has been made above of the pyxes and reliquaries belonging to the Temple, long since dispersed; to which may be added a note concerning one of them. The Burrell Collection in Glasgow has a tiny bronze panel showing three sleeping soldiers (holding long, Norman-type shields), almost certainly part of a group guarding the Holy Sepulchre. There is no inscription. It is known, somewhat ambiguously, as the Temple Pyx, because it is reputed to have been found within the London Temple. Several other sections exist elsewhere and it is possible that together they formed a box -shaped pyx or reliquary, of English or German make. The work has been dated between *circa* 1125 and 1150, so conceivably it belonged to the Templars.

Although war damage in 1941 caused some loss, previous centuries had already ravaged the church and its contents to a shameful degree. We learn that in the sixteenth century, in the body of the Church was 'a large blue marble inlaid with brasse', inscribed in Latin: 'Here rests Constance de Hover, formerly Visitor-general of the Order of the Temple in England, France and Italy.' Not a vestige of this monument remained when Charles Addison was writing his *History* in 1841. Regrettably, nearly all the archives of the Temple were destroyed by the followers of Wat Tyler in 1381, but most likely they would have disappeared anyway in a later age. Yet in spite of the losses, 'This great house of the unique order of vowed knights, shaggy of head and swarthy from the heat of the sun and the weight of their armour, (as St. Bernard of Clairvaux, who loved them, wrote), left behind them an ineffaceable impression on London.'[20]

Although from the Embankment we can see almost nothing of what was originally here, we can gain some impression of the extent of the Temple property. An excavation of the site might be informative, but extremely unlikely. Some limited excavation was done prior to 1951, in the Chapel under the south aisle; finds from which included a piscina.

If the spirits of the Knights should return here in these days, they would be amazed to find the Church obscured by later buildings of different character and, (stranger still), their Temple commemorated in the name of an Underground station! It all seems to be part of the irony of their history, to be immortalised almost unintentionally.

Reason should be given for having briefly referred to the east windows in the restored Church, the work of the stained glass artist Carl Edwards (*circa* 1954). It is surely unlikely that the Knights would have adorned their sanctuary with stained glass rather than plain windows to admit the light; yet what we see is appropriate to their memory. Here are little imagined glimpses of Geoffrey, son of Stephen, Amaric de St. Maur, Alan Marcel and Robert de Montfort (or Mountforde), four fairly early Masters of the Order in England, who would have known this Preceptory and lived here for a time. They are paired with Henry I, Stephen, Henry II and Henry III, four of the kings whom we encounter during the Templar period. These windows also incorporate the Temple seal of the *Agnus Dei.*

At a distance from the Temple, in the countryside to the northwest of London, were other properties. In 1237 the wealthy Otto Fitz-William, a goldsmith and Master of the Mint at London, granted the pre-Norman Manor of Lilleston (Lisson) to the Templars for a term of 40 years, repeating the gift without any limitation the next year and confirming it in 1240. In 1243 Hamo Fitz-Roger donated 80 acres of land with appurtenances in Lilleston, Hampstead and Hendon, probably lands lying along the Edgware Road. Other gifts of land in the neighbourhood were also made, in return for a share in the good works and prayers of the Temple. The Hampstead holding was of considerable value, its acreage being sown with wheat, winter wheat, peas and oats, besides meadow land. The name of Temple Fortune survives as a reminder of the Manor and estates in Hendon.

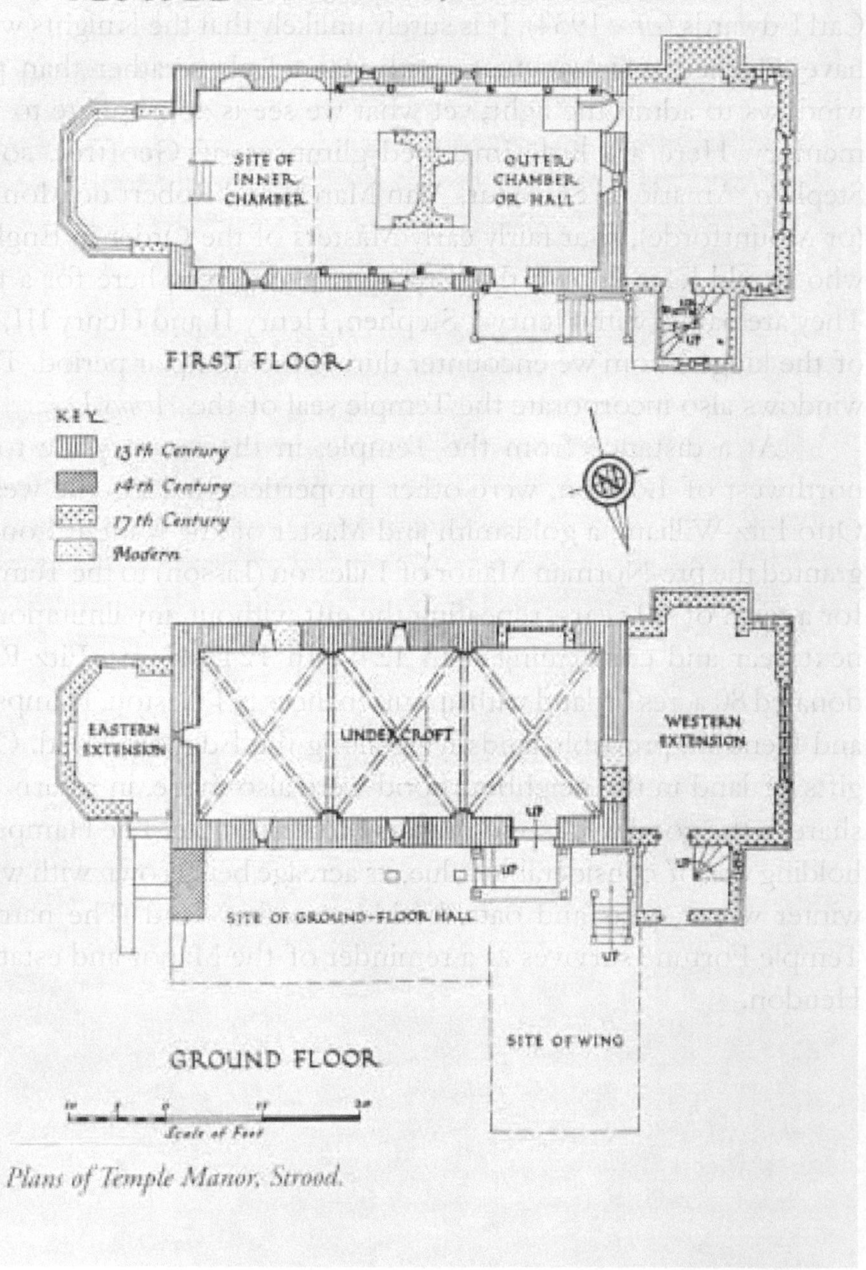

Plans of Temple Manor, Strood.

SURREY

Although there were no Preceptories in Surrey, the Templars had some properties there.

In 1166 the hide of Widefleet (or Wytheflet), on the south bank of the Thames at Southwark, was granted by the monks of Bermondsey Abbey to the Brothers of the Temple (presumably of the London Preceptory) to hold for a yearly rent of 10 marks, with its men, mills, waters, ponds and other appurtenances. Subsequently the Templars demised the manor to keepers or farmers, or as we might say, sub-let it.

They held lands in Capel known as Temple Elfold (or Elfande); much later the local family name became corrupted to Elephant! Temple Elfold, having 192 acres of arable land, was clearly of importance agriculturally. There must have been a chapel attached to the house, since in 1308 there was mention of a missal, a grail,[21] a chalice and vestment, implying a chaplain and several brethren in residence. A third of the manor of Merrow, near Guildford, was granted to the Templars in 1241. The manor of Addington Temple[22] was given to themin the same year by Walter de Merton. In 1249 Robert de Saunford (or Sanford) the Master, received a gift of further land in Addington. Evidently the Templars decided later not to farm this property themselves, since the last Master, Br. William de la More, demised it to John Blebury, clerk, for 20 marks per annum.

These holdings seem to have been intended for the support of the London Preceptory.

The Templars also had a foothold in Dorking by virtue of a charter (date unknown) from William, Earl de Warenne. This stated:

'For the health of my soul and the souls of my ancestors and successors I have granted to the Templars, in frankalmoin (i.e. free alms), Pagan Wrong, my man, with his whole tenement that he held of me in the vill of Dorking; to hold freely of me and my heirs quit of all secular service.'

The property in question (which later became known as the White Horse) apparently belonged to the manor of Shipley in Sussex, where a Templar Preceptory was established.

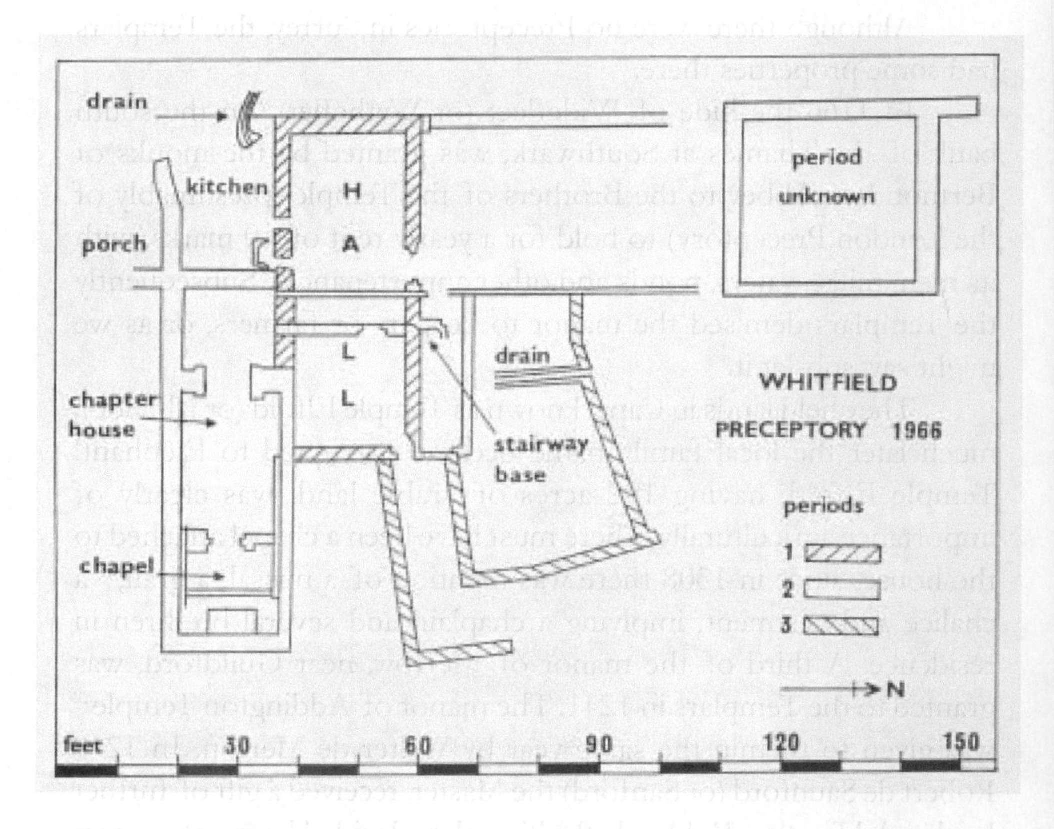

Plan of Temple Ewell, near Dover, as excavated 1964-66.

THE OTHER ENGLISH PRECEPTORIES

KENT

TEMPLE EWELL, near Dover, in the direction of Canterbury, was clearly of some importance in the Order. A Preceptory was established here before 1164 on a site given to the Templars by William, Henry II's brother and William de Peverell, Constable of Dover Castle. In the 1185 survey the Preceptory had an estate of over 300 acres. According to the monastic chronicler Matthew Paris, King John made his submission to the Papal Legate, Pandulph, on 15th May 1213 'in the house of the Templars near Dover', which must have been Temple Ewell. Nothing further is known of its history. In 1309 Ralph de Malton was the Preceptor and Robert de Sautre was a Brother at Ewell.

This Preceptory has also (more recently) been called after Whitfield, a local parish name signifying chalky ground; this is somewhat confusing, besides being unhistorical.

Despite the shortage of documentary evidence, archaeology has supplied some information about Temple Ewell and its appearance. There are no remains of the buildings above ground level, but the site was excavated in 1964-66. Some mediaeval floor tiles and iron objects of unknown purpose were unearthed. The site was later filled in, but significant data had been obtained from its ground plan. A rectangular Hall, dating from the twelfth century and very solidly built, with possibly a gallery or balcony at the west end, seems to have been the earliest part. In the thirteenth century a new wing was built, perhaps due to a need for more accommodation. The Chapel faced east and was only 15 feet square, with a single altar and smooth plastered walls. Fragments of glass from the window have been found. Adjoining the Chapel (and parallel to the Hall) were the Chapter House, where official business was transacted, and the Kitchen. The total area was 100 feet by 150 feet (see plan).

There is, however, more tangible evidence of the Knights' presence in this part of east Kent. On the Western Heights above Dover are the remains of a small church building, signposted as a Knights Templars' church. The impressive and well-preserved flint footings show that the building of this Church followed the same plan as the (completed) Church of the New Temple in London, but was smaller. The ground plan and photograph give an idea of its proportions. The external measurements are approximately: 54 feet total length: 32 feet the maximum diameter of the Round: length of the rectangular chancel 26 feet; and width of the chancel 20 feet. The site was excavated at a date prior to 1911.

It has been suggested that the Templars may have occupied this maritime site before moving a few miles inland to Temple Ewell. If this was so, it is enigmatic that they then built a much smaller chapel, at a time when the Order was prospering. The notion of a move appears unlikely. Rather it would seem that the Preceptory was at Temple Ewell from the start, the Dover Church being additional to it and built on land already belonging to the Preceptory. The tower may have been visible from the sea, serving as a daymark for shipping coming into the harbour. It was sometime believed that a house belonging to the Templars stood close by, but this rests on hearsay, as no trace of it remains.[23]

In the pleasant village of Temple Ewell, three miles northwest of Dover and near the source of the River Dour, which runs through it past an old watermill, the Templars founded the Church of SS. Peter and Paul. Although this has been altered and enlarged, traces of the original Norman work can be seen in the fine north doorway and the high narrow window in the north wall of the nave. The original length of their church cannot be determined, but from the lancet-headed window in the south wall of the chancel, belonging to

Dover: site of the Templars' church on the Western Heights, looking towards the chancel.

English Heritage drawing of the plan of the Templars' church, Dover.

the thirteenth century, it is clear that this part of the building also existed in their time. A somewhat mysterious stone slab with an incised cross was lifted from the chancel floor in 1874 and placed in the porch.

The Master of the Temple in England was the patron from 1185 to 1308, appointing the priests to the Church, which was not far from the Preceptory. Incidentally, the Dour, though not large enough to be navigable, provided the Preceptory with a supply of fresh spring water, which was an essential asset.

At Temple Ewell, services required by the Templar landlords of their tenants, the villagers, included salting fish caught off Dover and looking after sheep on the downlands, while links with the Manor's former landlords were maintained by the duty of carrying oats and straw to Dover Castle.

It will be seen that the busy town of Dover, on the Dour, stands between two Templar sites.

There were other Templar properties spread across this fertile county, strung out along the Dover road. Some are now little more than names; one has become better known because there is something to see and explore. At Strood, on the Medway, stands Temple Manor, in the midst of a modern industrial estate which covers the site of the Templars' farm. As was often the case, the farm was managed on their behalf. The Knights did not live here, but it was used as a convenient stopping place on the way from London to Dover and the Channel ports.

The Manor of Strood was granted to the Templars by 1159 at the latest, by King Henry II, one of their frequent benefactors. It was known as Templeborgh in 1292 and Templestrode Manor in 1337. The thirteenth century Manor House, built on a vaulted undercroft used for storage purposes, (with seventeenth century extensions added), has been carefully reconstructed from its former ruinous condition. The plain, austere style of the architecture reflects the disciplined influence of St. Bernard and the Cistercians. Nothing is included that is unnecessary or purely ornamental. What we see here is in fact the detached stone hall, *circa* 1240, which was then part of the *curia* or court, a complex (long since disappeared) of timber buildings, kitchens, barns, stables and probably a house for the bailiff's

Temple Ewell: church of SS. Peter and Paul, the doorway decorated for harvest festival (not as the Knights knew it).

residence, to which the Hall was added. The farm lands reached down to the west bank of the Medway. (Rochester Castle and Cathedral are within sight across the River) After careful restoration, Temple Manor is now an oasis of beauty and interest, despite its unbeautiful surroundings ironically called after it, Temple Industrial Estate.

There is no evidence of a chapel here, as might have been discovered had this been a Preceptory.

The Manor of Dartford and large areas of land in that part of Kent belonged to the Templars at the beginning of the thirteenth century. Temple Farm was later known as Templars (1311) and Le Temple (1360). Temple Hill, Godmersham, near Ashford, was part of the Order's property in that area. The village of Waltham, lying between Canterbury and Wye, was known as Temple Waltham because the Templars held the Manor there. This was a gift from the Archbishop of Canterbury in the mid-twelfth century. There was also a house in Canterbury and a smallholding at Deal, on the coast not far from Dover.

It seems highly probable that when time permitted, on their journeys between London and Dover, the Knights would have stopped in Canterbury and visited the shrine of St. Thomas, at first in the crypt and from 1220 upstairs in the cathedral. It is thought that their house in Canterbury may have been on a site later occupied by a Jewish synagogue in King Street, within the city walls and not far from the cathedral; but of this there is no convincing proof. Canterbury is only 12 miles from Temple Ewell by road.

SUSSEX

There were two Preceptories in mid-Sussex, with various properties attached to them.

SHIPLEY, some seven miles south of Horsham, in the northern half of the Rape of Bramber, was the larger Preceptory. Its origin is well documented.

About 1139 Philip de Braose (or Harcourt), son of Robert the Strong, bestowed the manor and church of Shipley on the Knights in these noble words: 'Moved by the words of the Gospel "Give unto Caesar what are Caesar's and unto God what are God's", and excited by the Holy Spirit, I give and grant unto God and to the Blessed Mary and the soldiers of the Temple of Solomon, for ever in perpetual alms a certain portion of the earthly lands which God has granted me to possess in this world, namely the land of Heschapelia (Shipley) and the Church...'

Apart from the fine early Norman church of St. Mary at Shipley with its plain square tower, there are no visible remains of the buildings occupied by the Templars, though traces of an old moat have been found, bounding the churchyard on the north and east and the fishponds of the Preceptory to the southeast of the church. St. Mary's is strong and austere, exactly suited to the Order. At Shipley the Templars trained knights, farmed their lands and perhaps also cared for sick and aged members of the Order. It must have been a good rural place in which to live, or maybe to end one's days after the hardness of service overseas. Even today this pleasant village is unspoilt and isolated from public transport, a place of peace and memories.

A special treasure preserved in Shipley church and dating from the time of the Templars, was a thirteenth century reliquary which, from its style, was probably made in Limoges. This was in the form of an oakwood casket about seven inches long with a sharply pitched roof, covered in copper and enamelled with Saints and the Crucifixion in gold, dark and light blue; essentially a tiny church or shrine for the Saints whose relics were here. Unfortunately, there is now only a replica of this priceless reliquary to be seen there, as the original was stolen in 1976. A reliquary-chasse in the form of a casket with a gabled roof, such as the one at Shipley, though costly, was not uncommon around 1200.

In fairness, it may be remarked that the Templars of Sussex were not so rich as was generally supposed. A royal commission in 1308 stated that their estates here contained many ploughs and other farm implements, with cows, horses and oxen, showing that their life at home was mainly agricultural. The library (if such a word is appropriate) comprised only two books: *The Book of the Kings* and a volume on animals. Besides the Shipley reliquary, their scanty hoard of valuables included 20 silver spoons, 3 gold rings and 13 silk purses - a disproportionate number considering the few coins they would have to contain, but doubtless gifts to the Order, of little practical use. In the inventory of chapel contents were "two irons for making oblates and wafers, a cup (the chalice used at Mass), two sets of vestments, three towels, two pewter candlesticks, one pewter pail". Perhaps it may be inferred from this that the Templars at Shipley made all the altar breads for their dependent churches in the vicinity. It is strange that only two sets of vestments were mentioned; the explanation may be that other sets had become worn and were not considered worth listing - or had been given to the church at Shipley for parish use.

A member of the prominent Norman family of de Braose donated further properties in 1154: St. Mary's church, Sompting on the South Downs above Worthing and the chapel of St. Peter at Cokeham.

Sompting church pre-dated the Templars by about a century, but the nave and chancel were then rebuilt on the original Saxon plan and significant additions to the exterior were made, so as to provide

Shipley, Sussex: the church from the south.

for the Templars to worship separately without needing to enlarge the church. What later became the south transept, being built (*circa* 1180) at a lower level than the rest of the church, certainly suggests separate use, as does the small eastward recess just sufficient to accommodate an altar. The doorway from the churchyard into this chapel had an exceptionally high arch, to admit the Templar standard (Baucent) when carried in. A local historian, Stanley P. Excell, stated that the present north transept also began as a separate chapel (with two altars?) for the Templars and that both transepts originally remained walled off from the main church building, though it is not obvious. If this is correct, the Order would have had three altars here for its exclusive use.

They also had the chapel at Knepp, near Shipley, and lands in Loxwood, Wisborough and Bramber. The house known as St. Mary's, Bramber, on the road which formed part of the great mediaeval east-west route through Sussex, leading from Southampton to Canterbury, is thought to have been owned by the Templars. This house still stands, though it has known much alteration since those days.

By about 1170 they had a chapel and burial ground in the port of Shoreham. Some of these places were of strategic importance; Shipley, Bramber and Shoreham all being on the navigable River Adur, were convenient for embarkation to France and the Holy Land. The Templars received Southwick church between 1173 and 1189 and the church at Kingston-by-Sea in 1206. The last Preceptor of Shipley was William de Egendon, 1304-8.

SADDLESCOMBE. About 1228 Geoffrey de Say granted the Manor of Saddlescombe, a hamlet in the parish of Newtimber at the foot of the Downs, some four miles northeast of Brighton, to the Knights with the assent of William de Warenne, Earl of Surrey. The latter added a grant of 40s. rent from Lewes, where he held the Castle. This Preceptory was a small establishment, seemingly dependent upon Shipley. It is thought that the L-shaped Manor House of later date represents approximately the original layout of the Preceptory. Little is known of its history, though one item affords lighter domestic insight into the Templars' life here: in 1308 their stores included two casks and a pipe of cider, probably produced locally in Sussex. They must have enjoyed quenching their thirst after labouring in the fields.

They also had a church at Woodmancote and certain tithes, land in New Shoreham and the Manor of Compton in Berwick.

Shipley church.

Sompting church, Sussex. Templars' Chapel.

HAMPSHIRE

The manor of TEMPLE SOTHERINGTON (or Southington) in the hundred of Selborne was called Sudynton or Sydynton in the thirteenth century. There seems some doubt as to whether this was a Preceptory, or if it remained one. The manor was granted to the Templars in 1240, as was also the manor of Blackmoor. There was a considerable holding of land in the vicinity, some of which was sold off. About 1250, Robert de Sanford, Master of the Order in England, granted all the tenements, lands and meadows which the Templars held in Selborne to the Augustinian priory of Selborne for 200 pounds, so as 'to buy other lands in aid of the Holy Land'. Various other dealings in property took place during the same century as part of the reshuffling process.

Sotherington Lane, leading towards Temple Manor, lies on the outskirts of the village of Selborne, the manor being in the southeast of the parish. One small farmhouse is the only building that now preserves the name of Sotherington. Nothing remains of the chapel. An old well 90 feet deep is supposed to date back to the Templars' occupation. They also held property in the manor of Kern, Kurne in the thirteenth century.

St. Mary's church, Selborne, has certain links with the local Templars. The two stone coffin lids with incised crosses, not identical but of unmistakably Templar origin and in good condition, stand against the wall of the south aisle chapel. In 1721 beneath the north transept were discovered the bones of a very large man, believed to be those of Adam de Gurdon (d. 1304 or 5), a Knight who lived at Temple Manor and was renowned for his size and valour. Whether in fact he was a Templar is not entirely certain, but probable.

At Fordingbridge in the New Forest, the north chapel (*circa* 1270) of St. Mary's church was non-parochial and belonged to the Templars. This presupposes the presence of Knights somewhere in the locality, though they were numerically not sufficient for the foundation of a Preceptory with its own chapel.

Cressing Temple, Essex. The two great barns used for large scale storage of grain. The Wheat Barn in the foreground, the Barley Barn to the right.

ESSEX

This county is unique in its traces of the Templars. Nowhere else can we find complete farm buildings such as the granaries which formed part of CRESSING TEMPLE. Cressing, 'the place where cress grows', lies southeast of Braintree. The Preceptory site is located south of the village itself, on the road from Witham to Braintree.

The Preceptory of Cressing Temple (and Witham) was one of the earliest Templar properties in England, if not the first. The manor with the advowson of All Saints church was granted to the Order by Queen Matilda by a charter dated at Evreux in 1136 and later confirmed by King Stephen. They received the manor and half hundred of Witham in 1147-48 and also land at Berecholt (Bergholt) and Newland.

The journey of about three miles between Witham and Cressing lies through gently undulating country, woods, cornfields and farmlands, the quiet fertile heart of Essex. Wheat, barley and oats were the crops grown in these parts. Here in this prosperous agricultural area the Templars, ever shrewd stewards of their resources, owned two great barns: what is nowadays called the Barley Barn was built *circa* 1200-1220 and a larger barn, now designated the Wheat Barn, *circa* 1260. These scientifically calculated dates leave no doubt as to the Templars' ownership. Being secular buildings of utilitarian value, the barns were not demolished in a later age, but were kept in use and repair. In 1987 the whole complex was acquired by Essex

County Council. These fine wooden barns are still standing and are the most famous in Essex, tangible evidence of the Templars' concern for producing cereal crops, for barns filled with corn presuppose cornfields round about and also mills available for grinding the grain into flour. The Preceptory had five corn mills. When in 1185 Geoffrey Fitz-Stephen, Master of the Temple, ordered a survey to be made of all the lands of the Order in England, one of the seven headings of the enquiry related to mills. These small and numerous manorial corn mills, mainly worked by water power, were a valuable part of the Templars' rural property, not only in Essex.

The Preceptory was seemingly well ordered, including in its buildings a hall house with chamber, pantry, buttery, kitchen, larder, bakehouse/brewhouse and dairy. There was also a cider mill, smithy and a store containing building materials. The farm stock comprised cattle, pigs, sheep, geese, chickens and peafowl. Ponds or moats would have provided fish and there would have been a dovecote. Even now the place has an air of spaciousness and calm, preserving a sense of well-being. There are Templars' Woods at Cressing, but no visible remains of the house, outbuildings or chapel, though the position of the latter is known.

Excavations on the site so far have revealed a shallow fishpond, probably constructed in the twelfth century. Slight traces of a ditch mark the extent of the site. Excavations are continuing. The name Temple End, which occurs four miles from Haverhill, Suffolk, to the north, suggests that the Preceptory owned land right across the county.

The Knights here maintained three chaplains to serve as chantry priests to pray for departed benefactors. Of course the chapel was dedicated to St. Mary and there was a cemetery attached to it. Brethren who died at Cressing Temple would have been buried there rather than in the parish churchyard of All Saints. The chapel was still extant in 1626. To the lands belonging to Cressing was added *circa* 1153-54 a market at Witham. This market, which had been established by Henry I, was one of the first in Essex after the Norman conquest. Cressing ultimately became the centre of an agricultural estate of some 2000 acres, including the five mills, two markets and an annual three days fair.

Before leaving Essex, a technical note on the construction of the Barley Barn may be of interest.

'It is a secular cathedral, a superb essay in carpentry which reminds us all of the great Norman timber buildings and roofs which we have lost. The Barley Barn has an aisled plan with opposed doorways in the centre of each long side. This central bay was used as a threshing floor and we must imagine the threshers working at the corn sheaves with flails...Here came the crops not only from the Cressing estate itself, but also from the Templars' other local possessions at Witham and Kirsting...But already by the Twelfth century such great barns, with their "passing brace" roof construction which was very demanding of good quality timber, were becoming a thing of the past and could only be built by rich and powerful owners...Next door is the Wheat Barn; these two great barns together make one of the most satisfying views of mediaeval England.'[24]

A new housing development in Witham is named Templemead. Essex is proud of its historic associations and its heritage from the Templars.

KNIGHT TEMPLAR

Cressing Temple: the wheat barn interior.

Cressing Temple: the barley barn interior.

HERTFORDSHIRE

TEMPLE DINSLEY, south of Hitchin, in an agricultural locality. There was a Preceptory here. In a chapter of the Order held in Paris in the Octave of Easter 1147, at which Pope Eugenius III was present, Bernard de Balliol gave to the Knights an estate called "Wedelee" (Dinsley). This was confirmed by King Stephen, who added two mills with the land and men and customs belonging to them. The date of the establishment of the Preceptory is not known.

A chapter was held at Dinsley between 1200 and 1205 by Aymeric de St. Maur, Master of the Temple. William de Bernewood, Preceptor of London, was present. Subsequently, a number of chapters were held there, at which the business and administration of the Order would have been discussed. The Preceptor's jurisdiction extended to Baldock; all of which suggests that this Preceptory was of some importance in the Order. In 1308 there were six Brothers living at Dinsley, besides pensioners.

The name Temple End occurs to the north-west of Temple Dinsley, presumably marking the boundary of their property. (This usage occurs elsewhere in England). Of this Preceptory nothing remains. A school now occupies the 'Vastum terre de Dynnesleya' (or Deneslai, in an earlier spelling).

A cemetery was disturbed by builders and among the items unearthed were many human skulls and part of a thirteenth century coffin lid bearing a long cross in low relief; the head of the cross was almost obliterated. Whether these have any connection with the Temple has not been proved.

BALDOCK, North East of Hitchin, was founded by the Templars, the feudal lord Gilbert de Clare, Earl of Pembroke, having given them 120 acres of land there, around the year 1140. As to the origin of the name, the theory has been advanced that the Templars adapted an oriental name with which they were familiar; a French rendering of Baudac or Baudoc, close in translation to Baghdad. This was gradually anglicised to Baldoc, Boldock and similar variants, ultimately becoming Baldock, according to John Stanley Rider, a local historian. There are no earlier traces of their occupation at Baldock.

At ROYSTON, archaeological research has been more fruitful. A cave that may have been used as a securely-hidden Templar chapel has been rediscovered, though this use cannot be proved with certainty. The cave, some 25 feet deep, is of a circular beehive shape, which would not be at all strabge to the Knights.

One of the last properties they acquired, by purchase, in Hertfordshire, was Leceworde - now known as LETCHWORTH.

OXFORDSHIRE

TEMPLE COWLEY, the original Preceptory, on the east side of Oxford, was founded in 1136 and functioned there for over a century. Bishop Robert Chesney of Lincoln granted the Templars freedom from market tolls at Banbury in the Twelfth century. Alan la Zouche, who was a great benefactor of the Temple, gave them much land in Sibford. A chapel at Sibford Gower was granted to them prior to 1153 by Agnes of Sibford. It then became independent of the mother church at Swalcliffe and acquired its own burial ground. She also gave Temple Mill, on a tributary of the Stour. The grange at Sibford was the centre of their Oxfordshire estates. Land granted to them frequently adjoined land which they already held, so that they were able to consolidate their estate, to the advantage of the crops and herds. There was also much heath land in those parts; around 1180 they received 30 acres on Sibford Heath.

After the foundation of Sandford, Cowley appears to have been reduced to the status of a *camera*, or cell. There remain no traces of the Preceptory, which stood near Temple Street, apart from the inevitable fish-pond. Cowley has long since been absorbed into Oxford.

SANDFORD, on the Thames just south of Oxford. The Preceptory was one of the largest houses of the Order outside London. Its history began *circa* 1239-40 when a local land-owner, Thomas de Sandford (junior), gave all his lands at Sandford to the Temple at Cowley in free alms. Further gifts followed and Thomas himself became a Templar, completing his oblation to the Order to which he was so devoted. Not long after this, the Preceptory removed (doubtless for reasons of greater convenience and efficiency) from Cowley to Sandford, a distance of only a few miles southward.

There remain part of the thirteenth century chapel, later used as a barn, south of Temple Farm and some conventual buildings incorporated in the farm, which is now a country club, between the church of St. Andrew and the river. Windows and fragments of stone carving have been preserved by being built into the farmhouse wall, and over the front doorway is a shield bearing the cross of the Templars. Of the chapel, two blocked-up portions of windows and a broad buttress can be identified. If what remains of this chapel is compared with the east end of the New Temple Church in London, some family likeness can be detected. The dates of both must be close, though Sandford (as we might expect) was plainer.

Somewhere on the site of the Preceptory was found an eleventh century metal reliquary of unique design. This must certainly have belonged to the Templars, though not made for them. It is now displayed in the Ashmolean Museum, Oxford. The Sandford reliquary, apparently intended to be worn on the chest, bears a figure of Christ the King in majesty, inscribed round the edge with the words: INTVS QVOD LATET CVNCTO NOS CRIMINE LAXET (may that which lies within release us from all sin). At the top a bird-like creature holds a suspension loop; at the bottom is a small hole which apparently held a pivot for a back plate (now missing), the top of which would have fitted under the bird's tail, to secure both parts. The interior is hollow to accommodate a relic (presumably of the Holy Cross). No similar object has ever been found. The style of workmanship is Romanesque.

It is noteworthy that the title 'Preceptor de Couele' (Cowley) was still used long after the transference to Sandford; perhaps because, after a century of residence there, Cowley was better known and enjoyed greater prestige than the more rural locality of Sandford. As early as 1139 Queen Matilda had given to the Knights of the Temple at Jerusalem all her land at Cowley, with its appurtenances, in pure and perpetual alms, and also rights in the royal forest of Shotover.

The Templars owned property in the city of Oxford, near the castle and in its suburbs, including Temple Cowley mills and mills which Queen Matilda gave them "apud Oxoniam".

Sandford did not completely vanish from history with the exodus of the Templars. It is an interesting fact that in post-Reformation times there remained staunchly loyal Catholic families, some of whom met in the old Preceptory at Sandford to pray the mass.

Oxford today has its Templar Road, on the outskirts of the city, to the north; not that this had any connection with the Order.

Sandford. Side view of the chapel, much altered.

From a thirteenth century engraving.
The various illustrations of the Templar habit show considerable discrepancies

BERKSHIRE

BISHAM (Temple Bistlesham and various other spellings). Preceptory, on a bend of the Thames near Marlow, on the opposite bank. The date of the foundation is uncertain, but the manor was the subject of charters of King Stephen and Henry II, *circa* 1154-55. The latter confirmed a charter of his predecessor relating to this property granted by the overlord Robert de Ferrers, in the following terms:

'Know that I have given and, by this my present charter, have confirmed to Brother Osto and the Knights of the Temple, the Manor of Bisham and forty acres of cultivated forest land and the mills and fisheries of the said manor in free and perpetual alms'...all to be held 'well in peace, free and quietly', with the church, wood, plain, meadows, pasture, lands and mills, freed from all secular exactions.

This must have been a choice site, although damp in the winter months and liable to flooding. The site of the mills, some way up stream from Bisham, is perpetuated by the name Temple. Besides Temple Lock and Weir, the whole district contains verbal reminders of the Order, such as Temple Park, stretching away to Hurley.

The first bridge across the river at Marlow is reputed to have been the work of the Templars. This timber structure, in use *circa* 1300, has long since been replaced, so we are unlikely ever to know the truth of this, but it seems to accord with the practical character of the Templars, if there was a need to cross the river, to have erected a bridge.

In this sparsely furnished Preceptory, needful rural trades were carried on - the churning of butter, baking bread, curing bacon by salting, fishing, and perhaps the making of cider, which was in use here. The livestock was varied; an inventory in *circa* 1308-09 listed 28 oxen, with boars and pigs, 49 in all, 2 horses, a palfrey for the Preceptor to ride, 2 donkeys, 9 peacocks and peahens, 3 swans and 6 hives of bees. The small number of horses in reserve would argue a correspondingly reduced contingent of Knights, if we could be sure that no horses had been taken away from Bisham at that time.

In addition to the usual provision of food to the poor, some fifty people living in this neighbourhood received each a loaf of bread, two herrings and a half-bottle of beer on the fifth day of March each year. Various other charitable provisions were made, including the payment of an annual pension of 5 marks and a bushel of corn to the vicar of Bray, near Maidenhead, where the Templars held some land.

Three resident chaplains were maintained at Bisham to ensure the regular cycle of services and to offer Mass for the souls of Richard I (d. 1189) and his predecessors, and more latterly for Queen Eleanor (d.1290) wife of Edward I, who must have been benefactors.

There are some remains[25] left of the Preceptory, although it was partially rebuilt as early as 1337, to become a priory of Austin Canons. The visible remains are the original entrance porch with Purbeck marble shafts, plain and noble in its dignity, the door leading into the great timber-roofed Hall, measuring approximately 52 feet by 33 feet. Behind the hall gallery is the solar. To the west of the porch are arches leading to the old kitchen, dairy, cellar and a 'lyttle wood yard'.

Certain lands known as the manor of Templeton (or Templeyngeflod) near Kintbury, belonged to the Preceptory. A fishery in Clewer, near Windsor, was granted to the Templars of Bisham in 1198. They held the advowson of St. Mary's Church, Speen, and the Vill of Sparsholt.

At BRIMPTON, east of Newbury, stands an old flint chapel which first belonged to the Templars and was latterly a farm storehouse. There is a Norman doorway with a tympanum on which is a Maltese cross and a pattern of overlapping fish scales.

BUCKINGHAMSHIRE

BULSTRODE, Hedgerley, near Gerrards Cross. A small and seemingly unimportant Preceptory was in existence here before 1276, though nothing seems to be known of it now. The Templars also held lands at Radnage and High Wycombe in the same county.

The manor of Radnage was granted by King John in 1214-1215 apparently to the Templars of London, which suggests that this was before the foundation of the Bulstrode Preceptory. They also held the advowson of Radnage church.

The Preceptory site is not known. A small estate in Chalfont St. Peter was held by the Templars and at Loudwater, near the manor of Temple Wycombe, a fulling mill belonged to them..

WILTSHIRE

The Manor of TEMPLE ROCKLEY (Rocleia) in Preshute (that is 'Priest's Cell'), in the parish of Ogbourne St. Andrew, on the high ground above Marlborough and south of Swindon, was granted to the Templars in 1155-56 by charter of John Fitz Gilbert the Marshal, a Wiltshire landowner and court official. It was not a Preceptory but was administered from the Oxfordshire Preceptory. The local names Temple Farm and Temple Bottom are evidence of their ownership.

The Rockley customs (existing before the coming of the Templars) provided labour for the dairies and sheep farms of the Wiltshire Downs, where the heavier work of sheep washing and shearing were done by women. When a feast day occurred during the harvest, the work specified to be done was reduced to ten sheaves.

Bristol Temple Church: altar place in the chantry chapel of St. Katherine

GLOUCESTERSHIRE

TEMPLE GUITING. Founded in the mid-twelfth century on land given by Gilbert de Lacy, this Preceptory gave its name to a secluded village on the upper reaches of the swift-flowing little River Windrush, near Winchcombe. The name Guiting means gushing or flooding. The donor Gilbert de Lacy became a Templar himself.

Stone slates for roofing were produced in the locality and this industry formed one of the sources of income for the Templars, who owned much land around Temple Guiting. The Abbot of Evesham leased meadowland in Bourton-on-the-Water to them. Nothing now remains of the Preceptory buildings, though there are traces of the numerous mills which ground corn for the Templars here. Guiting was the scene of much prosperous rural industry. In 1182 the Templars had a fulling mill here, one of the earliest in England. The cloth produced from the wool of Cotswold sheep was not the coarse cloth woven for home use, but a finer cloth made especially for the export market.

All the work to be done by the labourers on the Templars' estate was recorded in detail: the haymaking, reaping of crops, ploughing and sowing, washing and shearing the sheep, all the operations of a farming year, timed by the church calendar. Sometimes produce had to be carried from here by cart as far as Gloucester or Hereford. Guiting was the official centre for all Templar lands in Gloucestershire. It is significant that Temple Guiting Church, set in wide parkland, is dedicated to St. Mary.

It is possible that this foundation was preceded by that at Bristol, though precise dates are not available. Both were functionally well positioned, particularly with regard to the cloth trade.

BRISTOL held a valuable position on the Avon, even though its main development as a port came after the fourteenth century. The area still known as Temple Mead is the site of the marshy riverside meadows belonging to the Templars, which from the Temple Church extended to the bank of the river.

The Temple Church (or Church of the Holy Cross) was founded *circa* 1140, when Robert, Earl of Gloucester and Lord of the Manor of Bedminster, gave the Templars the district afterwards known as Temple Fee; it was the artisans and weavers quarter of Bristol. Here a small number of Knights settled, built their house and erected a small oval church measuring about 50 feet by 30 feet. The foundations of this building were discovered when the vaults were examined and repaired in 1870. Some excavation work has been done since. What we now see marking the site dates largely from around 1390; though still in existence, considerably altered, then badly damaged by enemy action in November 1940 and not re-roofed, it remains impressive with an exquisite leaning tower. It is probable that the Templars built part of this church, since it appears that the Chantry of St. Katherine, otherwise known as the Weavers' Chapel, standing at the east end of the north aisle, was in use in 1299, building having been comenced three years before. From this it seems that the Templars began from the east end the work of rebuilding, which was completed later by other hands. Due to the possibility of danger from masonry, only exterior viewing of the church is allowed, so the foundations are not visible.

Street names in the vicinity have borne silent witness to the Templars' presence: Temple Back, Temple Street, Temple Gate and Temple Way - one cannot be unaware of them. Property in Temple Street was marked with the cross and right of sanctuary was claimed there by Templar tenants, which led to trouble and litigation.

Strangely, it seems that Bristol was not a Preceptory, despite its importance, and there is some unresolved doubt as to whether it belonged to Guiting or to Templecombe in Somerset. It may be that some of the Knights from Bristol moved southward to Templecombe in order to found the Preceptory there, in more spacious countryside, leaving only a few Brethren in Bristol. It is unlikely that they would have abandoned such an old established and strategically important centre. Bristol was in fact the fiscal centre of a wide circumference of small rural properties, in Gloucestershire, Somerset, Dorset, Devon and Cornwall, which included mills at Broad Clyst, Devon, Launceston, Cornwall and Laycock, Wiltshire. Bristol itself was a wealthy centre of cloth manufacture (hence the Weavers' Chapel) in addition to its other crafts and trades.

From an impression of the Templars' old seal, showing the two Knights on one horse.

The Templecombe Christ; panel painting hung on the south wall of St. Mary's church. The location makes photography difficult, but the actual painting is reproduced in the sketch below.

SOMERSET

TEMPLECOMBE, a village standing on the edge of the Blackmore Vale, was once two separate parishes, but now one. In 1185 the Knights acquired the property of the manor on the south side of the village of Combe, which became known as Combe Templariorum (of the Templars), because here they established a Preceptory, the only one in Somerset.

The Preceptor who resided here was responsible for managing the Order's estates in the West Country, admitting new members and training men and horses for service in the Holy Land. Remains of the Templar buildings are visible at the manor house in Templecombe. On high ground adjoining the seventeenth century farmhouse, and at right angles to the road, stretches a long barn ending in what is considered to have been the Preceptory Chapel. The Templars who became considerable landowners received lands at Lopen and elsewhere in Somerset. Their estate at Williton was at one time known as the manor of Williton Temple.

The unique feature of Templecombe today is a panel painting of Christ's head by an unknown artist, now displayed on the south wall of the parish church of St. Mary the Virgin (which was in the manor of the Templars). This painting was discovered in 1951 in the outhouse of a cottage off the High Street, once the priest's house. During a gale the plaster of the outhouse ceiling collapsed, revealing the panel in the roof with a face looking down, covered with coal dust. Keyhole and hinge marks indicate that it had sometime been used as a door, before being hidden away and its origin forgotten.

This life-size painting was most probably connected with the Knights; indeed, it would seem to be an integral part of their history. It is believed to have been one of a number of similar pictures in the possession of the Templars, expressing their intense devotion to Christ and used as a focus of devotion in their chapel. The crucial point is that it does not appear to have a halo or nimbus, which usually surrounds the head of Christ. The painting we see is not idealised, but a realistic portrait as appears on the Holy Shroud[26], a likeness of the humiliated Christ, the Man of Sorrows, not yet the glorified King of Kings. When this is understood, the absence of the halo seems reasonable and obvious.

Despite the resemblance however, the Templecombe Christ is not an exact copy of the Holy Shroud; the eyes and mouth are open. The head, enclosed in a quatrefoil, is painted on four wooden planks in what now appear as quiet shades of brown, though there may originally have been more colour; unless these shades derive from the appearance of the Holy Shroud. Since the topmost plank of the panel (above the head) is missing, it is not absolutely certain that there was no halo, though this would tally with the strange historical circumstances leading to the Templars' downfall. At that time the absence of a halo in their portraits, which the Templars maintained were indeed paintings of Christ, appears to have been used by their inquisitors as evidence of 'idolatry'! They were said to worship a strange image - perhaps this is one such 'idolatrous image' which somehow escaped attention and was hidden away and then forgotten.

Thus, on close examination, the unprejudiced mind may find that the Templecombe Christ is not an icon of the dead Saviour (the Mandylion), but a vision of the living Christ, inspiring His Poor Soldiers to the defence and conquest of the Holy Land. So they kept their sights towards Jerusalem, even after the Holy City had fallen and hopes of recapturing it had faded.

It is not beyond the realms of possibility that the painting may have been imported into England, via Bristol, and thence brought to this remote Preceptory in Somerset - who knows?

One further thought about the Templecombe Christ may be helpful to our understanding: it is a well known phenomenon that the eyes painted by some artists were so realistic that they appear to move, to follow the observer. Possibly this was so with this picture when it was freshly painted (and not dulled by time and neglect) - and also the other Templar portraits of Christ which have not survived. This surmise could explain the naive awe in which they were held.

Templecombe. The manor house today, containing the remains of the Templar buildings, the chapel being on the extreme right of the picture.

Trebeigh, looking across the site of the preceptory.

Trebeigh. Templar Cross from the Preceptory, now standing outside St. Ive Parish church, a perpetual remembrance of those who bore the cross of service there.

CORNWALL

TEMPLE, a hamlet six miles north-east of Bodmin, and TREBEIGH, near Liskeard, together constituted the Preceptory of Trebeigh. The proximity of Bodmin Moor makes it seem likely that this westernmost of the Preceptories was a training centre for Cornish Knights joining the Order. It has been said (as a local tradition) that the Templars maintained a hospice here for the benefit of travellers across the lonely moor, or pilgrims finding their way to St. Michael's Mount - or ultimately to the Holy Land; feasible enough, though this was surely incidental to the Templars' main objectives. The Cornish property was not profitable in comparison with other counties.

The Church of St. Catherine at Temple stands on the site of the Templar chapel, of which a few stones and the base of the font are still extant. This lonely church in the desolate moor was a ruin, roofless and forsaken for about a century, until 1883 when it was rebuilt and restored to use. The new plans followed as nearly as possible those of the original building, on the existing foundations, using the old tower arch and other stones, some of them bearing engraved crosses.

In 1185 the Templars' estate here was described simply as 'one land on Fawimore' (i.e. Fowey or Bodmin Moor). It is known that the process of tin-streaming was practised in the valleys of the moor, so it is possible that the Templars became involved in the tin industry; which would make this Preceptory unique, though not prosperous. There is little more to be said. The whole area is mysterious, its history obscure. The Cornish Preceptory was in an isolated position, not only geographically, but also in relation to other Preceptories; there were none in Dorset or Devon.

However, the Templars have not been entirely forgotten here. Their red cross dominates the circular upper light of the east window in the church, and a tiny sepia window in a narrow opening on the north side of the tower shows a Knight Templar on horseback.

TREBEIGH. In 1150 the Lordship of the manor of Trebeigh (or Trebythe) was granted to the Order by King Stephen. While it is known that from 1259 the Master was patron of the neighbouring parish church of St. Ive, it is not certain whether the Templars were concerned with its building. Outside this church stands a well preserved stone Templar Cross which came from the Preceptory buildings and has been put here as a tangible reminder. Trebeigh Wood, alongside the main road from Liskeard, is close to the site of the Preceptory, in a wide green valley. Altogether the Cornish scene has little that survives from the Templar period as such.

Temple Church, St Catherine, Bodmin Moor, on the site of the original Templar building.

HEREFORDSHIRE

This county, at the heart of the Marches, the region where England and Wales meet, had two Preceptories and elements of special interest: round churches and fortified towers.

(1) GARWAY. An important Preceptory in an isolated country setting on the River Monnow, the Welsh border, to the south of Hereford. It was founded *circa* 1186 or earlier; some doubt exists about the date. Church House Farm is on the Preceptory site.

There have been two Templar churches here. Evidence for a round church has been discovered and a segment of the foundation was exposed in 1927 and can be seen abutting on the north side of the later nave (outside). This circular plan was abandoned in the late Thirteenth century, when the present rectangular church of St. Michael was built. The whole scene is dominated by an unusually massive tower originally detached, 33 feet square with narrow windows, standing at an oblique angle to the north-west of the church, which it pre-dates. Judging by the thickness of its walls, this plain impregnable tower must have been constructed for defensive purposes and as a refuge during border raids.

Between the nave and chancel of the present church is an arch enriched by transverse mouldings suggestive of Moorish or Saracen influence.

St. Mary's church, WELSH NEWTON, not many miles from Garway, was also built by the Templars. The stone 'Seat of Freedom' on the north side of the chancel was probably the official seat of the Preceptor when they used this church for services.

BOSBURY or UPLEADON, on the River Leadon, north of Ledbury. A small house for a Preceptor with a chaplain, clerk and other officials and servants.The moat at Temple Court belonged to the Templars. Bosbury Church, like Garway, has a massive detached tower, 29 feet square and lit only by lancet windows.

HEREFORD. St. Thomas de Cantilupe (1218-82), Bishop of Hereford, is reputed to have sometime held high office in the Order. His original Shrine (of 1287) is in the north transept of the cathedral, and on three sides of the pedestal can be seen 14 carved figures in different attitudes, usually said to be Knights Templar. This Shrine was damaged but not destroyed at the Reformation, because it did not then contain his relics, which had been translated to another shrine in 1349. The defaced statues are certainly of men in armour, but it is hardly possible to say whether or not they are intended to be Templars. There must surely have been some reason why the Holy Bishop's tomb was guarded by Knights, rather than saints, angels, or mourners[27].

What became known as St Giles's Hospital (almshouses), in Hereford, though founded in 1290 for the use of the Friars Grisey (i.e. Greyfriars) soon became the property of the Templars. Their occupancy was short-lived. Their chapel (thought to have been round) stood on a corner of St. Owen Street. All that remains of it there is the lower part of a slightly curved wall, scarcely noticeable. The rest has been obliterated by the pavement and road. St. Giles's hospital was totally rebuilt in later years. Built into the side wall is a badly weathered piece of sculpture depicting Christ in majesty, under a decorated Norman arch. This is presumed to be the tympanum from the doorway of the old chapel. It is being preserved as far as practicable at this late stage.

Garway: site of the round (see plan.)

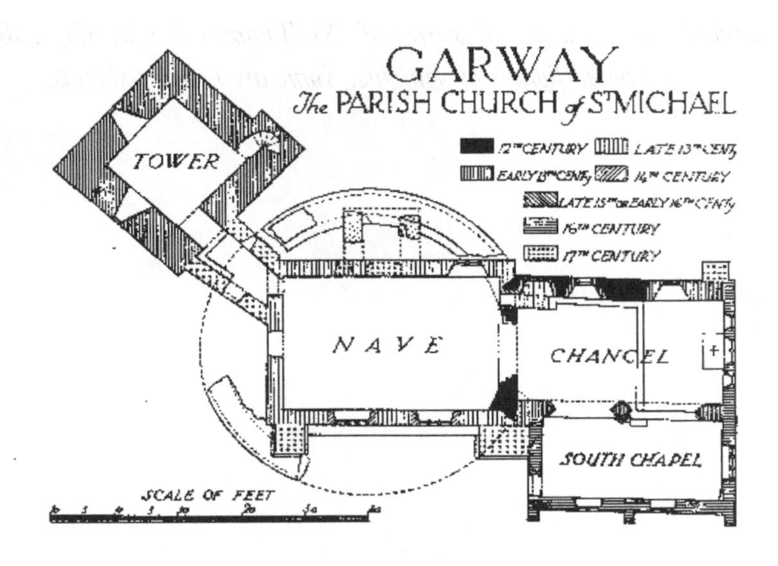

Garway. Plan showing position of the foundations of the original circular nave, uncovered in 1927.

Hereford cathedral: side of shrine of St. Thomas de Cantilupe, showing supposed figures of knights. Some are holding shields.

SUFFOLK

THE TEMPLE, DUNWICH. Surely the most intangible Templar site. Dunwich was in its time Suffolk's main seaport, probably the fifth largest harbour town in England and among its top ten cities. All that is left today, after centuries of marine erosion, is half a street and the ruins of a priory and a leper hospital, nothing relating to the Templars of Dunwich. Nevertheless a Preceptory was established in this ill-fated town in 1185, on an eight acre site granted to the Knights by King Henry II, in the west part of the town, just inside the rampart called Pales Dyke. Annexed to this Preceptory were various houses, tenements and lands in Dunwich and the neighbourhood. The church, the Temple of Our Lady in Dunwich, was covered with reeds (i.e. thatched). It was said to have begun as a round building, just as in London, which is not surprising since they were contemporary, though Dunwich was poorer and apparently obliged to make use of local materials. It was reputed 'to have been a Place of Great Privileges for Pardons' (Thomas Gardner, 1754) i.e. a sanctuary for fugitives from justice. It was known in 1252 as the 'bona Templiariorum de Donewico'.

In 1308 there were only two Knights in residence, Robert de Spaunton and John Coffyn. Grave losses in the Holy Land and the ultimate fall of the Latin Kingdom there may have made the austerity and discipline of the Templar life a less attractive calling. As we have noted, of this Preceptory nothing remains above the sea, which has tragically eroded this coast.

The Knights of this Preceptory also had a chapel at DINGLE, about a mile or so north of Dunwich. Since there was no church there, their chapel (being provided with a chaplain and a clerk) could have served as a mission or Mass station for the local people, some of whom were tenants of the Templars.

GISLINGHAM, in the country due west of Dunwich. A small house which is believed to have become a Preceptory *circa* 1305; surely the last Preceptory to be founded, perhaps intended to take the place of Dunwich in emergency? Local circumstances suggest this as a possibility. Erosion was a constant threat: the winter of 1286 brought disastrous storms and high tides to the Suffolk coast, wrecking much of the town and leading to various maritime troubles. It may be that the Templars of Dunwich had some premonition of their buildings subsiding into the North Sea and therefore they (partially) transferred to another property further inland, Gislingham, to cut their losses. In the event this did not prove necessary for them.

On the other hand, it seems from the inventory made in 1308 that the Dunwich house and church were still in use, even though there were only five or six persons, including the two Knights, then living there. Furthermore, there appears no record of the manor of Gislingham (or Gisleham Hall) belonging to the Templars, so this remains dubious. After the destruction of the harbour, when commerce and ship-building declined, the once prosperous Dunwich, now a 'place made desolate by the sea', would have lost its attraction for the Templars.

KNIGHT TEMPLAR

NORFOLK

HADDISCOE (or HADESCOE), north-west of Lowestoft, in the direction of Norwich. The Preceptory was founded before 1218. King Henry III was a considerable benefactor. In 1268 Thomas Rosceline conveyed by fine to Roger Fitz-John, Master of the Temple in England, 15 acres of land. In 1286, during the reign of Edward I, the Master claimed certain rights of his tenants, as Henry III had granted to them. In the same year the Preceptor of Haddiscoe set up crosses on the houses here and in Siveland belonging to the Order.

There are no visible remains. Being inland, Haddiscoe escaped the widespread storm activity which swept across the East Anglian coast and menaced Dunwich, but the Preceptory buildings vanished later by human agency.

Great Wilbraham church:
examples of heraldic decoration.

CAMBRIDGESHIRE

In this county were three Templar establishments, all of them within a ten miles radius of Cambridge, in the great monastic region of the Fenland. This may suggest some practical co-operation between them.

DENNEY, at Waterbeach, five miles north of Cambridge, was a preceptory of a special type. Previously built as a Benedictine Priory, transferred by the monks of Ely to the Templars *circa* 1170,[28] it became an infirmary where sick and elderly members of the Order were taken care of. The Preceptor was *Custos infirmorum.* Provision was made for eleven brethren to reside here, including the Preceptor and invalids, with the usual staff of chaplains, clerks and officials. In the middle of the thirteenth century the great tithes of Great Wilbraham Church were allocated to the support of the infirm brethren at Denney (Deneya); they received 'the ninth sheaf' (that is, one sheaf in every nine).

The Templars built the west doorway, still using the Norman style of architecture, and added the infirmary. The 11 beds stood together in a chamber. In the refectory or hall were two long trestle tables for meals and two 'tables dormant'. Denney had a well-appointed kitchen and bakehouse. During Templar occupation, structural additions and modifications were made to the original Benedictine plan and included buildings to the north of the church. A vast church was not needed by this small community, so we find that the mid-twelfth century cruciform church had a two-bay nave 27 feet long internally, with a south aisle, crossing and transepts,

Denney today. Photograph by Edward Harper.

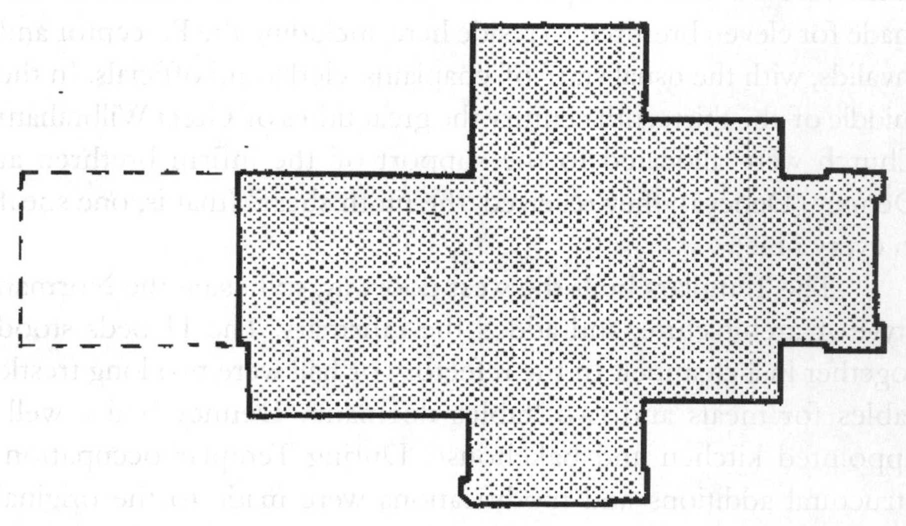

Denney. Ground plan of church with the Templars' cruciform building shaded.

culminating in a square-ended chancel of two bays (the latter destroyed). Remains of several graves have been found, and complex fish-ponds on either side of the drive.

The buildings have been much altered by later occupants, Franciscan Minoresses who added a cloister and enlarged the church for their use. The remaining part of it was still later incorporated into a farmhouse building, resulting in rather a hybrid structure, with the frater used as a barn. Owing to so many changes of user, it has not been easy for archaeologists to separate and identify the Templar elements, though much careful restoration work has been done.

It is clear that the long nave of Benedictine churches was not required here; consequently the church became disproportionate (see outline plan). It was no doubt ample for its purpose, since we know that the last *Custos infirmorum*, Br. William de la Forde, who had been transferred from Eagle, had in his care a total of nine or ten men. Of these, only two were comparatively young; another was described as senile, and two were crippled by age and infirmity.

For those Templars who had served overseas, in the Holy Land or in Cyprus (as had Robert the Scot, recorded at Denney in 1308), 'it must have seemed a strange contrast from the pulsating life of the Near East with its scorching, dusty summers and crisp, cold winters, its chivalry and brutality, its sophisticated court life and sudden death, to be sent to end their days at Denney surrounded by misty fen with its penetrating damps and agues, calls of waterfowl and the croak of frogs, and with servants whose worlds probably stretched no further than Ely or Cambridge.'[29] The active serving Knights would have known the wide expanse of sky (by which to predict the next day's weather) as they rode across the fens to visit their other properties. This quiet haven, never easy of access, between the Cambridge-Ely road and the River Cam, had originally been an island surrounded by ditches and moats.

GREAT WILBRAHAM (WILBURGHAM MAGNA). More than 20 variant spellings of the name have been noted! The site of Wilbraham Temple, now covered by a later house, is near the villages of Great and Little Wilbraham, east of Cambridge, in open fen country. The manor was transferred in 1226 to Brother Alan Martel, Master of the Knights of the Temple in England. This Preceptory was not a large establishment since, according to one account, its total personnel consisted of the Preceptor, one brother, a chaplain and certain servants who included the porter, baker and bailiff. There were two water mills and a windmill.

Wilbraham Preceptory was no great distance from Denney by horseback across flattish country. The dairy and sheep farm here kept the brethren at Denney supplied with fresh foodstuffs. The house and its chapel were very simply furnished, the most elaborate fittings being those used for dairying, presses for making cheese, a churn, a large fixed cauldron for heating milk and other utensils. The east end of Great Wilbraham is known as Temple End.

In the village of Great Wilbraham, St. Nicholas' Church, which is mainly of the thirteenth century, contains elements which most probably are directly linked with the Templars. In the south transept is a blocked-up archway which seems to have led into a built-on chapel, since demolished. The fine decorative work on the arch ends in a cross at either side, a very rare feature.

Great Wilbraham: St. Nicholas' church, the walled-up archway.

DUXFORD, Preceptory, five miles south-east of Cambridge on the River Cam or Granta. The Temple manor-house where the Preceptor lived included the hall and a chamber, the chapel, with a grange and other farm buildings, probably in the area called (in 1823) Temple Close, around the present Temple Farm. Traces of rectangular moat remain between this farm and the river.

This is also thought to have been a small house, the Preceptor being the only professed brother in 1308, when there were 15 dependants, mostly outdoor servants.

Great Wilbraham: St. Nicholas' church, the walled-up archway (external view).

Temple Balsall, St. Mary's Church, piscina.

WARWICKSHIRE

TEMPLE BALSALL, a remote hamlet in the midst of the Forest of Arden, south-east of Solihull. The name Balsall came from an Anglo-Saxon word denoting watery pastures. In the 1185 survey it was spelt Belesale. Here the Templars had a fairly large establishment, built on land given by Roger de Mowbray *circa* 1140. This had become a preceptory by 1226. The red sandstone church of St. Mary the Virgin, built *circa* 1290 as the Templars' chapel, without aisles or transepts, is remarkable for the fine tracery of its windows. Some mediaeval carving remains. This could not have been their original chapel here for obvious reasons of dating. The wide, spacious building we now see was the last church that the order built in England. It was restored in 1849 (after much neglect) by George Gilbert Scott, 'with due regard to the original form' and became a parish church in 1863.

In 1739 nearly all of the Preceptory buildings that had survived till then were pulled down, except for part of the hall and the Preceptor's chamber adjoining, which were encased in brick, in cottages to the west of the church. The great chimney remains. Some excavations were made in 1981. Three fish-ponds have been found nearby. However it is the church which makes Temple Balsall memorable as a place forever associated with the Knights. The striking effect of the mature red stonework contrasts with the more familiar grey of existing Templar buildings elsewhere, and points to the probable use of locally quarried stone. (They would have had their own stonemasons, as at the Temple in Jerusalem.) The piscina, with its clustered shafts and fine tracery, is unusual and beautiful.

TEMPLE MANOR, Warwick. Roger, Earl of Warwick, granted a small manor beyond the bridge on the south side of the town to the Templars. This became one of a group of Warwickshire manors contributory to the Preceptory of Balsall. A chantry chapel existed in the manor. In 1308 a chaplain received an annual stipend of £3 out of the income of the manor, for Mass to be offered for the Earl's ancestors and descendants, in return for the lands given by his ancestors to the Templars (as mentioned above).

Little more than a mile from the Lincolnshire village of Belton is an estate known as TEMPLE BELLWOOD which belonged to this preceptory. Some remains of their house are built into a farmhouse in the grounds.

Temple Balsall. St Mary's church; exterior from the south-west.

LINCOLNSHIRE

This county (once known as 'Mary's Meadow') had no fewer than five Preceptories, one of these being an infirmary.

TEMPLE BRUER, a lonely place in the East Kesteven district of South Lincolnshire. The Preceptory de la Bruere, or the Heath, stood a little to the west of the Roman highway, Ermine Street, and about ten miles from the city of Lincoln and six miles from Sleaford.

The foundation charter of *circa* 1150 delineated an area 'de terra vastata et brueria' on the plateau south of Lincoln, 'between the road to Sleaford and the road to Stamford'. By 1185 an agricultural village had grown up around the preceptory, the villagers paying the Templars rents in money, hens and services (cultivating the land belonging to the preceptory). A weekly market was held.

Among the greatest of local feudal magnates, the rents of the Preceptory's tenants and the profits of their farms went to swell the general resources of the Order. Remains of the church, a round nave with a tower attached to it, were in existence in 1726, but a hundred years later only the tower was left standing. Excavations since then (1908) have made it clear that the church had been lengthened and two towers added during the twelfth century. There was an apsidal crypt beneath the church. Now only one tower and a few fragments survive of this thriving preceptory, which was probably the most important in Lincolnshire. Curiously – in view of the amount of land available – the church was not correctly orientated..

The excavation reports are confusing, but certain facts emerge. The round church and crypt came first, the porch and and the towers later. The substantial square tower that remains is 54 feet high. Six stone steps lead to the round arched doorway of the tower, and a winding stairway to two upper rooms. The area inside the tower measures 15 feet by 16 feet. The ground floor is thought to have been either a chapter house or a chapel, for two of its walls contain the interlaced arcading of sedilia. There is also an old piscina and a stone carved with a priest's head. The mouldings are all of simple Norman work of mid-twelfth century. This tower was linked by a cloister to the round nave to the west. Some glazed tiles were found at the east end of the church. Temple Bruer was said to possess a portrait similar to that at Templecombe.

The village here was eventually deserted, possibly due to its isolated position, or because subsequent owners were less concerned with their tenants. Another factor we cannot overlook is the Black Death in 1348, which hastened the decay of many rural communities. Temple Bruer is not served by public transport.

Temple Bruer was the burial place of Br. Morinus, the Templar who was almoner to St. Hugh of Lincoln; mention was made earlier of this esteemed Brother whose death was revealed in a dream to the Bishop at Sleaford. He saw plainly the cell of Br. Morinus in the Bishop's manor-house at Stow Park, where he had fallen mortally sick. (St. Hugh, after administering the last sacraments to him, had been obliged to leave him and press on to Sleaford.) In his dream a white dove kept flying from side to side of the room, trying to find a way out. On waking, St. Hugh knew that Morinus was dead. Since he also knew that the dead Brother would be taken to Temple Bruer, the nearest preceptory, for burial, the Bishop ordered his horses to be got ready for him to ride there. He was saying his office when a messenger arrived bringing word of the almoner's death and arrived at Bruer in time to officiate at the funeral.[30] It would be unfair to cite this as the only instance (so far as we are aware) of any contact between Templars and a Carthusian in this country, since Carthusian monks were not usually made diocesan bishops.

Even if Temple Bruer was doomed to failure and desertion, the Templars cannot be held to blame for that.

WILLOUGHTON, seven miles from Gainsborough. This preceptory with its wide estates and many dependent 'camerae' (cells), founded before 1168, was the richest of English rural Templar houses. Now, in complete contrast, wide ditches overhung with trees in the fields around Temple Garth Farm, west of the village of Willoughton, are all that remain to substantiate memories of the preceptory.

ASLACKBY (pronounced locally 'Azelby'), south of Sempringham in the district of South Kesteven. This preceptory was founded *circa* 1154 or 1194. It had a round church, which by 1789 had been rebuilt as a farmhouse, still called the Temple. The embattled square tower remained standing until 1891 when it fell down through neglect.

The southernmost of the Lincolnshire Preceptories was WYTHAM, or South Witham, also in the district of South Kesteven. This, the administrative centre for all the Order's outlying estates within its area (which included parts of Lincolnshire, Leicestershire and Rutland), dates from *circa* 1164. The domestic and farm buildings, the foundations of which have been excavated, were arranged on a courtyard plan, that is, set about a great court with the gatehouse on the north, a fine range of barns on the west, the hall, chambers, chapel and kitchen on the south-east and a workshop area with ovens and kilns on the east. Beyond the great court, towards the River Witham, the preceptory had its own water mill and fish-ponds. As Dr. Colin Platt has remarked,[31] 'the concentration of the Templars' domestic range at Witham, with its own small court tucked into a corner of the great preceptory enclosure, echoes...the common monastic practice, the cloistered monk turning his back on the noise and activity of the farmyard by which he was sustained'. The excavations have been filled in and the area ploughed over, so we have to rely on the plan.[32]

The oldest monument in South Witham Church is a coffin stone with an ornate cross and the head of a bearded man – could this be a Templar memorial?

At EAGLE, (a name thought to be derived from 'ac leah' or 'the oak wood'), overlooking the wide valley of the Trent, the Templars had an infirmary similar to that at Denney, where members of the Order who had grown too old or infirm for active service were cared for in their last days. This seems to have been a later foundation. The legal devolution of the house is not clear; it was said to have been given by Henry II, but later, in 1275, King Stephen was stated to have granted the royal demesne manor of Eagle to maintain an infirmary for sick brethren of the Order. It seems that Stephen's grant was confirmed and enlarged by Henry; also that the hospital was there first and the Preceptory soon grew up around it. A farmhouse stands on the site.

It is by no means sure – scholars disagree – whether Mere was ever a preceptory, though in the thirteenth century there was a distinct community with breweries at Mere, a small manorial estate and a mill.

To sum up: in Lincolnshire, cattle grazing, dairy farming, fisheries, mills and pig-keeping in the woods were the Templars' main sources of profit, while road-making, trenching and ditching were the essential services to the locality. At Temple Farm, north-west of Grantham, they undertook the same kind of pioneer farming development as the Cistercians did elsewhere.

The Angel at GRANTHAM, reputedly Britain's oldest inn still in use, was Templar property in 1213. As with everything else, considerable changes have been made since then.

We have already noted the close association with the Bishop of Lincoln whose Inn was the Old Temple in Holborn, where the bishop and his retinue stayed when he was attending to business in London. The Diocese of Lincoln was at this time one of the largest and most important in the English hierarchy, extending over nine counties, so such an association was of certain advantage to the Templars.

LEICESTERSHIRE

ROTHLEY Temple stood between Leicester and Loughborough. The Templars already possessed land at Rothley in 1203 and further land in the vicinity was acquired later. The preceptory was probably established *circa* 1231, the year in which Henry III granted the manor and advowson of Rothley church to the Templars in free alms. Later on the preceptory came to include lands in thirteen neighbouring areas, several mills, large pastures for sheep grazing and five dependent chapels. The rent received from Rothley mills was used to provide a pittance (additional food on special occasions) for the Templars in the stronghold of Acre, in the Holy Land. At the granges of Baggrave and Gaddesby the Templars themselves carried on farming. In 1308 their flocks numbered more than 350 sheep and lambs. They also kept pigs.

In a beautiful rural setting still mostly agricultural, adjacent to Charnwood Forest and easily accessible, the site of the preceptory is occupied by an hotel; apart from the chapel (*circa* 1240) which remains intact. Architecturally this is impressive in its simplicity. It has been carefully restored and is used occasionally for weddings and other special events. Leading into the south side of this unpretentious rectangular chapel is a square vaulted porch, originally having doorways on all four sides. In Nikolaus Pevsner's opinion, this porch was probably part of a tower, or it may have supported an upper storey of the porch. The chapel has tall cusped lancet windows shafted inside. On the south wall of the sanctuary is a fine trefoiled pointed piscina with shafts. The east window was originally constructed as a triple lancet, familiar in other Templar buildings; it was altered later, as was the roof, but no substantial changes have been made to the chapel. During part of the nineteenth century it was used as a laundry and wine cellar. The long history of Rothley has certainly been eventful.

In the years after 1231 this manor in the fertile valley of the River Soar, in the Soke of Rothley, became a flourishing centre of Templar activity, with estates from Ashby Folville to Wymondham in Norfolk. At its greatest extent the Rothley (or Rothelee) Preceptory consisted of the chapel, the hall, a dormitory and the ancillary buildings necessary for a self-supporting community: stables, kitchen, various storehouses, bakery, buttery and brewery. The movable contents of the chapel indicate that it was furnished with the necessaries of worship not expensively, but sufficiently.

In 1285 the Order obtained from Edward I the right to hold a weekly market in the village and an annual fair on the eve, the feast day and the morrow of St. Barnabas (11th June).

The Templar Chapel, Rothley Court, Leicestershire

STAFFORDSHIRE

KEELE Preceptory had its beginning when an estate was given to the Templars by Henry II between 1155 and 1163. It was then completely uncultivated land and previous to this there had been no Templars in the vicinity, nor any village. It seems probable that this foundation was made by Knights from Temple Dinsley, since it was that preceptory which first administered Keele from a distance, as a dependency, a situation which became impractical. The Manor of Keele became a separate preceptory sometime after 1216, with its dependent estates elsewhere in north Staffordshire and across the border in Shropshire.

The range of buildings was extensive. In addition to the usual hall there was a separate chamber, probably used by the preceptor, chapel, kitchen, stable, ox-stall, dovecote, sheepfold, barn (*grangia*), watermill and windmill. This was predominantly a farming community. Crops of wheat, rye and oats were grown at Keele; cattle, sheep and pigs were kept. The Templars were responsible for the creation of Keele village and manor.

KNIGHT TEMPLAR

Garway, Herefordshire: the massive square tower and west end of the church.

SHROPSHIRE

LYDLEY Preceptory, near Watling Street (or Lydley Heys). The Templars had acquired various estates in Shropshire by 1158. It is not clear when this preceptory was established. They built a mill in the hamlet of Lydley before 1185 and seem to have had fish-ponds there, but the buildings of the preceptory stood on the site of Penkridge Hall, an isolated farmstead to the south- east. They maintained a large demesne, worked by a staff of permanent farm workers, ploughmen and a forester. There was much expansion and consolidation of estates for the growing of wheat and oats. Sheep were also kept, and stone was sold from a quarry, indicating the varied activities of this preceptory.

Land at Stanton Long, six miles up the valley and south of Much Wenlock, was acquired *circa* 1225. A small establishment was maintained there. In 1273 the Templars were given fishing rights in the Croud Brook.

Penhill: a lonely preceptory. Chapel ruins showing wall and site of altar.

Penhill: chapel, showing stone coffins in front of the altar.

YORKSHIRE

In the mid twelfth century the Templars began to acquire possessions in Yorkshire. This large county was of such importance to their organisation that no less than ten preceptories were founded and grouped together in a northern province. These formed the Yorkshire Preceptory, under a Chief Preceptor or Master, who was appointed for the whole of Yorkshire. The first known Chief Preceptor, Br. Walter Brito, was in office *circa* 1220. Although there are some large gaps in our knowledge in this respect, this group of preceptories is very interesting, since they illustrate how admirably organised the Templars were. Here they were settled yet mobile, one of the constant paradoxes of the Order.

The vast expanse of Yorkshire moors afforded fine training grounds for recruits (novices) to the order, before they embarked for active service in the east.

Nevertheless, Yorkshire was not only devoted to the training of Knights. The county was profitable in other ways, supporting the preceptories and raising funds through the woollen industry for example. Natural resources, including water power, were readily available. Watermills, more dependable than windmills, were used for mechanical fulling (the cleansing of cloth) and a variety of purposes besides the milling of wheat. Wherever they were erected, they gathered round them a cluster of houses which often led to shifts in population and industrial activity. The use of water power for fulling resulted in the concentration of English woollen cloth-making in the west and north-west. The fast-running streams of the

Yorkshire Dales were ideal for this purpose and some of the best sheep were bred in these parts. The Templars deserve the credit for their share in these developing projects.

It seems that in Yorkshire their farm work consisted mainly of stock raising and the growing of crops, with some sheep farming. The Templars held land in almost every Hundred in Yorkshire. Here, year by year as elsewhere, a small number of Templars occupied each provincial house and devoted themselves to the adjacent property, employing for the purpose the labour of the neighbourhood. Generally, the brethren worked the large farms themselves and sub-let their smaller properties.

As recognised guardians of travellers, much of their local work in the Preceptories was akin to that provided by a hospital (or hospice) for wayfarers. King Stephen (1104-1154) gave them the manor of Steynton in Yorkshire, on condition that they "find a chaplain to celebrate divine service daily and to receive and entertain poor guests and pilgrims there, and to bring and blow the horn every night at dusk, lest pilgrims and strangers should lose their way". We know of this instance, but it is not likely to have been the only one to cater for those important needs.

The oldest preceptory in the county was Temple Hirst. Considered within the old divisions of the county, the geographical distribution is fairly central, with four preceptories in the North Riding, five in the West and only one in the East.

COPMANTHORPE, to the south of York: the history of this foundation is not clear. It is known that the Preceptor of Copmanthorpe was keeper of the castle mills at York, which were first mentioned *circa* 1135 and were soon afterwards granted to the Templars. The mills have long since been demolished. The nearby St. George's chapel, north-west of the mills, also belonged to the Templars. The origin of this dates from 1232, in which year Henry III granted them 'a piece of land near the mill of the said brethren, without York', on which they erected the chapel of St. George where their chaplain officiated. It was well furnished, possessing a gilt chalice, nine service books of different kinds, and various vestments and ornaments. Not a fragment of this chapel now remains standing.

At some time prior to 1258 William Malbys gave the manor of Copmanthorpe and other property, on condition that the Templars should support a chaplain to celebrate Mass for the donor and his relatives in the chapel of the manor. At Copmanthorpe there was a small house with a Preceptor resident in 1292, but later it was joined to Ribstone and became part of that preceptory for the last fifteen years or so. (This would seem to have been part of a general reorganisation after the fall of Acre and the consequent departure of Knights from the Holy Land.)

Robert de Reygate, Preceptor of Copmanthorpe, with John, chaplain of the castle mills, was accused in 1292 of having set nets below the mills to catch the King's fish, somewhere near the confluence of the Ouse and Foss rivers.

The village of Copmanthorpe has in modern times become assimilated into York and no obvious traces of Templar occupation are left. The Parish Church of St. Giles, a long low building of great simplicity and retaining some Norman windows, may well have Templar associations, though not obviously so.

FAXFLEET, the only preceptory in the East Riding of York, was among the most important in the county and one of the chief recruiting centres. The date of its foundation is not known. Faxfleet marks the confluence of two rivers, the Ouse and the Trent. It was a recognised port of call for little ships, though not as important as Hull. Being the only Templar house in the county with a direct outlet to the sea, by way of the Humber, Faxfleet was most probably the embarkation point for all the Knights travelling from Yorkshire to Outremer.

The chapel there was well provided and there was 'a certain treasury with many written deeds and bulls relating to estates in Yorkshire', which was duly locked and sealed with the seals of the Sheriff and the Preceptor of Yorkshire. This sounds as though the title deeds of all the Templar estates throughout the county[33] were lodged here; it could also be that other land owners lodged their documents with the Templars at Faxfleet for safe custody. In any event this was considered a secure place and well guarded.

Perhaps the treasury was in fact a central chancery where the legal work was done. This would be necessary to record the transfer of property from a donor – possibly a feudal knight joining the Order and bringing his lands into its possession. This function would have required a staff of literate and learned clerks (clerics), probably priests of the order rather than Knights, concentrated at this Preceptory. William de Grafton, the last Preceptor of Faxfleet, was also Chief Preceptor of Yorkshire.

Excavators of Temple Garth, at the west end of the village of Etton (in 1965-67), found fragments of green glazed pottery and local York and Humber ware, together with half a dozen horseshoes, one with a nail still protruding: simple and practical artefacts, just the kind of things we should expect to find on a Templar site in this area.

FOULBRIDGE, near Yeddingham (North Riding). Founded before 1226. Little is known of this preceptory. The contents of the chapel included four crosses, 'two with images and two without'. The Templars supported a chaplain and fulfilled the work of charity by giving alms three days a week to any poor persons who came. (The Templars' Rule commanded the brothers to give daily to the almoner a tenth of their bread for distribution to the poor.)

PENHILL, West Witton, in Wensleydale (North Riding)
This preceptory (founded not later than *circa* 1200) was also known as Temple Dowskar or Dove Skar. It was a very small house and was founded by William Fitz Hervey, or by Roger de Mowbray, a crusader who by a charter of *circa* 1155 granted to the Templars the right to cut timber in his Yorkshire forests at Nidderdale, Malzeard and Masham, for the building of three houses wherever they might wish at Penhill, Cowton and Stranghow. These lay at some distance apart, between Wensleydale and Whitby. It seems that Stranghow never became a preceptory, since nothing more is heard of it. Grants of money were made for maintaining the lights of St. Catherine and the Holy Cross at Penhill; that is, lights kept burning for the donors at those altars or shrines. The chapel was dedicated in honour of Our Lady and St. Catherine.

Some excavation was begun at Penhill in the nineteenth century. The chapel ruins were uncovered in 1840. The excavation revealed the stone base of an altar and some stone coffins in the chapel. These remains are listed as a 'Scheduled Ancient Monument', protected by a fence, and there the matter rests. Foundations of the residential buildings of the preceptory have not been exposed, though their position is known. Outside the east wall a number of stone coffins were found (at some time prior to 1884) lying side by side and containing bones. Pieces of armour, bits and spurs were also discovered, suggesting that this site may have been a cavalry station. What has become of these artefacts is not known.

Enlarging on this, all that can now be seen above ground lies compactly in a grassy field on high ground up Temple Bank, an isolated site which has become part of the Yorkshire Dales National Park. There would seem nothing further to be discovered within the four walls of the plain rectangular chapel, which has neither bases of columns nor indications of windows left. Remains of the walls stand approximately three feet high and four feet thick, with interior walls at the east end only a few inches above ground level. In size and shape this chapel bears no resemblance to the spacious Cistercian churches of Yorkshire. Three empty unmarked graves (the stone coffins mentioned above) are visible in front of the altar and possible remains of a piscina. Entrance was by a south doorway.

There is no direct access by road. A farm in the vicinity is still known as Temple Farm. Some land in the hamlet of Swinithwaite, lower down in the Dale (or valley) of the Ure, belonged to the Templars. There is something of a mystery about this since, according to an Itinerary written by Charles Fothergill in 1805, 'the place near Swinethwaite yet called the Temple has immemorably borne that title.' He mentions a local tradition 'that there stood a Temple in which the Knights Templar were accustomed to meet', then relates that several years previously, 'perhaps twelve' (that is, *circa* 1793), 'in making some alterations on the estate, the green mounds and part which had generally been supposed the foundation of the ancient temple was opened when…not only the foundations but a considerable portion of the lower walls of the temple were discovered entire: the building was circular and of about ten yards diameter; within the outer wall was another and like it circular and about two feet within forming a walk all round the centre being a circular hollow space. There were several entrances into it at stated distances: the whole was remarkably strong, the cement in particular and well built and amongst the rubbish were found several capitals and parts of columns…' Unfortunately, the remains were, in the absence of the owner, totally destroyed by workmen, to build new walls on the estate of Swinethwaite Hall.

From the description of this temple being larger and circular, as well as comparison of the material dates, it is clear that this could not have been on the site of the Penhill Preceptory, but was a separate building which we cannot now see.

RIBSTONE (or Ribstan) and WETHERBY together formed a single preceptory (West Riding). Founded *circa* 1217.

Robert Lord de Ros, a great benefactor, granted the Manor of Ribstone and the advowson of the church. Besides other land and windmills, the Templars here received grants of woods nearby. There are some remains of their buildings.

The chapels at Ribston and Wetherby were simply furnished; however Ribstone possessed two silver cups, three masers and ten silver spoons, more secular plate than all the other preceptories in Yorkshire. As mentioned earlier, Copmanthorpe became joined to this preceptory.

An unsuccessful attempt was made to establish a roadside market at Walshford Bridge in 1227. Within thirteen years the Templars found it advantageous to transfer the place of trading from there to Wetherby, three and a half miles south.

TEMPLE COWTON (or East Cowton), (North Riding). Founded *circa* 1155. The Preceptor and two other brothers lived here. Their buildings comprised a hall, chamber, chapel, kitchen, brewhouse and smithy. There must have been some local labourers employed to help in the work of this preceptory. In the chamber (of the Preceptor?) was kept a sealed chest which contained 'all the charters of the Temple of Scotland together with various charters of certain estates in England'. From this it would seem that Cowton performed a similar legal function to Faxfleet, for different areas.

The church at Kirby Fleetham was probably used as the chapel of this house for a time. TEMPLE HIRST, south of Selby (West Riding). Founded *circa* 1152 by Ralph de Hastings, who with William de Hastings gave lands at Hurst and Wyxham. (At that time Richard de Hastings was Master in England.) Little is known of this preceptory. The buildings comprised a hall, chapel, kitchen, larder and outbuildings. Though there were 200 acres of land, it was inferior to Newsam in its quantity of livestock.

The church at Kellington was used by the 'brethren of the soldiery of the temple'. The chapel at Hirst must have been built before 1185, as 40 acres in Fenwick were given prior to that year for the support of a chaplain at Hirst. They also had a chapel at Norton. Some remains of the preceptory have been embodied in the buildings of Temple Farm.

TEMPLE NEWSAM, three miles from the centre of Leeds in the Vale of Aire (West Riding). The date of foundation of this preceptory is uncertain. Henry de Laci, founder of Kirkstall Abbey, gave the site some time before 1181. After 1185 further land was acquired, until the preceptory had about 765 acres.

The buildings comprised the chapel, kitchen, dormitory, brewhouse, furnace, hall, the 'pistrina' (or pistrinum, the bakehouse, which may also have included the apothecary and farrier's drug store) and dairy; clearly a large and very important establishment. There was a grange at Skelton. The church of Whitkirk became the chapel of the preceptory and remained in the patronage of the Master. It has since been rebuilt.

Temple Newsam was predominantly a cavalry depot. The whole economy of the estate was directed towards supporting the Knight and his charger. Granaries were well filled with oats and wheat. Stables were abundant with a farrier's shop nearby, but the accommodation for the Knights was restricted to mere sufficiency governed by rigorous frugality. Military efficiency demanded that every emergency should be anticipated and provided for. A perfectly organised community would have been found at Temple Newsam when at the zenith of its efficiency. The blacksmith, the baker, the farmer, the herdsman, the farrier, the armourer, as well as the brethren in arms or esquires, with the chaplain(s) and Knights, made up the personnel of the preceptory. The first fulling mill in England, mentioned in 1185, was at Temple Newsam.

Nothing remains of the preceptory except the name. The Temple also survives in the names of local farms and streets. On buildings in the Ainstey region of Leeds have been found the crosses with which the Templars marked their possessions, as has been shown at Sandford; though the Leeds examples were mostly double barred types which they sometimes used, unlike the more familiar Templar cross at Sandford (the 'Cross Patee'). Examples of such markers, taken from property in Templar Street, Leeds, are kept in the museum at St. John's Gate, Clerkenwell, London.

In York Minster library are some 15 documents under seal, grants and confirmations of gifts to the Templars at Middleton, near Ilkley, and Temple Newsam. They are each about the size of a postcard, written on parchment.

WESTERDALE (North Riding). Founded before 1203, since on 25th June of that year King John confirmed the gift of the estate, for which free warren was granted to the Templars in 1248. The preceptory consisted of a hall, chapel, kitchen and outbuildings.

WHITLEY (West Riding). The manor of Whitley came to the Templars before 1248. Otherwise nothing seems to be known of it in this conection. It has been suggested that Whitley was raised to the status of a preceptory late in its history, perhaps even at the beginning of the fourteenth century; but this is only conjecture and of no real help.

As Professor Frank Barlow remarked[34], 'It is significant, perhaps, that the bulk of the endowments given to the Temple in England were situated in the eastern half of the kingdom…in the sheep-rearing counties and those connected with Flanders and the fairs of Champagne.' The counties on the eastern side of England are for the most part less than 300 feet above sea level and amenable to cultivation (even if with some initial difficulty). We have seen why Yorkshire and Lincolnshire were especially favoured by the Templars. On the other hand, the rocky infertile Cumbrian region to the west did not attract them. Agriculture was the key to the Temple's economy before their financial activities developed, and it remained indispensable. Their policy was unaltered; whatever fluctuations of fortune affected the Order, it had to be self-supporting, the land had to produce sufficient for their needs.

The Chief Preceptor of Yorkshire, being very distant from the London headquarters, was a powerful official having responsibility for oversight of all those properties. Their work seems to have epitomised Templar activity in all its varied forms: training in the duties of knighthood; farming; the growing of crops, dependent upon climate and soil; all the skills necessary for the support of their communities. In addition, water-driven cloth-fulling mills may have been introduced into England by the Templars, taking root in the West Riding and other localities and stimulating the Anglo-Flemish wool trade. If their policy was generally unchanging, so too was the essential agricultural environment, alongside of such industrial progression.

Alfred Duggan[35] has pointed out that with regard to the Latin Kingdom of Jerusalem before 1187, 'there was just not enough agricultural land to support the knights necessary for its defence'. We can see from our study of the Templars how well they realised the importance of this factor in their own situation. Their agricultural lands were widespread and never limited to Outremer. It has been the recurrent theme running through their story here: in Templar England they were well provided for. From first to last their resources were developed so that there was always enough, and to spare. With less land at their disposal, this might not have been so in a year of poor harvest. The fact that each brother handed over a tithe of his daily bread ration to be given to poor wayfarers points to the working of an efficient economy. What was produced for use in the preceptory allowed for this distribution to the poor, while also ensuring that the brothers still had adequate nutrition to maintain their strength. The standard of living may not have been the same throughout the English preceptories, since (from various causes) some were more productive than others; yet the minimum bread and water promised to each Templar was more symbolic than actual.

Whether the early circular churches were demolished and then superseded by larger rectangular churches, or whether the two co-existed (as will be considered later), their purpose was the same: to be the fixed centre of Templar life in that place, the focal point where quiet recollected worship linked them for ever to Jerusalem, Rome and the whole Church.

BRINGING IT ALL TOGETHER

From the information available, it should be possible to form a true, unfanciful picture of the Templars' life and their place in the economy of England.

To the ordinary people in town and village they must have seemed aloof, concerned with their own business, shrewd in their dealings, yet most Christian in their quest. They renounced the world, as did all monks, but over and above that, they undertook a special commitment, which marked them out as the spearhead of Christendom.

An early corporate seal, said to represent the founders of the order, shows two knights riding on one horse; this has been taken as symbolic of the monastic poverty of the Templars. There was always a note of austerity about the lives of these sturdy, bearded men. In a small treatise 'On the Praise of the New Knighthood', St. Bernard wrote idealistically of the Templars:

'First of all, there is discipline and unqualified obedience. Everybody comes and goes according to the will of the commander. Everybody wears the clothing given to him, and no one goes in search of food or garments according to his whim. They live in a community, soberly and in joy, without wife or children: and to reach evangelical perfection, they live in the same house, in the same manner, without calling anything their own, solicitous to preserve the unity of spirit in the bond of peace.'

Their chapels were straightforward buildings[36], seemingly without aisles or transepts, obviously not intended for processions and elaborate worship. They were not public like parish churches, but simply for the brethren residing in the Preceptory and any guests who might be there. The Temple in London was an obvious exception to this, since it was the most important Preceptory and the headquarters of the English Province. The church was therefore bigger, to accommodate the various important personages who visited there. Even so, it was not enormous compared with the great abbey churches. It is clear that although the English Templars received large donations of land and had sufficient income from their properties, they did not invest a fortune in buildings, which would have diverted funds from the Holy Land. Similarly, they had no reason to build highly fortified castles in England, apart from the Welsh border perhaps, and it is certain that they would not have incurred needless expenditure.

The first Templars were practical, single-minded men who banded themselves together to protect Christian pilgrims; that was their distinctive vocation. In order to fulfil it, they had to develop resources: hence the need for country estates. It seems that quite often the Templars managed to acquire the best and most fertile regions, suited for their use, for which they can hardly be blamed.

The Preceptories in England (and elsewhere) were established to provide support for the Knights on active service. If that fact is lost sight of, the Templars here would seem very similar to any other international religious order, except that those in authority were not priests. From its particular nature, the Order of the Temple consisted mainly of lay brothers neither in Holy Orders nor preparing to be. Before 1172 it was wholly non-clerical, depending upon Canons Regular or secular priests for administrations; after that date priests were admitted to the Order, in a non-combatant role.

Just as the early Cistercians were said to be 'the new soldiers of Christ, poor men with the pauper Christ', so too were the Templars, in a more physical sense. They were able to accept the harshness of the Gospel as well as its sweetness. Life in the Preceptories was wholesome, well-regulated, certainly not luxurious or easy.

Besides the Preceptories, a large number of manors or *camerae* belonged to the Order, a secular chaplain, a bailiff and other dependents and servants usually being maintained there. In some country districts there were also granges. These were monastic farm settlements, at first probably comprising only a barn and small dwelling place, but sometimes becoming almost a replica of the parent house.

It is clear from the history of the Templars that they were not averse to moving their Preceptories from one place to another, given sufficient reason, as from the Old Temple in London to the New, from Cowley to Sandford, and perhaps at Dover. Such moves were never to distant sites since they needed to manage the same estates. The Benedictine virtue of stability was of less value to the Templars than their absolute loyalty to the Order. This was a high standard and very few Knights seem to have failed or acted dishonourably, as far as we know.

The fact that there were in England only two infirmaries specially dedicated to the care of the sick (Denney and Eagle) may suggest that the Templars were a remarkably robust body of men not prone to illness, or that the wounded did not usually live to return home! Such conclusions are not reliable. There is so much that we do not know.

If there is an air of mystery about the Templars at home, it is because in their life and worship they were essentially private, even secretive about their customs; there was no reason to be otherwise. Their interior contemplative life was the necessary source of strength for great deeds in the field. A delicate balance had to be kept between the spiritual and material aspects. They lived and died in the faith. The core of their life was the Mass and they were expected to to attend the daily Office unless legitimately prevented.[37]

In addition, senior professed members of the Order, wearing their distinctive white cloaks, would gather at night in the candle lit chapel and in honour of the Head of Christ would sing the psalm: 'Deus misereatur nostri, et benedicat nobis: illuminet vultum suum super nos…' (May God have mercy on us and bless us: may He make His face to shine upon us) words which occur in the Mass of the Holy Cross. We have no details of their nocturnal adoration, but it may have concluded with the veneration of a relic of the Holy

Cross or some other relic brought from the Holy Land or Constantinople; or, after 1264, some form of Benediction of the Blessed Sacrament, then a new devotion not widely practised.

We can appreciate that there was nothing intrinsically wrong about secret services when we think of the 'hidden churches' in Holland (several centuries later), where the faithful gathered in secret for worship.

The key to understanding the spirit of the Templars is their intense devotion to the person of Christ (and there followed, in consequence, protection of the Holy Places and the Christian pilgrims). In the era of the Crusades this was not in the least strange or surprising. That is why Templars sometimes built circular churches, to remind themselves (and people who could not make the pilgrimage to Jerusalem) of the rotunda covering the Holy Sepulchre of the Lord. Furthermore, the impetus of the Franciscans led to devotion to the Passion becoming popular throughout western Christendom. St. Louis, King of France and a Franciscan tertiary, brought the Crown of Thorns to Paris in 1239. By that time most of the Preceptories were well established and the Templars were bound to have been influenced by such an event, so close to the Paris Temple.

The Templecombe Christ is a powerful image of the Head of Christ probably derived from the Holy Shroud folded over. This has already been discussed but is of importance in this context. According to a Minorite friar, there were known to be four copies of a portrait of Christ in England in the possession of the Templars: one in the sacristy of the Temple Church in London, another at 'Bristleham' (either Bristol or Bisham), a third at Temple Bruer and the fourth at a place beyond the Humber (i.e. in the Yorkshire preceptory). Of course there may have been more copies; either the friar did not know of the Templecombe Christ or it was moved there from another preceptory.[38]

The present devotion to the Holy Shroud in Turin, as the only true likeness of Christ, can be seen as a belated vindication of the Templars. Their picture of Christ was not an untrue one far removed from reality.

While not suggesting that the Templars were mystics – though some may have been – it does seem that this special attraction to the person of Christ and the saving Cross was always essential to their life and character.

The day to day life of the English Templars at home was much less spectacular than the heroic incidents involving the Knights in Egypt and the Holy Land. Ordinary domestic life rarely made news and so we know less about it. However, we do know that Templars slept in dormitories (or dorters) in their shirts and breeches. At night they had to keep a light burning as a moral precaution 'lest the dark enemy, from whom God preserves us, should find some opportunity'. They were allowed to drink wine with every meal, though some English Knights seem to have used cider, perhaps because it was cheaper or easier to obtain. They were allowed to eat meat three times a week; meals were eaten in silence, so they could listen attentively to readings from the Holy Scripture.

These domestic customs were not at all unusual for monks, yet compared with some of the other religious orders active at that time the Templars showed marked differences. They were not men of immense learning like the Dominicans, nor mendicants like the Franciscans. They did not spend long hours in libraries or scriptoria like the Benedictines, advancing the cause of learning. They were not professional scholars, writers or theologians. Their enterprise took other forms, varying from one Preceptory to another, but always serving the common good. They were farmers, millers, expert horsemen, landlords, administrators and much more. They turned their hand to whatever needed to be done. They would have fished (as monks were always supposed to have done!) in the river at Sandford and possibly in London, but their fishing was more highly developed than the traditional method.

Fish was a staple item of food and manorial fishponds were frequently planned to serve a dual purpose as moats. Excavations at one such Templar property at Washford, near Redditch in Worcestershire, have unearthed remains of a fish-house and curing furnace associated with the ponds and breeding tanks. The finest mediaeval fishponds are at Harringworth in northern Northamptonshire which were also owned by the Templars. The ponds are so large and complex in their arrangement that they were clearly used as commercial fish farms, for breeding and selling fish elsewhere. This trade, no doubt, provided a valuable source of income.

In the latter part of its existence, members of the Order won fresh fame as bankers and money-lenders, showing the trust that people had in them. Royal funds were held in safe deposit at the New Temple in London. It was recognised that the Templars' honesty was solid and dependable. Being armed knights, they were often entrusted with the conveyance of money and valuables. Of course they had always carried money belonging to the Order itself between the Preceptories[39] and for deposit in the Temple in Paris and London; they were also engaged by kings and private persons to guard shipments of money and valuables, all of which brought its own dangers.

There was also what might be described as another public service, of a very different nature and not exclusive to the Temple. Templars had the right of sanctuary, which could be claimed by any persons who were fugitives under the law, before they abdured the realm and went into exile. By various Papal Bulls it was enjoined that no person should lay violent hands upon the persons or property of those fleeing to Templar houses for refuge. This was very much in keeping with the Christian principles of mercy and justice, which were integral parts of the Templar way of life. Their houses were often referred to as hospices, but, unlike the Hospitallers, they did not run almshouses to give permanent shelter to poor men.

In those years when Jerusalem was accessible and pilgrimage to the Holy Places was not interrupted by hostilities, pilgrims liked to travel on Templar ships. This was with good reason, for on board them they felt safe; they could rest assured that the captain would not jettison the poorer passengers in a sudden emergency, in order to conserve his stores for the safe transport of the wealthier travellers, as happened all too often. Neither would there be the risk of being held to ransom on the high seas, nor kidnapped and taken to some Moslem port to be sold into slavery, a practice which also occurred frequently. Such hazards naturally made pilgrims fearful of the journey to Outremer and all the more ready to trust themselves to the Templars, who would take care of them.

Matthew Paris, the learned chronicler of St. Alban's Abbey, described, in a memorable passage, a departure of Knights for the Holy Land:

'They set out, passing through the town with spears held aloft, shields displayed, and piebald banners advanced, in unbroken formation, and sought a blessing from the people who crowded to see them pass. The Brethren uncovered, bowed their heads from side to side, and recommended themselves to the prayers of all.'

Whether or not this is strictly an eye-witness account of the Templars' ride, it has a ring of truth about it. There seems no reason why Matthew should not have been in the crowd himself and seen the Templars leaving one of our southern ports, such as Dover. It was not such an unusual sight, but one which would always arouse interest and even a sense of pride akin to patriotism, for these champions of Christendom were 'athletes of God' and the 'new Maccabees' (as St. Bernard had called the Order), deserving of prayers and goodwill to encourage them.

Given the business sense and practical nature of the Templars it does not surprise us that the first ships to sail eastward under the red cross swiftly grew into a well organised fleet. In addition to transporting Knights they began to appropriate much of the pilgrim traffic which, from England alone, was considerable. From what we know of the pilgrims and the Templars it would have been strange had it not been so. We can see the working out of this east/west transport. Pilgrims to the Holy Land had a special dependent relationship with the Templars; was it not for their protection that the Order was established? No one knew that territory better, nor the journey with its hazards. Pilgrims were often inexperienced and needed guidance as well as reliable transport.

It has been shown that certain of the English houses were strategically placed in relation to navigable rivers and ports of embarkation, particularly Bristol. This falls into place as part of the overall planning. Regular voyages were made from Europe by way of La Rochelle or Marseilles to the Holy Land twice a year, in the spring and summer, under the conduct of the Templars and the Hospitallers of St. John. On these voyages newly admitted Knights went from the Preceptories. They took with them hired foot soldiers, armed pilgrims and large sums of money raised from the possessions of the brethren. By this means a continual succour was afforded to the Latin Kingdom of Jerusalem and other colonies in the Holy Land. At one time the Templars conveyed 6000 pilgrims in one year. Navigating the seas in the depth of winter was always considered too dangerous an undertaking, not surprisingly so. Sea journeys were never popular with mediaeval man because of the risks and uncertainty involved, as mentioned by such chroniclers as Joinville. This is well known, so the point need not be laboured.

Sometimes the ships returned with more specialised cargo, as when in 1247 Br. William de Sonnac, Master of the Temple in Jerusalem, sent a distinguished Knight Templar to bring to England and present to King Henry III 'a portion of the Blood of our Lord, which He shed on the Cross for the salvation of the world, inclosed in a handsome crystalline vessel'. The relic was authenticated under seal by the Patriarch of Jerusalem, the bishops, abbots and nobles of the Holy Land. After the King 'going on foot' had personally carried it from St. Paul's to Westminster, he presented it to the Abbey of St. Peter to be kept there, as related by Matthew Paris. Templars were much in evidence on that occasion.

A contemporary event related to Templar life in this country was the naming of St. George the Great Martyr as Patron Saint of England, at Osney Abbey, Oxford, in 1222. The English Templars were in all probability active in spreading devotion to St. George. This is a reasonable surmise since the Knights knew his shrine at Lydda in the Holy Land, and as a Roman cavalryman St. George appealed strongly to Crusaders and Templars; their chapel near the castle mills in York was dedicated to St. George. At Balsall an annual fair on the vigil, feast and morrow of St. George (April 22-24) was granted to the Templars by Henry III *circa* 1216-17. This suggests some local *cultus* already popular.

It is disappointing that (apart from formal church dedications) we know nothing of any Marian devotion practised by the Templars, though it is very probable that they made use of the eleventh century antiphon 'Salve Regina' as an evening devotion in the Preceptories. It is a known fact that in western Christendom the twelfth and thirteenth centuries saw an intense growth in Marian devotion, expressed in many ways. In somewhat romantic fashion, without evidence, Fr. Vincent McNabb O.P. called the Salve Regina 'the war-song of the Crusaders, sung when the army of Christians first caught sight of Jerusalem'. Whether this was always the case and to what extent it would have influenced the Templars we cannot tell. The antiphon did not originate in the Holy Land, so there is no special reason for such an association of ideas.

What else do we know of the religious practices peculiar to the Order? Practically nothing with certainty. The devotional exercise of the Via Crucis, now known as Stations of the Cross, existed then in a fairly rudimentary form which may have been familiar to the Templars. More than that we cannot say. We can only suppose that something so linked to Jerusalem (being in fact a spiritual pilgrimage) could have a strong appeal to them. The special services of Holy Week would have a similar attraction to those for whom wearing the red cord was a constant reminder of the Passion of Christ.

It also seems probable that at times of grave necessity (as in 1245) their prayer was supplemented by night vigils. Corporate prayer would have been limited by the number of men available at a given time. The prescribed prayers repeated in lieu of the daily offices of the church were counted on the beads of a rosary, attached to the sword belt when travelling. At other times the Knights, in common with other Christians, joined their hands ('junctis manibus') to pray. None of this would be unusual or novel. Indeed it underlines the fact that the Templars were not singular in the practice of their religion. In an age of faith and liturgical development they were open to the same influences as other orders and the church at large. Frequent communion was not usual.

In some respects, corporate worship in the Preceptories would have been simpler than the late mediaeval liturgy which we have inherited. In the absence of direct evidence, it seems probable that from the first the Templars followed the liturgy of the Canons Regular of the Holy Sepulchre in Jerusalem (which was of French origin), as did the Knights of St. John of Jerusalem and the Teutonic Knights, both contemporary orders in the Holy Land. However, in England the Templars may well have adopted the Sarum use.

On board ship, when the normal celebration of Mass was considered impossible, the chaplains followed the custom of the time and compromised with a *Missa Sicca* (dry mass), an abbreviated form without consecration. This was also known as *Missa Nautica*; though not restricted to voyages, it was not a substitute for Mass on *terra firma*.

What can be learned from the buildings permanently set apart for the Templars' worship, at the heart of the Preceptories? If they are in keeping with the Rule, we should expect to find simplicity, integrity and strength expressed there in the stones; buildings fit for their purpose, without ostentation. This was doubtless true, so far as we can judge from viewing the relevant sites. Certain conclusions may also be drawn as to the transition in architectural styles in this period (whatever technical names are used).

However frustrating it may seem, we could not expect to find any church interior remaining exactly as it was when the Templars knew it. The New Temple in London and Temple Balsall have both been altered substantially; probably the chapel at Rothley (*circa* 1240) gives us the most authentic impression, though here the east window and roof were modified in the fourteenth century, in the style of the time. The ruins of Penhill still have a sense of solidity, even though we now see the altar and tombs long since broken and plundered. Without the shelter of a roof it is not easy to reconstruct such a place of worship and to imagine services being held there. Certainly, if the present font in Sompting Church was replaced by a simple stone-built altar, the Templar chapel would bear a closer resemblance to its original appearance.

Since there was then plenty of land available for Templar buildings it would be very surprising if their altars were not correctly orientated. From the examples we are able to investigate, it appears that eastward position was indeed the normal practice. To all Christians, looking eastward in church always symbolised their looking towards Jeruslem; more especially so for Templars. Tracing a line eastward from anywhere in England would not lead to Jerusalem, but geographical exactitude was less important than the symbolism of the orient. As the sun rose in the east, so did Christ the unconquered 'sun of righteousness'. Towards Him they looked.

The rectangular termination of the east end (instead of an apse) was a Cistercian feature which was reflected in Templar churches e.g. the New Temple, Sandford and Penhill. They probably built in that plain style for reasons of economy, both of labour and expense, as well as from a desire for simplicity. However, the triple lancet windows where they occurred had obvious Trinitarian inspiration. Porches at the west end were not often a feature of Templar churches, though one outstanding example exists. Gilbert Scott recognised the large open porch of the New Temple as a 'priceless example of mediaeval architecture', and who would disagree? There is nothing like it on any other English Templar site.

It is most unlikely that the Templars troubled themselves about the acoustics of their church buildings, since no one else did in this period. The sound of Divine worship - the 'opus Dei' – was for the praise of God, not to please human ears with its beauty.

Looking now more closely at the architectural aspect, we find that Templar church building passed through two distinct phases; (1) the round or oval church, as at Bristol, Temple Bruer and Garway, and (2) the rectangular or square shape, to be seen at Rothley Temple and Temple Balsall. This explodes the oft-repeated theory that the Templars always built round churches (because of their origin in Jerusalem). They sometimes did so, but it was not an inflexible rule. Rather it can be said that they began building circular churches, but, as Gothic influence from northern France grew stronger, they adopted the rectangular plan. From the dates available, it would seem that sometime after 1186 the change of style occurred. All the round or oval churches of which we have knowledge date from before then, though some rectangular ones were also built during the twelfth century. The smaller chapels, as at Temple Ewell and Sandford, were of the square or rectangular type, probably for reasons of utility. At the New Temple in London (*circa* 1185 and 1240) the two phases fused into a synthesis which clearly demonstrates the old and new, making the best of both[40]. In the first type, which formed a double apse, the altar would have been in the east with the brethren ranged around the wall (under those curious heads!) and perhaps also in the centre of the Round. The second type provvided for an inward facing, monastic or collegiate arrangement of seating, which has become more familiar.

It has been remarked that Templar churches (i.e. those built for their own use) were generally designed without transepts, side aisles, or towers. Like all generalisations, this raises difficulties, since we can find exceptions to the rule.

The twin towers at Temple Bruer were an unusual feature, so far unexplained. In open county the erection of towers for observation and defensive purposes cannot be entirely ruled out. It seems somewhat unlikely in the Templar period, though there is the strong detached tower at Garway; while the ornamental aspect of the towers was an unwarranted luxury which would not have entered into the builders' minds. The remaining possibility seems more satisfactory: in England (then as now) church towers housed one or more bells, to alert the people to the time of service and call them to church. This may well have been the case at Temple Bruer where tenants lived nearby. In areas where the Templars were more an enclosed community without close neighbours dependent on them, this need for bell towers did not arise; but why were *two* towers necessary at Temple Bruer? The question remains unanswered. Possibly one of the towers was planned to contain a secret chapel where a portrait of Christ's head could be kept securely; we do not know.

Certainly in such counties as Lincolnshire one can hear church bells ringing out across the flat country long before one comes to town or village. Perhaps it became customary for people in these parts to travel several miles to Mass at Temple Bruer, guided by the sound of its bells: not that that adds to our appreciation of the varied styles of Templar buildings.

Having established the principle that the round came first, we should notice that the later rectangular building was projected eastward of the round, thus preserving the orientation. It has been noted that wherever possible the worshippers faced east at the most sacred moments. It could even be suggested that the round was associated in the minds of the Knights with the field chapels in the centre of the camp; while the extension was typical of the permanent chapels of the Preceptories at home. The idea is fanciful, but not wholly irrelevant. Further, a circular building is not normally suggestive of fortification.

If Bristol was typical of the first phase, Temple Balsall is the final statement of the second phase of architecture which evolved, but continued to be functional and avoided excess of detail. Although we have that much certainty about Templar churches, the rest of their buildings are problematical, for no preceptory in England survives in anything like complete condition. Of all too many there is nothing left to assist our mental reconstruction of the buildings as they were. Wytham in Lincolnshire preserves the foundations of a courtyard plan suitable to a farm environment, as has been described. This was more spread out than Temple Ewell which had a small compact plan, known from excavations: nothing could be simpler, or less pretentious. From comparisons such as that, it can be seen that Preceptories had no standard layout. Practical reasons for the differences can be adduced - the type and size of site, the precise use intended and the amount of money available to the Preceptor for domestic building. In some cases an existing manor house may have been used or added to. Not all would have been farms.

The Old Temple in London, besides having a round church built of imported Caen stone in the old style, had a garden and an orchard, a cemetery and outbuildings protected by a ditch. Even so, by 1161 this property had become too small for the expanding needs of the Knights. They required two halls and more space for military exercises. This was a special case owing to its national importance as headquarters.

As builders the Templars played a quietly ubiquitous part in the life of England, which should not be overlooked. It has been shown, with reference to Sompting parish church, how they added to existing churches for their own use without interfering with the course of parochial worship. This is unlikely to have been an isolated case. Something similar may have been done at Wilbraham and other places. What is obvious to us is the Templars' diligence in providing for their own spiritual and temporal needs, while honouring their obligations to others. It is not through any fault of their craftsmanship that many of their buildings have not endured.

Large churches like those at Shipley and Temple Balsall could not have been intended solely for the Templars' own use; they would not have needed buildings of such size and the notion of building for posterity would not have arisen. Future permanence was not to be had here.

The time-scale of their building seems somewhat compressed, when we remember that only fifty years elapsed from the completion of the New Temple Church to the building of Temple Balsall Church. During that half-century, a medieval man's lifetime, much had changed. Some people would see this reflected in their architecture, but this idea should not be pressed too far. They did not build for future scholars to study and analyse their work..

Of course it hardly needs saying that circular churches were not peculiar to England in this period; there was one founded by the Templars at Brindisi, southern Italy, and the more famous one in Paris. If in Marie Madeleine Gauthier's phrase, referring to the Holy Sephulcre in Jerusalem, 'the rotunda is the monumental reliquary of the dead and risen Christ', it had an essential quality for the unknown builders of these churches. While there was nothing in the nature of a 'blueprint' to guide them, it was natural that they should be inspired by the same principles.

An important factor in the extension of the original churches in the mid-thirteenth century could be that, by then, more funds had become available for the purchase of building materials (whether imported or produced locally) in addition to increased manpower. That may well be so, but the thrifty Templars did not demolish and rebuild. It was more practical and possibly more economical to add to the existing structure, bringing together both styles. Garway was an exception to this, for there the Twelfth century circular nave was supplanted by a rectangular nave on the same axis (see plan). Of the vanished round churches of Lincolnshire little can be said with certainty.

In 1174 the so called 'Gothic' architecture reached England (at Canterbury Cathedral) and its subsequent progress is well known. It would be unrealistic to suppose that the new style of the Ile de France did not affect Templar churches here, though the apse seems to have been less acceptable amongst Templars in England. Had this not been so, we could surely expect to find an apse at the New Temple in London. As it is, we have no certain knowledge of apsidal churches in any of the Preceptories here, with the possible exception of the crypt at Temple Bruer.

For many people visiting the London Temple, this is the only Templar church they have seen (or will ever see) and because of its unusual features they conclude that it is the model of all Templar churches, or that all round churches belonged to the Templars. Both incorrect opinions need to be disproved

For purposes of comparison, it seems convenient to select Paris. It is fair to compare the English and French headquarters for, although the latter was wantonly destroyed as a result of the French revolution, sufficient details of the structure remain. Its church 'resembled the Temple Church in London which has been considered the most beautiful of the remarkable churches with which the Templars marked their western properties.'[41] There were certainly resemblances in plan, in the familiar two stages of building, but differences in architectural proportions. What was done on Thames-side was not necessarily the same as by the Seine. The New Temple was not a copy. One fundamental difference is that here width was preferred to length; the New Temple is considerably shorter.

The church of the Paris Temple, Sainte Marie du Temple, patroness of the Order, had at first just a circular nave (or rotunda) 60 feet in diameter, built circa 1140, and a bell tower [42] which included a Chapel of the Holy Sepulchre on the ground level. In the thirteenth century the great porch, measuring about twenty feet wide by thirty feet deep, was added, with a new nave and choir ending in an apse, altogether some 100 feet in length, giving a total length of 190 feet. The absence of aisles or transepts would have tended to make the Church seem even longer. Tall windows with pointed arches rose almost to the roof. The whole appearance must have been cathedral-like, with proportions not found elsewhere.

Such building (on either side of the Channel) was an art of craftsmen working in anonymity for the glory of God and the spiritual health of the Order.

From such evidence as we have, it would seem that, while we can identify a Benedictine plan or a Carthusian plan, such is not the case with the Templars. Certain features, like a Hall and a Chapel (or Church) were common to all the Preceptories wherever they were situated, but there was no specific layout of buildings instantly recognisable as Templar.

At Strood we can see the thirteenth century type of stone-built first floor hall, above a vaulted undercroft and approached by an external flight of stairs; architecturally, the secular parallel to a church and its crypt. The Hall at Temple Ewell may have been similar, though earlier. As will be shown, halls were not always bare nor devoid of colour, if we consider the effect of shields hung up on special occasions, with Baucent and possibly other standards belonging to distinguished visitors. We also know of another simple and less militant kind of decoration: the wall plaster might be painted with red lines, to imitate ashlar masonry. This was a common type of early medieval wall decoration and traces of it still exist at Strood.

The purpose of the Hall is not entirely certain and may have varied. It was not ornamental. It probably contained the dormitory and if divided, may also have housed the refectory and a guest chamber. The smaller Preceptories would have done little entertaining of guests, unlike the more important centres, Temple Dinsley and London for example, where the Hall would have been large enough to accommodate a number of eminent visitors who came on business. The master of the Order, the Latin Patriarch of Jerusalem and several Kings of England are among those of whom we know. The Hall would have been as well used as the Church. On such occasions, there may have been some relaxation of those restrictions which St. Bernard thought so praiseworthy. Hospitality would have been adequate.

When Henry III was in France with Br. Robert de Sanford, Master of the Temple in London (in 1254), he was entertained by the Knights at the Temple in Paris. There, according to Matthew Paris, 'They feasted in the great hall, where hang the shields on every side, as many as they can place along the four walls,[43] according to the custom of the Order beyond our seas. ' The knights in England likewise exercised a magnificent hospitality and constantly entertained royalty, nobles, prelates and foreign ambassadors in the Hall of the New Temple, which was probably decorated with shields in a similar way. Immediately after the return of King Henry, some illustrious ambassadors from Castile came on a visit to the Temple; as the King 'greatly delighted to honour them', he commanded three pipes of wine to be placed in the cellars of the Temple for their use, together with meat from the royal forest in Essex.

A conjectural impresion, several centuries later.
The building in the background has not been identified.

Like most people, the Templars may well have enjoyed occasions, although events of this kind must be regarded as external to their proper life and really a compromise. Worldly wise in their dealings with the world's great ones, who found the Templars useful, the more spiritually minded brethren possibly found such trafficking irksome. Unlike the Cistercians, they could not avoid all contact with the world and its commerce. Walter Map, a twelfth century official not entirely in sympathy, wrote that the Templars, 'because of their offices, are held dear by prelates and kings, and high in honour, and carefully see to it that means for their exaltation are not wanting.' This seems to be a backhanded compliment to their honest efficiency. There can be no doubting the high regard in which the Order was held by several English kings. A Templar was chosen to be Almoner to Henry II. The same monarch bequeathed five thousand silver marks to the Order and it is said that he caused almsboxes to be placed in all the churches of his realm for contributions to aid the Templars which doubtless annoyed some of his parish clergy.

The Order of the Temple is frequently called a wealthy order, but corporately it needed to amass substantial funds: the cost of clothing and equipping the Knights with armour and weapons was very considerable, in addition to the horses. In the Rule, each Knight was allotted three horses. Feeding and maintaining even a small body of men and their horses, both here and overseas, was a constant expense which could not be shelved. There were many contingencies to be provided for in uncertain times.

Throughout the Order, in all its functions, ran a sense of balance. Individual members may have passed their lives in obscurity, but at the same time Templars served as advisers, messengers, envoys and sometimes arbiters to the Kings of England, France and Germany. In contrast to such privileged positions, every Templar was bound to remember that he was called to be a Christian warrior 'par excellence', the Knight who served God through the profession of arms no less than through his monastic discipline. There was no romantic ethos about the life; that was a much later invention.

The twelfth century Renaissance brought a more professional interest in the law and legal documents. This was reflected in the care for the Temple's charters at Faxfleet and Temple Cowton, besides the work of the London Temple. Official correspondence and legal work would have been the employment of clerks and chaplains, not serving Knights. Apart from a few carefully written Grants, we have little opportunity to examine their work. The Sandford Cartulary is the only surviving cartulary or register book of the English Templars.

Seen in the larger context of the Order as a whole, England, France and Spain were the three western countries of most importance to the Order, as its granaries and armouries. England was a source of revenue, derived from both trading and banking. No doubt the Templars' transactions had a beneficial effect on the national economy, for here they developed a flourishing export trade in wool, grain, fish, and dairy products. When a large section of the population were countrymen born and bred, it was natural that Templars should engage in those occupations when they were not on duty overseas. The fertile counties of Yorkshire and Lincolnshire together provided nearly half their total income. The medieval wool producing region stretched across the eastern counties from Northampton to Beverley. Every religious house in the Fens of Lincolnshire derived some part of its income from the sale of wool, so it need not surprise us that the Templars prospered in this trade. In the south and east of England particularly, they sold surplus grain - wheat oats and barley. They also grew peas and beans and in Kent, then as now the 'Garden of England', they specialised in fruit growing.

There was clearly no such person as a 'typical' Templar. Such modern terminology could have no meaning, for the Order embraced so many varied talents and its achievements were in so many fields. Such men do not conform to a type. In addition, the Temple (like other Religious orders and indeed all organisations made up of fallible human beings) suffered changes during its span of existence. Trading, financial concerns and any form of banking could hardly have been further from the minds of the founders, yet these things overtook the Templars and affected their lives - for good or ill.

Thomas W. Parker[44] concentrating on the non-religious aspects of the Templars, has made this assessment of their activities: 'When all is said and done, the Templars contributed much to western civilization as their participation and leadership in the Crusades and their services - political, administrative, and financial - to the Kings of England, and to the rulers of other states, indicate …' The most comprehensive charter favouring the Templars here was that granted by Henry III in the 11th year of his reign. Under this King the Templars were at the height of their influence in royal matters. They were, at that time, (the mid thirteenth-century) the foremost bankers of western Europe.

By his charter, Henry III showed himself to be one of the greatest benefactors of the Templars, confirming all previous donations and privileges granted to them. Extracts from this document will give some idea of their rights and possessions in England.

'…all reasonable donations of lands, men, and eleemosynary gifts … as well churches as worldly goods … with all liberties and free customs and immunities, in wood and plain, in meadow and pasture, in water and water mills, on highways and byways, in ponds and running streams, in marshes and fisheries, in granges and broad acres, within burgh and without the burgh [various legal rights] in season and out of season, at all times and in all places...

We ordain, likewise, that the aforesaid brethren shall for ever hereafter be freed from royal aids and sheriff's aids and officer's aids [and various services] and from the works of castles, parks, bridges and enclosures; and from the duty of providing carriages and beasts of burden, boats and vessels, and from the building of royal houses, and all other works …

And we concede also to the aforesaid brethren the privilege of cutting down trees in all the woods they possess … and of clearing and bringing the land into cultivation without any licence from our bailiffs, so that they may never at any time hereafter be in any way called to account by ourselves, or our heirs, or any of our bailiffs…

We ordain, moreover, that the aforesaid brethren and their men shall be quit and free from every kind of toll in all markets and fairs, and upon crossing bridges, roads and ferries, throughout the whole of our kingdom, and throughout all lands in which we are able to grant liberties … also that if any of their men be condemned to lose life or limb for crime or shall have fled from justice, or have committed any offence for which he has incurred forfeiture of his goods and chattels, the goods and chattels so forefeited shall belong to the aforesaid brethren ... as our bailiffs would or ought to have siezed them into our hands, had such goods and chattels belonged to ourselves, without the molestration or hindrance of the sheriffs or bailiffs , or any other person whatsoever

We moreover ordain, that if any of the liberties and privileges contained in this our charter shall happen to have been disused for a length of time, such disuse shall in no disrespect prejudice the right, but such liberty or privilege may again be exercised without contradiction, notwithstanding that it may have been discontinued and disused as aforesaid... and we prohibit all persons, on pain of forfeiture, from proceeding against them or their men contrary to this charter, for we have taken the aforesaid brethren and all their goods and possessions, and all their men, under our especial guardianship and protection ...'

Such an array of privileges was bound to arouse some envy and the accusation of arrogance, even if undeserved. Freedom from traditional feudal restrictions meant a lot to the Templars as it left them to do their work in their own way, untrammeled for the most part. Of course there were occasional disputes - some of which have been mentioned - when people were aggrieved by the independence of these men who seemed to be above the law; all law except that of God and the Pope (that is the moral law and canon law).

We cannot tell what opinions the rank and file of Englishmen held of the Red Cross Knights, though we can infer from Matthew Paris that the ordinary people who crowded to see them departing for service in the Holy Land were well disposed and enthusiastic. Otherwise they would have stayed at their work, or in their homes. Those who benefited from the Templars, directly or indirectly - and a great many people did - would have good reason to acclaim them. It is only fair to mention also that the Templars seem to have quenched their thirst freely; to 'drink like a Templar' became a proverbial saying. Not that they were alone in this respect, nor does it appear to have been detrimental to the Order.

Their living conditions were communal. They did not eat and sleep in separate houses like the Carthusians. Templars had their dormitories where (as has been said earlier) they slept with a lamp burning all night. They would be familiar with the scriptural implications of this: darkness represented an environment in which evil flourished unchecked. The single light pointed to the Lumen Christi conquering the darkness. It was like a continuing reminder of the night Office of Compline, reinforcing its message that they must be ready at all times to resist evil 'steadfast in the faith'.

In some of the small remote Preceptories where few were in residence at a time, there may have been a sense of loneliness, but men who had foresaken all worldly ties for the sake of their vocation were not easily daunted. Had such feelings worried them, they would have been of little use in action overseas. They lived (as we might say today) in a healthy environment unpolluted by noise, which was surely a blessing. We should not dwell too much on hardships; these men were Knights, prepared for such things.

One aspect of the Templars which has not been sufficiently appreciated by historians of the past is their colonizing of country districts, resulting in shifts of population. We know that, at Temple Bruer and Keele for example, the Templars established new villages and encouraged people to come and settle around the Preceptories as their tenants. This was a deliberate policy for obtaining farm workers in remote areas where little or no cultivation had been done and it seems to have worked well. There was no shortage of land, much of it still forest, awaiting only the labour, aided by the skill of the Preceptory staff, to make it productive. Whether the Templars made any lasting contribution to farming in England we cannot estimate; too much has happened since.[45]

The properties settled on the east side of England must have been extremely cold in the winter, with winds blowing in from the North Sea, across the bleak open fenland. Yet clearly, from the number of Preceptories founded there, the potential was worthwhile and if life was spartan, that was nothing strange to the Templars. Life in the wayfaring state was always a pilgrimage, as they well appreciated. Here they were called to dedication, efficiency, sacrifice, with few concessions to human comfort. Some people would say this was life stripped down to the essentials, the irreducible minimum; but it could also be argued that it was simply an exact following of Christ's counsels.

It will be remembered that St Bernard used a dual image, likening the Templars to both lambs and lions. There must always be a sense of incompatibility and paradox here: the hereditary knight becoming a monastic brother seems a vocation of opposites, which is not easy to understand. To many people it may seem irrational, like pursuing peace and war at the same time; yet in our own time, the French government has conscripted monks and seminarians into the armed forces in wartime. We are in no position to question the motives of the Templars, or the cruelty and horror of warfare in any age. Perhaps the key to our understanding is that the Templars lived to 'fight with a pure mind for the supreme and true King'. Cut off from the world, yet thrust into the world, they combined the roles of Martha and Mary (to use another dual image).

F. C. Woodhouse,[46] writing over a century ago (not exclusively about the Templars), gave an opinion of this idea of dual vocation, taking a monastic view of the question rather than looking only at the need for such an Order in the Holy Land. He was concerned to show the practicability of this vocation and its appeal to those who were drawn to it.

'The idea itself was certainly noble and grand. In those times the military and the religious life alone offered a promising field for great and energetic minds. But there would be men whose religious instincts drew them to the cloister, while their vigorous frames and fiery energy disposed them also to the soldier's life. It was a happy thought, therefore, that devised a method to combine these two vocations and put a sword into the monk's hand who had little taste for the spade or the library.'

Given the historical background, the argument is convincing and doubtless would have seemed so to many English knights of good character. There was seldom any shortage of recruits. Clearly it was not every man's vocation to be a Red Cross Knight. Some words of Christ might be applied to the situation: 'Let him who can take it, take it'.

During the greater part of the Order's existence, the monk with a sword in his hand was able to justify his calling. St Bernard and the founders were not mistaken, despite later criticisms. Bruno S. James, an authority on St Bernard's life and work[47] thought that

'Perhaps it is asking too much of human nature to expect men to live for long the life of a soldier according to those high ideals' proposed by St Bernard. 'Yet the Knights of the Temple … fulfilled a noble purpose in their day. The mere presence of knights trying sincerely to be knights of Christ and, above all, independent of the feudal lords, did very much to raise the whole tone of warfare and to check the worst excesses of the common soldiery.'

Enough has been said about the uniqueness of this vocation, so well suited to men of the crusading generations, whether of noble families or not. Of course, celibacy was an essential component of the life. Apart from the monastic aspect, it was practical for Templars to be without responsibility for wife and children. It could not have worked otherwise.

The Temple provided a vocation for feudal knights who would probably not have been drawn to any other Order of more conventional character. They were not ashamed of their birth and background, which might have made them unacceptable elsewhere. What they brought to the Order was an oblation of great worth: their lands and their skills.

A good deal has been written about the occupations followed in rural Preceptories, to offset the warlike activities which find their place in the chronicles of the Crusades. Referring particularly to Yorkshire, Dr. Martin[48] made a telling point: 'The devotion of the provincial houses to the pursuits of peace is seen in the entire absence of arms in the very complete inventory of property made in 1308.' It is understandable that then very little money was kept in the Preceptories and that evidence of luxury was markedly absent.

Earlier it was remarked that the positive note of austerity ran through all the Templar way of life, not merely in the avoidance of luxury and strict dedication to duty. (That could have been true of many soldiers and minor officials, for whom life was equally spartan.) Spiritually too this austerity prevailed, continuing somewhat in the spirit of the founders and their obedience to the admonitions of St Bernard. We know of no mural paintings or stained glass windows in their Churches and Chapels, neither silks nor rich fabrics, which would have seemed needless luxury. Their treasure was not in such things. However, St Bernard's anti-art principles did not prevent them from accepting beautiful and simple things as gifts, to the glory of God. This is probably how they came by such objects as the 'Temple Pyx' and the Sandford Reliquary. Perhaps it should be mentioned in passing that these would have been treasured solely for their devotional value, not as works of art. The latter is a modern concept and therefore not relevant here.

As far as is known, no books from Templar sources in England have survived. How are we to interpret this fact? Apart from missals and other necessary books used by the chaplains, there was little demand for books. Some may have been destroyed, but it is safe to assume that normal wear and tear accounted for a number of volumes.

What was the impact of a Preceptory on the local community? The question would not have been asked at the time and it is difficult for us to find more than a partial answer, given the partial state of our knowledge. We can look at some of the examples available. In the new village planted around the preceptory at Temple Bruer were settled 37 tenants, inhabiting 34 crofts. A weekly market was started, possibly for marketing wool and surplus grain and perhaps other commodities also. There can be no doubt that while the Templars flourished here, their impact on the locality as landlords was beneficial in building up a stable economy. The fruits of their labour were tangible enough and although the village was deserted at a later date, we have the evidence of aerial photography to reveal its extent.

Keele, similarly a village founded by the Templars, was more fortunate in surviving. It is probable that the Preceptories at Temple Guiting and Lydley both employed a considerable part of the local population. This may have been true of most rural Preceptories in the mid thirteenth century. Of course, it was all severely practical; there was no social programme. Templars did not think along those lines. Nobody would have thought of the Order as a benevolent institution, even though their origin was charitable in the truest sense and they had a duty to share their bread with the poor and hungry. The latter may well have been wanderers and pilgrims passing by, rather than local people. Mention has already been made of the Templars' activity as church-builders, which obviously had a spiritual impact on the locality.

It would seem that, apart from employing such essential artisans as blacksmiths, the London Temple had less direct impact on its neighbourhood; or perhaps we should say it was more formal. Nevertheless, a number of men must have worked on the periphery of the Temple, performing services necessary to the use and maintenance of its properties, but having little contact with the Knights. Individual members of the Order, except those in positions of authority, would have exercised very little impact outside the Preceptory which was their temporary home. In this respect they were no different from the stricter houses of monks.

Whatever their local impact - and it would have varied widely according to circumstances - there is no doubt that the importance of the Templars greatly exceeded their estimated numerical strength in England (and probably elsewhere). Of their beneficial influence here, Edward II (almost at the end of the Templar era) declared plainly: 'the Master and the Brethren are very much esteemed by us and all our Kingdom in living as well as in morals.'

It is refreshing to find that a modern historian, Dr Peter Partner, declares that the Templars' '… most striking characteristic was their ordinariness; they represent the common man, and not the uncommon visionary.' We know of no visions by which they were favoured. Certainly, the ordinary man can set himself high ideals, practice courage and reach heroic virtue, without being appreciated or canonised. They were not necessarily perfectionists, but the willingness to renounce their own wills and to sacrifice everything, ultimately earthly life, for the Christian cause argues the highest ideals to which man can aspire. Of course there were failures (as in every religious order then and now) but for those ordinary, perhaps unlettered, men who could rise to this vocation, the responsibilities were great.

Some modification is needed however. Ordinary is not intended in a derogatory sense; nor should we be too ready to classify them indiscriminately as unlettered men. We do not normally associate the Templars with literary or musical activity, but this may be doing them an injustice. In such a varied body of men, there must have been hidden talents which found an outlet in the quieter life of the Preceptories, when they were not over tired from manual work.

The fact that most of the Knights were not intellectuals and could not read Latin should not be taken to mean that they were all illiterate. This was not so. It is known that they produced several poets, troubadours and trouveres, who included one Master of the Temple, Br. Robert de Sable (d. 1193) Towards 1180 an otherwise anonymous 'Templar of Temple Bruer' was writing Norman French verse translations of 'Thais' and of Latin poems on Anti-Christ and on St Paul's descent into Hell; one is dedicated to his superior, Henri d'Arci, frere del Temple Salemun (of Solomon). This unknown English poet of the Order also made a prose translation of the 'Vitae Patrum' (Lives of the Fathers), this being thought suitable for the edification of brother-Knights. For the most part, Templar talents lay in other directions however, as noted above. Some clerical contemporaries sneered at the the military brethren's lack of erudition; yet this may not have been an altogether fair criticism since, for knights in general, the use of pen and stylus was regarded as imcompatible with the use of the sword and lance, the active manly life of a warrior. It underlines the essential dichotomy of the uncloistered monk on a foreign battlefield.

In the Preceptories we see them as ordinary men who for the love of God and for the good of their souls, were ready to turn their hands to any honest labour, without having to be experts. The Temple had need of all. Up and down the country, in varied circumstances, the Templars heeded the precept of St. Benedict, 'Idleness is an enemy of the soul'. They certainly found no time for trivialities.

It is rather strange that, according to St. Bernard, the Knights abhorred the game of chess; if in fact they always did. By contrast, it is said of St. Louis, a true friend of the Templars, that chess was one of his favourite pastimes. He found in it, said the chroniclers, a peaceful image of warfare; and it gave him scope for a leisured study of the principles underlying the tactics of this most tumultuous of sciences; but of course the Templars were not in the position of the King of France who needed such recreation, nor would they theoretically plan to fight a battle according to the rules like a game of chess. Too many strategic factors were involved.

We know that such games of chance as chess and dice, together with a variety of worldly pastimes, were to St Bernard and his followers time-wasting and useless occupations, associated with secular knighthood and courtiers. This undoubtedly was why the Templars shunned them as harmful. Time and talents must not be wasted or misused. All in all theirs was a remarkably uncluttered existence.

Perhaps anyway they had little time for pastimes; no long winter evenings to be occupied until Compline, since generally their daily timetable would be governed by the rising and the setting of the sun. This may also be another reason why our English Templars seemingly neglected reading. In their priorities, prayer, manual work and necessary rest excluded pastimes, even if they were not harmful or considered to be so. Yet we know that books were not entirely absent from the Preceptories. Not only were the rank and file of Templars less literate than the older monastic Orders, they had less opportunity to amass books and manuscripts to form libraries. This because, from the nature of their vocation, they were much less static than the monks of other foundations who could work systematically at the making and study of books.

If little effort was expended in the writing of books, there was certainly written communication of important news; letters were received by the English brethren, to be circulated amongst them. One such letter from Outremer, written in 1240, began with this salutation: 'Brother Hermann of Perigord, by the grace of God humble Master of the poor Knights of the Temple, to his beloved brother in Christ, Master Robert Sandford, Preceptor of the house of the said Knights in England, greeting in the Lord.' Br Hermann (otherwise known as Armand de Peragors) wrote again in 1244, on the state of the Holy Land. Matthew Paris preserved the text of another letter, this being from Br. William de Sonnac 'by the grace of God Master of the poor soldiery of the Temple, to his beloved brother in Christ Robert Sandford, Preceptor in England', giving news of the capture of Damietta in 1249.

Having made mention of literary work by Templars, we cannot omit a glance at one other book of which we have knowledge. Its significance will be obviouss, since it was an early translation of parts of the Bible, carefully selected. Two influential Knights, Master Odo de Saint-Amand and his close friend Br. Richard de Hastings (who was Master in England *circa* 1160), together commissioned a volume of extracts from the Old Testament translated into French. It comprised abridged versions of Genesis, Joshua, Kings, Maccabees, Tobias, Judith and Judges, with a rhymed preface obliquely boasting of the literary difficulties the translator had overcome. He also added a rationalist commentary and some anecdotal material taken from the Talmud and Moslem texts. This work was clearly intended to be read within the Order, probably by the reader during meals, so that the Knights might be well schooled in the heroic and warlike exploits of the ancient warriors from Israel's past. (Hardly the best models for Christians to copy, we might think.) The volume was noteworthy because at that time translations of the Scriptures into vernacular languages were not allowed in general use.

In an age of brutality and idealism, such examples of leadership and zeal for the faith of of their fathers and their worthy deeds seemed relevant for the formation of the new Maccabees. Indeed the more imaginative Templars may have seen some parallels between those Jews who defended their inheritance from heathen forces and the Crusader armies.

Crusading was not an intellectual or philosophical movement, but like all pilgrimages was intended to be of practical value and not undertaken lightly. Only those who were adequately trained could hope to achieve success as valiant athletes of God. Much of that training was done on the estates of the Bailiwicks here, though the building up of physical and spiritual fitness was continuous. Those ordinary men, not always very enlightened, who grasped the opportunities which came to them to develop their talents, were in a state of perpetual readiness to be the spearhead of Christendom. We may suppose that most of those who joined the Templar ranks were young men in the prime of life, prepared to stay the course. This could be the reason for their energetic and sometimes impetuous nature. When there was need for a choice to be made, the principle was followed that the better man and not the better born was put first. They must serve God in efficiency. Neither wastage nor insubordination could be tolerated.

In a life seen to be joyous but frugal, where in matters of food and clothes only necessity was considered, a seriousness of purpose prevailed; these were serious men. Yet there seems no reason to suppose that they practised the vicarious penance of the Cistercians, for mankind. Nor, going to the other extreme, was there a neo-classical cult of the body and athletic sports.

There is no doubt that the Templars had a great capacity for strenuous devotion when the cause demanded it. Theirs was a muscular Christianity which could work hard and pray hard. In 1245, a time of dire distress in the Holy Land, when all the newly admitted Knights and novices who were available were sent out to the succour of their brethren, the aged Knights and those whose duties made them unable to leave the western Preceptories, prayed long and earnestly for their brethren. They observed extraordinary fasts and mortifications and continual prayer was offered throughout the Order.

Like all monks and in keeping with the order of nature, the Templars rose early in the morning. It was not their custom to eat breakfast, but they were not encouraged to fast so rigorously that bodily strength was impaired. The day's work was more important.

There was nothing singular, or sinister, about wearing a beard. If one wants a mystical reason, it is not far to seek - both Christ and St John the Baptist had beards and so, we may believe, did most of the Apostles; but beards were commonplace among men of all classes, saints and sinners alike. For the Templars it was most probably a discipline, which achieved a certain uniformity of appearance. Theirs was not the carefully trimmed beard of courtiers, but the shaggy beard of those who rode through arid deserts. Personal vanity was strongly discouraged by the Rule.

As we have seen, Knights of the Temple were ordinary men, trained and many of them hardened by long spells of duty in a hostile climate: those men of silence, who spoke when it was necessary, but did not indulge in futile argument, may well have felt some sense of affinity with those earlier desert dwellers; but this idea should not be over-stressed. They were never solitaries. Any who had that vocation were free to leave and join a stricter order. It would not be alien to medieval thought to say their life was sacramental; outward actions expressing inward reality. The wearing of the red cross and its meaning has already been considered. The white cloak stood for purity of life and intention. Living together in community (however small) expressed unity in the family of Christ ... and so on. The belt or cord which the Templars wore at all times was a tangible reminder of their vows, binding for so long as they remained in the Order, which normally meant until death.

Infirmity and death have their natural place in the human story of the Templars, within the intimate fellowship of the Brothers and generally hidden from the outside world. To say that Templars looked after their own would be altogether too slick - and too modern a response to their situation. The exercise of Christian charity was seen as a duty, endorsed by the Rule and the Gospels. Knights who had grown old and feeble in the service of the Temple rightly received special consideration from their brethren, in an honourable retirement. Whether in all cases they were transported to the Order's infirmaries and so ended their days in tranquility we cannot tell. That was certainly the ideal: whether ideals always worked out in practice is another matter, which we are not in a position to judge. Since the Templars were less publicly concerned with social and hospital work than was the Order of St John of Jerusalem, we have fewer insights into this hidden side of their domestic life; nor should we expect it to be chronicled. Accommodation for the sick was far from sumptuous as can be deduced from the inventory of Denney Preceptory, but comparison should not be made with modern standards, for obvious reasons. Longevity may not have been general in the Templar era, neither would stress and many of the diseases prevalent in our society today. They are more likely to have suffered from exhaustion and from wounds received in battle.

One intriguing item of invalid fare was fried slices of stag's horn in soup laced with wine and prepared in three different flavours, in honour of the Holy Trinity. This would have been considered especially nourishing for an elderly invalid.

We cannot compute the mortality rate for the military orders, but the proportion of those who died as a result of active service must have been high. This would have kept the Templars' numbers well below those of more conventional monks who remained within the confines of their monasteries.

Mortality was the Templar's ultimate oblation, his final act of renunciation, the gentle stripping off of human strength. Metaphorically speaking, death the great leveller made no distinction between Master, chaplain, knight, or servitor. All were equally Brothers of the Temple, as on their profession: all wore the same red cross. In their last moments they may have recalled St. Bernard's comforting words, 'Living or dead, Lord, we are Thine'. After all, death has always been an inevitable fact in life's cycle, yet it came as the final enemy to individuals and to the Order. In the medieval phrase they were 'paying the debt of nature'.

When they died, professed Knights were buried in their habit and whenever possible were so represented on their tombs. This was a break with the earlier custom of monks having plain graves marked with a simple cross. There is a certain logic here, for the Templars also had the secular status of knighthood which they retained on their profession , incorporating it into their vocation. Thus they were shown wearing the long white mantle or cloak with a red cross on the left side over the heart; it had a short cape and a hood behind and fell down to the feet loosely without any girdle. Associates of the Temple, like William Marshall and the others represented in effigy in the New Temple, are not so attired because they were not fully professed Knights Templar, though sharing in certain benefits of the Order. Provision was made for prayers for the departed brethren and benefactors and this continued until such time as there was no one left to fulfil this charitable duty.

From the nature of their calling, it seems unlikely that many of the Templars met death unprepared; surely not those who died peacefully in the English Preceptories, attended by their brethren. Those who reached the autumn of their lives before the fateful fourteenth century were the fortunate ones, who died here in peace, fortified by the sacraments of the Church. Although a considerable number of Templars must rest in English graves, we cannot with any certainty say more than that as to their identity.

> 'The Knights are dust,
> Their swords are rust:
> Their souls are with
> The Saints, we trust' - Anon.

Whether we see them now as knights carved in stone in Hereford Cathedral, or as in the colourful modern windows of the London Temple, makes little difference; the reality is more than either. Even if they have no corporate memorial (and it is very unlikely that they would have wanted one) we can visit over a dozen churches associated with the Templars, without leaving England. Otherwise we have to rely on circumstantial evidence. Templars have no place in the art historian's field of study, yet their immortal power can arouse our interest in various ways.

Sometimes confusion has been caused by people investigating old effigies of cross-legged knights and hazarding a guess that what they saw was a Knight Templar's tomb. For instance, in the south transept of Pershore Abbey church, Worcestershire, is a badly mutilated figure - thought to be a Templar - in mail armour, *circa* 1280, with a long shield on his left arm. A hare, carved at the feet of the effigy, seems to indicate that he belonged to the old local family of Harely (or Harley). There is much uncertainty about his identity, if only because Pershore was a Benedictine Abbey with no Templar connections and there were no Preceptories in that county; though there were some properties, such as the Manor of Temple Broughton. He might have been an associate who served with the Order for a specified term in Outremer and then returned home honourably; or he might have been a crusader.

Such problems of identity are ever-present and are unlikely to be solved. It is fitting that in death the Templars should remain enigmatic and anonymous. That lessens neither their unique fascination, nor our respect for them.

The *Agnus Dei* appears yet again - this time in the archaeologists' mud: small metal objects which have been identified as signs of the Order (similar to pilgrims' tokens) have been recovered from the Thames at London (some time prior to 1940). Who wore them, and for what purpose, is uncertain; possibly returning pilgrims from the Holy Land who owed their safety to the Knights. Perhaps the sign was the equivalent of a ticket or a pass? The point is not greatly important.

We started by likening history, rather naively, to a puzzle in which we are not able to make all the pieces fit neatly together. Some have been found unexpectedly, like those mentioned in the Thames mud; many artefacts will never be found and even if they were, would not substantially modify our overall view. Bringing together all the known traces of the Templars, spiritual and material, in England, does not answer all the questions that might be asked.

1291 was the end of an age for all who were concerned with the Christian defence of the Holy Land and the uninterrupted 'general passage' of pilgrims. Nothing could be the same after the stronghold of Acre had fallen. It foreshadowed the last decade of Templar activity. Did they have an inkling of future unhappy events at home and in Europe? It is possible, but we do not know. There was much movement and regrouping of the remaining Knights. Even when the Latin Kingdom and their own historic Temple headquarters had been lost, their hopes were still Jerusalem-orientated. The English Preceptories were outposts of Outremer.

UNANSWERED QUESTIONS

Should anyone wish to speculate on what might have happened to the Order had not cruel fate overtaken it, there seem to be three distinct possibilities: it might have died out, through an insufficient supply of vocations; or merged with the Hospitallers; or continued to exist separately, but changed its character in some way. Any of those courses would have been, in a sense, surrender, and that would have been unthinkable.

Had they managed to continue to lead a separate existence, the Order might now have a safe headquarters in Rome, within reach of the Vatican; an ironic thought. There had been a Templar house in Rome.

Doubtless some writers consider that the closure of the Order was inevitable. Once Outremer was no more and the dreams of reconquest faded, the Order lost its main reason for existence. At home, not all of the Preceptories, granges and other small dependencies would have survived. In the changed circumstances after 1291, some consolidation and economy measures would have been necessary, to preserve as much as possible of their monastic life. It is significant that at Temple Balsall, the church completed around this time was the last Templar church to be built. The brethren were becoming disheartened and perhaps apprehensive of future prospects of the Order as such.

The failure to retain a foothold in the Holy Land was not attributable to any fault or cowardice on the part of the Templars. To the end they were ready to support a new crusade, but the call never came. Our reaction to the subsequent tragic mistakes of history must surely be sympathetic to the Templars. It is indeed 'appropriate to remember the honest image of the knights, sergeants and humble serving-brothers, clad in their mantles of white or brown, living, farming, trading, fighting, and dying with the red cross of martyrdom on their chests and the battle-standard above their heads'.[49]

Mature with accumulated wisdom and their crusading experience, the Order was yet unable to adapt to the situation following the fall of Acre. Christian history can never vanquish its collective memory of 'those dedicated warriors of the Knights Templar … how many of those died as unknown martyrs at the hands of the infidel? How many lived the lives of the saints?'[50]

The Templecombe Christ remains witness to their simple devotion. The red cross also remains, in a totally different (though no less humanitarian) context, as a symbol of compassion. Cardinal Newman (in 1848) was of the opinion that in theory the Jesuits were 'the Knights Templar of modern history'. Of course we are free to disagree with him.

In modern terms we might imagine an unlikely combination of the Foreign Legion and the Little Brothers of Jesus, founded by Charles de Foucauld. If a fusion of those two passionately French inspirations was possible, the result might have been something near the Templars, though still lacking in their essential ethos. The secret of their power might be analysed as masculinity harnessed to the hardest of callings.

In England today not a few of our fellow countrymen would deem the Templars, equally with the Cistercians and the Carthusians, completely out of touch with the so-called realities of ordinary life; but such a judgement would be unjust and utterly irrelevant. The Church Militant of that time was truly conscious of being the earthly counterpart of the *militia cælestis*, with the Templars forming part of the militant wing: anything but out of touch with everyday activity in the Preceptories and their estates, or with the defence of Christendom in a wider field. As decision makers and leaders the Knights were used to taking the initiative.

Our reading of history may sometimes lead to confusing results, if it becomes over complicated. Here however, the Templars' character remains clear. Their outlook on life was for the most part healthy and straightforward. The Poor Soldiers of Christ were men to be trusted; men of the world as well as being men of the Spirit. Perhaps we find it difficult to appreciate the amazing paradox of their lifestyle: lions and lambs, combining the fierce heroism of Old Testament leaders and Christian virtues; astute men of business and withdrawn monks, in the world yet not of the world, attractive to some people, repellant to others: Biblical contrasts, all found within the pages of Scripture.

Though it is not possible to visit all the sites (Temple Dinsley and Bulstrode for instance), the unanswered questions are fewer than might have been expected. This is encouraging, for in considering such men of deep faith, we cannot conclude on a negative note. There is much more we would like to know about their architecture, its variations and the extent of the Cistercian influence (if indeed they were aware of any). Answers to some questions have been attempted in the foregoing pages. More minor enigmas may yet be solved. The Templars are no longer strangers to us.

We can contemplate a little group kneeling silently in their distinctive white habits, in the peace of an old church. We know that they can never be forgotten. We can treasure those traces of their work which remain as part of our national heritage and also, in a wider international setting related to our Christian civilization. Of course, no one studying the Templars would claim that they were all, without exception, noble examples of St. Bernard's ideals; that would hardly be possible, since every organisation of human beings contains both good and bad members, though not necessarily extremes of either, but we are not called to pass judgement.

'Though the Order sometimes abused its chartered rights, we have no evidence that these acts were so frequent or flagrant as to attract general dislike. Its wealth in lands, and especially in moveable property, and the number of its members, have ben much over-estimated ... though the Templars' shrewd business management and financial operations may have aroused dislike in some quarters, it does not appear to have been general … Most of the English Templars were industrious and enterprising men of business, living at peace with their neighbours'.[51]

It is of interest to note that Br. John de Stoke, Treasurer of the New Temple in London, gave his opinion that the Order needed correction in two respects, namely that a year of probation should be required of prospective members and that their reception should be public. The secrecy of their proceedings was undoubtedly a cause of suspicion and distrust, which could have been avoided. Unfortunately those reforms were never able to be instigated.

A Templar in his habit—white with a plain red cross on his shoulder.
From P. Helyot, *Histoire des Ordres Religieux, Monastiques et Militaires* (Paris

A Templar in his habit.

EPILOGUE - REMEMBERING MARYTRS

There is a certain irony in the fact that the Order of the Temple ceased to exist in England two centuries before the Reformation, so that no Templars were victims of Henry VIII. No comfort to them, however! There seems to be little point in drawing a parallel as some writers have done. History teaches us that Religious Orders are rarely dissolved without violent methods being employed, which later ages deplore but cannot reverse.

In memory of the Templars might be quoted what Pope Innocent II wrote to them, in the document *Omne datum optimum*, on 29th March 1139, when their future was full of promise:

' ...Through the inspiration of grace you have become receptive to the message of the Gospel and having left behind worldly pomps and your own possessions ... you have humbly chosen the hard road that leadeth to life; and to prove it you have most conscientiously worn on your breasts the sign of the living Cross, because you are especially reckoned to be members of the knighthood of God.'

What finer praise could they expect to receive? Time redeems their memory from the intrigues of enemies, and from the fire of persecution, the gold shines clearer.

The total number of Templar martyrs is untold, their heroic virtue for the most part unrecorded. A contemporary of the Templars in the Holy Land, Jacques de Vitry (d. 1240) Bishop of Acre, expressed his view that the Templars slaughtered in battle, whose bodies were hanging from the walls of Ascalon, were martyrs already enjoying heavenly rewards. We can safely say that a large proportion of the Templars gave their lives as martyrs for the faith of Christ. The red cross which they proudly wore was indeed prophetic of that martyrdom which they accepted, defending the perpetually blood-stained land of Him who said, 'I came not to bring peace, but a sword'. We have no sure means of knowing how many of the Knights from England died in that unhappy land fought over by so many nations.

NOTES

[1] *The Knights Templar,* p. 68. This book is an excellently readable short history.
[2] For a clear general outline of the Templars, see *Medieval Monasticism* by C. H. Lawrence, Longman, 1984.
[3] *The Common Man,* 1950.
[4] Thomas Merton *The Last of The Fathers* pp. 56-57 (1954).
[5] Fratres Servientes, or Frères Serjents (serving brothers).
[6] C. G. Addison, *The History of the Knights Templars*, p.38. They may have been confused with the Trinitarians who were sometimes called Red Friars.
[7] In the London Temple there seems to have been some segregation, for there existed two halls, a Hall of Priests and a Hall of Knights, perhaps because there were so many coming and going in the capital.
[8] *The Knights Templar in England* pp. 7-8.
[9] However, what we now see at Strood is all that remains of a much larger building that survived until the 1940's See ground plan for the extent of this.
[10] *The History of the Knights Templars.* The manuscript of this survey (Inquisitio or Feodary in technical language) is kept by the Public Record Office. A small volume, written in Latin in a fair and clear hand, bound in beech boards covered with dark brown leather, it was not an inventory but a trustworthy record of holdings and rents. The text is reproduced in Miss B. A. Lee's substantial volume, *Records of the Templars in England in the Twelfth Century.*
[11] Ecologists tell us that in the Middle Ages a large part of the country, perhaps as much as 75%, was covered with forests.
[12] The widely felt urge to liberate Jerusalem was paralleled geographically as well as spiritually, for the contemporary *Mappa Mundi* showed the then-known world as Jerusalem centred.
[13] *Dante the Maker,* p. 375.
[14] Perhaps it would be unpardonably facetious to suggest that the Lamb was also appropriate in a more material sense, since much of the English Templars' income came from wool!
[15] That is their maximum time-span running from the foundation until the death of the last Grand Master, Jacques de Molay. The last seven years were taken up by trials and cruel tortures of the French Templars. Their English brethren were treated with less severity. A time-span of less than two hundred years is not long in the history of the Church.
[16] An inscription inside over the west doorway records the event. It was a singular distinction for a church in England to have been consecrated by a Patriarch of Jerusalem, even though this particular prelate was notorious in his personal life.

[17] Plaster casts of four of these effigies, taken before they were damaged, can be seen in the Casts Room of the Victoria and Albert Museum, London.
[18] 17 Fleet Street, (now known rather obscurely as Prince Henry's Room) stands on a site which formed part of the Templars' extensive property.
[19] Douglas Newton, *London West of the Bars*, p. 69.
[20] Douglas Newton, *Catholic London*, p.258.
[21] 'Grail' can mean either a graduale (a large book of chant) or a paten. In this context the latter is the more probable meaning.
[22] Traces of medieval buildings have been found in the locality of Addington, but there is no clear indication of where the Manor house stood.
[23] Between 1236 and 1287 terrific storms swept England, not least the Kent coast. Whether such calamities seriously damaged the old church on the Western Heights, or even led to its abandonment, we cannot say.
[24] From Nigel and Mary Kerr, *A Guide to Norman Sites in Britain*, pp. 58-59. Some idea of the elaborate carpentry of the roofing timbers can be gained from interior photographs of the barns.
[25] There is not enough of the Preceptory buildings remaining for the plan to be completely traced; the site of the chapel is uncertain.
[26] For a discussion of whether the Templars ever possessed the Holy Shroud itself, see *The Turin Shroud* by Ian Wilson (Victor Gollancz, 1978). An earlier book, *The Story of the Relics of the Passion* by H. M. Gillett (Basil Blackwell, 1935) made no mention of the Templars. In a general sense this theory is not of paramount importance since, as Mgr. A. S. Barnes pointed out, in 1934, the Holy Shroud seems to be the only possible source from which the likeness of Christ in art (from the fourth century onwards) can have originated.
[27] An explanation may lie in the fact that Hereford was not only a diocese, but an episcopal barony held by the Bishop, who was then answerable for fifteen knights' fees. *The Life and Gests of St. Thomas Cantilupe*, by Richard Strange, SJ, 1674, (which drew on the records of his canonisation) made no mention of the Templars. This book was republished in 1879 with supplementary material which refers (on p. 237) to the tomb, 'the former resting-place of the relics ... in the north transept, with its stone-cut Templars guarding the honour of their sainted Provincial Master', without giving any authority for such a statement. Bosbury was one of the Bishop's manors.
[28] The Templar Rule provided that 'a most watchful care is to be bestowed upon sick brothers, and let their wants be attended to as if Christ himself was the sufferer ..' Furthermore, 'it behoves you to support , with pious consideration, all old men , according to their feebleness and weakness, and dutifully to honour them ...'
[29]From the English Heritage Guide, p. 6.
[30] Details from the *Magna Vita S. Hugonis* by Dom Adam.
[31] *Medieval England*, p. 60.
[32] The Witham site was totally excavated in 1965-66.
[33] It would seem that the documents mentioned in connection with Temple Newsam were originally kept at Faxfleet

.

[34] *The Feudal Kingdom of England 1042-1216*, p. 250.
[35] *The Story of the Crusades*, p. 254.
[36] 'The Templars ... were not great patrons of the arts. Their buildings were utilitarian and any enrichment (such as the doorway of the Temple in London, very modest.' Prof. George Zarnecki, *The Monastic Achievement*, p. 109, Thames and Hudson 1972. We would not expect them to commission works of art, but they may have been given some.
[37] An obligation binding the lay brothers (of any Order) to personal recitation of the Office would have been unrealistic, since many of them would have been illiterate.
[38] If 'Bristleham' was Bristol, it could have been sent to Templecombe, perhaps for better security?
[39] One of the routes of which we know was between London and Dover, with a half-way stop at Strood.
[40] The plan is best seen from the south (river side) where the five bays of triple lancet windows contrast with the Norman windows of the Round.
[41] Frederick W. Ryan, *The House of the Temple* (1930), p.36
[42] The tall, lean tower of the Paris Temple had no counterpart here.
[43] This custom is also reflected in the decorative use of painted shields in Great Wilbraham church, Cambridgeshire. It may have originated in the Mother-house in Jerusalem which (according to their founder, as quoted by Frater Felix Fabri) was 'gay with arms, not with gems or ancient crowns of gold; the wall ... covered with shields slung thereon instead of chandeliers, censers and flagons; the whole house ... fenced about with bridles and lances.' since there dwelt 'the Knights of Christ, ... in the holy house together with their horses and their arms.' (Translated in *Jerusalem Journey*, H. F. M. Prescott, p. 169).
[44] In *The Knights Templars in England*, p. 120.
[45] According to Dr Martin, 'the business acumen and financial capacity of the Templars were probably their most important contribution to their age'. Though this seems rather too materialistic an estimate, we can see what is meant.
[46] *The Military Religious Orders* ... preface, p. xxi.
[47] *St. Bernard of Clairvaux, An Essay in Biography* (1957) p. 75.
[48] Rev. Dr. E. J. Martin, article on 'The Templars in Yorkshire', in *Yorkshire Archaeological Journal* Vols. 29 and 30 (1929-31).
[49] Stephen Howarth, *The Knights Templar*, p. 312.
[50] Douglas Newton, *Catholic London*, p. 245.
[51] Clarence Perkins, 'The Knights Templar in the British Isles', in *The English Historical Review*, No. XCVIII, April 1910.

A modern artist's impression of a Templar fully dressed, looking more chivalric than monastic. © Denys LeFevre

APPENDIX 1.

List of Masters in England

R. de Pointon	
Rocelinus de Fossa	
Richard de Hastings	1160
Richard Mallebeench	
Geoffrey (son of Stephen)	1180
Thomas Berard	1200
Amaric de St. Maur	1203
Alan Marcel (or Martel)	1224
Amberaldus	1229
Robert Mountforde	1234
Robert de Sanford	1241
Amadeus de Morestello	1254
Himbert Peraut	1270
Robert Turvile	1290
Guido de Foresta	1292
Jacques de Molay	1293
(who became the last Master of the Temple)	
Brian de Jay	1295
William de la More the Martyr	d. 1312

Note: a complete list of the Masters in England cannot be drawn up because of the lack of evidence. The above list, derived from Addison's book, is said to have come from a list made by the Hospitallers. It differs in some respects from the list given by Parker, which is as follows:.

Name	Dates
Hugh of Argentin	*circa* 1140
Otto (Osto)	*circa* 1150
Richard de Hastings	1155-1164
Geoffrey Fitz Stephen	1180-1185
William Newham	?
Aymeric de St. Maur	1200-1218
Alan Martel	1218-1228
Robert de Sanford	1229-1248
Rocelin de Fos	1251-1253
Amadeus de Morestello	1259-1260
Ambresard	1264
Himbert Peraut	1271
Guy de Foresta	1273-1274, 1291-1294
Robert de Turvill	1276-1290
Jacques de Molay	1295
Brian de Jay	1296-1298
William de la More	1298-1312

Temple Church. Traces of the Templars here - archway incorporated into the present church.

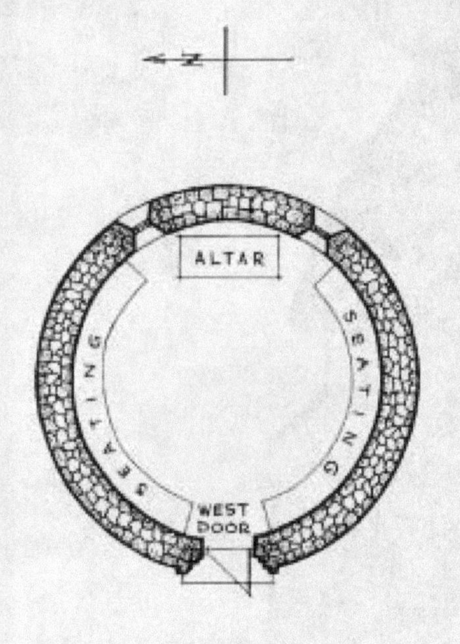

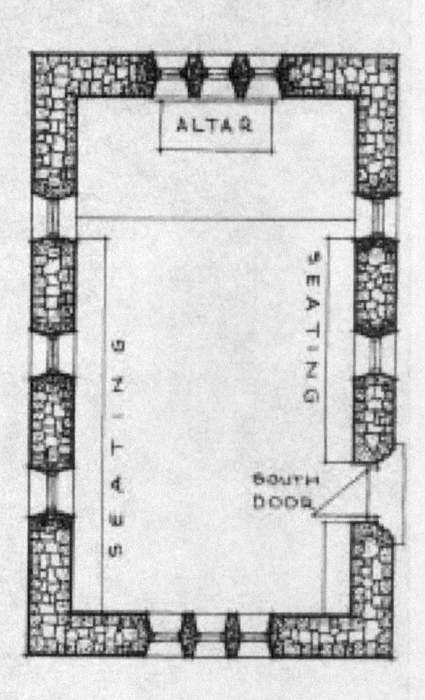

Phase 1 – CIRCULAR or OVAL CHURCH

Phase 2 – RECTANGULAR (Basilica type) CHURCH

GROUND PLANS OF TEMPLAR CHURCH BUILDINGS

APPENDIX 2

It is of interest to mention these, since it seems that those still existing may have been connected with Crusaders, being modelled on the Church of the Holy Sepulchre in Jerusalem and possible Templar influence may be detected in the design. That is not to say that they were ever officially Templar churches: it is unlikely, more than that we cannot be sure of. In order of building, they are:

(1) The Holy Sepulchre, NORTHAMPTON (? *circa* 1115) which is perhaps the most enigmatic.
(2) The Holy Sephulcre, Bridge Street, CAMBRIDGE (*circa* 1130) much restored and added to in 1841-1842. It replaced an earlier church of St. George.
(3) St John of Jerusalem, LITTLE MAPLESTEAD, Essex. This church could have had no connection with the Templars, since it was built circa 1335 by the Hospitallers of St. John. It is the smallest and youngest of the group of round churches.

There is also a chapel with a circular nave within the castle at LUDLOW, Shropshire. This is dedicated to St. Mary Magdalene and dated later than the eleventh century. There is no connection with the Templars.

A modern illustration depicting aspects of Templar life - the brother sowing seed, the Knight preparing for action and the monk at prayer, all necessary to each other.

INDEX

BIBLIOGRAPHY

General

Charles G. Addison	**The History of the Knights Templars** Longman, Brown, Green and Longmans, 1842.
Edward Burman	**The Templars: Knights of God** Crucible, 1986.
G. A. Campbell	**The Knights Templar** Duckworth, 1937
Stephen Howarth	**The Knights Templar** Collins 1982.
David Knowles & R. Neville Hadcock	**Medieval Religious Houses** Longmans, Green and Co., 1953.
Beatrice A. Lees	**Records of the Templars in England in the Twelfth Century** Oxford University Press, 1935.
Thomas W. Parker	**The Knights Templars in England** University of Arizona Press, 1963.
Desmond Seward	**The Monks of War** Eyre Methuen, 1972.
Edith Simon	**The Piebald Standard** Cassell & Co., 1959, White Lion Publishers Ltd., 1976.
F. C. Woodhouse	**The Military Religious Orders of the Middle Ages, Part II** SPCK, 1879.
Frances Gies	**The Knight in History** (chapter 6) Robert Hale, 1986.

Local

Christopher Harrison (Ed.) **The History of Keele,** chapter 1 by Robin Studd University of Keele, 1986.

S. E. Rigold **Temple Manor (Strood)** Ministry of Works Official Guide Book 1962.

H. P. Stokes **A History of the Wilbraham Parishes** Cambridge, 1926.

William Wheater **Temple Newsam: Its History and Antiquities** Goodall & Suddick, Leeds, 1889.

Victoria County History Various volumes

Piers Compton **The Story of Bisham Abbey, Part I.** Thames Valley Press, 1973.

George Godwin **The Middle Temple** Staples Press Ltd, 1954.

M. C. Wadhams *et al.* **Cressing Temple; A Brief Guide.** Essex County Council, 1990.

Rev. Arthur A. R. Gill **The Knights Templar at York** MS, undated.

Acknowledgements

Thanks are due to Denys Le Fevre for drawing the cover illustration, the map of Templar England and the ground plan showing the phases of Church building; to Nigel and Mary Kerr for permission to quote from their book *A Guide to Norman Sites in Britain*, published by Granada; to Simon Le Fevre, Archivist of the Priory of England - Order of the Temple of Jerusalem, for much help and information; Miss Stephanie Harding and the Royal Commission on the Historical Monuments of England; English Heritage, which has four Templar sites in its custody; The Institute of Archaeology, University of London; Sutton Library and various other libraries which have assisted my research. I am especially grateful to St. Gregory's library, at the London Oratory, where I have made certain unexpected finds which were most helpful. Various church guides and other pamphlets have been consulted, but since these are not easily accessible they are not listed in the bibliography.

All the colour photographs are the author's own copyright, except that of Denney which was taken by Edward Harper.

Special thanks to the archivist of the Minster Library, York.

By kind agreement of the family of the late George Tull, royalties from the sale of this book go to support the Templar Heritage Trust. The Trust is a project of the Order of the Temple of Jerusalem and the Industrial Temple in England and Wales (www.templars.org.uk). Its aims are to help preserve heritage sites and to promote historical research associated with the medieval Knights Templar."

L - #0060 - 210219 - C0 - 234/156/10 - PB - DID2450176

▶ Plant cells

Look at the plant cell below.
In what ways is it different from the animal cell?

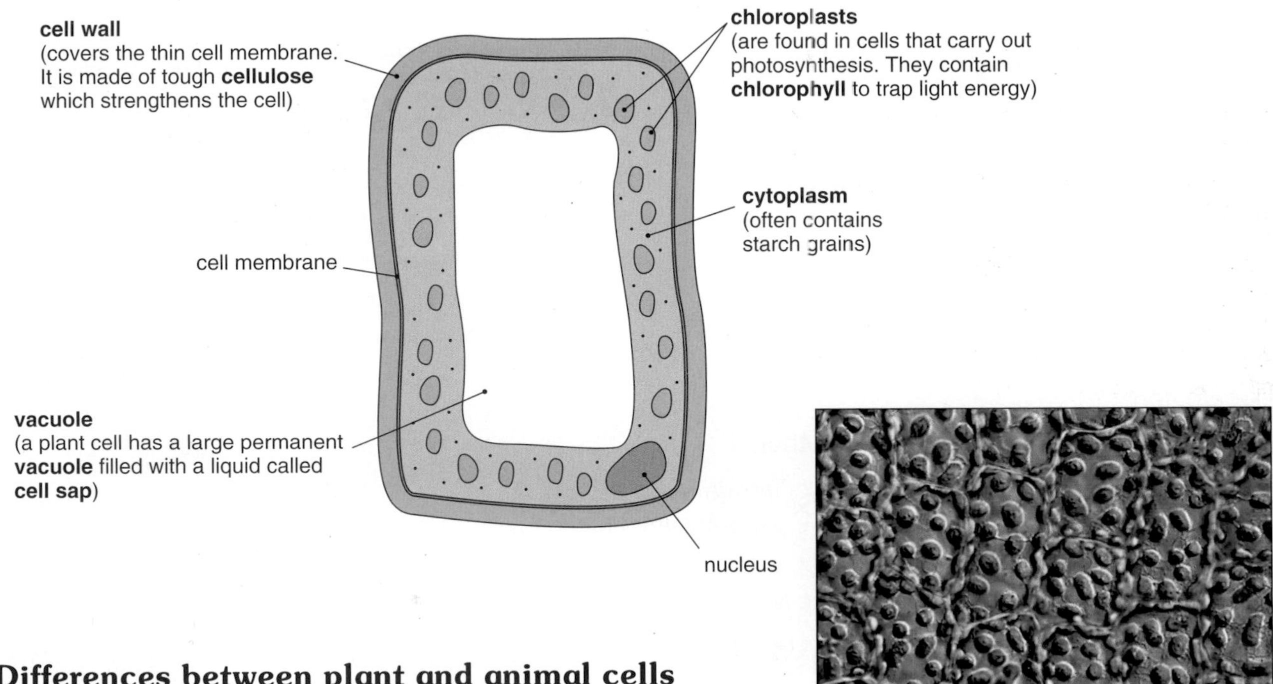

Chloroplasts in moss cells

Differences between plant and animal cells

There are similarities and differences between plant and animal cells.
In what ways are they similar?

Here are some differences between them:

Plant cells	Animal cells
• have tough cellulose cell walls • have chloroplasts • have a large permanent vacuole containing cell sap • many have a box-like shape • have a nucleus to the side of the cell	• do not have cellulose cell walls • do not have chloroplasts • sometimes have small vacuoles but they never contain cell sap • shape varies • have a nucleus in the middle of the cell

If you look at animal and plant cells with a powerful microscope you can sometimes see tiny dots in the cytoplasm.
Many of these are **mitochondria**.
At a much higher magnification they look like the diagram:

Respiration happens inside a mitochondrion to release energy from food molecules.

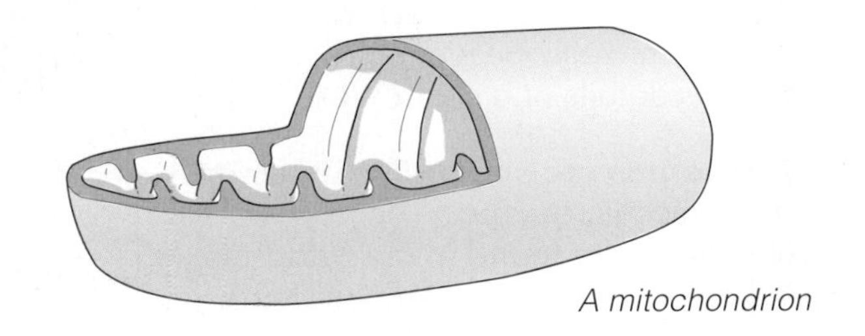

A mitochondrion

▶ Microscopes

As you know cells are too small to see with the naked eye.
So we use a **microscope** to magnify them.

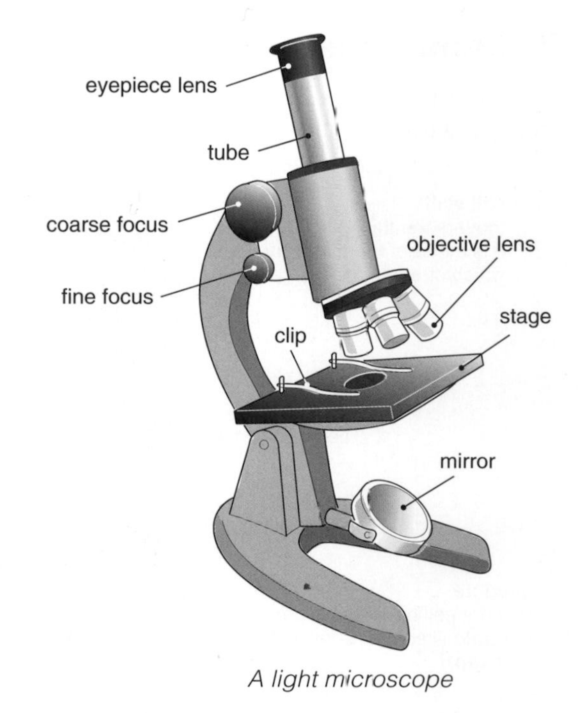

A light microscope

Light microscope

You have probably used a **light microscope** like the one shown :

Can you remember what all the different parts are for ?

This type of microscope has ***two*** lenses, the **eyepiece lens** and the **objective lens**.

How do you work out the total magnification ?

You multiply the magnifying power of one lens by the magnifying power of the other.

$$\text{Total magnification} = \text{magnifying power of eyepiece lens} \times \text{magnifying power of objective lens}$$

Work out the total magnification if the eyepiece lens is ×10 and the objective lens is ×40.

Light microscopes can magnify up to 1000 times.

Electron microscope

Some things are too small to be seen with a light microscope.
Instead we use an **electron microscope**.

An electron microscope in use

Electron microscopes use a beam of electrons instead of light rays.
The image shows up on a fluorescent screen.
This can be photographed.
Electron microscopes can magnify up to 500 000 times.

Electron microscopes help us to see the structures ***inside*** cells in detail.
This photograph was taken with an electron microscope :
It shows details of a chloroplast.

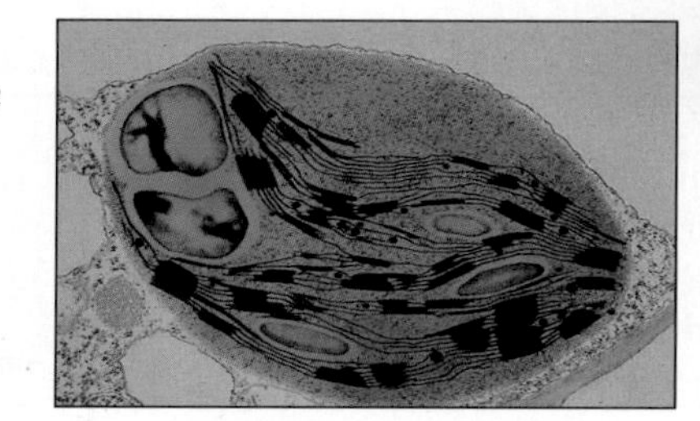
A chloroplast

Ribosomes are only visible under an electronic microscope.
Ribosomes are found in the cytoplasm and are involved in making proteins.

▶ Looking at plant cells

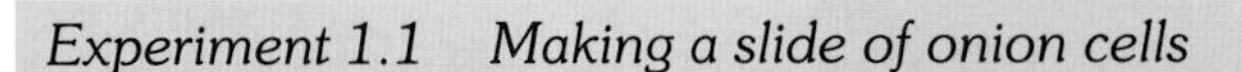

Experiment 1.1 Making a slide of onion cells

First you must peel off a very thin layer:

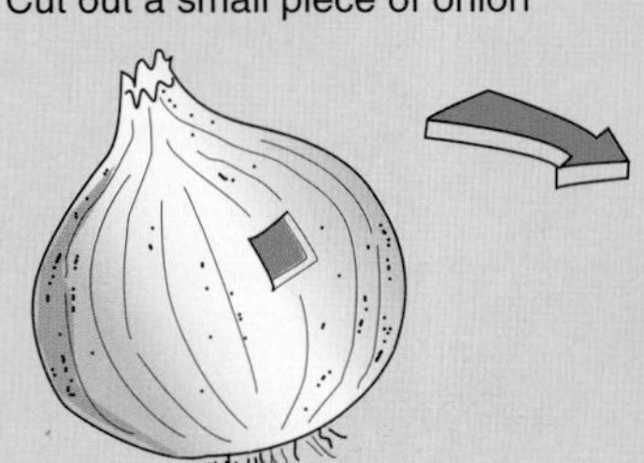

3 Put the piece of onion 'skin' flat on a slide and add two drops of iodine solution

4 Gently lower the cover-slip onto the slide using a mounted needle

cover-slip

5 Place the slide onto the stage of the microscope

6 Focus carefully onto the onion skin using the lowest power objective lens in your microscope

7 Turn on the high power objective lens to see details of the onion cells

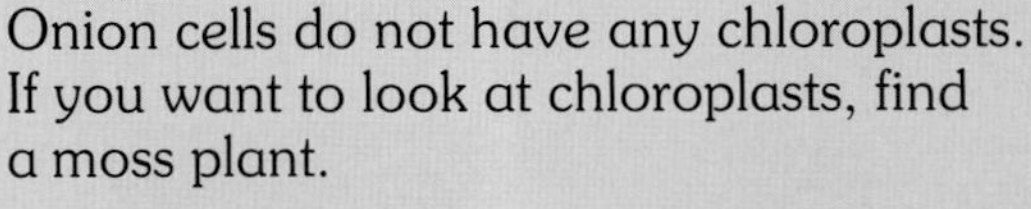

Onion cells do not have any chloroplasts. If you want to look at chloroplasts, find a moss plant.

Use tweezers to remove one of the smallest leaves from the tip of the plant.

Put it onto a slide with a drop of water and place a cover-slip over it.

Look at it under high power with your microscope.

▶ Looking at animal cells

Experiment 1.2 Making a slide of cheek cells

To avoid any chance of infection carry out these instructions carefully: 

1. Your teacher will give you a cotton bud from a freshly opened pack.
2. Gently wipe the lining of your cheek with one end of the cotton bud.
3. Smear the cotton bud over the centre of a slide.
4. Immediately dispose of the cotton bud into a beaker of disinfectant provided by your teacher.
5. Put a drop of methylene blue stain on top of the smear.
6. Place a cover-slip on top and look for cells under the microscope at high power.
7. At the end of the activity put the slide with its cover-slip into a beaker of disinfectant.

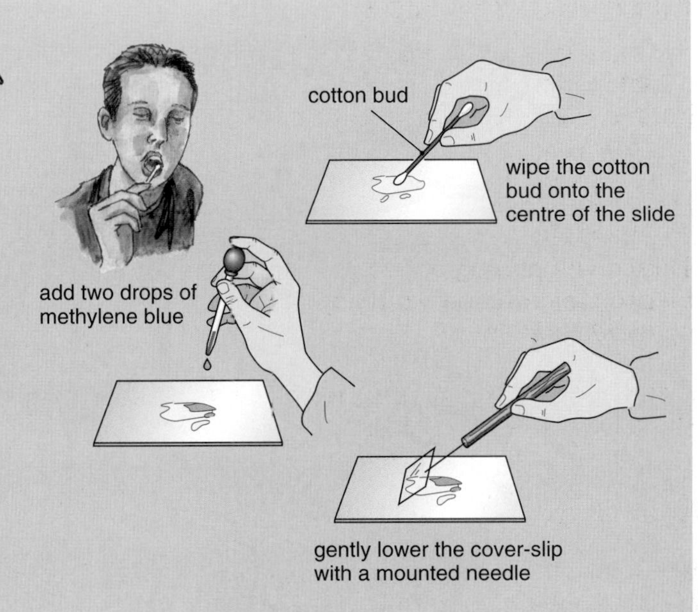

▶ Specialised cells

Many cells look different.
This is because they have their own special jobs to do.
During their development, these cells have changed shape, we say that they have **differentiated**.
Different cells do different jobs.
They share the work of the whole organism.

xylem cells are small tubes that carry water up the stem

leaf palisade cells contain lots of chloroplasts for photosynthesis

root hair cells are long and thin to absorb water from the soil

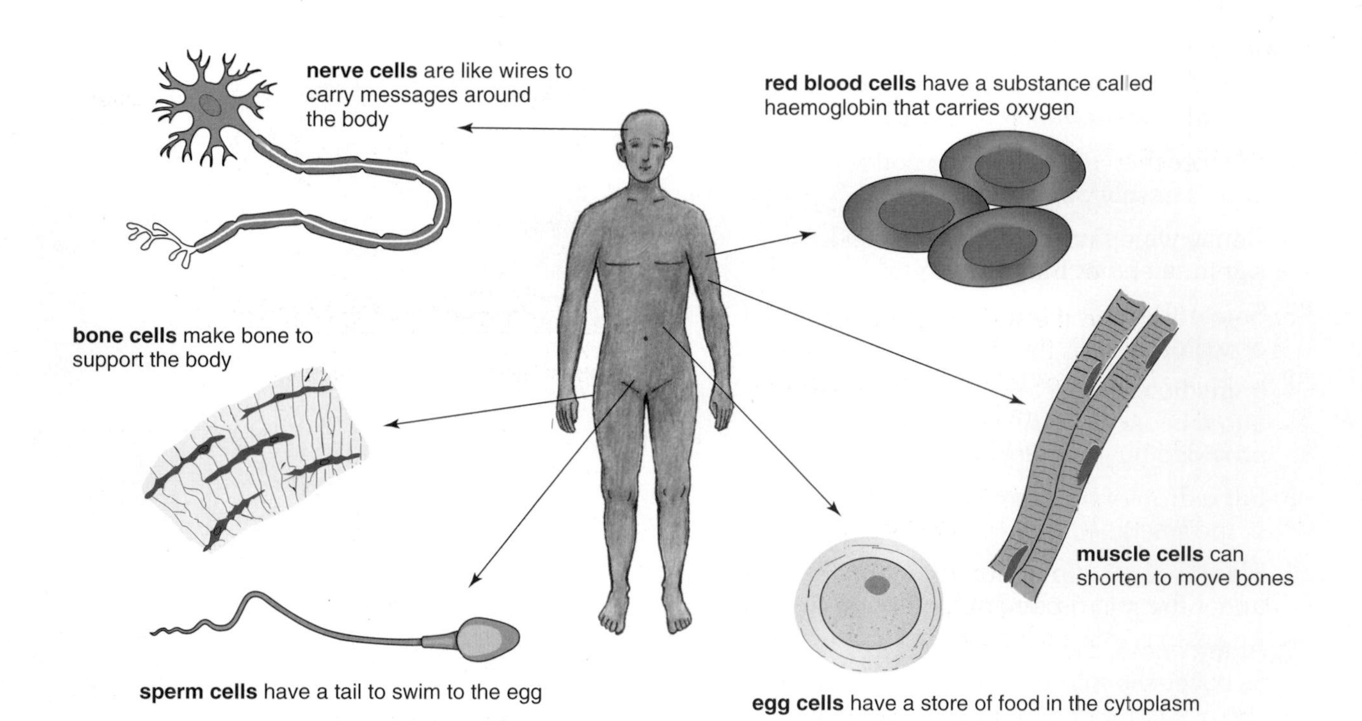

▶ Single cells

Some living organisms are made up of just ***one*** cell.
We call them **unicellular**.

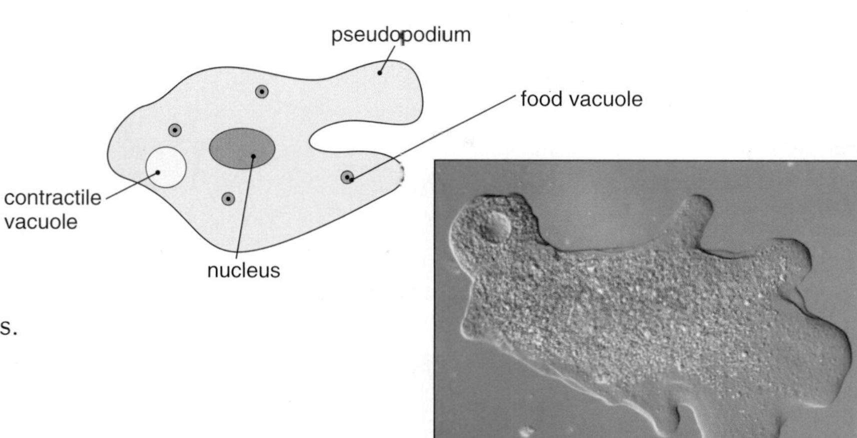

Amoeba is unicellular.
All seven life processes take place inside the one cell.

Amoeba lives in ponds and ditches.
It moves by changing its shape.
It pushes out **pseudopodia** in the direction it wants to go.
The rest of the cell 'flows' after them.

Amoeba feeds on smaller things like bacteria.
Pseudopodia flow around the food.
The food is taken into the cytoplasm in a **food vacuole**.

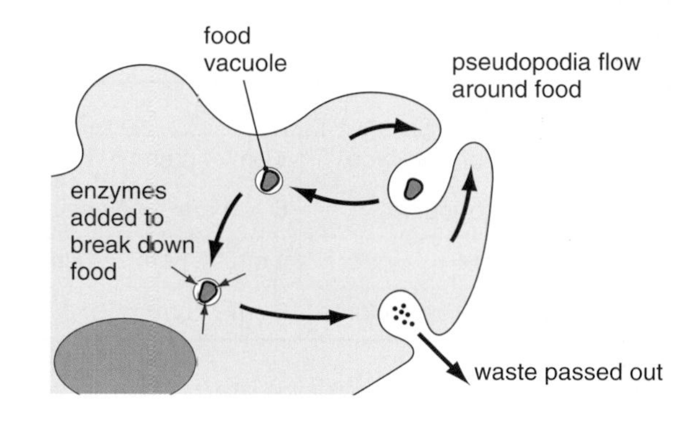

Chemicals called **enzymes** are added to the food to break it down.

Oxygen is dissolved in the water around the Amoeba.
It passes into the Amoeba by **diffusion**.
Waste substances like carbon dioxide diffuse out into the water.
You will find out more about diffusion in Chapter 2.

Amoeba reproduces by splitting into two.

▶ Many cells

Spirogyra is a very small living thing too.
But it is made up of more than one cell.
We say that it is **multicellular**.

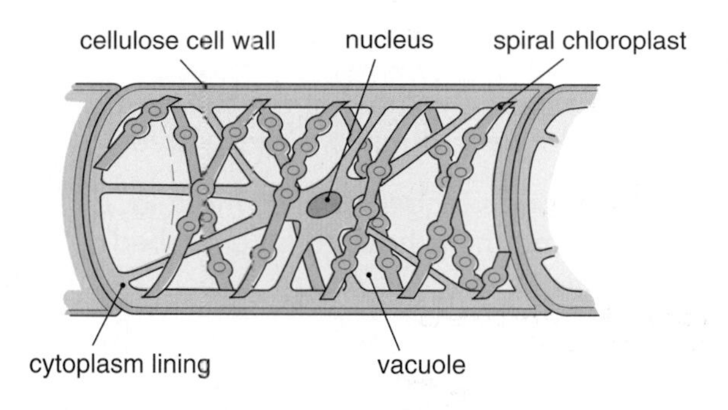

Spirogyra floats on the surface of ponds.
It is made up of cells that look alike.
All seven life processes take place in each cell.
In Spirogyra the cells are joined end to end to make **filaments**.

Spirogyra has a spiral, green chloroplast.
It makes its own food by photosynthesis.

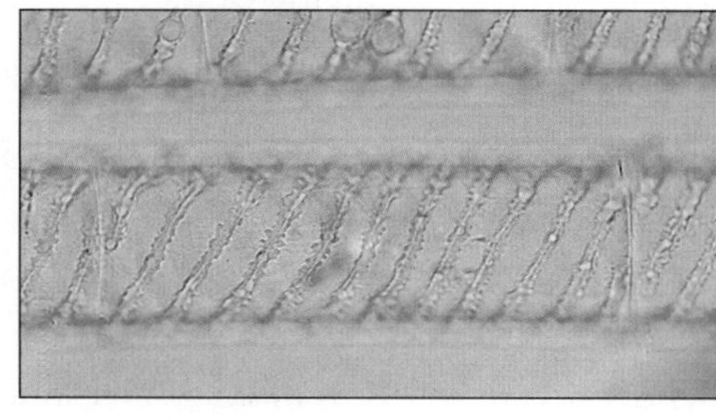
Spirogyra filaments

Both Amoeba and Spirogyra belong to a group of organisms called **Protists**.

You can find more about Protists on pages 236–7.

Cell size

Cells are very small.
You need a microscope to see them.
As they grow they get bigger.
But eventually they divide into two.
Why do you think this is?

Surface area and volume

Look at the three cubes.
They are different sizes.
A cube has six faces.

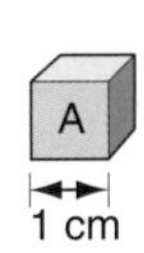

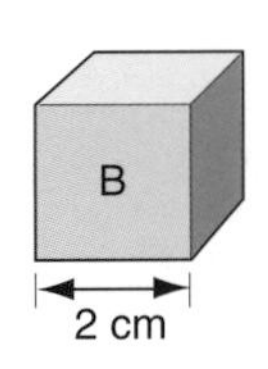

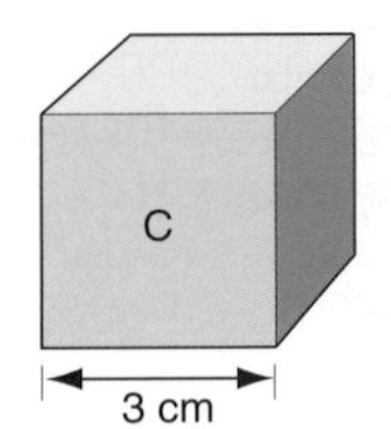

Copy and complete the table:

	Cube A	Cube B	Cube C
Surface area of one face	$1\text{ cm} \times 1\text{ cm} = 1\text{ cm}^2$		
Surface area of cube	$6 \times 1\text{ cm}^2 = 6\text{ cm}^2$		
Volume of cube	$1\text{ cm} \times 1\text{ cm} \times 1\text{ cm} = 1\text{ cm}^3$		
Ratio: surface area / volume	$6\text{ cm}^2/1\text{ cm}^3 = 6:1$		

What happens to the surface area/volume ratio as the cube increases in size?

As a cell grows its surface area/volume ratio gets smaller.
This means that the volume of the cell is increasing a lot faster than its surface area.

But as the cell gets bigger it needs more food and oxygen and these have to be absorbed through its surface.

Eventually the surface area becomes too small for enough food and oxygen to get into the cell.
The cell must now divide or die.

Look at the different cells sizes in the diagram:

Bigger cells tend to use up food and oxygen quicker than smaller cells.

Which cells here would use food and oxygen quickest?

What sort of materials need to pass ***out*** of a cell? (***Hint:*** think of respiration.)

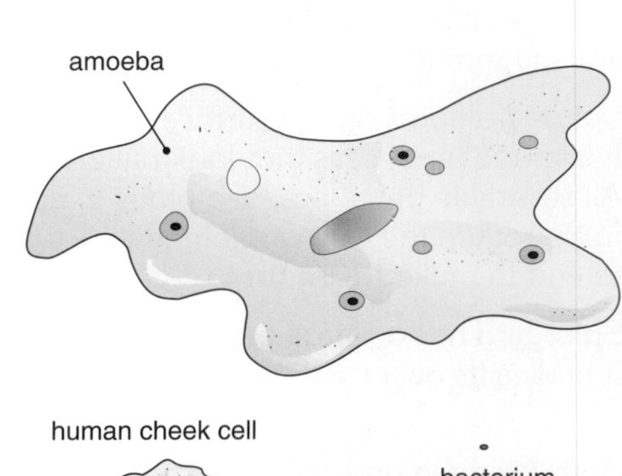

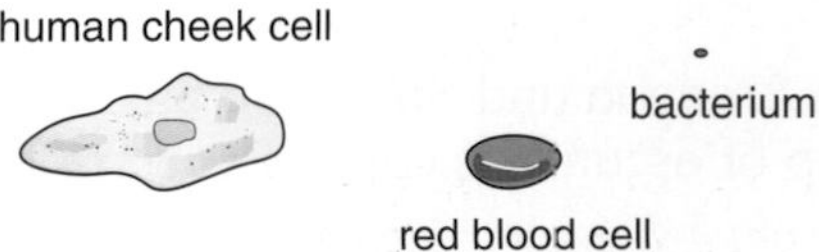

These cells are drawn to the same scale

▶ Tissues and organs

A group of similar cells is called a **tissue**.
All the cells in a tissue look the same and do the same job.
Your muscle tissue is made up of identical muscle cells.

An **organ** is made up of different tissues.
These work together to do a particular job.
Your heart is an organ.
It is made up of different tissues that work together to pump blood around your body.

Your stomach, lungs, brain and kidneys are all organs.
Do you know what each of them does?

Different organs work together as part of an **organ system**.
Your heart and blood vessels work together as part of your circulatory system.

All of your organ systems make up a living **organism** – that's you!

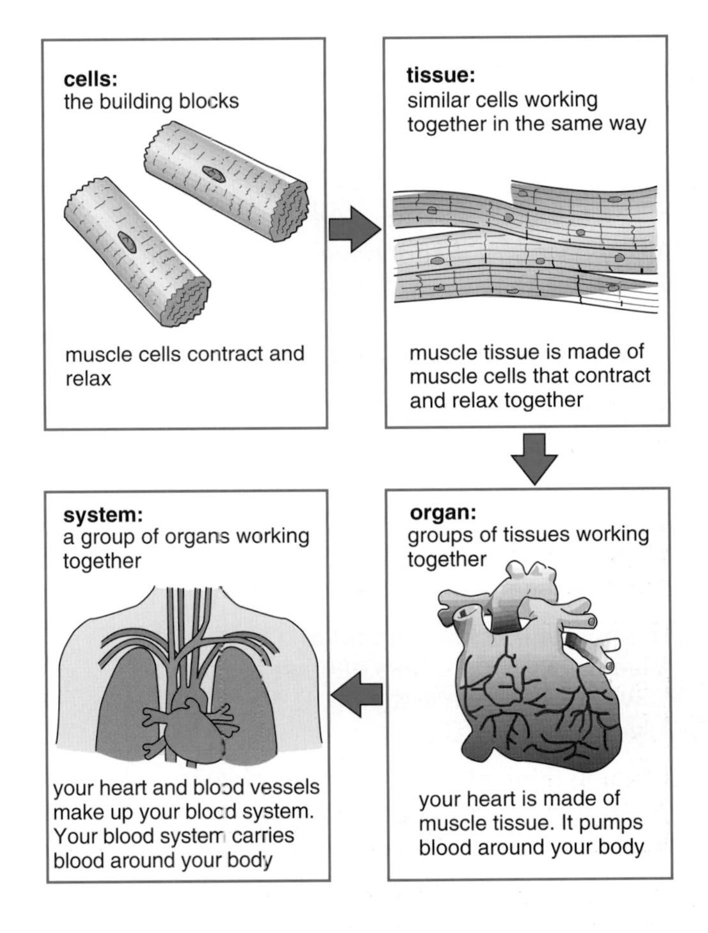

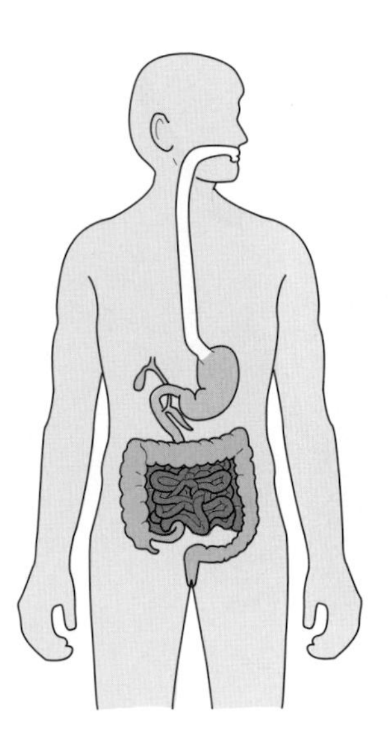

The digestive system is made up of your oesophagus, stomach and intestines

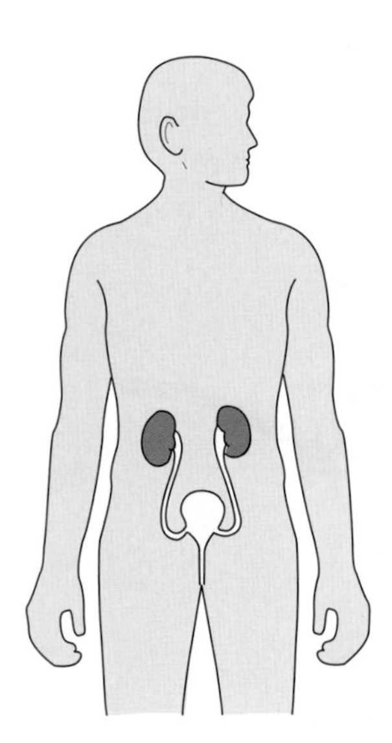

The excretory system is made up of your kidneys, ureters and bladder

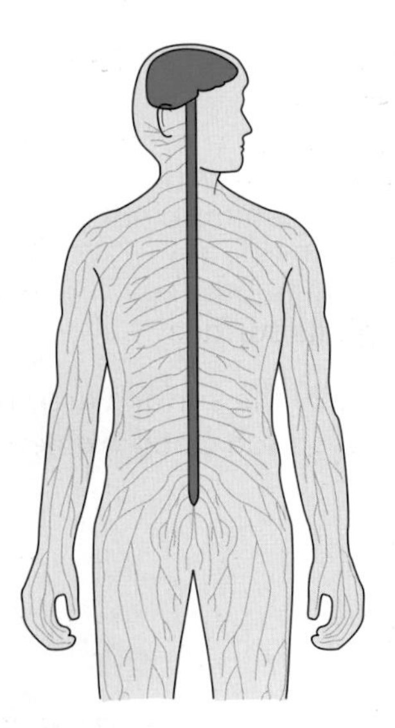

The nervous system is made up of your brain, spinal cord and nerves

▶ Plant organs

Try putting these words into the correct order, starting with the smallest and ending with the largest:

organ system tissue organism cell

Although plants do not have proper systems like we do, they do have tissues and organs. Let's look at an example:

The cells that carry out photosynthesis are called **palisade cells**.
They are rectangular and full of chloroplasts.

Lots of palisade cells make up the **palisade tissue**.
All the cells making up this tissue look alike and do the same job – they make food for the plant.

The palisade tissue is found in a **leaf**.
A leaf is made up of lots of other tissues as well as palisade tissue.
A leaf is an organ.

Can you think of any other plant organs? Roots, flowers, stems and fruits are all organs too.

All these different organs make up an organism – the buttercup plant.

cells: the building blocks

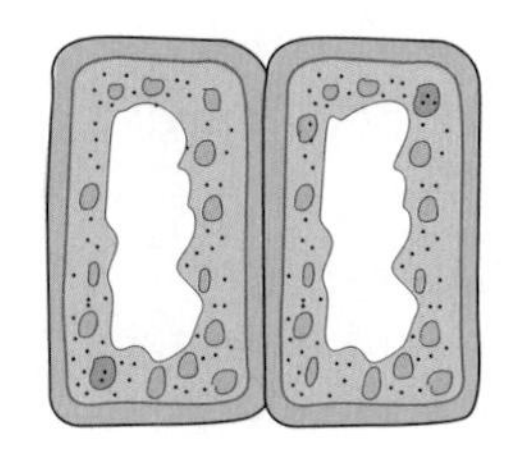

Leaf palisade cells absorb light

tissue: similar cells working together in the same way

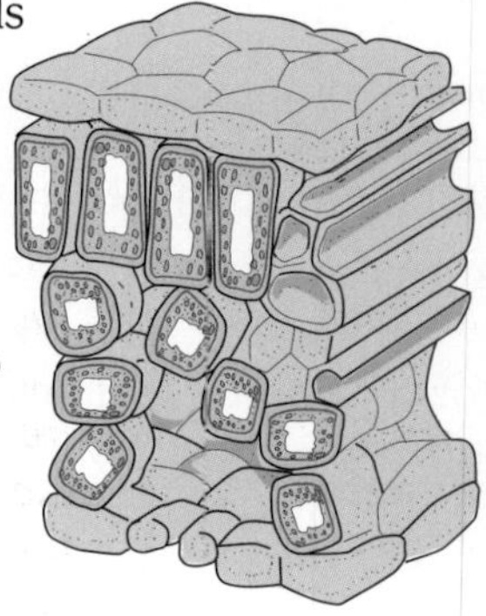

Photosynthesis takes place in the palisade tissue

organ: groups of tissues working together

organism: the buttercup plant is made up of many organs

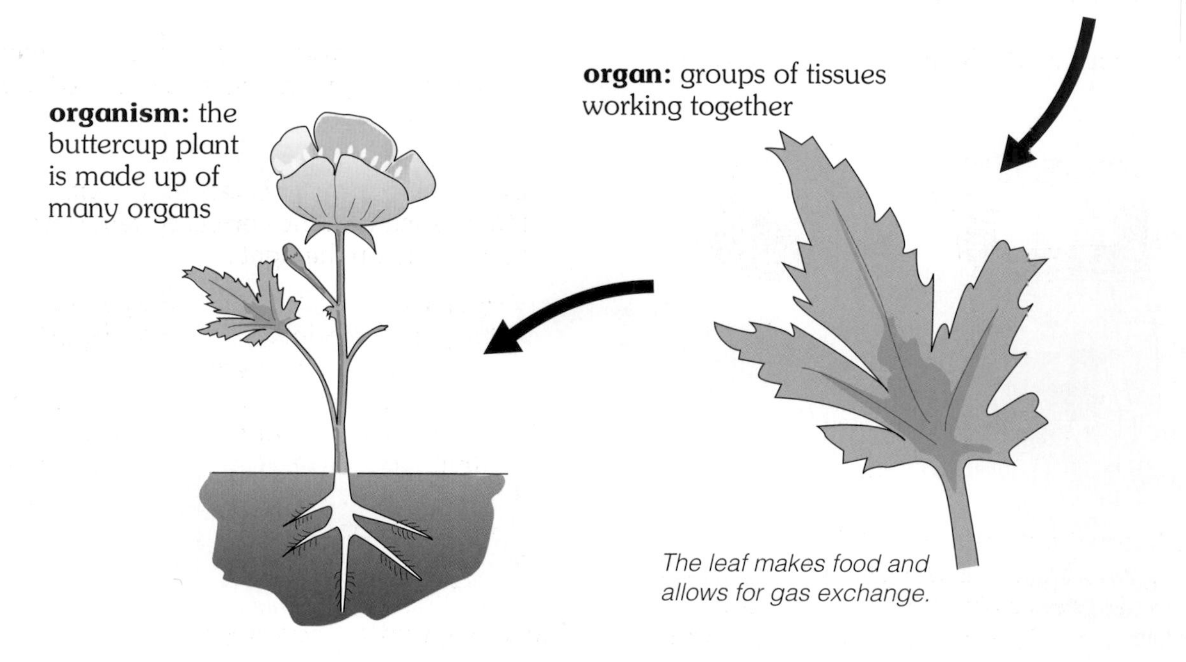

The leaf makes food and allows for gas exchange.

Summary

- The seven life processes are feeding, respiration, movement, growth, excretion, sensitivity and reproduction.
- Cells are the basic units of which all living organisms are made.
- There are differences in the structure of plant and animal cells.
- As a cell's size increases its surface area/volume ratio gets less. This limits the size of a cell.
- Some organisms are unicellular and some are multicellular.
- Cells differentiate as they develop and become specialised to do a particular job.
- In a multicellular organism the jobs are shared by all the cells.
- Cells that do the same job are grouped together into tissues.
- Different tissues make up organs and different organs make up systems.

▶ Questions

1. Copy out the activities listed in the left-hand column, then match each with the correct example from the right-hand column :

growth	***escaping from danger***
respiration	***laying eggs***
excretion	***making new leaves***
feeding	***hearing a whistle***
sensitivity	***sweating***
movement	***using up energy in a race***
reproduction	***having a snack***

2. The three cells A, B and C are not drawn to scale.

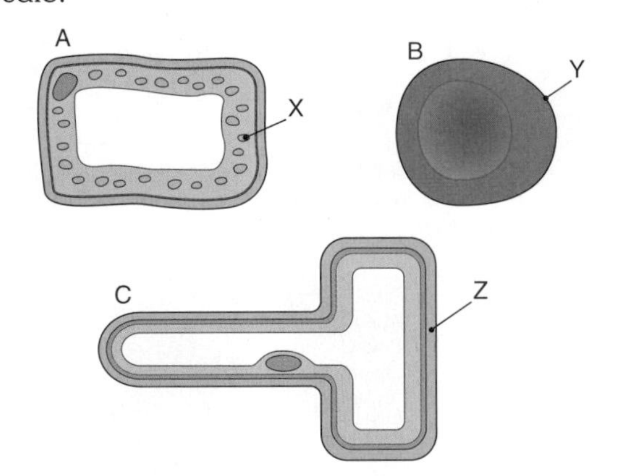

a) Name the parts X, Y and Z.
b) Give two reasons why cell A is a plant cell.
c) State one way in which the structure of each cell helps it to carry out its function.

3. a) What are the structures A, B and C in the diagram ?
b) What is the function (job) of C ?

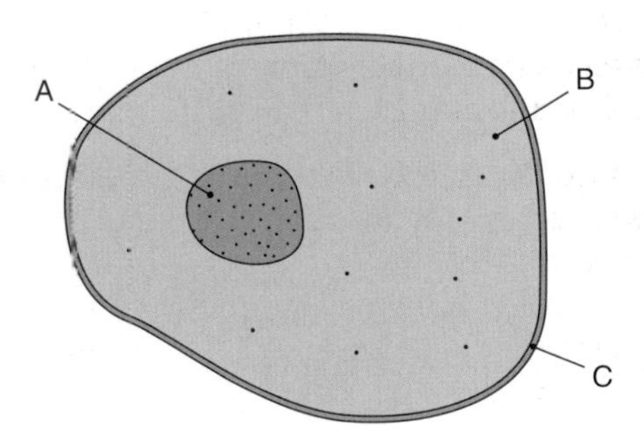

c) Draw and label three extra structures that would change this animal cell into a typical plant cell.

4. Copy out the organs listed on the left. Match each with the correct system from those listed on the right :

Organs	*System*
• lungs and windpipe	• digestive
• heart and blood vessels	• nervous
• brain and spinal cord	• respiratory
• ovaries, oviducts and uterus	• excretory
• oesophagus, stomach and intestines	• circulatory
• kidneys and bladder	• reproductive

Further questions on page 38.

chapter 2

Many substances dissolve in water.
How does this happen?

There are tiny spaces between the water molecules.
When something like sugar dissolves, each grain breaks up into thousands of tiny sugar particles.
These tiny particles spread out and fit into the spaces between the water molecules.

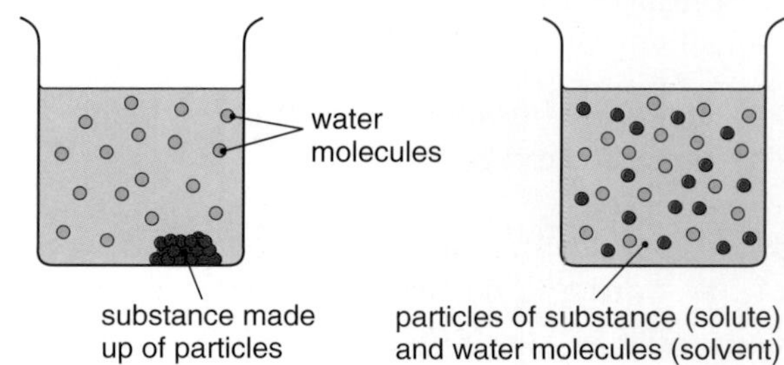

Look at the photographs:

- A purple crystal was dropped into the test-tube of water.
  At first the molecules were concentrated in one place – in the crystal.
- After 30 minutes some of the purple molecules had left the crystal and spread out.
- After 24 hours all the purple molecules had spread evenly through the water.

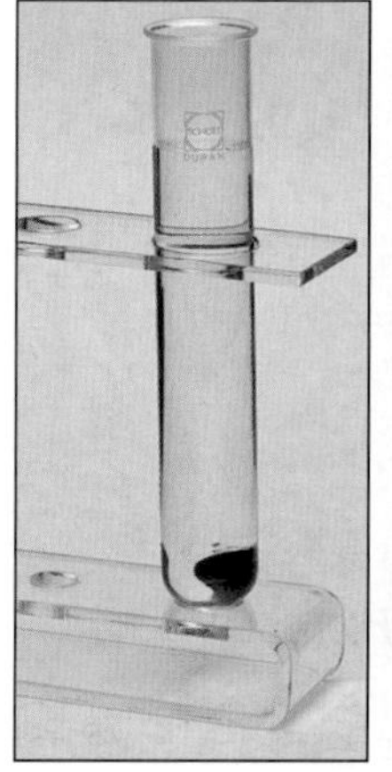
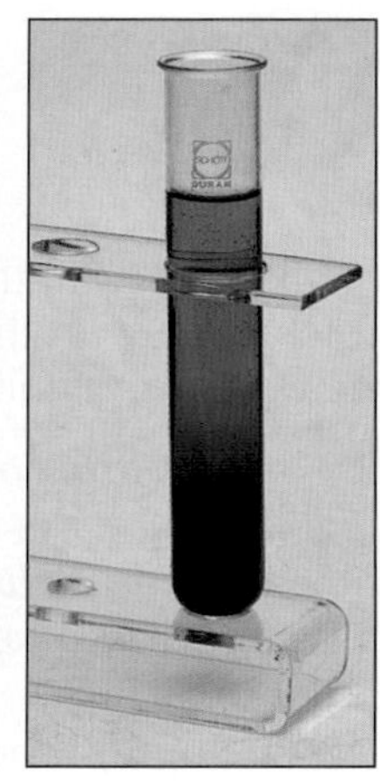
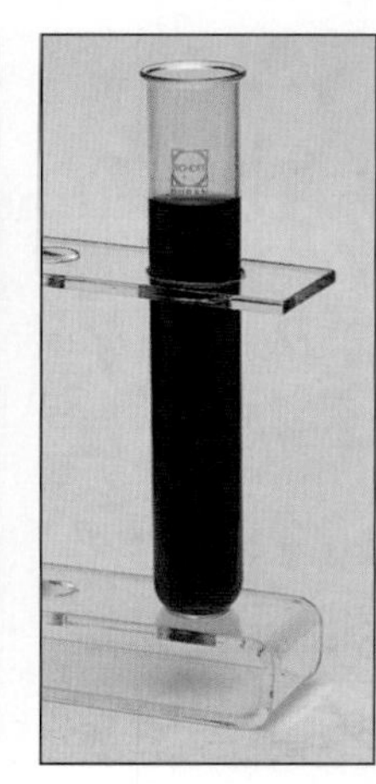

The purple molecules spread out by **diffusion**.

When molecules diffuse they spread out from where there are lots of them (a high concentration) to where there aren't many of them (a low concentration).
They do this until they are spread out evenly.

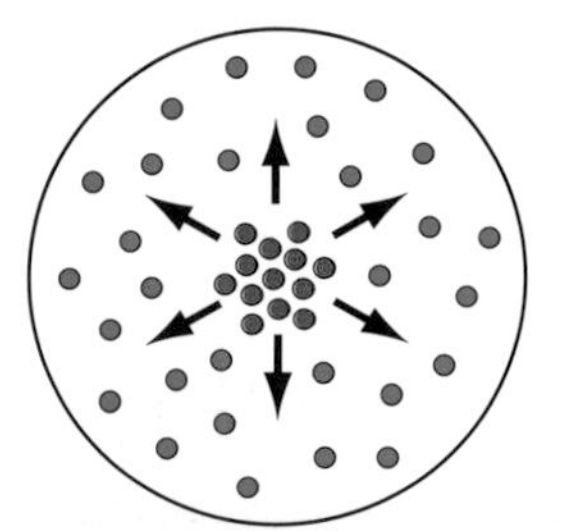
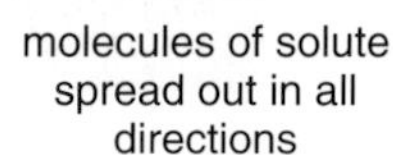
molecules of solute spread out in all directions

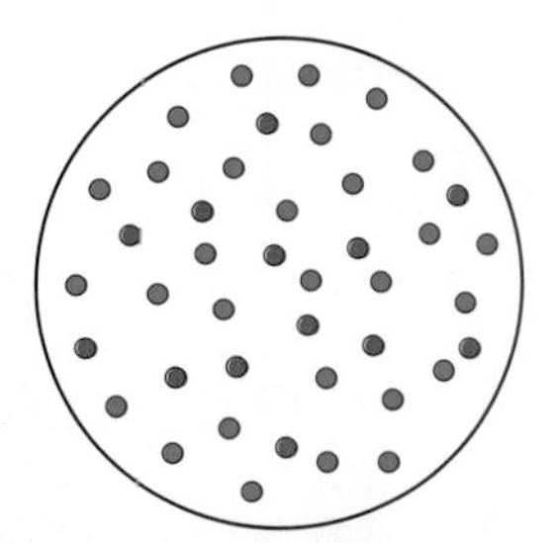
solute molecules spread out evenly

A **solution** is made up of two parts, the **solute** and the **solvent**.
The **solute** dissolves in the **solvent**.

If you dissolve sugar in water you make a sugar solution.
The sugar is the solute and the water is the solvent.

The solute is not always a solid like sugar.
Liquids and gases can be solutes as they can dissolve in solvents too.

A **concentrated solution** has a lot of solute dissolved in the solvent.

A **dilute solution** has a small amount of solute dissolved in the solvent.

▶ Diffusion

When food is cooking in the kitchen you can smell it in other rooms in the house.
This is because molecules are leaving the food as a gas and moving around at high speed, eventually reaching all parts of the house.
This is called **diffusion**.

Diffusion is the movement of particles from a high concentration to a lower concentration until they are spread out evenly.

Demonstration 2.1 Diffusion in a gas

⚠ bromine is toxic and corrosive

Your teacher may be able to show you the diffusion of some bromine.
This brown gas is very poisonous.
What will happen when the gas jar of air is put on top of the gas jar of bromine?

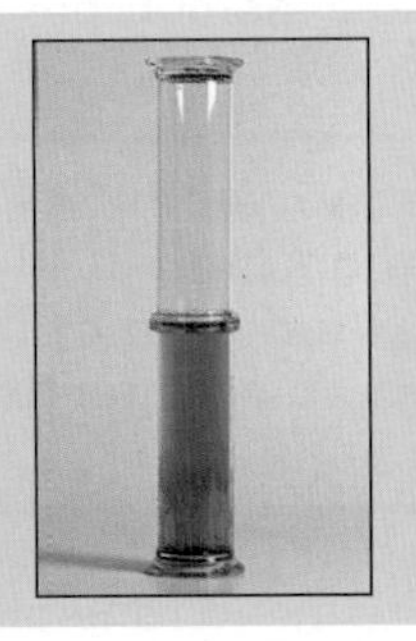

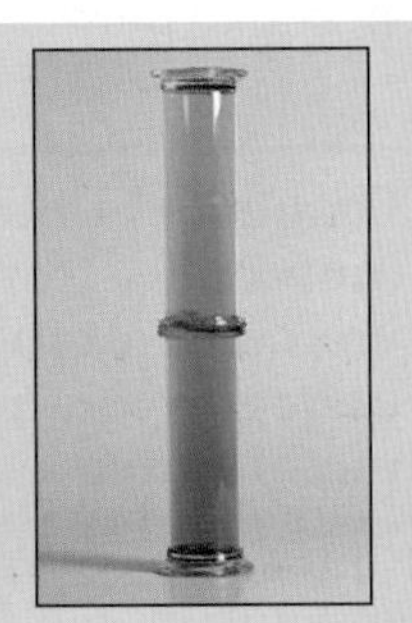

Gases diffuse quicker than liquids.
Why do you think this is?

Demonstration 2.2 Rate of diffusion

⚠ ammonia is toxic and irritant

Your teacher may show you this experiment.
Eight pieces of red litmus paper are hung in a glass tube as shown in the diagram:
Some ammonium hydroxide solution is added to the cotton wool pad and placed into the hole in the bung.
As alkaline ammonia gas diffuses along the tube it turns the litmus paper blue.
Time how long it takes for each piece of litmus paper to turn blue.
The greater the difference in concentration, the faster the rate of diffusion.

cotton
glass tube
red litmus paper
cotton wool soaked in ammonium hydroxide solution

Your body cells need food and oxygen for respiration.
These are carried to our cells in the blood.
What happens when the blood reaches the cells?
The molecules of food and oxygen diffuse out of the blood and into the cells.

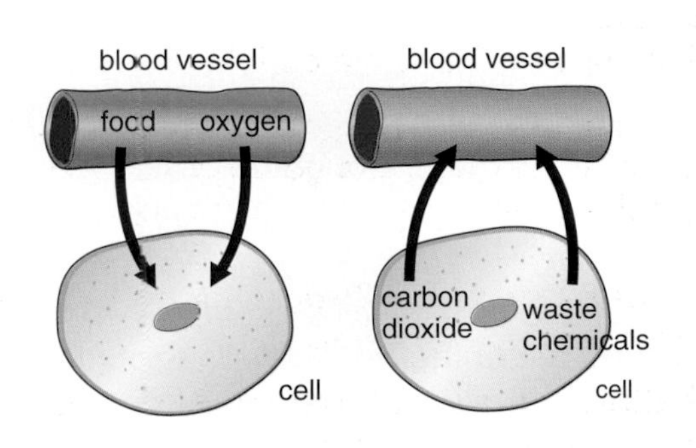

As cells use up food and oxygen they make waste.
This waste is carbon dioxide and waste chemicals.
These will poison the cells if they build up.
Carbon dioxide and waste chemicals diffuse out of the cells and into the blood.

▶ Osmosis

Each cell is surrounded by a cell membrane.
It separates the contents of the cell from the outside.
The cell membrane has tiny holes in it.
This allows small molecules to pass through but not large ones.
The cell membrane is **partially permeable**.

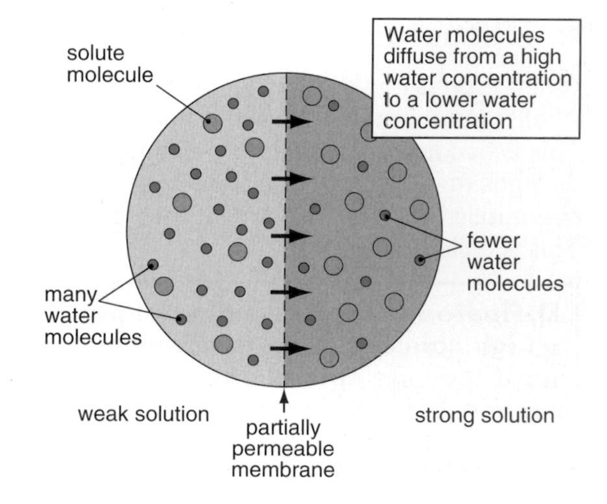

Osmosis is a special kind of diffusion involving water molecules.
It occurs when two solutions are separated by a partially permeable membrane.

Osmosis is the movement of water molecules from an area of high water concentration to an area of low water concentration across a partially permeable membrane.

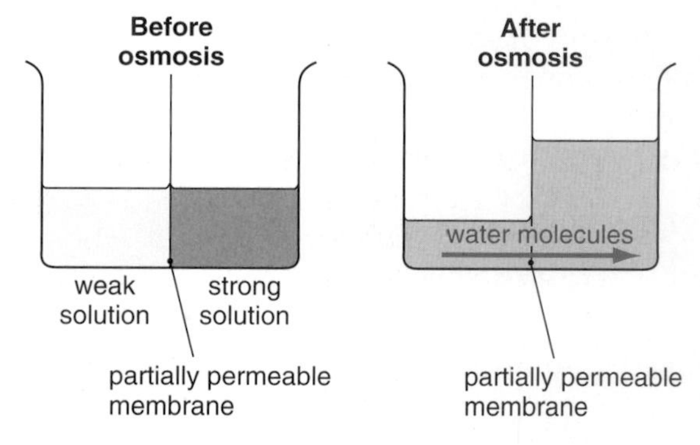

The tiny holes in the membrane allow small water molecules to pass through.
But the large solute molecules are too big to pass through the partially permeable membrane.

Experiment 2.3 A model cell

Visking tubing is partially permeable.

Cut two pieces of Visking tubing 12 cm long.

Tie one end of each with cotton.

Fill 'cell A' with sugar solution and 'cell B' with water.

Tie the other end and weigh each 'cell'.

Put 'cell A' into a beaker of water.

Put 'cell B' into a beaker of sugar solution.

After 30 minutes re-weigh each 'cell'.

Cell A increases in weight because water has passed into the cell, into the strong solution by osmosis.

Cell B decreases in weight because water has passed out of the cell, into the strong solution by osmosis.

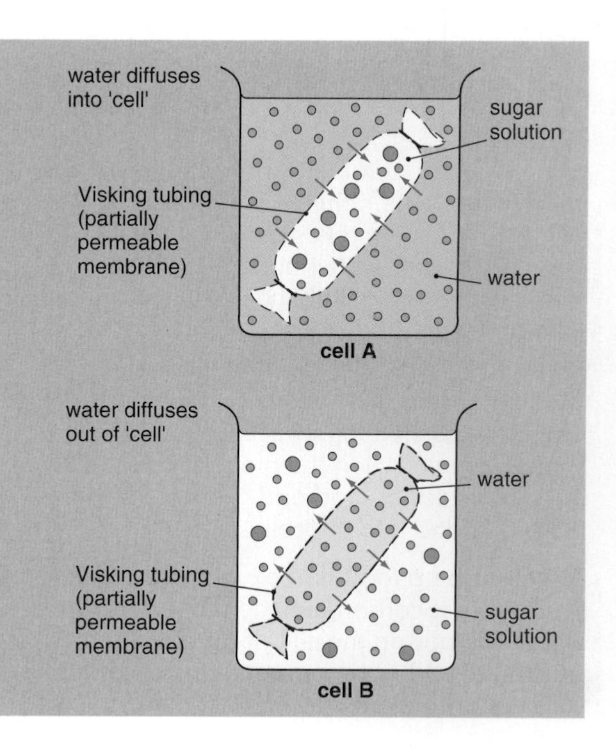

▶ Osmosis in plant cells

Osmosis is the way in which many living things take up water.

Experiment 2.4 An osmometer

You can see the effects of osmosis if you set up this apparatus:

Fill the partially permeable membrane with strong sugar solution.

Tie it to a capillary tube and stand it in a weak sugar solution.

Use your ideas about osmosis to explain why the liquid rises in the tube.

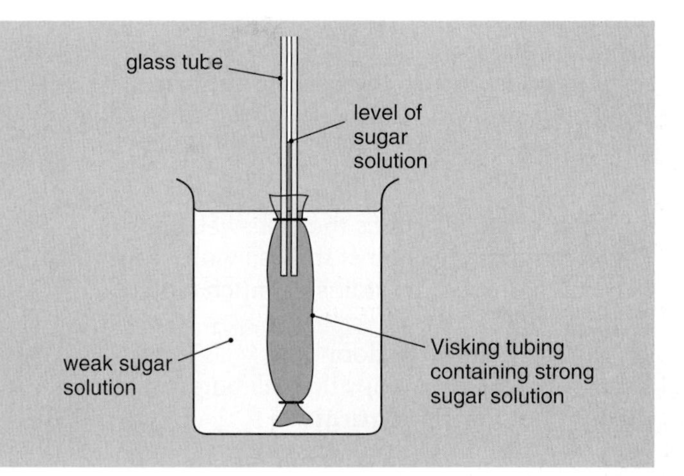

Water will move into plant cells by osmosis.

- The cell membrane of the plant cell acts as a partially permeable membrane.
- The cell sap inside the vacuole is a strong solution.
- Water passes into the plant cell by osmosis.
- The concentration of the sap in the vacuole is now weaker.
- Water passes from the weak solution into the strong solution in the next cell by osmosis.

cell wall (fully permeable)
cytoplasm
weak solution
osmosis
strong solution
cell membrane (partially permeable membrane)
vacuole

Experiment 2.5 Osmosis in potato cells

Cut three potato chips to exactly the same size.

Measure their length and write it down.

Set up the following test-tubes:
test-tube A – distilled water
test-tube B – weak sugar solution
test-tube C – strong sugar solution.

Place one potato chip in each test-tube and leave it for 30 minutes.

Re-measure each chip.

- Which chip has increased in size? Is this because it has taken in water by osmosis?
- Which chip has got shorter? Is this because it has lost water by osmosis?
- Feel the chip that was in test-tube A. Why does it feel firm?

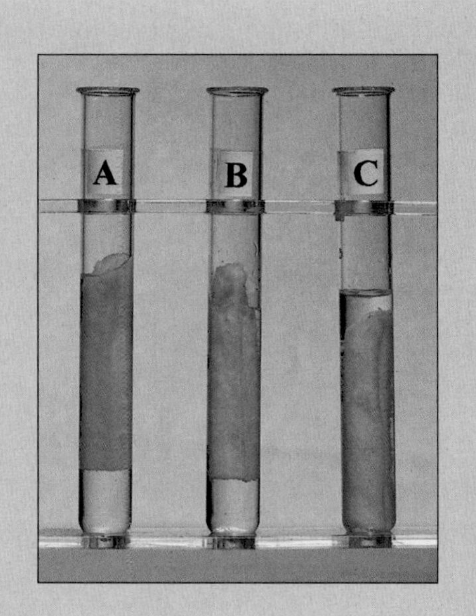

▶ Turgidity

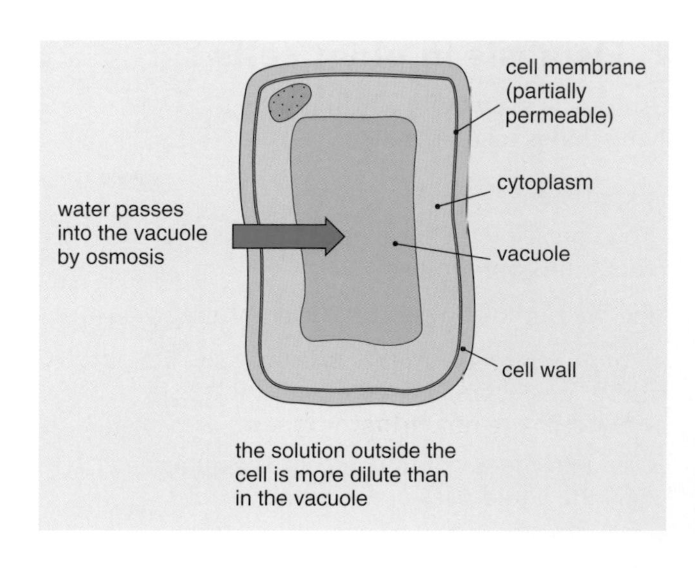

When plant cells are placed in water, the water enters the cells.
This is because their cell sap contains a strong solution.
So water passes ***into*** the cells by osmosis.
The cell membrane is the partially permeable membrane.

As water enters it makes the cell swell up.
The water pushes against the cell wall.
Eventually the cell contains as much water as it can hold.
It's like a blown-up balloon.
The strong cell wall stops the cell bursting.
We say that the cell is **turgid**.

If you've cut chips and put them into water you will know that they soon go firm.
This is because they have taken in water by osmosis and are now turgid.

Can you think why turgid cells are useful to plants?

Turgid cells give the plant support.
They keep the stems of many plants upright.

But what happens when these cells lose water?
The cells are no longer firm and turgid.
Plant stems that have lost water **wilt**.

Investigation 2.6 Plan an investigation into the effects of sugar solution on potato cells

You could find out how different concentrations of solutions affect the mass or the length of potato chips.

You could also measure the flexibility of the chips.

You could find out the effect of temperature on turgidity.

Before carrying out your plan, check with your teacher that it is safe to do so.

▶ Plasmolysis

When plant cells are placed into a strong sugar or salt solution water passes ***out*** of the cells by osmosis.
As water passes out, the sap vacuole starts to shrink.
These cells are no longer firm, they are limp.
We say that they are **flaccid**.

As more water leaves the cells their cell membranes start to peel away from their cell walls.
These cells are now **plasmolysed**.

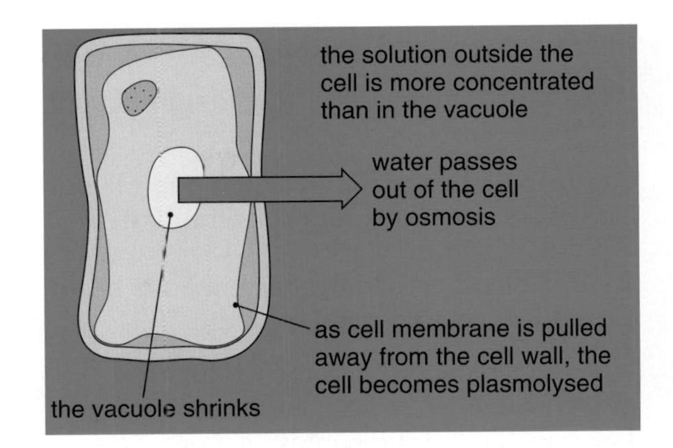

Experiment 2.7 Plasmolysis

Put some red onion skin onto a slide with a drop of water.

Put a cover-slip on the slide and focus it under the microscope.

Add a few drops of strong sugar solution to the edge of the cover-slip.

Describe what happens to the cells.

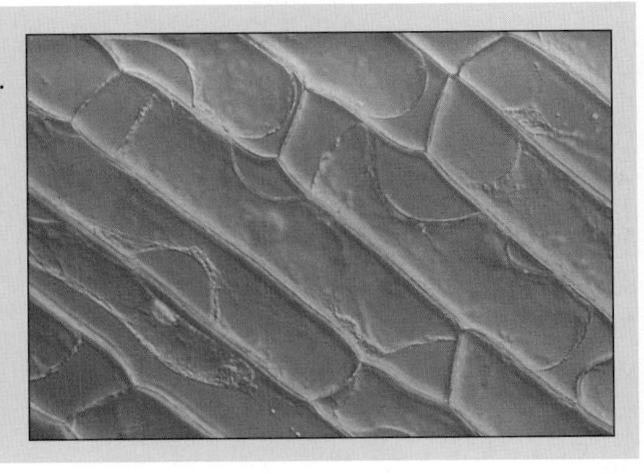

▶ Osmosis in animal cells

What do you think animal cells will do if placed in different strengths of solution?

The cell membrane is the partially permeable membrane in animal cells.

The red blood cells in the picture have been placed in distilled water.
Their cytoplasm is a strong solution.
Water passes into the cells by osmosis.
But animal cells have no cell wall to stop them swelling too much – so they burst!
We call this **haemolysis**.

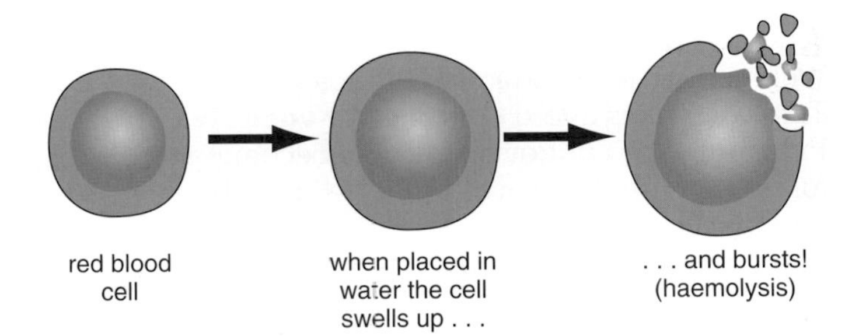

▶ A constant blood concentration

What would happen if the liquid part of your blood was too watery and dilute?

What would happen if the liquid part of your blood was too strong and concentrated?

The red blood cells in this picture have been placed in a concentrated solution:

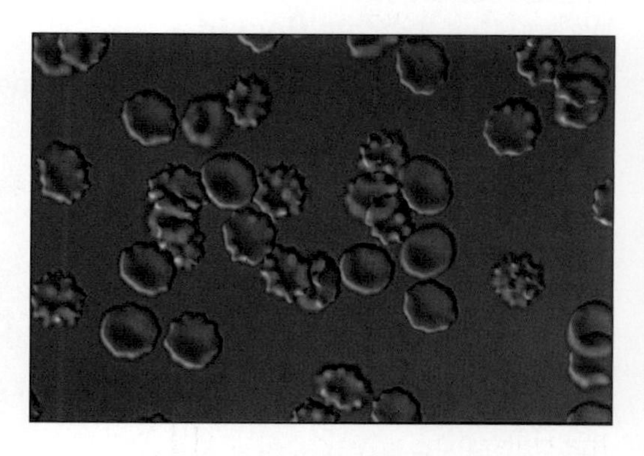

Water has moved out of their cytoplasm by osmosis.
The cells have shrunk.
Do you think these red blood cells would be able to do their job properly?

Can you see why it is so important to keep the concentration of our blood constant? (We will find out more about keeping our water content constant in Chapter 7.)

The red blood cells in this picture are in a solution that is the same concentration as their cytoplasm:

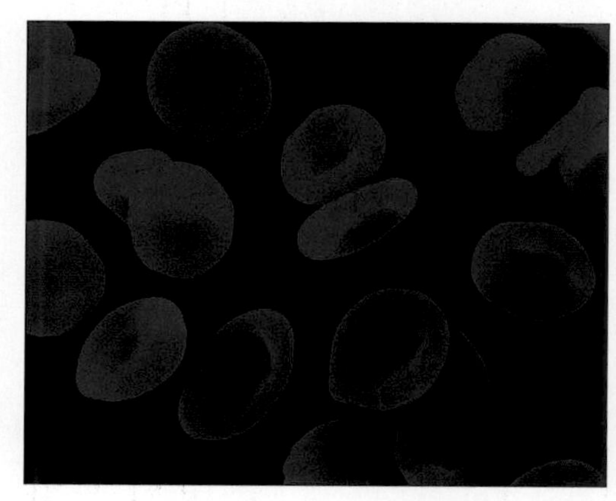

Why have they kept their shape?

The solutions on each side of their cell membranes are the same concentration. So the cells neither gain nor lose water.

Why doesn't Amoeba burst?
Water enters the Amoeba by osmosis.
The water goes into a **contractile vacuole**.
Eventually the contractile vacuole becomes so full of water that it moves to the cell membrane and bursts.
The water has been removed from the cell.

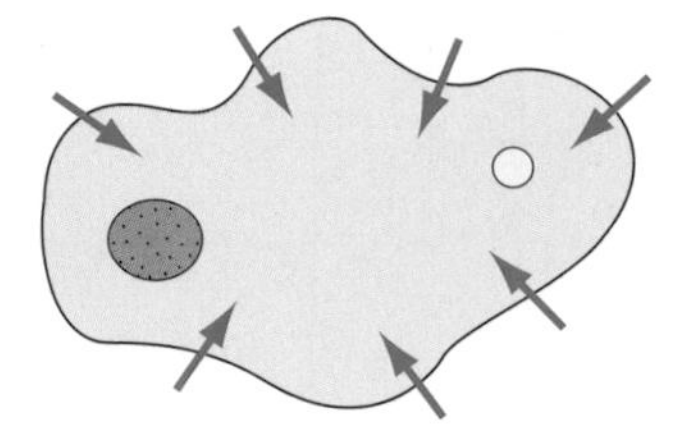

water enters *Amoeba* by osmosis

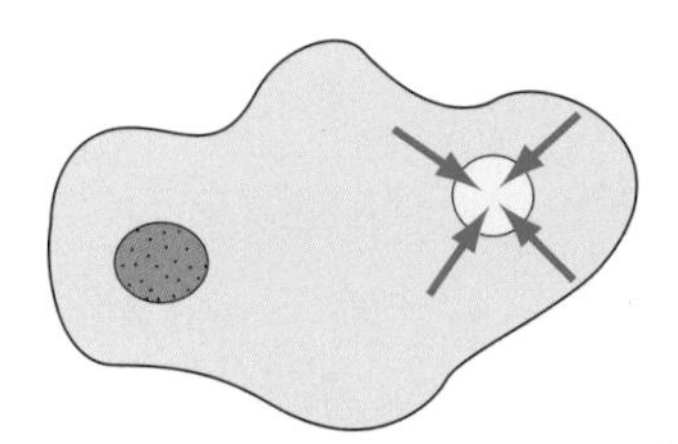

water taken into contractile vacuole

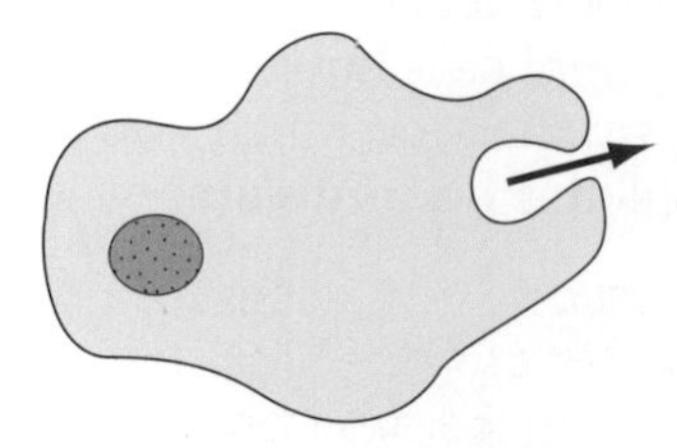

contractile vacuole bursts removing water from the cell

▶ Active transport

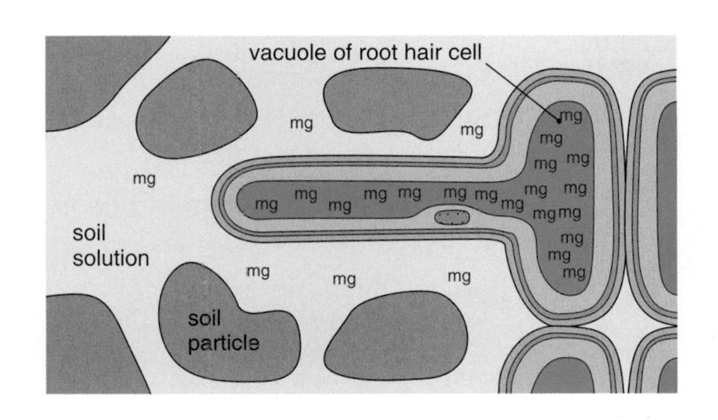

Cells can take up some substances from dilute solutions and keep them in high concentrations.

Look at the concentration of magnesium ions in the root hair cell :

Look at the concentration of magnesium ions in the soil solution :

Which way would you expect magnesium ions to move by diffusion ?

Sometimes cells can keep hold of particles and not let them diffuse out.
What's more they can even take in ***more*** particles against a concentration gradient.

Look at the histogram :

It shows the concentrations of some salts inside the cells of a water plant and outside in the water.

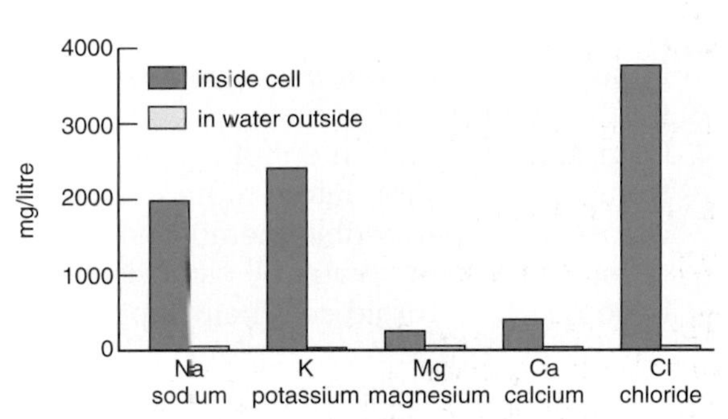

The concentrations of salts found inside and outside the cells of a freshwater plant

These salts cannot have been taken in by diffusion.
They are taken in against a concentration gradient.
They are taken in by **active transport**.
Active transport needs energy from respiration to make it happen.

Active transport is the uptake of particles by cells against a concentration gradient. Active transport needs energy.

Sugars can be absorbed from the small intestine and from the kidney tubules by active transport.

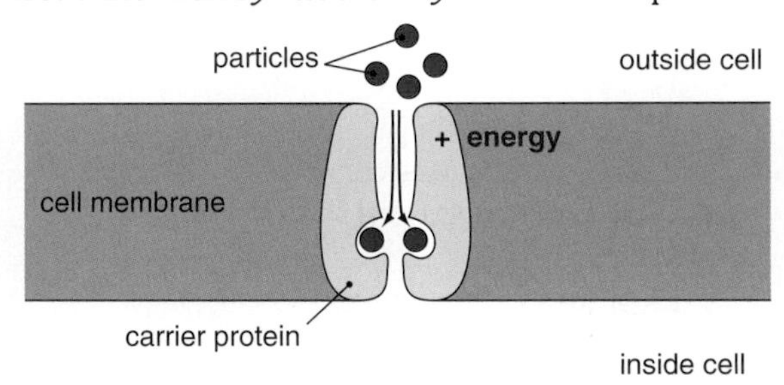

Carrier protein takes up particles on outside of membrane

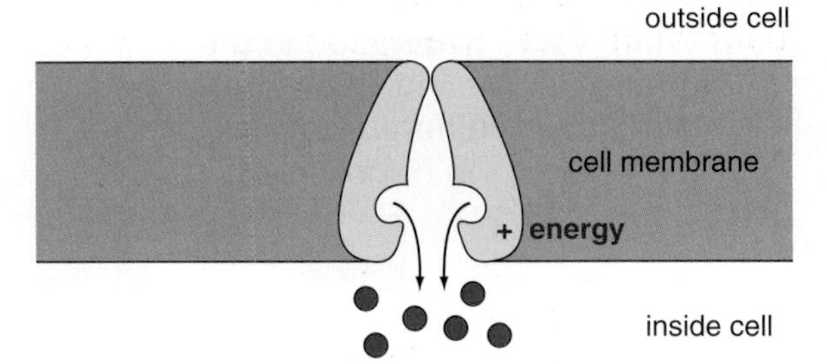

Carrier protein releases particles on inside of membrane

The carrier protein uses energy to transport molecules or ions across the membrane.
This energy comes from respiration inside the cell.
Poisons like cyanide can stop respiration.
Do you think that this would stop active transport too ?

Summary

- Molecules move from a high concentration to a lower concentration by diffusion.
- The greater the difference in concentration, the faster the rate of diffusion.
- Food and oxygen diffuse into cells. Carbon dioxide and waste substances diffuse out.
- Osmosis is the movement of water molecules from a dilute solution into a more concentrated solution through a partially permeable membrane.
- Water passes into plant cells by osmosis. A plant cell that is full of water is turgid. If plant cells are placed in a strong solution, water passes out by osmosis. As the vacuole shrinks the cell membrane eventually peels away from the cell wall – the cell is plasmolysed.
- If animal cells are put into a weak solution they take in water and burst.
- Particles can be taken into a cell against a concentration gradient. This process needs energy so is called active transport.

▶ Questions

1. Copy and complete:
Molecules move from a .... concentration to a .... concentration by .....
Osmosis is the movement of .... molecules from a .... solution into a more .... solution across a .... permeable membrane. When plant cells take up water by osmosis they become ..... Turgid cells help support parts of a plant like the ..... If plant cells lose water the stem lacks support and ..... If plant cells lose a lot of water the cell .... peels away from the cell .... and the cell is said to be .....

2. a) Which diffuses faster, a liquid or a gas? Why is this?
b) What would heating do to the rate of diffusion of a salt crystal in water?
c) What things diffuse:
i) into cells ii) out of cells?

3. The test-tube containing agar jelly and blue dye was set up as shown in photo A.

A

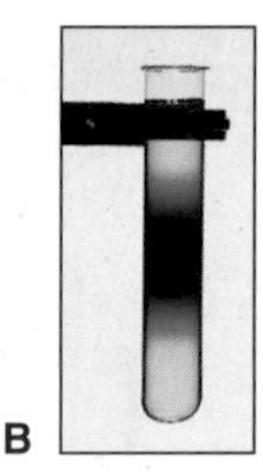
B

Photo B shows its appearance after a week.
a) Explain as fully as you can what has happened to the blue dye.
b) Why did it take a week for this to happen?

4. a) Is a cell membrane permeable, impermeable or partially permeable?
b) Is a cell wall permeable, impermeable or partially permeable?
c) These two chips were cut from a potato. Each ***was*** 50 mm long. One was put into water and the other was put into strong sugar solution. Use your ruler to measure each chip.

chip A

chip B

i) Which chip was put in water? Explain your answer.
ii) Which chip was put into strong sugar solution? Explain your answer.

5. a) Explain why red blood cells burst if they are put into water.
b) Explain why Amoeba does not burst when put into water.
c) Some plant cells are put into a solution. They neither take up water nor lose water. What can you say about the strength of the cell sap and the external solution?

6. The experiment was set up as shown :

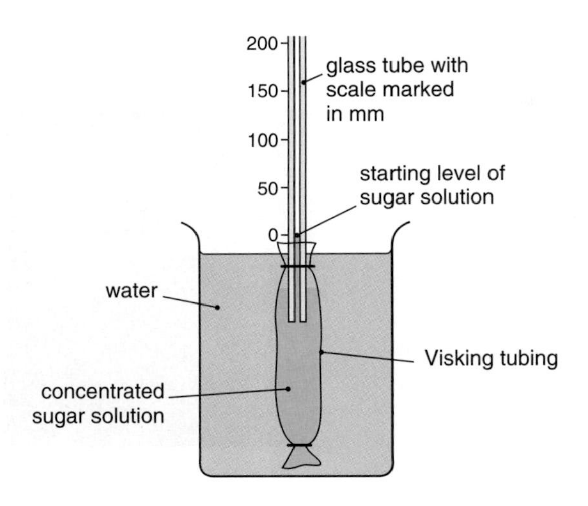

The level of the liquid in the tube was measured every minute.

The results are shown in the graph.

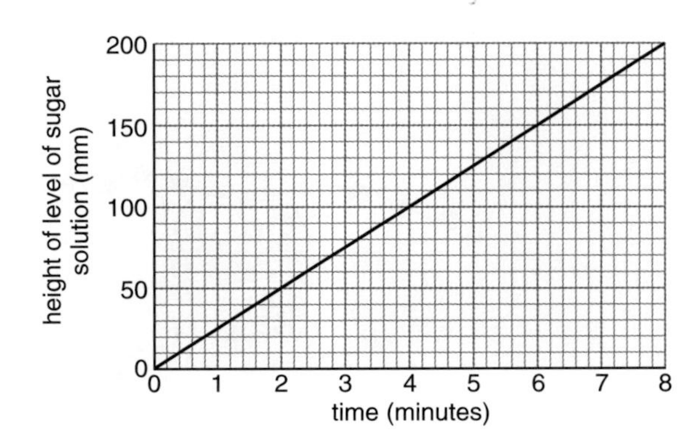

a) Explain why the liquid rose in the tube.
b) What was the level of the liquid after 4 minutes?
c) How much longer did it take for the liquid to reach the top?
d) Would the liquid take longer to reach the top if the sugar solution was weaker? Explain your answer.

7. Two freshly cut potato chips were set up as shown.

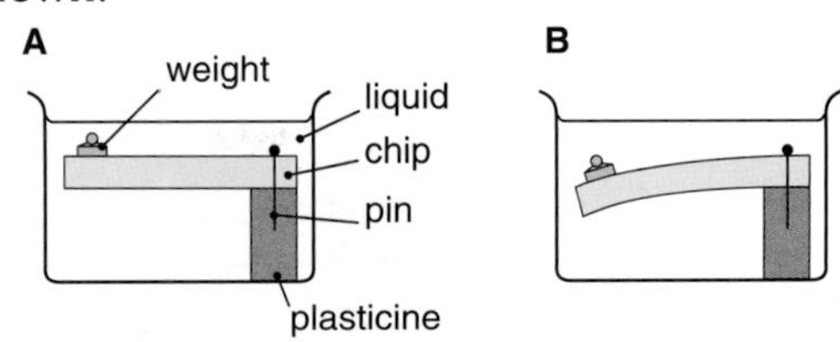

Each was covered with a colourless liquid.
a) What liquid was used in **A**?
b) Explain why the chip in **A** was able to support the weight.
c) What sort of liquid was used in **B**?
d) Explain why the chip in **B** bent under the weight.

8. Batches of 10 potato discs were weighed and then placed into one of 10 different concentrations of sugar solution. After 30 minutes the potato discs were removed and re-weighed. Their percentage change in mass was worked out. The results are shown in the graph :

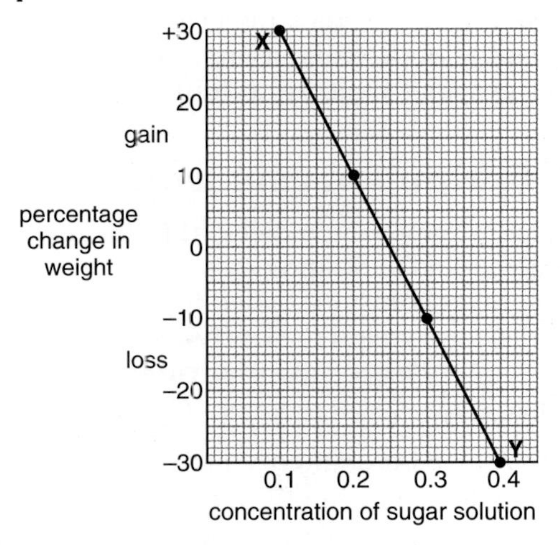

a) What process caused the change in mass of the potato discs?
b) What would the potato discs be like at **X**?
c) What other differences apart from weight would you be able to observe between the discs at **X** and **Y**?
d) Use the graph to find the concentration of sugar solution that would cause no change in the weight of the potato discs.

Further questions on page 38.

chapter 3

Thousands of chemical reactions take place in our cells.
We need these reactions to happen quickly to keep us alive.
Luckily for us there are chemicals called **enzymes**.
Enzymes make reactions happen at a much faster rate.

Chemicals that speed up reactions are called **catalysts**.
Since enzymes speed up chemical reactions in our cells, they are often called **biological catalysts**.

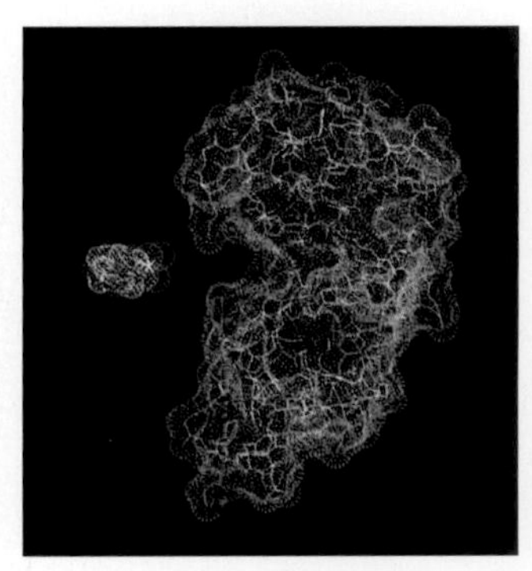
Computer model of an enzyme

Breakers and builders

Enzymes come in two main types :

Breakers
Sometimes we need to break down large molecules into smaller ones. Breaker-enzymes speed up these reactions. This is important in digestion when large food molecules are broken down into small ones so that we can use them.

Builders
In other reactions small molecules are joined together to make large ones. Builder-enzymes speed up these reactions. These enzymes build important molecules inside our cells.

▶ How an enzyme works

Enzymes are protein molecules made up of long chains of amino acids.
These long chains are folded to produce a special shape called the **active site**.
Other molecules called **substrates** fit into the active site and a reaction takes place.

This is how a breaker-enzyme works :

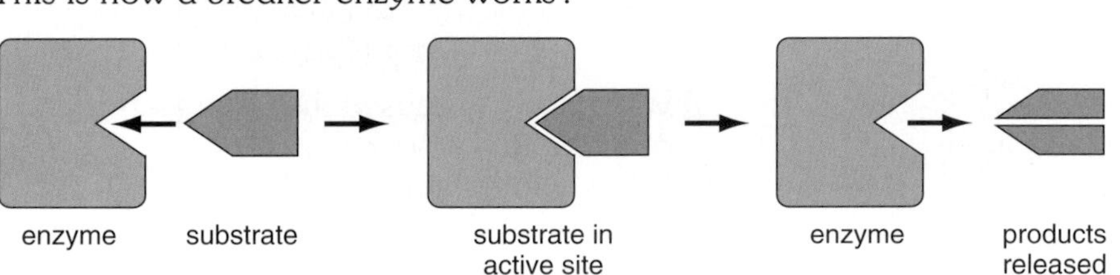

Use the diagram below to explain how a builder-enzyme works :

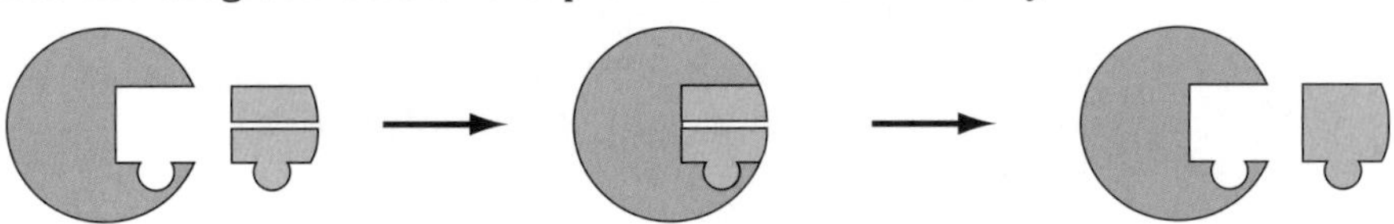

Enzymes are particular ...

All enzymes have five important properties:

> **1. They are all proteins.**
> **2. Each enzyme controls one particular reaction.**
> **3. They can be used again and again.**
> **4. They are affected by temperature.**
> **5. They are affected by pH.**

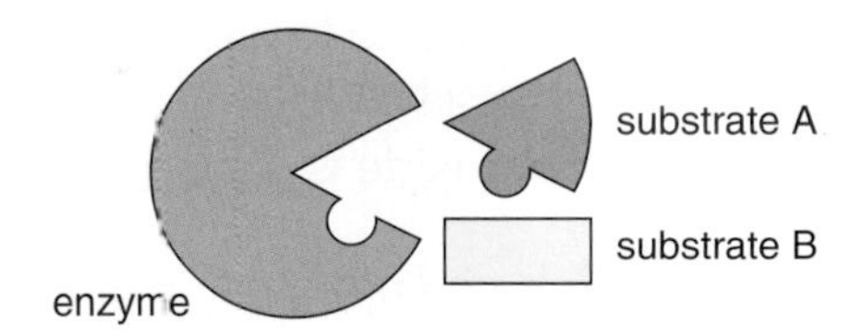

Which substrate fits the active site?

Look at the diagram:

Use it to explain why each enzyme will only work on ***one*** particular substrate.
Does the shape of the active site decide this?

Why is only a ***small*** amount of enzyme needed to control a reaction?

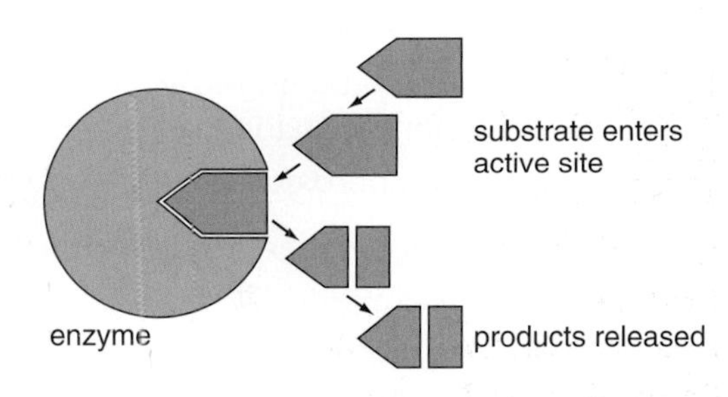

An enzyme can act on lots of substrate

Enzymes can be used over and over again.
Once the products leave the active site, more substrate can enter.
So the enzyme will keep on working until all the substrate is used up.
Just a little enzyme goes a long, long way!

Enzymes in digestion

Enzymes break down large food molecules into smaller ones inside your gut.
This is called **digestion**.
Why do these food molecules have to be broken down into smaller ones?

Look at the diagram:

The wall of the gut works a bit like a net.
What sort of molecules can get through?

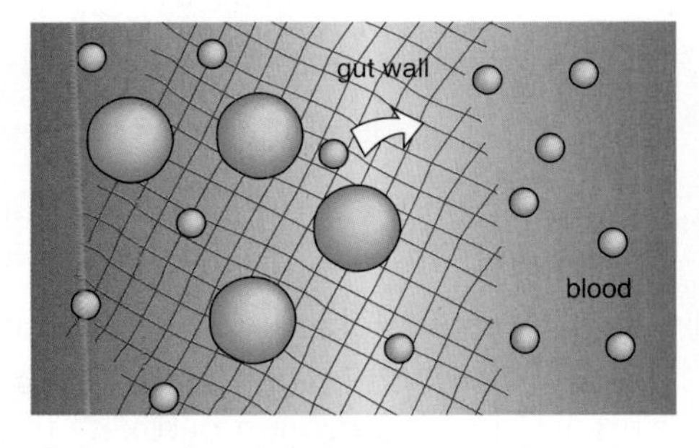

Only small molecules can get through the gut wall into the blood

Two large food molecules are shown below.
Copy and complete these sketches to show what they would look like ***after*** enzymes have digested them.

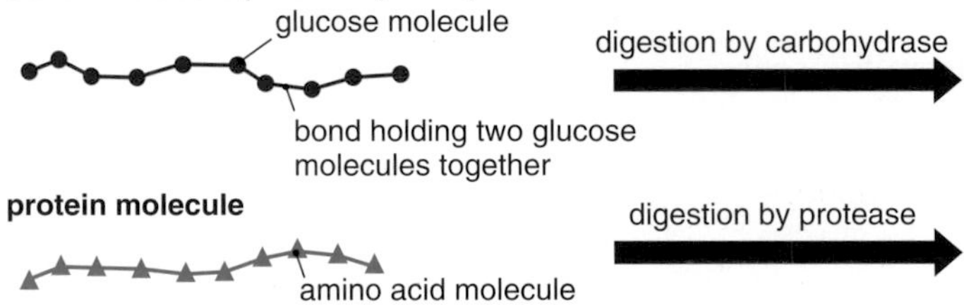

The fastest enzyme in the west!

Potato cells contain an enzyme called **catalase**.
It speeds up the breakdown of hydrogen peroxide into water and oxygen.

Do you remember how to test for oxygen?
Add a small piece of potato to 5 cm^3 of hydrogen peroxide in a test-tube.

⚠ eye protection

CARE: hydrogen peroxide is corrosive and an irritant.

Test the gas which is given off with a glowing splint.

Experiment 3.1 Fast froth

Cut two pieces of potato to the same size.

⚠ eye protection

Put one piece into a boiling-tube containing 5 cm^3 of hydrogen peroxide.

CARE: hydrogen peroxide is corrosive and an irritant.

Use a ruler to measure the ***highest point*** that the froth gets to in the tube.

Now do the same with the second piece, but this time chop the potato up into small pieces first.

- Which tube made the most froth?
  Why do you think this is?
- Where is the enzyme found in this reaction?
- Was the enzyme a breaker or a builder?

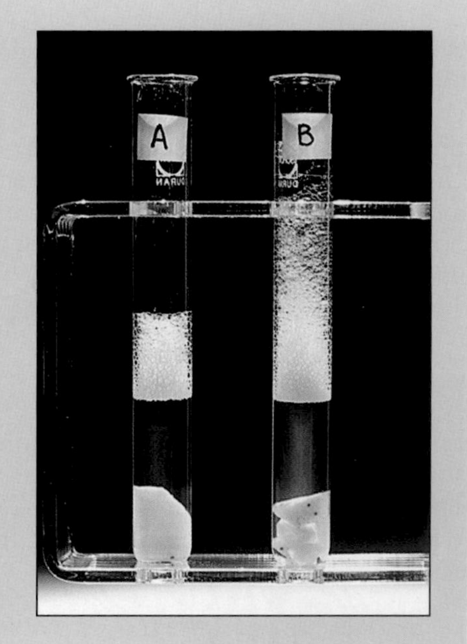

Catalase is found in many living cells.
It breaks down hydrogen peroxide to water and oxygen, that's where the bubbles come from.

$$\text{Hydrogen peroxide} \xrightarrow{\text{catalase}} \text{water} + \text{oxygen}$$

Chopping up the potato releases ***more*** catalase from the cells.

Catalase is the fastest enzyme known.
Hydrogen peroxide is often formed as a product of reactions in cells. It can be poisonous if it builds up.
Why do you think catalase has to work so quickly?

The right enzyme for the job

There is a **carbohydrase** enzyme in our saliva.
What type of food does it act upon?

The carbohydrase in our saliva is called **amylase**.
It breaks down starch to sugar:

$$\text{starch} \xrightarrow{\text{amylase}} \text{sugar}$$

Experiment 3.2 The effect of amylase on starch

Starch turns iodine solution blue–black.
When starch is broken down it will not turn iodine blue–black.

Put one drop of iodine into each well on a spotting tile.

Add 1 cm^3 of 1 % amylase solution to 5 cm^3 of 1 % starch solution in a test-tube.

Start the stop-clock immediately.

At the times shown in the diagram take a drop out of the test-tube and add it to the iodine on the spotting tile.

Wash out your dropping pipette between each sample.

add one drop of starch alone to this well

add one drop of starch/1% amylase to this well

add one drop of starch/1% amylase to this well after 30 seconds

0 min | 30 secs | 1 min

1 m 30 secs | 2 min | 2 m 30 secs | 3 min

3 m 30 secs | 4 min | 4 m 30 secs | 5 min

Record your results in a table like this:

starch alone	mixture straight after mixing	mixture after 30 secs	mixture after 1 minute
Black (starch present)	Black (starch present)		
after $1\frac{1}{2}$ mins	after 2 mins	after $2\frac{1}{2}$ mins	after 3 mins
after $3\frac{1}{2}$ mins	after 4 mins	after $4\frac{1}{2}$ mins	after 5 mins

- How did you know when all the starch had gone?
- How long did it take before all the starch was broken down?
- What did the starch form when it was broken down?
- How could you prove this?

Could a **protease** have broken down the starch?

Remember, an enzyme is **specific**.
It can only control ***one*** kind of reaction.

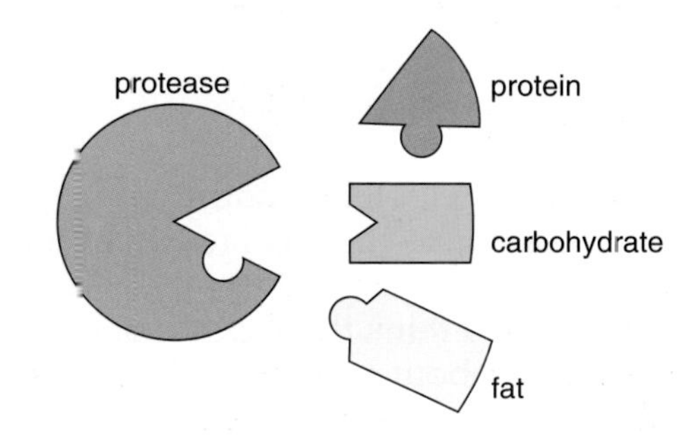

Carbohydrases can only break down carbohydrates.
Proteases can only break down proteins.
Lipases can only break down fats.

▶ Hotting up

Enzymes are affected a great deal by temperature.

This graph shows the effect of increased temperature on an enzyme-controlled reaction:

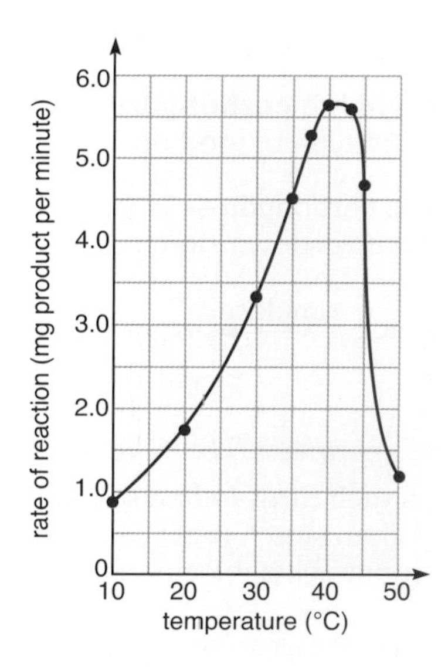

Look at the graph.

- How fast is the reaction going at 10 °C?
- How fast is the reaction going at 20 °C?
- How much faster is the reaction at 20 °C than at 10 °C?

- At what temperature is the reaction going fastest?
- Why do you think the reaction goes faster as the temperature increases?
  (***Hint:*** what happens to molecules when they warm up?)

- How fast is the reaction going at 50 °C?
- What do you think is happening to the enzyme at high temperature?

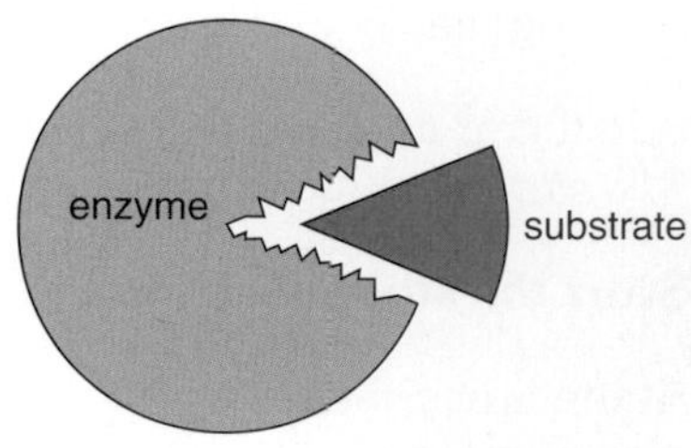

Enzyme denatured – substrate no longer fits the active site

As you know, all enzymes are proteins.
At high temperatures the special shape of the protein chain breaks down.
The active site is changed, so the substrate no longer fits.
We say that the enzyme has been **denatured** and it no longer works.

Investigation 3.3 Effect of temperature on enzyme action

Plan an investigation into the effect of temperature on the action of an enzyme.
You could use amylase.

- What temperatures will you use?
- How will you tell how fast the reaction is going?
- How will you know when the enzyme has finished working?
- How will you show your results?
- Check your plan with your teacher before you begin.

Enzymes are useful in industry.
They can make chemical reactions take place at lower temperatures.
Why do you think this saves money?
(For more about enzymes in industry see Biology at Work, page 34.)

▶ Enzymes and pH

An enzyme is affected by how much **acid** or how much **alkali** is present.
Many enzymes work best in neutral conditions, but some prefer acid and some alkali.

Look at the graph showing the action of enzymes X and Y :

- At what pH does enzyme X work best ?
- At what pH does enzyme Y work best ?
- What happens to the action of enzyme X above pH 5.5 ?
- What happens to the action of enzyme Y below pH 5 ?

The active site of an enzyme can be changed by very acid or very alkaline conditions.
How do you think that this could reduce the rate of a reaction ?

Experiment 3.4 The effect of pH on the action of a protease

Exposed photographic film contains black grains of silver.
These are stuck on by a layer of gelatin.
Gelatin is a protein.

You can investigate the effect of a protease on gelatin at different pHs.

Set up the experiment as shown in the diagram :

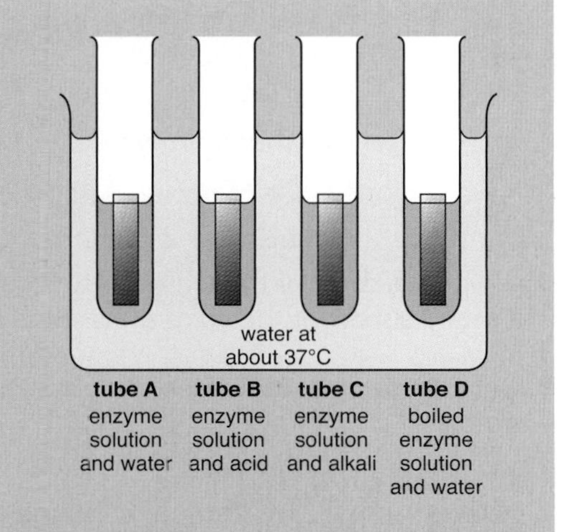

After 30 minutes, take out each strip with tweezers.

Gently rub the film, between your finger and thumb, under a cold tap.

If the gelatin has been digested, the film will turn colourless.

Record your results in a table.

- In which test-tubes did the protease break down gelatin ?
- What effect does boiling have on the action of the protease ?
- In which conditions of pH does the protease work best ?
- Why do you think that the test-tubes were kept at 37 °C ?

This protease breaks down proteins to amino acids in the small intestine.
It works best at a pH of about 8.5 and at 37 °C.
Like other enzymes, it is denatured at high temperatures.

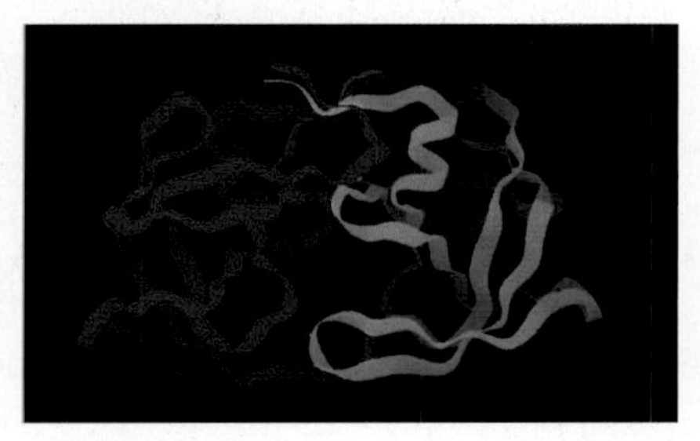

Computer model of a protease

▶ Enzymes as builders

Proteases break down the proteins into amino acids. The amino acids are small enough to get through the gut wall and into our blood.
These amino acids join our body's amino acid pool. When we grow we take amino acids out of this pool. Enzymes join these amino acids to make new proteins.

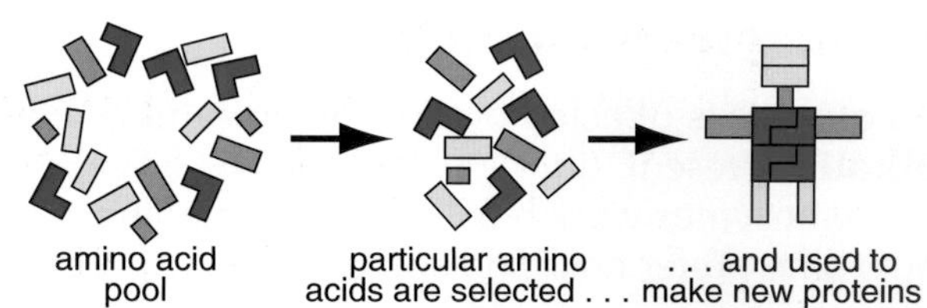

Experiment 3.5 Building starch from glucose

Green plants make glucose during photosynthesis.
Many plants store this glucose as starch.
Potato has an enzyme that changes glucose into starch.

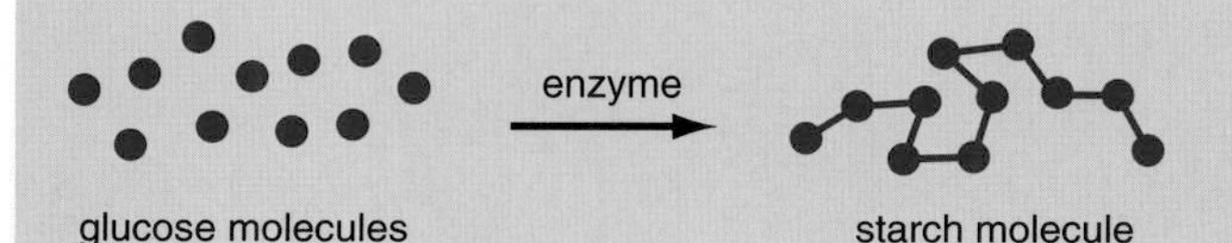

First you have to make an extract of potato enzyme.

Grind a small piece of potato with 5 cm^3 of water.

Centrifuge the extract for 2 minutes.

Now test a drop of the extract with some iodine to make sure that the solution is starch-free.

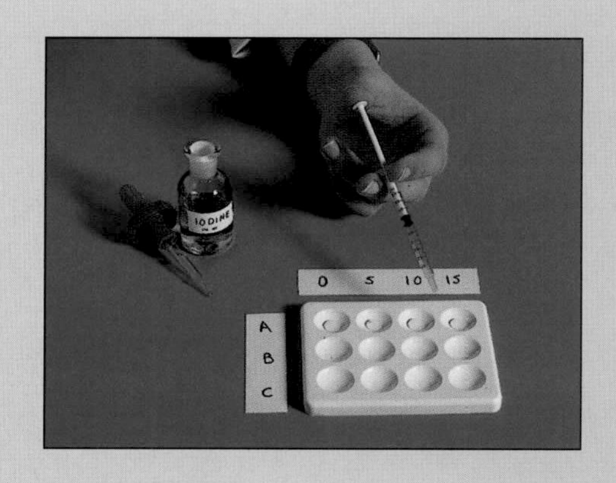

You will use 1 cm^3 syringes to deliver drops of liquids.

Now get your iodine ready.

Make up row A and immediately add one drop of iodine to the first well on the spotting tile.

Repeat at the times shown.

Copy the table and record your results in words or with crayons.

Row	To each well add:	Time (minutes)			
		0	5	10	15
A	2 drops glucose monophosphate, 2 drops potato extract				
B	2 drops glucose monophosphate, 2 drops water				
C	2 drops water, 2 drops potato extract				

Starch forms when the iodine turns blue–black.

- How long did it take for starch to form in row A?

Now set up rows B and C using clean syringes.
Repeat the procedure.

- Will row B make starch without any enzyme?
- Will row C make starch without any glucose?
- Would there be any starch in potatoes without this builder-enzyme? Why not?

▶ Immobilised enzymes

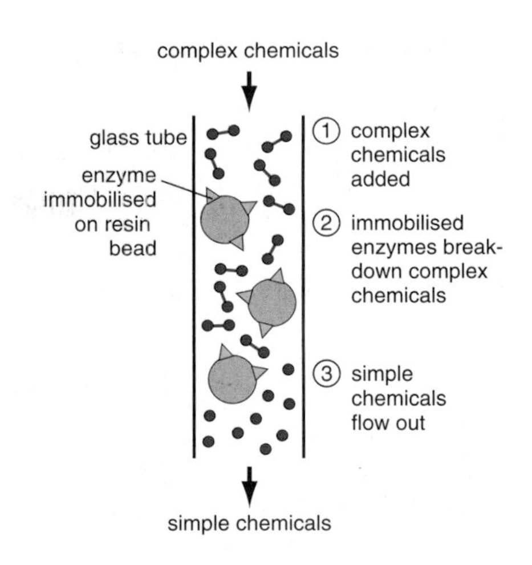

Breaker-enzymes break down complex chemicals into simple ones.
At the end of the reaction, the enzyme and these simple chemicals are mixed together.
In industry, it can be very expensive to separate the enzyme from these simple chemicals.

We solve this problem by ***fixing*** the enzyme to small resin beads.
In this form, we say that the enzyme is **immobilised** because it can not move.

The resin beads are packed into a glass tube.
The complex chemical is poured in at the top.
As it trickles through the beads, the reaction takes place.
Simple chemicals run out of the bottom of the tube.

Lumpy ice cream

Sucrose forms crystals more easily than simple sugars like glucose.
This can cause sweet foods, like ice cream, to go hard and lumpy.
Manufacturers use yeast enzyme to break the sucrose down into simple sugar molecules.

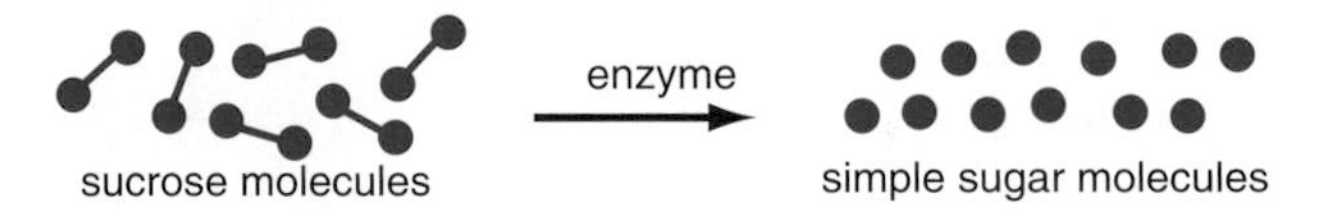

Experiment 3.6 Changing sucrose into simple sugars

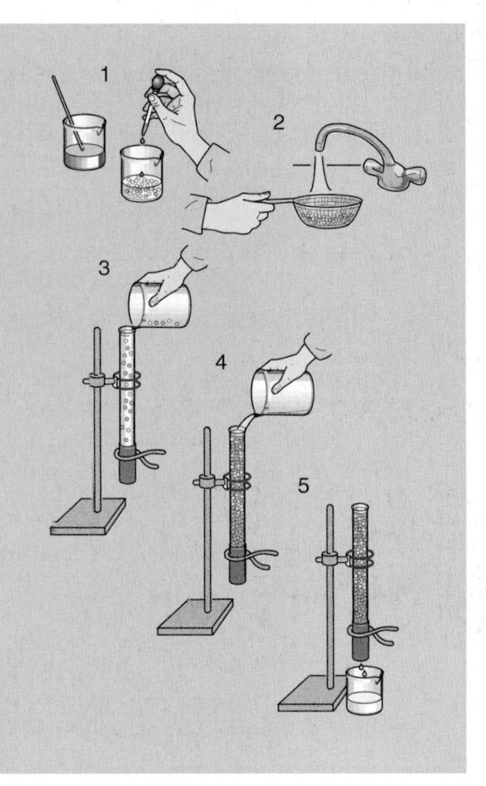

1. First make your resin beads.
   Mix some yeast paste with some sodium alginate paste in a beaker.
   Add drops of the mixture into calcium chloride solution.
2. Wash the beads (coated with yeast enzyme) in a sieve.
3. Fill a glass tube with the beads, leaving a space at the top.
   Make sure that the tap on the glass tube is closed.
4. Test the sucrose solution with a glucose-detecting strip.
   No glucose should be present.
   Pour the sucrose solution into the glass tube and leave for 5 minutes.
5. Open the tap and run out the solution into a clean beaker.
   Test the solution with another glucose-detecting strip.

- Does the second glucose-detecting strip turn purple? Why does this happen?
- How do you think the sucrose has been changed to glucose?
- Where was the enzyme in this experiment?
- Why can this enzyme be used again?

▶ Biology at work: Enzymes in industry

Enzymes have become very important in industry.
They are versatile and far more efficient than other catalysts.
They work at relatively low temperatures.
So this reduces fuel costs, making them cheaper to use.
Also enzymes can be reused and therefore they are only needed in fairly small amounts.

Biological washing powders

Biological washing powders contain proteases and lipases.
These break down the protein and fat stains such as grime and sweat.
These washing powders work at quite low temperatures.
What would happen to these enzymes if they were boiled?

Enzymes are unstable at high temperatures and at extremes of pH. But there are some bacteria that can thrive at high temperatures, like those found in hot springs and thermal vents on the ocean floor. These bacteria contain thermostable enzymes. This means they are unaffected by high temperatures.
Scientists have been able to isolate the genes that code for these enzymes and transfer them into the bacterium ***Bacillus subtilis***.
The bacterium then multiplies, in a fermenter, producing lots of the enzyme **subtilisin** for commercial use.

Subtilisin is a protease that works best in alkaline conditions.
It can tolerate the alkaline phosphates in washing powders.
It is active at 60 °C so can be used in a wide variety of wash programmes.

Investigation 3.7 The effects of different factors on enzyme action

How can you make enzyme reactions faster or slower?

Investigate the effect of one factor on the action of a biological washing powder.

Which factor will you look at?
How will you judge how well a powder containing enzymes works?

You could compare how well the stains have been removed.
Plan a fair and safe test. Show it to your teacher before you start.

Alternatively you could compare the action of biological and non-biological washing powders.

▷ Biology at work: Other uses of enzymes

Sweeteners

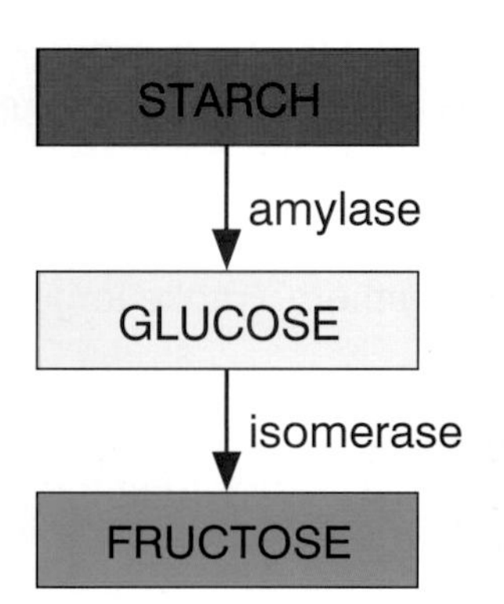

There is a worldwide demand for sweeteners mainly in confectionary and fizzy drinks.
Traditionally sucrose (the sugar you put in your tea) has been used. It is extracted from sugar beet or sugar cane.
In recent years a sucrose substitute, **high fructose syrup**, has been introduced since it is cheaper to produce.
Fructose is sweeter than sucrose and can be made from starch, a relatively abundant and cheap food stuff.
Amylase is first used to convert the starch to glucose.
Then **isomerase** converts the glucose syrup into fructose syrup (isomerase is used as an immobilised enzyme, see page 33).
Fructose, being much sweeter than sucrose, can be used in smaller quantities in slimming foods.

Do you like those chocolates with the soft, gooey centres?
Have you ever wondered how they are made?
The chocolate is poured over a solid mixture containing sucrose and a carbohydrase enzyme.
The chocolate sets and the enzyme breaks the sucrose down into glucose and fructose. These smaller sugars are much more soluble than sucrose, and dissolve in the small amount of water in the original mixture.

Extracting fruit juice

Experiment 3.8 Getting the juice

Cut an apple in half.

Chop each half into small pieces and put them into separate beakers.

Pour 10 cm^3 of pectinase over the apple in beaker A and 10 cm^3 of water over the apple in beaker B.

Place both beakers in a water bath at 40 °C for 20 mins.

Filter the juice from each of the beakers of apple pieces.

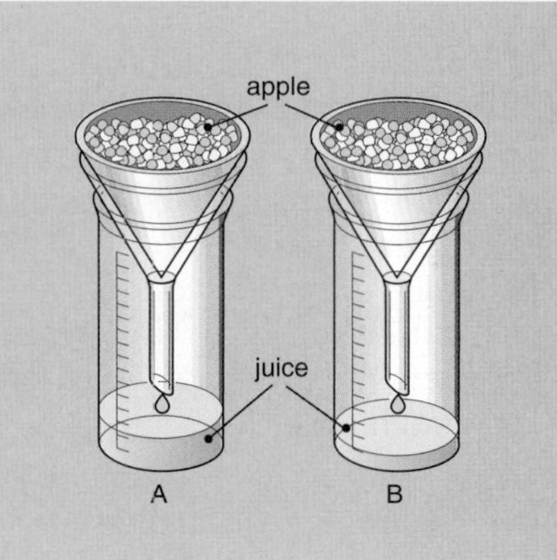

- Which of the apple pieces will make most juice?
- How does the pectinase release this juice from the apple cells?
- Why were 10 cm^3 of water added to beaker B?

Some other uses of enzymes:
Proteases are used to tenderise meat and remove hair from skins.
Proteases are also used to 'pre-digest' the protein in baby food.
You can find out about the enzymes used to make cheese and yoghurt and those used in brewing and baking in Chapter 21.

Summary

- Enzymes speed up chemical reactions inside cells.
- Breaker-enzymes split up large molecules into smaller ones.
- Builder-enzymes join small molecules together to make large ones.
- Enzymes are specific. They will only act on one particular substrate. This is because the substrate has to fit the enzyme's active site.
- An enzyme is unchanged after the reaction, so can be used many times. This is why only a small amount of enzyme is needed.
- Enzymes work faster as the temperature increases up to 40 °C, but eventually they are denatured at about 60 °C.
- Each enzyme works best at a particular pH.
- Enzymes are extensively used in industry because they are cheap and more effective than other catalysts.

▶ Questions

1. Copy and complete:
a) Enzymes .... up the rate of chemical ..... .
b) Enzymes are .... because they only work on one substrate.
c) The substrate fits into the .... site on the surface of the ..... .
d) With an increase in .... , the rate of reaction ..... . But eventually a temperature is reached which .... the enzyme.
e) Enzymes can be re-used, so only .... amounts are needed.

2. a) To which group of chemical compounds do enzymes belong?
b) Which enzymes work on
i) carbohydrates ii) proteins iii) fats?
c) Name the products which are formed in each case.

3. An enzyme has an 'active site' on its surface on which the reaction takes place. Use the idea of an active site to explain:
a) Why an enzyme is specific for a particular substrate.
b) Why enzymes are denatured at high temperatures.
c) Why an enzyme can be used again and again.

4. Lipase is an enzyme that breaks down fats. We can use an indicator to follow this reaction. The indicator is red to start with but turns yellow when all the fat has been broken down.

Test-tube	Temp. °C	Original colour	Final colour
1	0	red	red
2	10	red	orange
3	40	red	yellow
4	60	red	orange
5	100	red	red

Look at the results:
a) At what temperature does lipase work best?
b) Why do you think the colour did not change in test-tube 1?
c) Why do you think the colour did not change in test-tube 5?
d) Predict what you think would happen if you warmed test-tubes 1 and 5 up to 40 °C. Try to explain your prediction.

5. A number of factors can alter the rate of an enzyme-controlled reaction. Say what each of the following would do to the rate of reaction, and give your reasons:
a) An increase in enzyme concentration.
b) A decrease in temperature.
c) A lowering of pH.

6. The following experiment was set up to investigate the action of protease on egg-white. When enzymes break down the protein in egg-white, it changes from cloudy to clear.

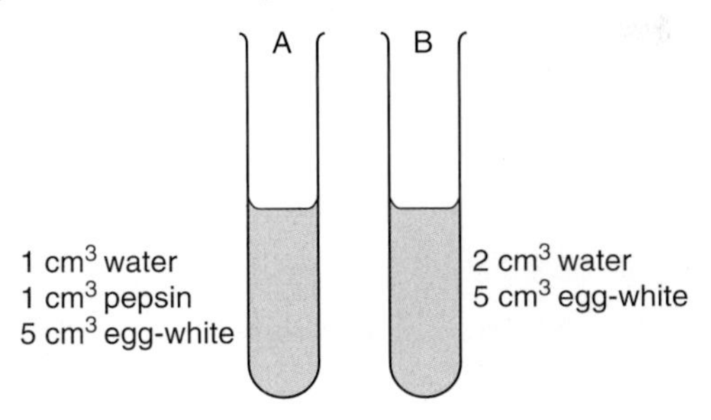

a) Explain why the contents of test-tube A went clear after 15 minutes.
b) Explain why the contents of test-tube B stayed cloudy after 15 minutes.
c) How could you increase the speed of the reaction in test-tube A?
d) What do you think the egg-white protein was broken down to form?

7. The graph shows how temperature affects an enzyme-controlled reaction.

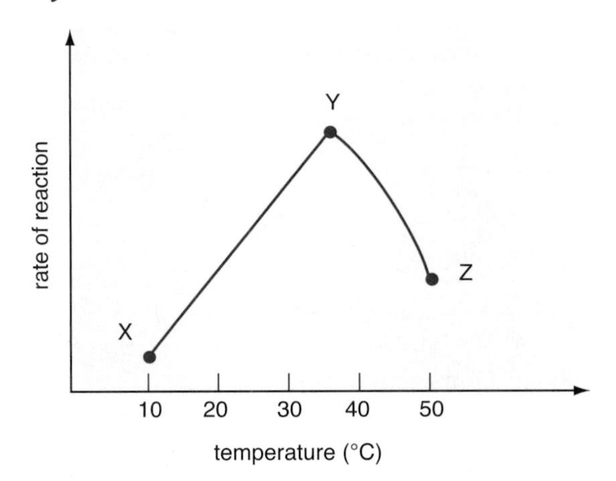

a) Explain what is happening:
   i) between X and Y
   ii) between Y and Z.
b) Suggest how increasing the temperature affects the rate of reaction of the enzyme.
c) What is happening to the active site of the enzyme at the higher temperatures?

This graph shows how pH affects the rates of two enzyme-controlled reactions.

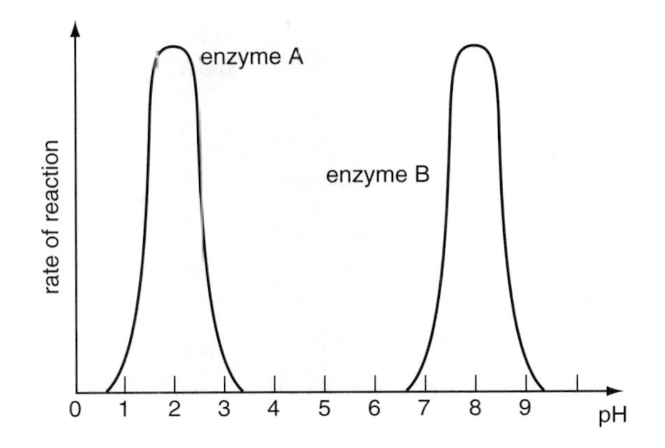

d) Which enzyme works best in acid conditions?
e) Which enzyme works best in alkali conditions?
f) What does the graph tell you about the ***range*** of pH over which each enzyme is active?

8. In 1989 a new fat-digesting enzyme was found in a fungus.
This enzyme works best at a pH of 7.5.
The enzyme can act at low temperatures and, after a few days, breaks down into carbon dioxide, nitrogen and water.

a) Give two reasons why this enzyme is now used in washing powders.
b) Why do you think that this enzyme is 'environmentally friendly'?
c) Why would a washing powder of high pH or low pH be difficult to handle?

Further questions on page 38.

▶ Cells

1.

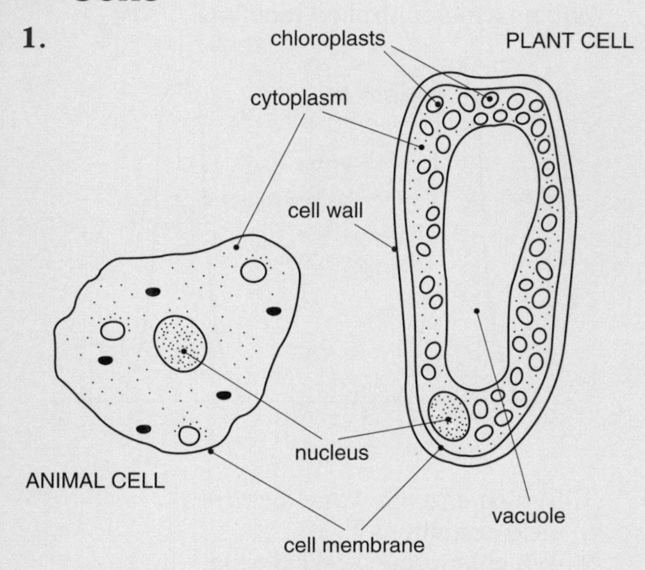

a) Use **only** the drawings above to copy and complete the table below to show **three** differences between plant and animal cells. *[3]*

	Plant cells	Animal cells
1		
2		
3		

b) What is the job of **each** of the following parts of a cell:
   i) nucleus ii) cellulose cell wall
   iii) cytoplasm iv) cell membrane? *[4]*

c) i) What substance is contained in the chloroplasts?
   ii) Why is this substance important to **all** living things? *[2]* (WJEC)

2. The key below lists organs of the human body.

Letter	Organ
A	Brain
B	Heart
C	Lung
D	Diaphragm
E	Stomach
F	Large intestine
G	Kidney
H	Bladder
I	Uterus

The table which follows shows a function of each of these organs. Copy the table and match the correct function to each organ by writing the correct letter in each box.

The first one has been done for you.

Function	Letter
Stores waste fluid called urine	H
Breaks food down into smaller chemicals	
Can contain a developing fetus	
Controls other organs	
Filters the blood to help remove waste	
Helps oxygen to enter the blood and carbon dioxide to leave	
Helps to move air in and out of body	
Pumps blood through the body	
Takes water from food into the blood stream	

[8] (EDEX)

3. The diagrams below show five cells, some from animals and some from plants. Note that the diagrams are not all drawn to the same scale.

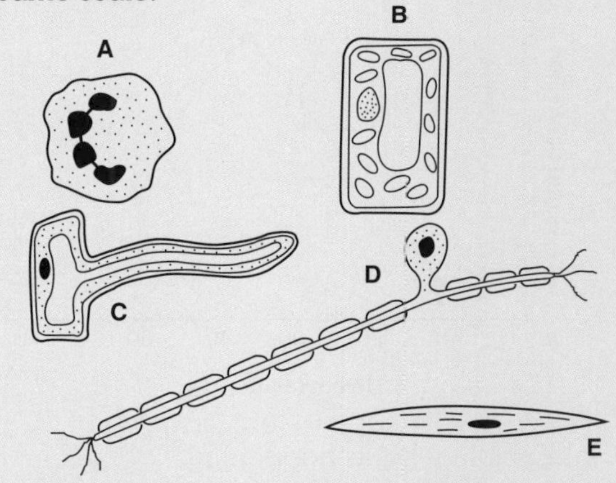

The cells are specialised to carry out certain functions. The list below gives the functions of these five cells.

1. absorbs salts and water from the soil
2. kills bacteria
3. makes food by photosynthesis
4. carries electrical impulses
5. shortens to bring about movement

 Note: although a question may be marked (EDEX) etc, it will often be relevant to other examinations as well.

a) i) Copy and complete the table below by matching the cells with the letters from the diagrams.

ii) Complete the column ii) of your table by matching the cells with the correct number from the list of functions. [4]

Name of the cell	i) Letter of diagram	ii) Number of function
Muscle cell	E	5
Palisade cell		
Root hair cell		
Sensory neurone		
White blood cell		

b) Choose **two** of the cells shown in the diagram and for each one describe how its structure allows it to perform its function efficiently. *[2]* (EDEX)

▶ Diffusion

4. The diagram shows two potato cubes, X and Y, that were placed in distilled water for one hour.

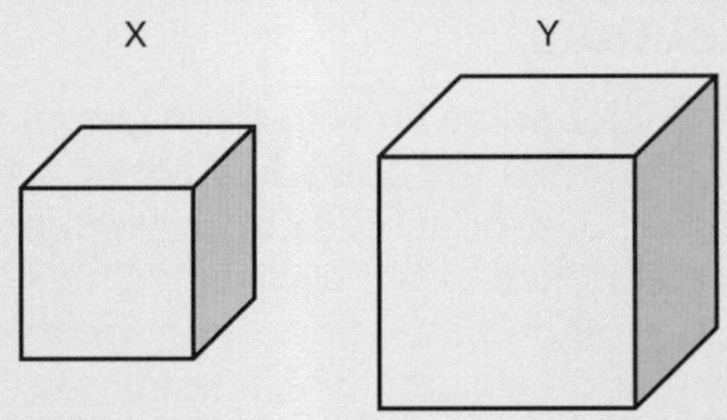

a) Explain why both cubes gained in mass after one hour. *[3]*

b) Copy the table and put a tick in the row that correctly describes the change in mass for cube X compared to cube Y.

Mass of water absorbed in g	Percentage increase in mass	Tick
more	lower	
less	lower	
less	higher	
more	higher	

[1] (AQA)

5. Lengths of Visking tubing were set up as follows:

A contained 1% starch and amylase;

B contained 1% starch and boiled amylase.

Both were left in water at 30 °C for one hour. They were then placed in beakers of dilute iodine solution and left for five minutes as shown below. Iodine solution can pass through Visking tubing.

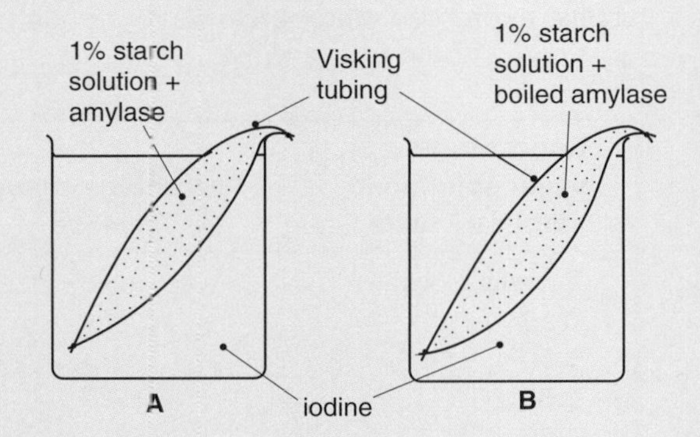

a) What colour would you expect to see inside
   i) A
   ii) B? *[2]*

b) Explain what has happened inside **A**. *[2]*

c) i) Describe a test to prove your explanation. *[2]*
   ii) State the expected results. *[1]*

d) What appears to be the effect of boiling the amylase? *[1]* (WJEC)

6. A teenage boy was pulled out of the sea after he got into difficulty. The boy coughed up some sea water and the lifeguard insisted he was taken to hospital for observation. The boy said he felt fine so the lifeguard explained that there is a danger of secondary drowning if you inhale sea water and it stays in your lungs. After a short time the air sacs could fill with water and gaseous exchange would be impossible.

Explain as fully as you can, using scientific terms, why the boy's air sacs could fill with water after he is taken to hospital.

[5] (AQA)

7. A student carried out an investigation on the effects of various sugar solutions on rods of potato tuber. The student used a cork borer to remove the rods which were gently blotted and weighed.

Each rod was then placed in distilled water or in one of several sugar solutions of different concentrations. After 2 hours the rods were removed, gently blotted and reweighed. The results, expressed as a percentage change in mass, are shown in the table.

Concentration of sugar solution in arbitrary units	Percentage change in mass
0 (distilled water)	+8
0.25	+4
0.50	−1
1.00	−7
1.50	−10

a) i) Plot a line graph of the data on a sheet of graph paper.
Put concentration of sugar solution in arbitrary units on the horizontal axis and percentage change in mass on the vertical axis. *[3]*

ii) From the graph, work out the concentration of sugar solution which would result in no change in mass of the potato tuber. *[1]*

b) Name the process which causes the mass of the potato to change in this experiment. *[1]*

c) What else might the student have measured to investigate the effect of the sugar solutions on the rods? *[1]*

d) Some people soak salad vegetables, especially lettuce, in salt water to remove animals such as slugs and greenfly. However, if the lettuce is left too long in the salt water the leaves become limp.

i) Explain why the lettuce leaves become limp. *[1]*

ii) Suggest how the lettuce leaves could be made crisp again. *[1]* (EDEX)

8. A pupil set up the apparatus shown in the diagram.

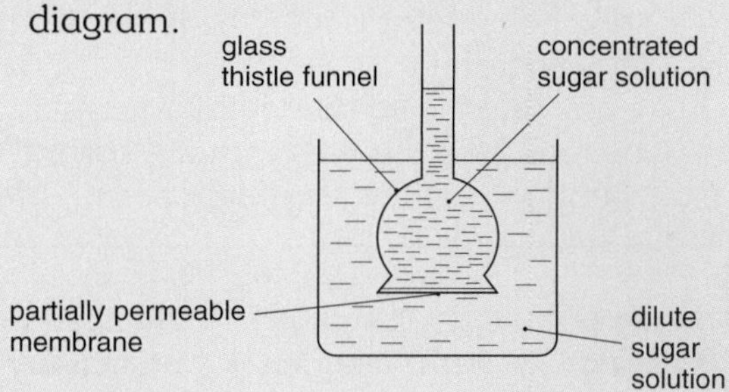

a) What happens to the height of the sugar solution in the funnel? *[1]*

b) Explain why this happens.
You may use the diagram below to help with your answer.

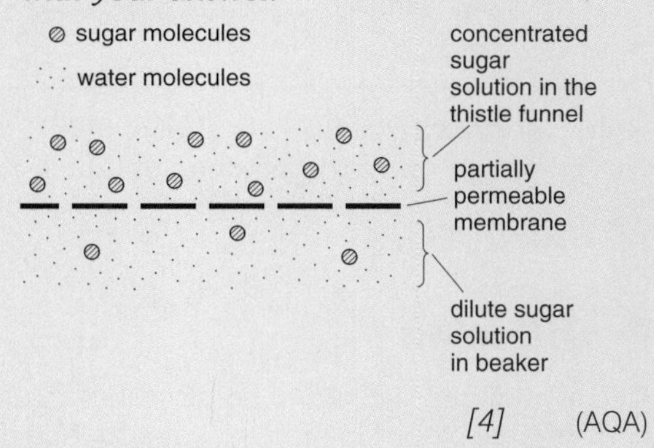

[4] (AQA)

▶ Enzymes

9. a) i) What name is given to an enzyme which catalyses the breakdown of protein? *[1]*

ii) What product is formed when protein is broken down by the enzyme? *[1]*

The table shows the effect of pH on the activity of an enzyme which catalyses the breakdown of protein.

pH	1.0	2.0	3.0	4.0	5.0
Rate of formation of product in mmol per minute	10.5	23.0	10.5	2.5	0.0

b) Draw a graph of the data in the table.

c) The enzyme is produced by the human digestive system.

i) At what pH does this enzyme work best? *[1]*

ii) Suggest which part of the digestive system produces this enzyme. *[1]*

d) Why is it necessary to break down proteins in the digestive system? *[3]* (AQA)

10. Sucrose can be digested to give glucose and fructose. This reaction is speeded up by the enzyme sucrase.

$$\text{Sucrose} \xrightarrow{\text{Sucrase}} \text{Glucose} + \text{Fructose}$$

a) 'Disaccharide' is the term used to describe sucrose. What term is used to describe glucose? *[1]*

b) A student carried out an investigation into the effect of increasing the concentration of the enzyme sucrase on the rate of this reaction.
He kept the concentration of sucrose constant. He used six different concentrations of the enzyme (sucrase) and for each of these he measured the time taken for the sucrose to be completely digested. He carried out all the reactions at 40 °C. The student's results are shown in the table below.

Enzyme sucrase concentration (%)	Time taken to digest sucrose in seconds
0.10	950
0.25	600
0.50	470
1.00	290
1.50	225
2.00	160

i) Plot a graph of these results. Join the points with straight lines. *[5]*

ii) Describe how increasing the concentration of the enzyme (sucrase) affected the time taken for the sucrose to be digested. *[2]*

c) i) Suggest why he carried out all of the reactions at 40 °C. *[1]*

ii) Describe **one** way that he could keep the temperature constant (at 40 °C). *[1]*

d) The student then repeated this experiment, first at 20 °C and then at 80 °C.
Suggest what would happen to the time taken for the sucrose to be digested at 20 °C and 80 °C. In each case give a reason for your answer. *[4]* (EDEX)

11. Some cats become ill if they drink cow's milk. Scientists have found out that the milk sugar, lactose, is responsible for the illness. In the pet food industry, lactase is added to milk to change the lactose into simple sugar as glucose, but lactase is an expensive substance.

The lactase is mixed with a type of jelly and small beads are produced which are put into a long tube. The milk is poured into the tube and collected at the bottom.

The diagram shows a laboratory model of the industrial process.

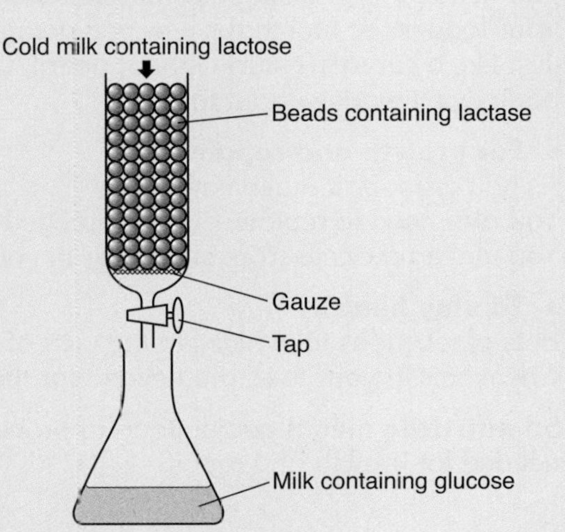

a) What sort of substance is lactase? *[1]*

b) State two advantages of putting the lactase into beads. *[2]*

c) Suggest one modification which would speed up the change of lactose to simple sugar. *[1]*

d) After using the beads for several days the manufacturers find that there is still lactose in the milk product and they have to replace the beads.
Explain why the lactase does not work after several days. *[1]* (AQA)

chapter 4

Your body is made up of chemicals.
You get these chemicals from the food that you eat.
What do you think your body uses your food for?

- **For energy**
You need food to work your muscles and other organs.
Your food is the fuel that keeps you going.
Just like a car won't start without petrol, your body won't work without food.

- **For growth and repair**
As you grow, you make new cells.
You also need to replace old or damaged cells.
You make new cells from chemicals in your food.

- **To stay healthy**
Lots of reactions take place in the cells of your body.
Chemicals in your food are needed for these reactions.

So **nutrition** means getting food to provide energy and substances needed for growth and repair.

What's in the food we eat?

These are some of the nutrients that are in our food:

proteins carbohydrates fats water
vitamins minerals fibre

Which is the better balanced meal?

Some foods may have a lot of protein in them.
Other foods may not have much protein at all.
Some foods may have a lot of carbohydrate or fat.
Different foods have different vitamins and minerals.

If we are to stay healthy our bodies must have:

- enough food
- a variety of foods – so that our body gets all the different things it needs.

We need a healthy, **balanced** diet.

Remember also that a balanced diet will change depending upon a person's age, gender and how active they are.

▶ Proteins

Your body is made up of billions of cells.
These cells are made mainly from protein.

Some protein-rich foods

Proteins are made up of the elements carbon, hydrogen and oxygen, but they also contain nitrogen (N) and many have sulphur (S).

When you grow your body needs protein to make new cells.
Your body may need to replace old or damaged cells.
You need enough protein in your food for this as well.

Proteins are made up of lots of **amino acids**.
There are about 20 different types of amino acids.

Here are two different proteins:

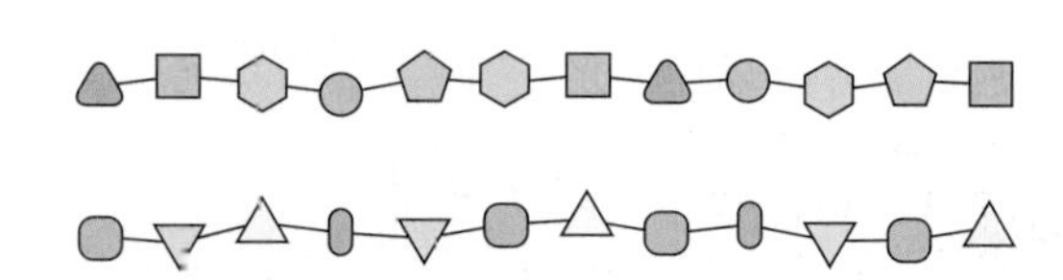

Can you see what makes them different?

Haemoglobin, enzymes, antibodies and some hormones (e.g. insulin) are soluble proteins.
Keratin is a fibrous protein found in the skin and hair.

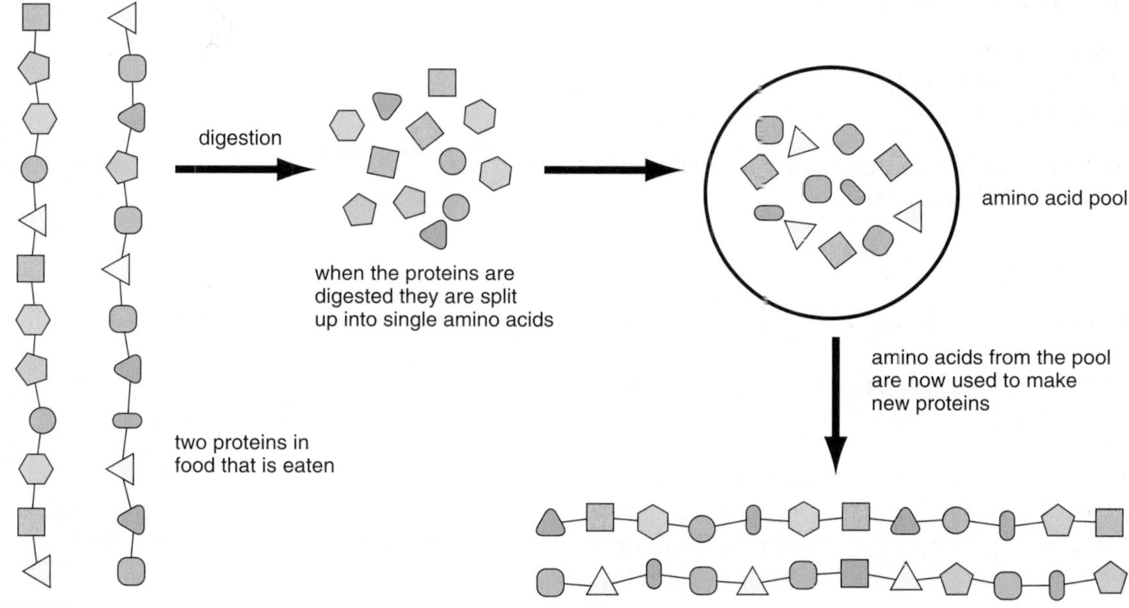

Experiment 4.1 Testing for protein

⚠ eye protection

Add a few drops of copper sulphate solution to some protein solution in a test-tube.
Now ***carefully*** add a few drops of sodium hydroxide solution.
Take great care as sodium hydroxide solution is **corrosive**.

Did the protein go purple?

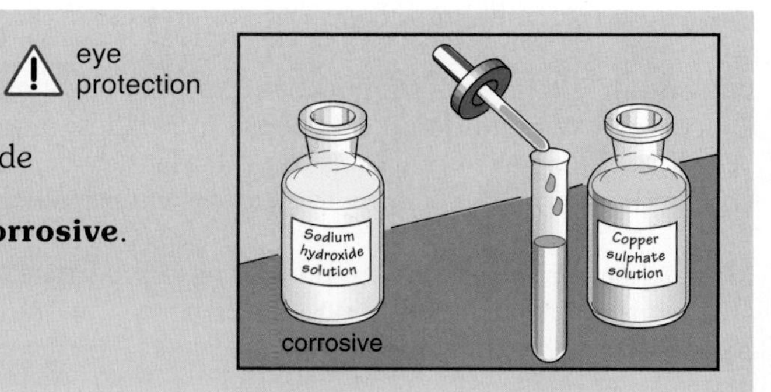

▶ Carbohydrates

Carbohydrates are made up of the elements carbon (C), hydrogen (H) and oxygen (O).

Sugars are carbohydrates.

Did you know that there are different kinds of sugars? The kind of sugar you put in your tea is called **sucrose**. The kind of sugar that is in milk is called **lactose**. The sugar that our bodies use most is **glucose**.

We need carbohydrates to give us energy. Sugars are the fuel that our bodies need.

Some foods rich in carbohydrates

Experiment 4.2 Testing for glucose

⚠ eye protection

Pour some glucose solution into a test-tube.

Add a few drops of Benedict's solution. (Be careful, this is harmful.)

Carefully heat the test-tube in a water bath.

Did the glucose turn orange?

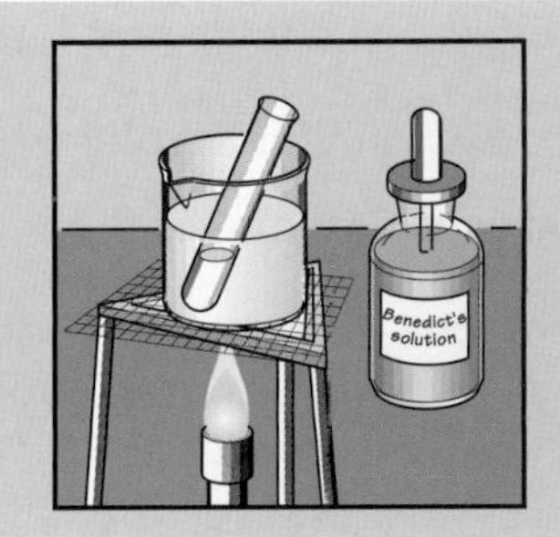

Starch is also a carbohydrate. You already know that starch is a large molecule. It is made up of lots of smaller glucose molecules joined together.

large starch molecule → digestion → small glucose molecules

What do you make when you digest starch?

Experiment 4.3 Testing for starch

⚠ eye protection

Half fill a test-tube with starch solution.

Add two drops of iodine solution.

Does the starch turn blue–black?

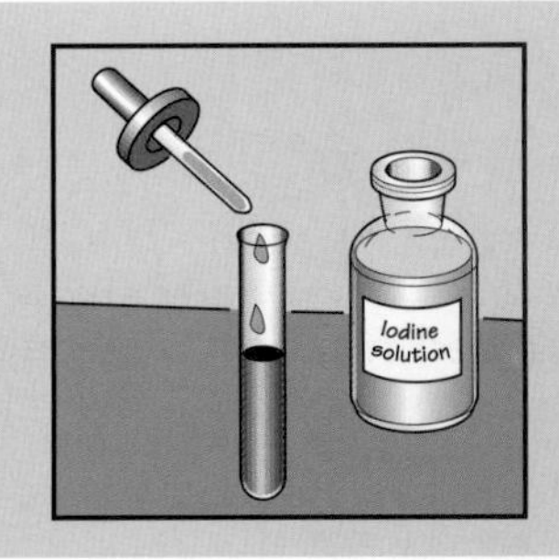

Plants often turn their glucose into starch to store it.

Glycogen is a large carbohydrate molecule like starch. Glycogen is also made up of glucose molecules joined together. We store glycogen in our liver and muscles. Our bodies change glycogen to glucose when we need it.

Many cheaper foods contain a lot of carbohydrates. Do you think foods containing a lot of protein would be more or less expensive?

► Fats

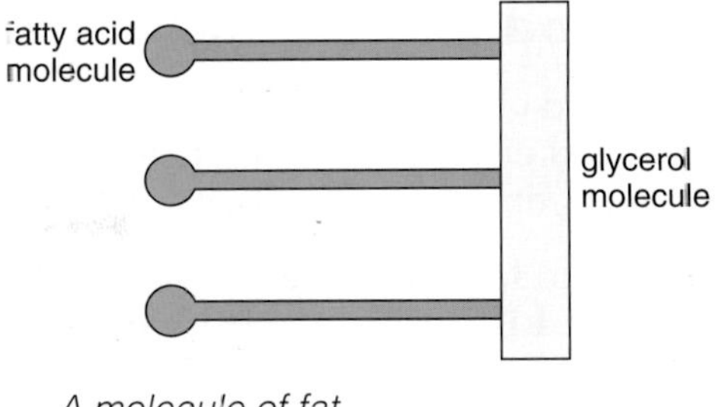

A molecule of fat

Fats are made up of the elements carbon, hydrogen and oxygen.
There are many different kinds of fats.
Fats are made up of three **fatty acids** joined together.
There are different kinds of fatty acids.
Do you think that different fats have different kinds of fatty acids in them?

Fats also give us energy.
Fats actually contain more energy than carbohydrates.
Our bodies use fats as an energy store.
We store fats under the skin and around the heart and kidneys.
When we are short of energy our body uses the fat.
What do you think happens if we eat too much fat?

Experiment 4.4 Testing for fat

⚠ ethanol is highly flammable

Put four drops of cooking oil into a test-tube.

Add 2 cm^3 of ethanol to the oil and shake the test-tube.

Add 2 cm^3 of water to the test-tube and shake again.

Does the oil turn cloudy white?

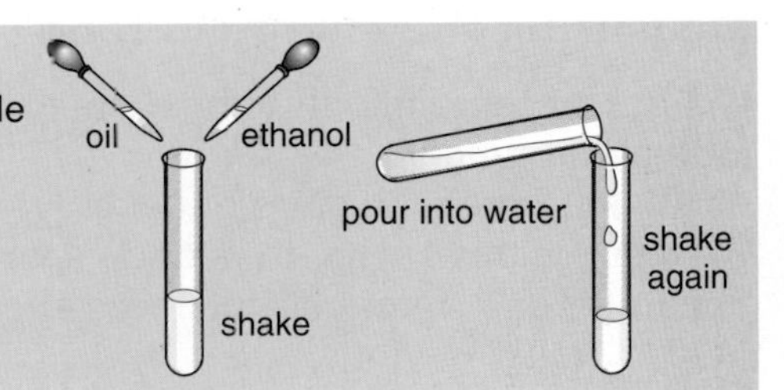

Fats are good insulators. They cut down heat loss.
Which animals have a lot of fat under the skin?
Fats also give buoyancy.
Why do whales have a thick layer of blubber?

Some foods rich in fat

We need: proteins for growth and repair of cells
carbohydrates for energy
fats as a store of energy and for warmth

Why can fat be bad for us?

There are two main types of fat:
saturated fat that comes from animals and
unsaturated fat that comes from plants.
Saturated fats increase the level of **cholesterol** in our blood.

Cholesterol is a chemical made in the liver and found in the blood.
The amount of cholesterol that we produce depends upon our diet, but also inherited factors.
High levels of cholesterol are linked to an increased risk of heart disease and an increase in blood pressure due to a narrowing of the blood vessels (see page 85).

Mono-unsaturated fats have little effect on blood cholesterol. Poly-unsaturated fats may help to reduce cholesterol levels.

What would your advice be to reduce heart disease?

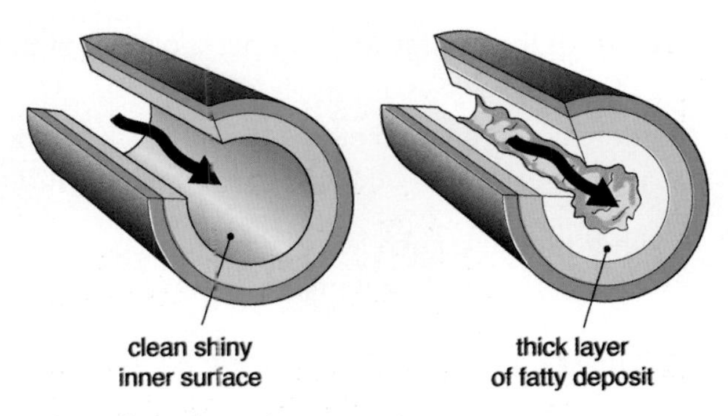

How a fatty deposit can narrow an artery

▶ Food and energy

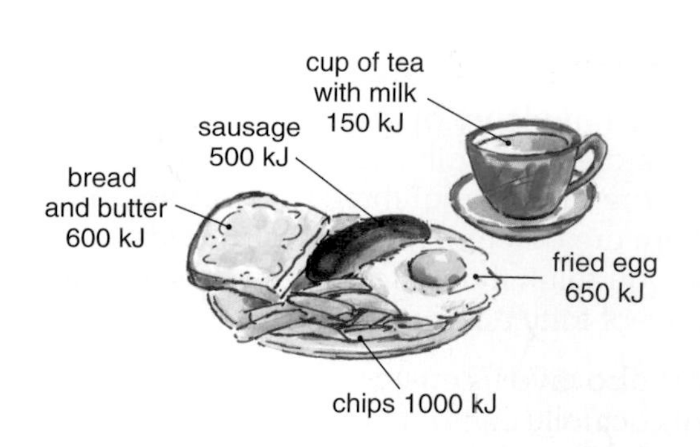

Our food gives us our energy.
We need energy for all the activities that we do.
Carbohydrates and fats are high-energy foods.

Energy in food is measured in **kilojoules (kJ)**, where **1 kilojoule = 1000 joules**.

Look at these two meals:

Which meal has the highest energy content?
By how much?
Which meal is the most healthy?
How could you reduce the energy content in the first meal?

Measuring the energy in food

We can measure the amount of energy in some food by burning it.
As the food burns, it gives out energy.
We can use this energy to heat up some water.
The hotter the water gets the more energy is in the food.

Experiment 4.5 Measuring the energy in a peanut

Copy the results table.
Use a measuring cylinder to pour out exactly 20 cm^3 of water into a boiling-tube.
Take the temperature of the water and write it down in your table.
Weigh a peanut and write down the weight in your table.
Put the peanut on the end of a mounted needle.
Set the peanut alight and hold it under the boiling-tube of water.
When the peanut has burnt out, take the temperature of the water again. Write your result in your table.

Weight of peanut (g)	Temp. of water at start (°C)	Temp. of water at end (°C)	Temp. rise of water (°C)

⚠ eye protection
peanut allergy

Work out how many joules of energy were given out by your peanut using this equation:

Energy (joules) $= 20 \times 4.2 \times$ temperature rise of water

Work out the energy content per gram (g) of peanut using this equation:

$$\text{Energy content (joules/g)} = \frac{\text{energy given out by your peanut (J)}}{\text{weight of your peanut (g)}}$$

Rather than use such large numbers, you can change the units from joules to kilojoules by dividing by 1000.

Try the experiment again using a pea instead of a peanut.

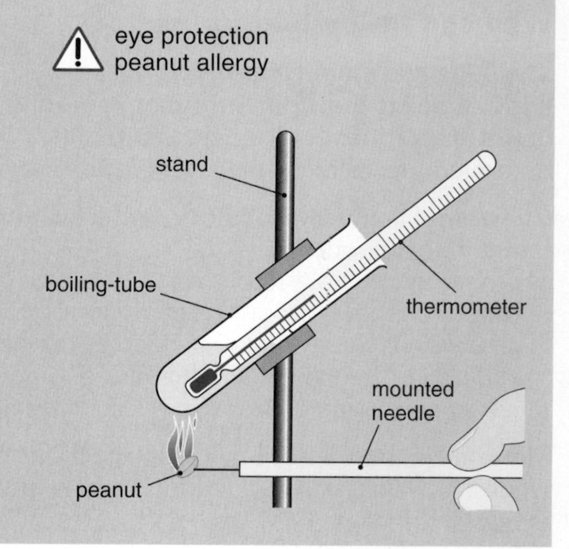

▶ How much energy?

Most foods have their energy content on the label.
The amount of energy is given in kilojoules per 100 g of food.
How much energy is there in 100 g of these foods?

BRANFLAKES

Wheatflakes Enriched with Bran

INGREDIENTS

Wheat, Wheat Bran, Sugar, Malt Extract, Salt, Niacin, Iron Pantothenic Acid, Thiamin (Vitamin B1), Vitamin B6, Riboflaviv (Vitamin B2), Folic Acid, Vitamin B12, Vitamin D.

INGREDIENTS

Typical Values	Per 100g	Per (30g) serving
Energy	1411 kJ (333kcal)	422 kJ (100kcal)
Protein	10.1g	3.0g
Carbohydrate	67.7g	20.3g
of which sugars	16.9g	5.1g
starch	50.8g	15.2g
Fat	2.4g	0.7g
of which saturates	0.4g	0.1g
mono-unsaturates	0.4g	0.1g
polyunsaturates	1.6g	0.5g
Fibre	12.7g	3.8g
Sodium	0.7g	0.2g

WALKERS CRISPS

Prawn Cocktail Flavour

INGREDIENTS: potatoes, vegetable oil, prawn coctail flavour [flavouring, acidity regulator (sodium diacetate), flavour enhancer (monosodium glutamate), citric acid, sweetner (saccharin)], salt.

Typical Nutrition Information

	Per 100g	Per 28g pack
Energy	2300 kj 550 kcal	644 kj 154 kcal
Protein	6.0g	1.7g
Carbohydrate	46.0g	12.9g
Fat	38.0g	10.6g

DAWN

Rice Pudding

NUTRITION INFORMATION

100 grams of this rice pudding typically provides:

Energy Value	363 kj
(calories)	(86 kcal)
Protein	3.4 grams
Carbohydrate	16.0 grams
Fat	0.9 grams

Activity 4.6 Energy content of different foods

Look at the labels of 10 different foods.
Sort the foods in order of their energy content.
Start with the one with the highest energy content per 100 g and finish with the least.
Make a table of your findings.
Now look at your labels again.

- What do you notice about the fat and carbohydrate content of the foods at the top of the table?
- What about those at the bottom?

How much food do you need?

The amount of food that you need depends upon how much energy you use up every day.
The amount of energy you need depends on:

- your body size
- how active you are
- how fast you are growing.

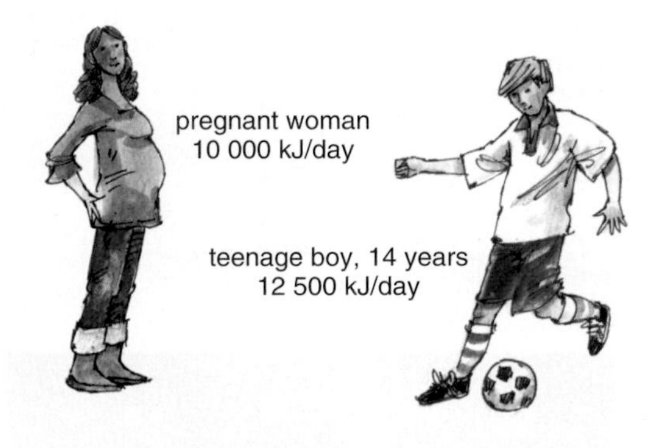

	Energy used in a day (kJ)	
	Male	**Female**
8-year-old	8 500	8 500
Teenager, aged 14	12 500	9 700
Adult office worker	11 000	9 800
Adult manual worker	15 000	12 500
Pregnant woman		10 000
Breast-feeding mother		11 500

- Why do you think that males usually need more energy than females?
- Why do manual workers need more energy than office workers?
- Why does the 14-year-old boy need more energy than the male office worker?
- Why does pregnancy increase the energy needs of a woman?
- Why does a breast-feeding mother need more energy than a pregnant mother?

► Getting the balance right

The food you eat in a day should provide you with enough energy to get through that day. Even if you are lying in bed, completely inactive, you are still using energy to keep:

- your heart beating
- your lungs working
- your body temperature constant
- all the chemical reactions in your body going.

A well-balanced meal is important at lunchtime

This 'ticking over' speed at which our bodies work is the **basal metabolic rate (BMR)**.
The BMR varies from person to person, but roughly it uses 7000 kJ per day. So even if you lie around doing nothing you still need this amount of energy.

What happens if we eat too much?

If you eat more food than you need, your body stores the extra as fat.

Your **energy intake** is the amount of energy you get in your food in a day.

Your **energy output** is the amount of energy your body uses up in a day.

If our energy intake is greater than our energy output, then we put on weight.
We may run the risk of becoming fat **(obese)**.
People with a low BMR are more likely to get overweight.
Why do you think this is?
Fattening foods are those with most energy content.

So how could someone lose weight?
They could:

- eat less high-energy foods (lower their energy intake),
- take more exercise (increase their energy output).

A sensible approach to slimming should combine:

- a balanced lower-energy intake, and
- a gradual increase in exercise.

Fast food often contains a high proportion of fat

► Obesity

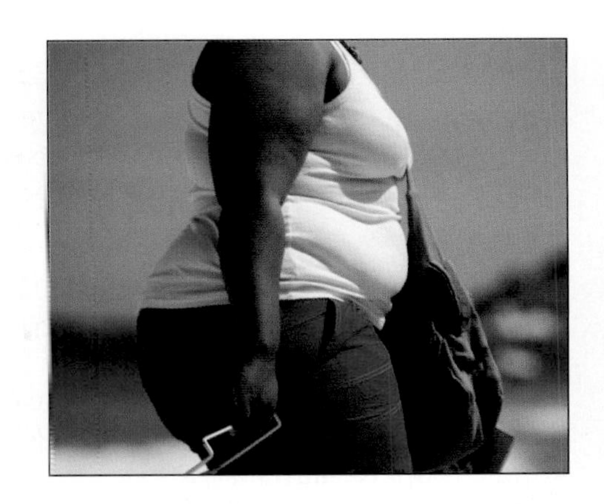

In rich, industrialised countries, like Britain and the USA, more people suffer from overeating than from eating too little. As we have seen, if a person takes in more energy in food than they use up, then the excess is stored as fat.
Taken to extremes, people can put on so much weight that they become **obese**.

Major causes of obesity include:

- high intake of fatty foods and refined foods containing a lot of added sugar
- too little exercise
- social and emotional stress, leading to 'comfort eating'.

There are two ways in which people can identify being obese:

- being 20% above the recommended weight for his or her height
- having a **body mass index (BMI)** greater than 30.

$$\text{body mass index} = \frac{\text{body mass (in kg)}}{\text{height (in metres)}^2}$$

A person with a BMI of less than 20 is underweight, between 25 and 30 is overweight, and more than 30 is obese.
If you are 20–24, then you are just right!

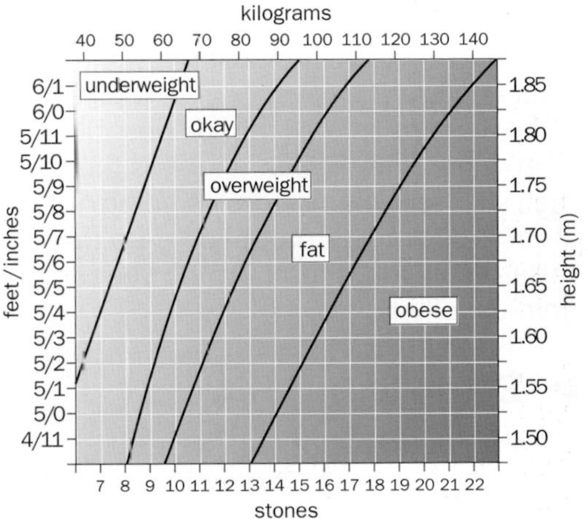

Average height to weight ratios

Waistband measurements are easier to calculate than BMI. Scientists have shown that women with waistband measurements of over 80 cm (31.4 inches) and men with over 94 cm (36.9 inches) are twice as likely to develop heart and circulatory diseases.

Overweight people are much more likely than thinner people to have the following health problems:

- heart disease (see page 85)
- high blood pressure (see page 92)
- diabetes (high blood sugar) (see page 99)
- arthritis (worn joints) (see page 136).

Which of the following actions would be best for an obese person to lose weight?

- cut down on all carbohydrates
- cut down on fat
- cut down on starchy and fibrous foods.

Which of these would be the least helpful?
Give reasons for your answers.

A person's desire for perfection, low self-esteem and a poor self-image, can lead to a poor diet and the increased risks involved.

Oiiver Hardy (right) died of a massive stroke, aged 65. Stan Laurel died aged 75.

▶ Anorexia nervosa

Slimming programmes usually involve eating less energy-rich foods and taking more exercise.
Normal slimming seldom leads to a person becoming too slim.

A few people eat so little that they suffer from **anorexia**.
They worry so much about fat that their body mass drops dangerously low.
Most anorexics are women, aged between 15 and 25, and may develop health problems like:
- pale, papery skin
- reduced resistance to infection
- irregular periods.

Anorexia is more than just slimming and loss of appetite.
Sufferers have an 'attitude' to their bodies.
They want to stay as thin as possible.
Even when they weigh a lot less than they should, they still 'see' themselves as being 'fat'.
Treatment focuses on building up their self-esteem and if this is achieved, then normally eating patterns and weight gain usually follow.

▶ Dietary influences

Lots of vitamins and minerals here

Vegetarians do not eat meat.
But there is more to it than just leaving the meat at the side of the plate.
It is important to replace the meat with other forms of protein, like cereals, seeds and nuts.
There are different kinds of vegetarians.
Some people do not eat meat but eat fish.
Others eat no meat or fish but eat dairy products.

Vegans eat no animal products at all.
Vegans have to make sure that they have enough vitamins and minerals (like iron and calcium).

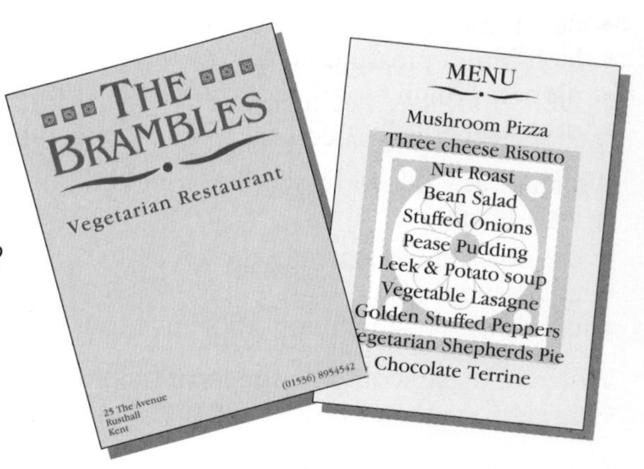

In what ways might vegetarians be healthier than other people?
Would they eat less saturated fats?
Would they have more fibre?
Why do you think people choose to become vegetarians?

There might be religious influences on a person's diet.
Halal meat has to be prepared in a special way under Muslim law. There are Jewish laws requiring the preparation of **Kosher** food.

There may be medical influences on personal diets.
Some people have food allergies and need a gluten-free or dairy-free diet.

► Vitamins and minerals

You need small, regular amounts of vitamins and minerals.
Vitamins and minerals are essential for good health.
They must be present in our balanced diet.
If they are missing we can become very ill.

Name	Rich food sources	Use in body	Deficiency disease
A	carrots, milk, butter, liver	good eyesight, healthy skin	sore eyes, poor night vision, unhealthy skin
B_1	yeast, cereals, beans, egg yolk	healthy nerves, growth	a disease called beri-beri, retarded growth
C	oranges, lemons, other citrus fruits	tissue repair, resistance to disease	a disease called scurvy (bleeding gums)
D	fish oil, milk, butter, made by body in sunlight	strong bones and teeth	a disease called rickets (soft bones)
iron	liver, meat, cocoa	healthy red blood cells	anaemia
calcium	milk, green vegetables	strong bones and teeth	soft bones
iodine	fish, iodised salt tablets	thyroid gland	goitre (enlarged thyroid)

Deficiency diseases are caused when the body doesn't have enough of a certain vitamin or mineral. They are easily cured by eating the right kinds of food.

Look at the information in the table above and answer these questions:

- Why does a pregnant woman need lots of calcium and iron in her diet?
- A 13-year-old girl starts her 'periods'. Why might she become a bit anaemic?
- In olden days sailors developed scurvy on long sea voyages. How do you think they cured it?

Salt

Fast foods often contain a lot of salt.
Too much salt in a diet can lead to high blood pressure. Many people eat too much salt each day because some processed foods contain large amounts of salt.

Experiment 4.7 Estimating the amount of vitamin C

DCPIP is a liquid that loses its colour when it comes into contact with vitamin C.

Pour 1 cm^3 of DCPIP solution into a test-tube.

Take a 1 cm^3 syringe of vitamin C and see how many drops it takes to decolourise the DCPIP.

Compare the amounts of vitamin C in different fruit juices.

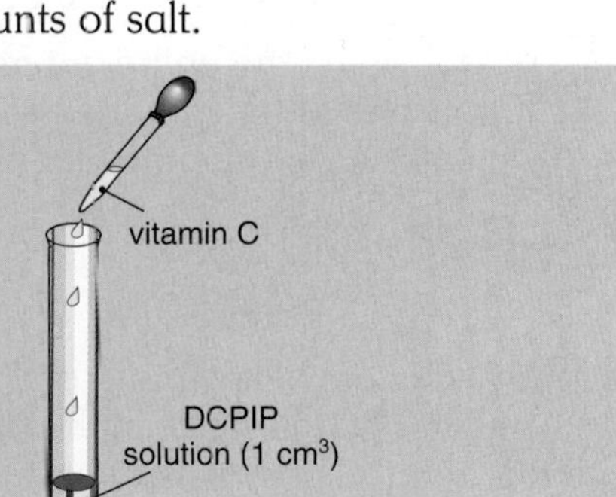

▶ Water

Water makes up two-thirds of your body weight.
You take in water when you drink or eat.
You could go without food for a number of weeks.
But you would die in a few days without water.

Why do we need water?

- In our cells, chemical reactions take place in water.
- Waste chemicals are passed out of our bodies in water.
- Our blood transports substances dissolved in water.
- Water in our sweat cools us down.

Water: our daily losses and gains

Gains (cm^3/day)		Losses (cm^3/day)	
drinks	1400	urine	1500
food	800	faeces	100
respiration	300	breath	350
		sweat	550
Total	2500	Total	2500

▶ Fibre

Dietary fibre or roughage comes from plants.
It is mainly cellulose from plant cell walls.
Although it can not be digested, it is an important part of your diet.
High-fibre foods include bran cereals, potato skins, sweetcorn and celery.

Why is fibre important?

- Fibre adds bulk to our food. Since it is not digested, it passes down the entire gut from mouth to anus. The muscles of the gut need something to push against. It's like squeezing toothpaste out of a tube.
- Fibre absorbs poisonous wastes from digesting foods.
- It prevents constipation.
- Many doctors believe that a high-fibre diet lowers the level of cholesterol in the blood. Fibre reduces the risk of heart disease and bowel cancer.

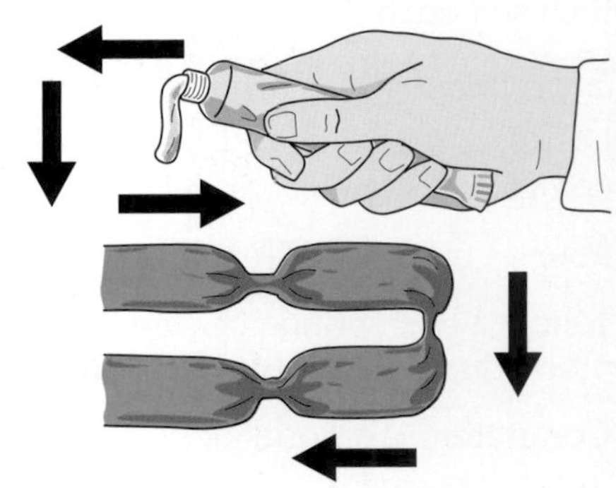

► Food additives

When some foods are manufactured, chemicals are put in them.
These chemicals are called food additives.
They are added for a number of reasons:

Preservatives *keep the food fresh*

Flavourings *replace the flavour of the food that is often lost when it is processed*

Colourings *make the food look more attractive and appetising*

All food additives must be tested before they can be used.
Over 300 additives are approved in Britain.
Most of these have 'E numbers'.
Additive E215 is a preservative called sodium ethyl para-hydroxybenzoate!
Try fitting that on a food label!

Some people avoid eating food additives because they think that they are harmful.
Some may cause asthma and headaches.
Others are blamed for over-activity in children.
There is evidence that some additives destroy vitamins.

Additive number range	Use of additive
100–181	colouring (tartrazine is 102)
200–290	preservatives (ethanoic acid is 260)
296–385	anti-oxidants and acids (ascorbic acid – vitamin C – is 300)
400–495	emulsifiers and stabilisers
500–585	anti-caking agents and mineral salts
620–640	flavour enhancers (monosodium glutamate is 621)
900–1520	others, such as sweeteners and wax glazes on fruit

Activity 4.8 Looking at food labels

Look at some of the food labels in your home.
Make a list of the additives and find out why they are put into the food.

If the E number starts with 1, it is a **colouring**.

If it starts with a 2, it is a **preservative**.

If it starts with 3, it is an **antioxidant** which helps to stop the food from going off.

If it starts with 4, it is to help with the **texture** of the food.

► Digestion

What happens to your food when you eat it?

Before your body can use the food you have eaten it must be broken down to very small molecules.

Large food molecules like proteins must be broken down into small amino acids.
Large carbohydrate molecules like starch must be broken down into small sugar molecules.
Large fat molecules must be broken down into small fatty acids.

The breakdown of large food molecules into small food molecules is called **digestion**.
It's a bit like pulling Lego bricks apart.

When the food has been digested, it is **absorbed** through the wall of the gut into the blood.
Before the food molecules can go through the gut wall they must be dissolved.

Large food molecules are insoluble; they will not dissolve.
Large food molecules can not get through the gut wall.
Small food molecules are soluble; they will dissolve.
Small food molecules can get through the gut wall.

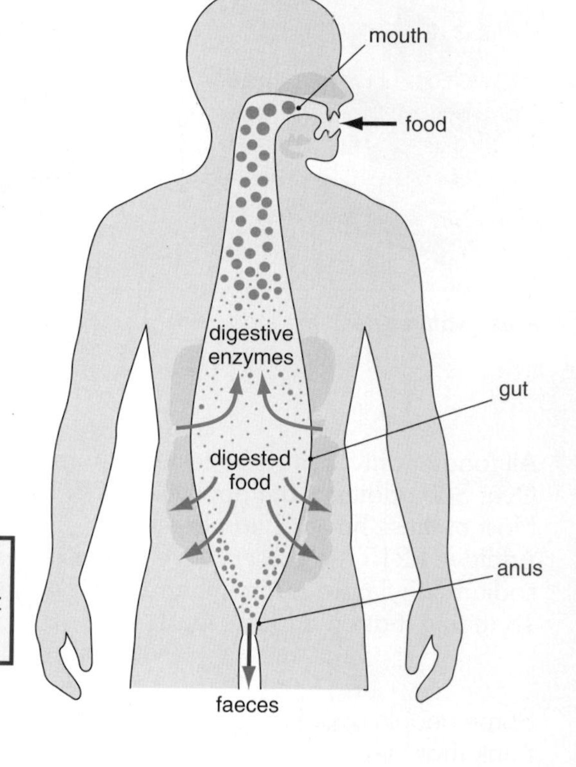

Digestion is the breakdown of large, insoluble food molecules into small, soluble food molecules so that they can be absorbed into the bloodstream.

You know that enzymes are important chemicals.
They help digestion by breaking down large food molecules into small food molecules.
There are three main kinds of enzymes in your gut:

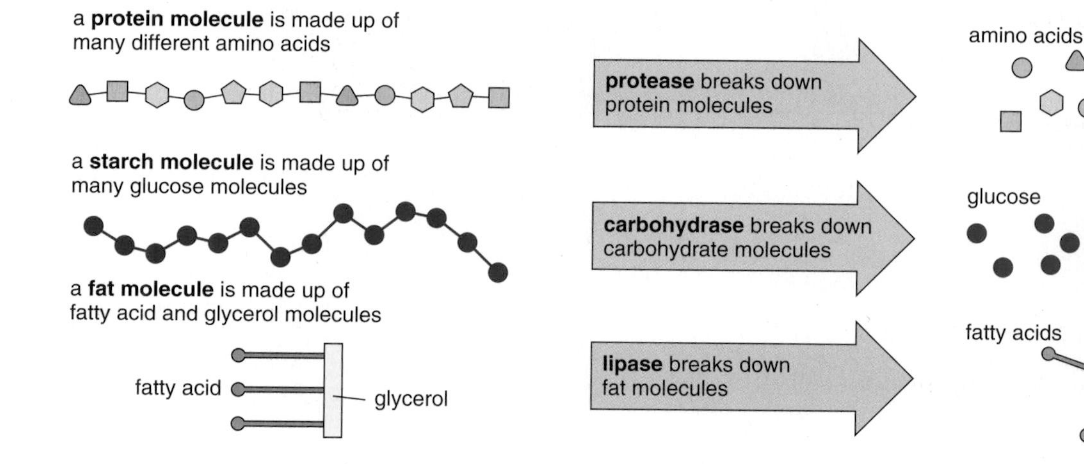

▶ The gut – your inner tube

Your gut or digestive system is about 9 metres long.
It starts at your mouth and ends at your anus.
It bends and twists a lot to fit inside your body.
But your gut is not just a simple tube.
There are many different parts to it.

▶ In your mouth

Ingestion is the process of taking food and drink into the body through the mouth.
Food enters your mouth in bite-sized chunks.
Chew your food well – it's important for digestion.

The chewed food is mixed with **saliva**.
Your **salivary glands** make saliva.

- Saliva contains a carbohydrase enzyme called **amylase**. This starts to digest starch to sugar.
- **Mucus** is a slimy substance in saliva. It helps the food slip down your throat!

Swallowing

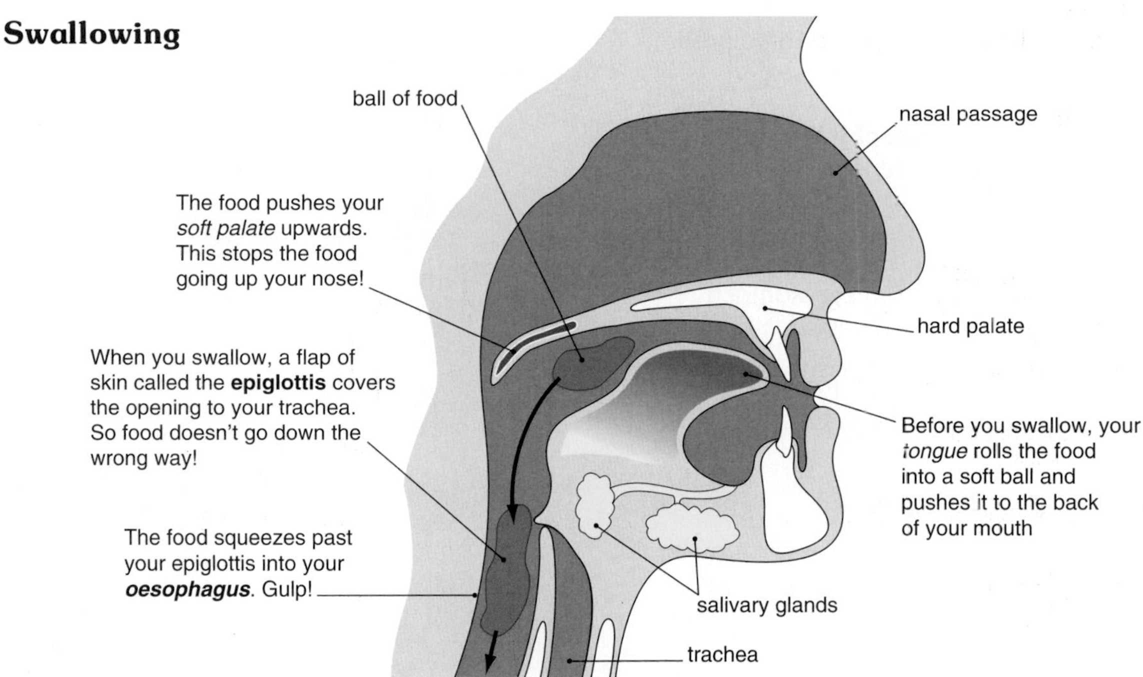

Swallowing is a reflex – it happens without you thinking about it.
Next time you swallow, think about all the things that are happening.

▶ Down the tube!

The **oesophagus** (also known as the gullet) passes the food down to your **stomach**.

The oesophagus has circular muscles in its wall. These muscles contract and squeeze in behind the food to push it along. It's a bit like squeezing toothpaste out of a tube.

In front of the food the muscles relax.

This way of moving food down your gut is called **peristalsis**.

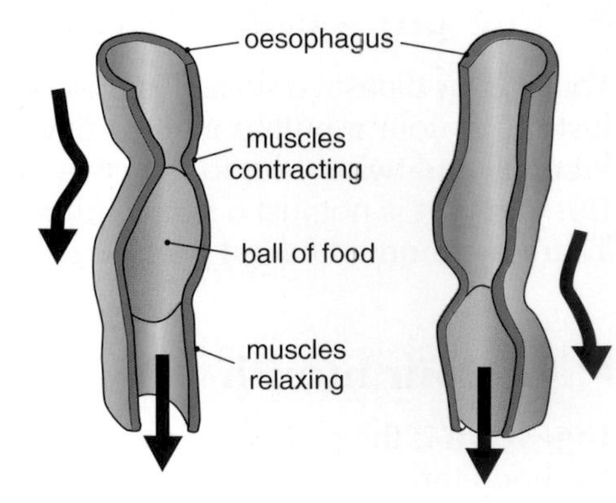

Peristalsis in action

▶ In your stomach

Your stomach is a muscular bag that will hold up to 2 litres of food. When food reaches your stomach it really gets the treatment!

- The stomach makes digestive juices. These contain proteases which start the digestion of proteins to amino acids.
- The juices also contain **hydrochloric acid**. This is because stomach protease works best in an acid pH.
- Babies make the enzyme **rennin**. It makes milk solid so it stays in the stomach longer. The milk can then be digested.
- The muscular walls churn up the food making sure that it is mixed up well with the juices.

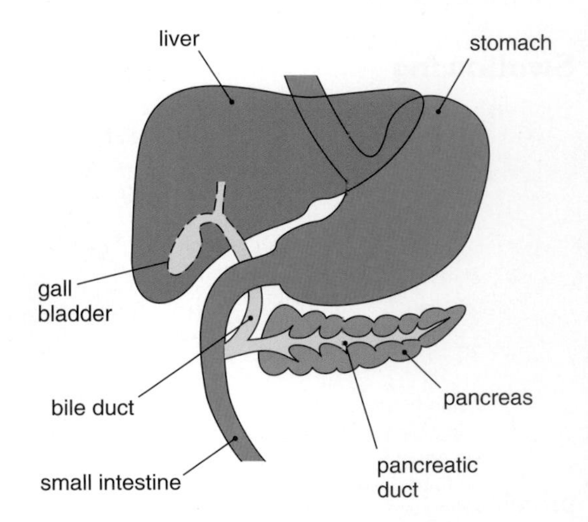

The stomach acid also kills germs.

After 2–3 hours of churning, the food is a runny liquid. A ring of muscle opens to let the food squirt out. It passes into the **small intestine** a little at a time.

Investigation 4.9 What affects the clotting of milk?

Plan an investigation into how quickly rennin clots milk. What sort of factors will affect how quickly the rennin works?
Choose ***one*** factor and investigate its effect.

▶ In your small intestine

This is not really so small, it's about 6 metres long!
Everything is much calmer here.
The liquid food is squeezed gently along.

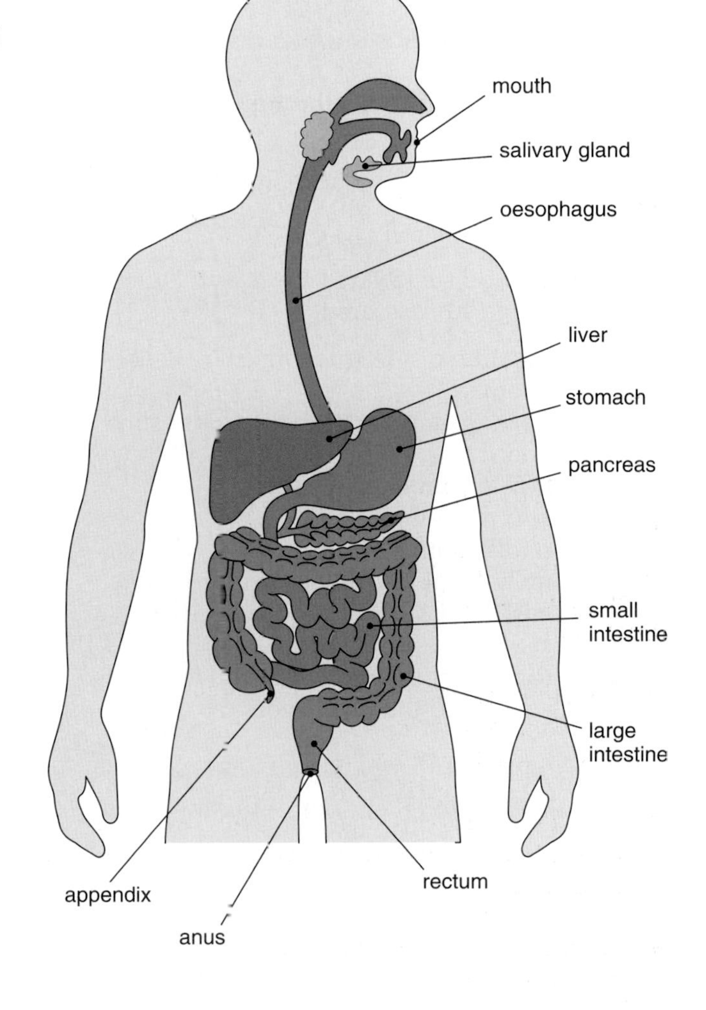

Three important liquids are added to the food:

- **Pancreatic juice** contains carbohydrases, proteases and lipases. These enzymes carry on digesting the food.
- **Bile** enters the small intestine from the **bile duct**.
  Bile is made in the **liver** and is stored in the **gall bladder**. It has two important jobs:
  i) Bile is alkaline and neutralises acid which was added to the food in the stomach. This gives the best pH for enzymes in the small intestine to work.
  ii) Bile **emulsifies** fats (breaks large drops of fats into small droplets). This increases the surface area of fats for lipase enzymes to act upon.
- **Intestinal juice** is made by glands in the wall of the small intestine.
  It also has carbohydrases, proteases and lipases in it.
  These enzymes complete the digestion of the food:

starch $\xrightarrow{\text{carbohydrases}}$ sugar

proteins $\xrightarrow{\text{proteases}}$ amino acids

fats $\xrightarrow{\text{lipases}}$ fatty acids and glycerol

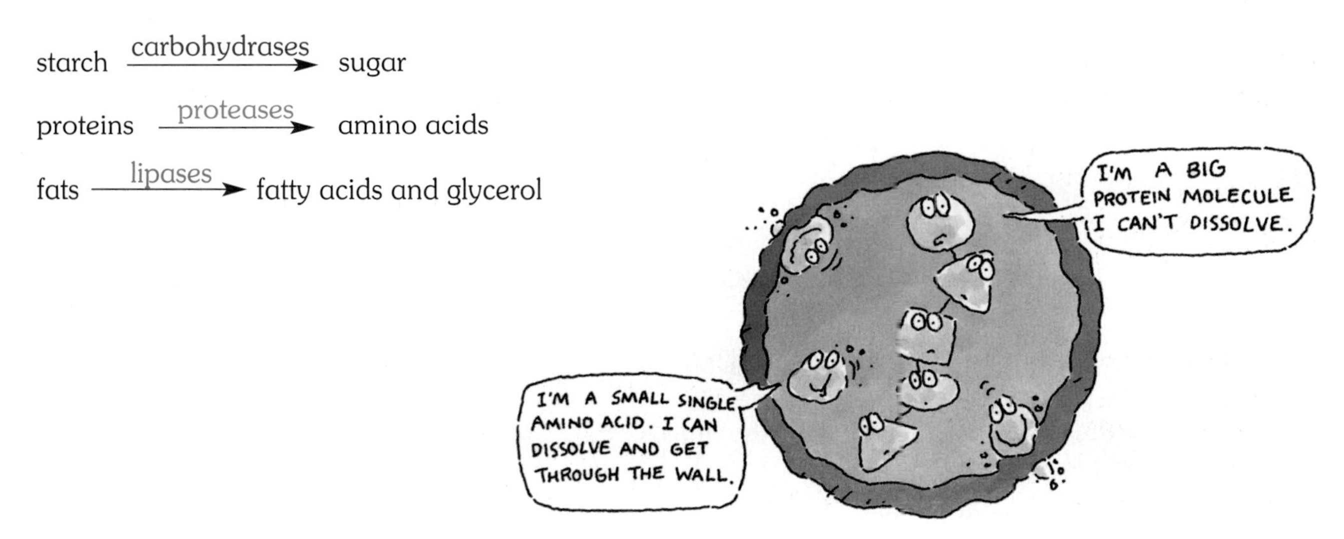

► Absorption

The small intestine has another important job apart from digestion.
Digested food has to pass through the wall into the blood.

The small intestine is well designed for absorption. It has:

- a thin lining
- a good blood supply
- a very large surface area.

The surface area of the small intestine is about 9 square metres.
How is this large surface area fitted into such a small space?

- The small intestine is very long (at least 6 metres).
- It has a folded inner lining.
- It has millions of tiny, finger-like processes called **villi** (the singular of villi is **villus**).

All this means that the digested food can pass through easily into the blood vessels.

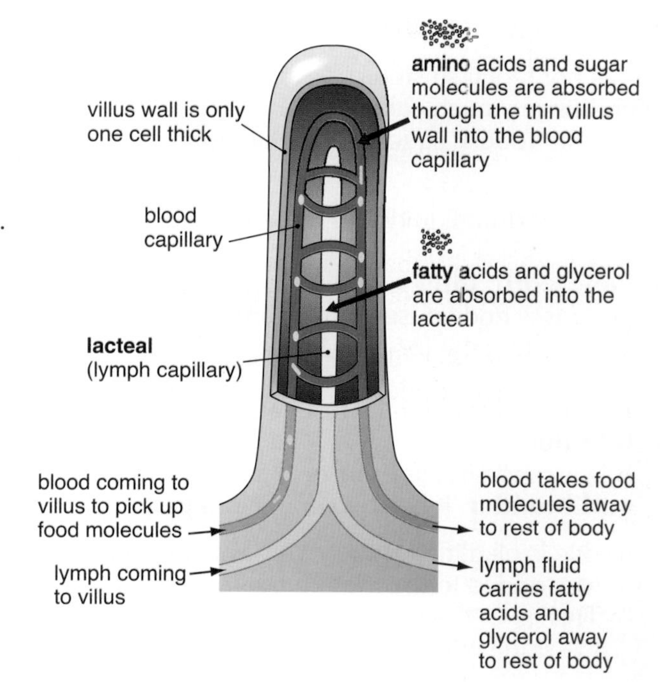

Experiment 4.10 Making a model gut

Try making a model gut out of Visking tubing.

Wash a 12 cm length of the tubing in warm water to soften it. Then tie a knot in one end.

Fill the tubing with 5 cm^3 of starch solution and 2 cm^3 of amylase solution. Put it into a boiling-tube of water (as shown).

After 10 minutes, test the water for starch and for sugar.
What do you find?

⚠ eye protection

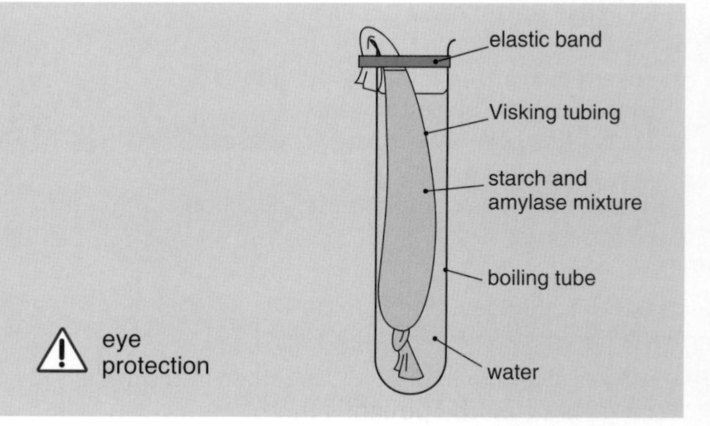

Your large intestine

By the time your food gets here there's not much useful food left.
It's mainly fibre, dead cells, bacteria and water.
As it passes along the large intestine some of the water is absorbed into the blood.
The solid waste or **faeces** are stored in the **rectum**.
Eventually the faeces are egested through the anus.
The passing out of indigestible food through the anus, in the form of faeces, is called **egestion**.

Normally it takes between 24 and 48 hours for food to pass along the whole length of your digestive system.

► Biology at work : Pictures of the gut

X-rays

How can a doctor see inside your gut without opening you up?
The answer is to use **X-rays**.

A machine sends a beam of X-rays through your body. But the X-rays do not pass through dense material like bone.
If the photographic film on the other side is then exposed, it goes dark except where your bones are.

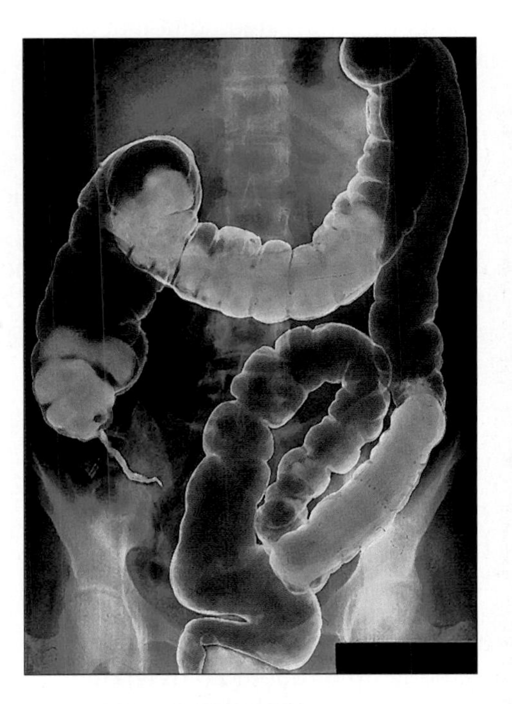

But what happens if we want to take pictures of the gut?
Here there is no dense material.
The doctor gets the patient to drink a liquid that will not let X-rays through.
The liquid drunk is barium sulphate and it is called a **barium meal**.
The fluid fills the stomach and intestines so they show up clearly when X-rayed.
The doctor uses the photograph to see if anything is wrong with the patient's gut, such as a stomach ulcer.
An ulcer forms if the acid attacks the lining of the stomach.

Optical fibres

Doctors use optical fibres to look inside the stomach.
Many optical fibres are held together in a bundle that goes down the patient's throat.
Light passes down some of the fibres to illuminate the stomach.
Reflected light passes back up the other fibres to give the picture.

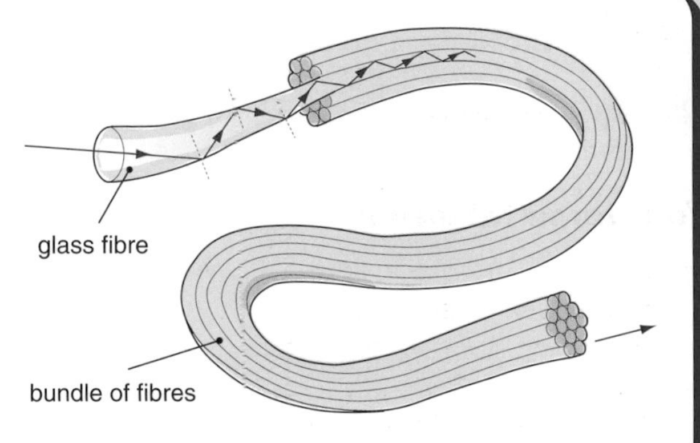

The doctor may find a stomach ulcer.
If so a laser beam can be sent down to burn and seal the ulcer.

Summary

- You need a balanced diet if you are to stay healthy.
- Proteins are needed for growth.
- Carbohydrates and fats are our energy foods.
- We can measure the energy that these foods give in kilojoules.
- Different people need different amounts of energy depending upon their age, size and activity.
- It is important to get the balance right between our energy intake and our energy output. Otherwise eating disorders, such as anorexia and obesity can occur.
- We only need vitamins and minerals in small amounts but if they are missing we can be very ill. Water and fibre are also important in our diet.
- Digestion means breaking down large molecules like proteins into small, soluble molecules like amino acids. Chemical digestion involves enzymes.
- Different parts of our digestive system have different functions.
- In the stomach protease enzymes work best in acid conditions.
- In the small intestine, bile from the liver makes conditions alkaline.
- When digestion is complete, the soluble food is absorbed into the blood.
- Water is absorbed in the large intestine before waste food is passed out of the body.

▶ Questions

1. Copy and complete:
   a) Starch and sugar are examples of . . . . .
   b) Foods rich in . . . . supply you with a quick source of energy.
   c) . . . . are body-building foods. They are made up of about 20 different . . . .
   d) Citrus fruits contain plenty of . . . . .
   e) Bran cereal and wholemeal bread contain lots of . . . . .
   f) Fats provide the body with a . . . . of energy.

2. Copy and complete the table of vitamins and minerals:

Nutrient	Rich source	Deficiency disease
	citrus fruits	scurvy
iron		
		goitre
Vit. B_1	yeast, cereals	
calcium		
		poor night vision, unhealthy skin

3. The table shows the energy content (in kJ per 100 g) of some common foods. The columns A, B, C and D show the percentage of either protein, fat, carbohydrate or water in each food.

Food	Energy (kJ/100 g)	A (%)	B (%)	C (%)	D (%)
milk	290	3	89	4.5	3.5
butter	3000	0.5	16.5	–	83
potatoes	370	2	82	16	–
beef	1300	25	55	–	20
tuna	700	18	70	–	12

   a) Which food has:
      i) the highest energy content
      ii) the lowest energy content?
   b) Look carefully at the figures and try to work out which of A, B, C or D is carbohydrate, which is water, which is protein and which is fat. For each choice you make give a reason.
   c) Give two important food materials which are not in the table, but are essential for a balanced diet.

4. a) Which food in the table below contains
   i) most protein   ii) least carbohydrate?
   What do you need protein and carbohydrates for?
b) Which foods have no fibre?
   What do you need fibre for?
c) Which food gives
   i) most energy   ii) least energy?
d) Which food has most iron?
   Why do you need iron?
e) Which foods contain no vitamin C?
   Why do you need vitamin C?
f) How much energy is there in
   i) 50 g of milk   ii) 200 g of sausage?

Food	Energy (kJ per 100 g)	Protein (%)	Fat (%)	Carbohydrate (%)	Fibre (%)	Iron (mg per 100 g)	Vitamin C (mg per 100 g)
milk	272	3.3	3.8	4.7	0	0.1	2
sausage	1520	10.6	32.1	9.5	0	1.1	0
chicken	599	26.5	4.0	0	0	0.5	0
cabbage	66	1.7	0	2.3	54	0.4	23
watercress	61	2.9	0	0.7	25	1.6	60
apples	196	0.3	0	11.9	20	0.3	5

5. a) Calculate the body mass index (BMI) for a man with a mass of 85 kg and who is 180 cm tall.
b) What advice would you give to this man about his weight? Give reasons for your advice.
c) Explain how the balance between energy intake and energy output affects obesity.
d) Regular exercise increases the basal metabolic rate (BMR).
   i) What is meant by the basal metabolic rate?
   ii) Explain how an increase in BMR could decrease the chances of heart disease.

6. Look at the diagram of the digestive system:
a) Name the parts labelled A–J.
b) Match the labels on the diagram to these functions:
   i) absorbs a lot of water
   ii) contains acid
   iii) stores faeces
   iv) makes bile
   v) stores bile
   vi) joins the throat and stomach
   vii) most absorption takes place here
   viii) has no function in humans
   ix) faeces pass out here
   x) makes pancreatic juice

7. Match up each of the parts of the body in the first column with its function in the second:

a) mouth	1) is very acidic
b) colon	2) makes bile
c) pancreas	3) most food is absorbed here
d) liver	4) food is chewed here
e) small intestine	5) makes pancreatic juice
f) stomach	6) most water is absorbed here.

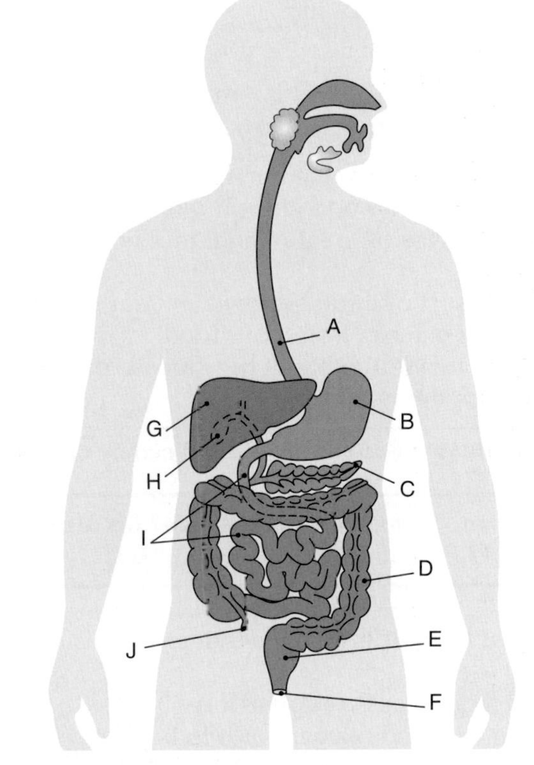

Further questions on page 171.

chapter 5

Breathing and Respiration

How long can you hold your breath for?
After about a minute it becomes too difficult and – gasp! – you have to breathe in.
But why is breathing so important to you?

If you look at the pie-charts, they will give you a clue.
They show the proportions of the gases that we breathe.
What do they tell you about the amounts of oxygen that you breathe in and out?
What do they tell you about the amounts of carbon dioxide that you breathe in and out?

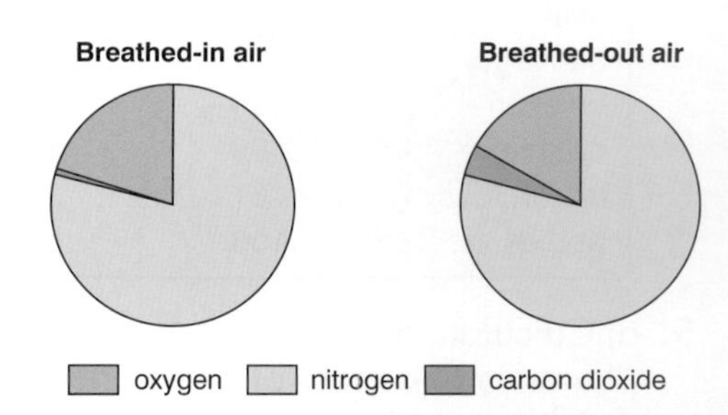

We use up oxygen in our bodies and produce carbon dioxide.
But why?

▶ Releasing energy

What happens when we burn a fuel like petrol?
Oxygen is used up and carbon dioxide is made.
The flame gives off a lot of light and heat.

The same sort of thing happens in your body.
Your fuel is glucose from your food.
Oxygen is needed to break the glucose down and release the energy.

Look at this equation:

glucose +	**oxygen** →	**carbon dioxide** +	**water** +	**energy**
$C_6H_{12}O_6$	$6\,O_2$	$6\,CO_2$	$6\,H_2O$	

The most important point is that ***energy*** is released.

We call this process **respiration**.
Because we need oxygen for it to happen, it is called **aerobic respiration**.

Burning petrol

▶ Using energy

Your body needs energy for many different things.
Energy is used up :

- working your muscles
- transporting chemicals
- absorbing food (active transport)
- sending messages along nerves
- building cells for growth
- keeping your body temperature constant.

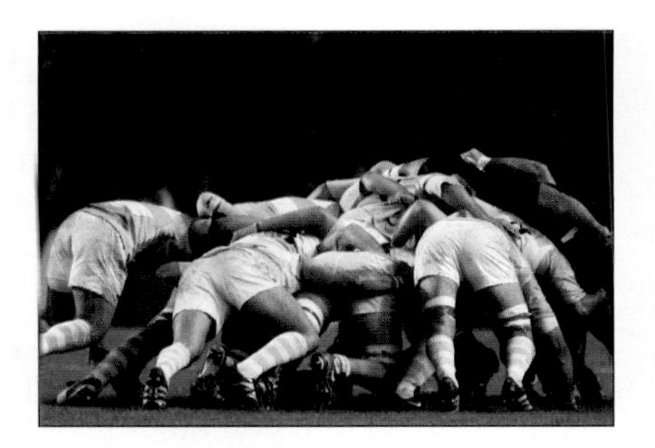

Respiration takes place in ***all*** our cells ***all*** the time.

Our cells contain tiny structures called **mitochondria**.
This is where energy is released from glucose.

Muscle cells use up lots of energy.
They have lots of mitochondria.

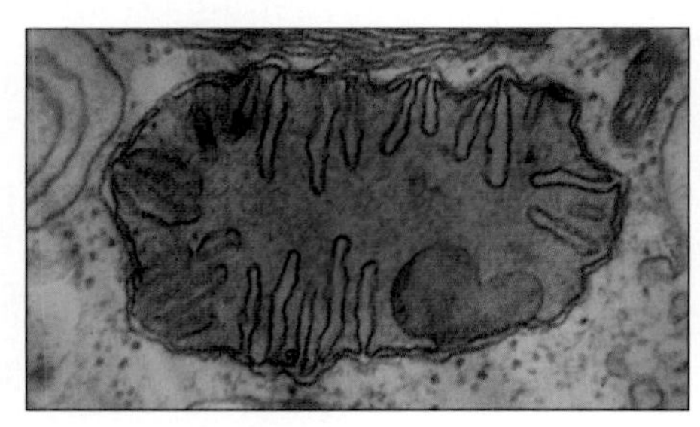

An electron micrograph of a mitochondrion

> **Living things need energy to keep alive.**
> **They transfer chemical energy from the food they eat.**
> **The energy is released to do work during respiration.**
> **You use this energy to keep going.**

Experiment 5.1 Measuring the heat energy from germinating seeds

During respiration a lot of energy is lost as heat.

You can show that heat energy is released as follows :

Set up the two thermos flasks as shown.
Use surface-sterilised germinating peas or beans.
Measure the temperature of each flask at the beginning of the experiment and each day for a week.

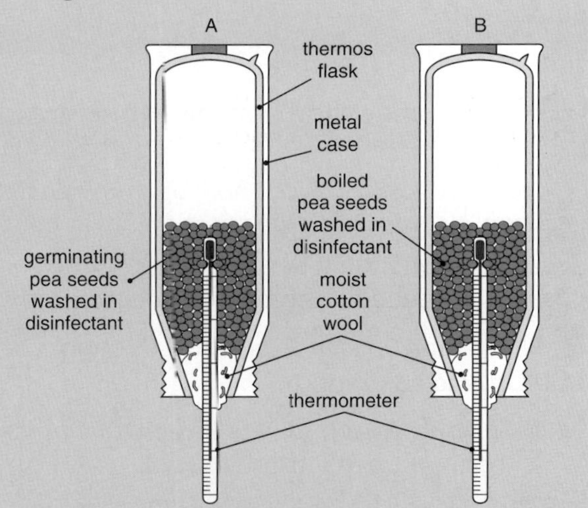

- How was the heat produced in flask A ?
- Why was there no rise in temperature in flask B ?

Microbes respire too.
- So why was it important to sterilise the surfaces of both sets of peas ?

A thermos flask keeps heat energy in.
- Why was this important in this experiment ?

The cotton wool lets gases pass in and out of the flask.
- Why was this important for respiration ?

	Day 1	Day 2	Day 3	Day 4	Day 5
flask A (°C)					
flask B (°C)					

▶ Breathing out carbon dioxide

Carbon dioxide is a waste gas made in respiration.
It can become toxic if it builds up in our cells.
The more exercise we do, the faster and deeper we breathe to get rid of the carbon dioxide.

Experiment 5.2 Testing for carbon dioxide

You can show that you breathe out carbon dioxide.

Breathe out gently through a straw into a test-tube of lime water.
Carbon dioxide makes lime water go cloudy.

⚠ eye protection

Now try doing the same thing, but this time breathe into hydrogencarbonate indicator in a clean test-tube.
Carbon dioxide changes hydrogencarbonate indicator from red to yellow.

Respiration for all

All living things carry out respiration.
Animals, plants and bacteria all respire.
So all living things give out carbon dioxide.
You can find out about respiration in plants on page 192.

Your teacher may show you this demonstration :

Demonstration 5.3 To show that germinating seeds release carbon dioxide during respiration

Your teacher should set up the apparatus as shown in the diagram :

⚠ eye protection

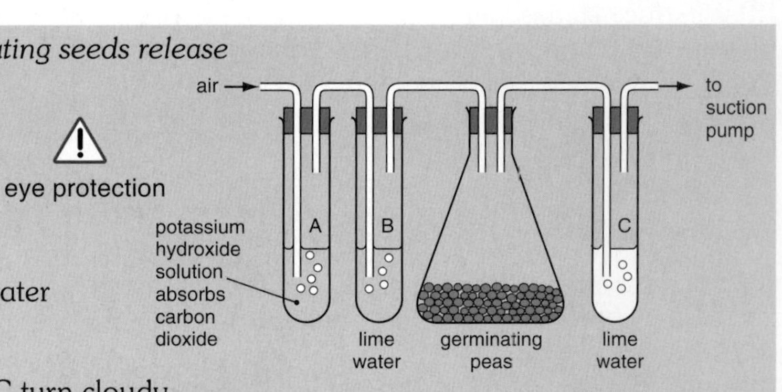

A filter pump is used to suck air through the apparatus.

- How long does it take before the lime water in boiling-tube C turns cloudy ?
- Why did the lime water in boiling-tube C turn cloudy before the limewater in boiling-tube B ?

More carbon dioxide out?

Look at the table:

Gas	Inspired air (breathing in)	Expired air (breathing out)
oxygen	21%	16%
carbon dioxide	0.04%	4%
nitrogen	78%	78%
water vapour	variable	saturated

It shows that we breathe out more carbon dioxide than we breathe in.
How could you prove this is true?

Experiment 5.4 Carbon dioxide in breathed-in and breathed-out air

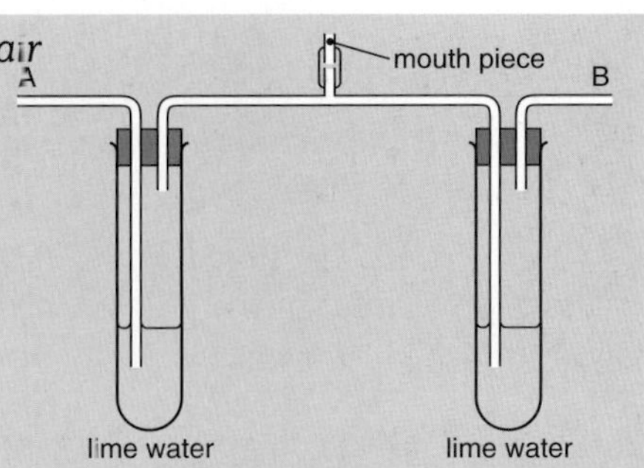

Set up the apparatus as shown in the diagram:
Breathe gently in and out of the mouth-piece several times.

- When you breathe in, does the air come in through A or through B?
- When you breathe out, does the air go out through A or through B?
- In which tube did the lime water turn cloudy first?

Less oxygen out?

When we breathe in our bodies use some of the oxygen for respiration.
The rest is breathed back out again.

Our cells use up the oxygen to break down the glucose and release energy.

The table shows that we breathe out less oxygen than we breathe in.
How could you prove that this is true?

Experiment 5.5 Oxygen in breathed-in and breathed-out air

Time how long it takes before the candle goes out in:
i) fresh air
ii) breathed-out air
(you can collect this by breathing out through a rubber tube as shown in the diagram).

- What does this experiment tell you about the amount of oxygen in fresh air and in breathed-out air?

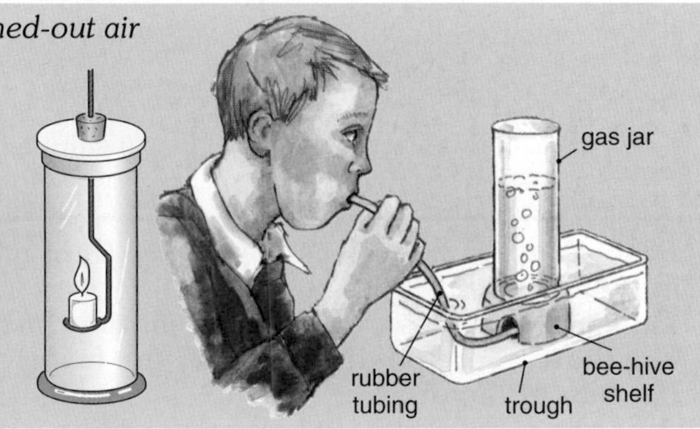

► How fast?

You can measure how fast respiration takes place.
This is the **rate of respiration**.
We measure either the rate at which oxygen is used up, or the rate at which carbon dioxide is produced.
To do this we use a **respirometer**.

Experiment 5.6 A simple respirometer

⚠ eye protection
soda lime is corrosive

You could use the simple respirometer in the diagram:

It will tell you how quickly germinating seeds use up oxygen.

- How do you think it works?
- What does the soda lime do?
- Why is it important to keep the apparatus at a constant temperature?
- How could you find out the effects of different temperatures on the rate at which oxygen is used up by the seeds?

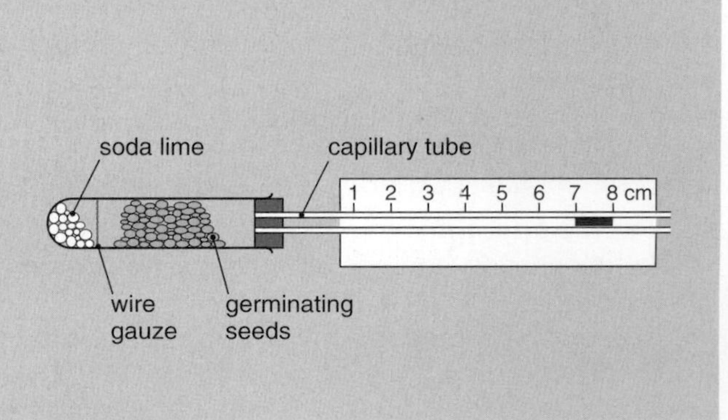

Experiment 5.7 A more accurate respirometer

⚠ eye protection
soda lime is corrosive

You can measure the rate of respiration more accurately with this apparatus:

Put some mealworms or woodlice into the boiling-tube.

Set up the rest of the apparatus as shown.
Be very careful not to touch yourself or the animals with the soda lime. It is corrosive.

Close the clip and find out how much the coloured liquid rises in 30 minutes.

Soda lime absorbs carbon dioxide.

- Explain how you think the apparatus works.
- Can you think of a control for the experiment?
- Why was the boiling-tube kept at a constant temperature?

plastic tubing
clip
capillary tube
small animals
wire gauze
soda lime
water bath to keep temperature constant
coloured water

Respiration is the release of energy from glucose in living cells.
This energy release takes place all the time.
The more energy that is needed, the faster the rate of respiration.

▶ Your breathing system

You need to breathe in air to get oxygen.
You breathe air out to get rid of carbon dioxide.
We call this **gas exchange**.

In humans it takes place in our lungs.
But there are other important parts of
our breathing system.

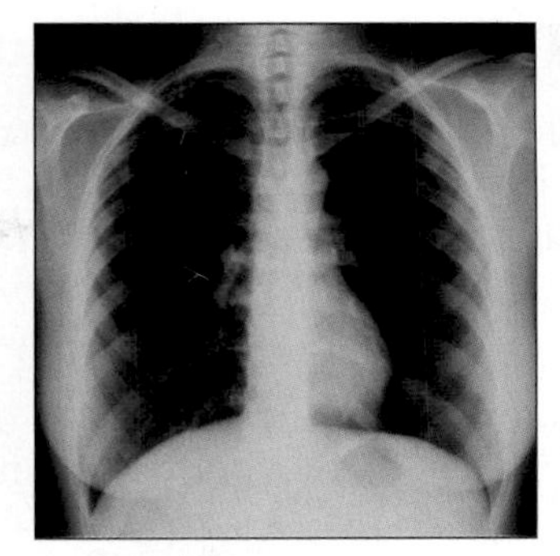

A chest X-ray

Finding your lungs

Where do you think your lungs are?

You'll find them inside your chest or **thorax**.
They are surrounded and protected by your ribs.

Many people don't realise how big their lungs are.
Each of your lungs is as big as a rugby ball.
They fill the whole of your chest space.

Below your lungs is a sheet of muscle called the
diaphragm (dia-fram).
It separates your thorax from your **abdomen** below.

Your diaphragm and ribs help you to breathe.

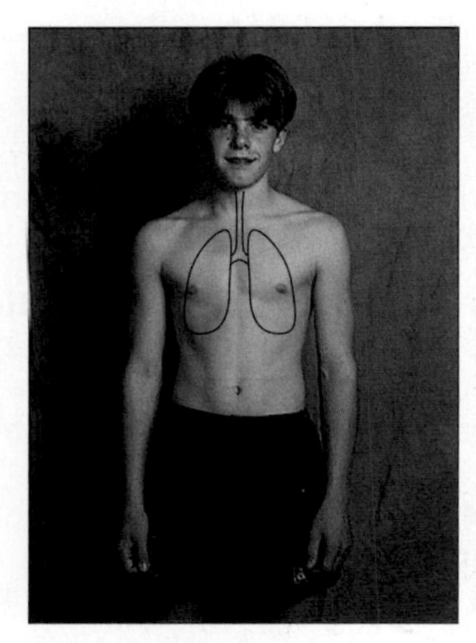

Do you know where your lungs are?

Air-conditioning

Air enters through your nose and mouth.

It then passes down your windpipe or **trachea**.

This first part of your breathing system treats
the air before it reaches your lungs.
Cold, dry and dirty air might damage your lungs so
it is:

- warmed
- moistened
- filtered and cleaned.

The cells lining the nose and trachea make slimy **mucus**.
Dust and germs get trapped in the slime.
The cells have tiny hairs or **cilia** on them.
These beat to carry the mucus up to your nose and throat.
What happens to it then?

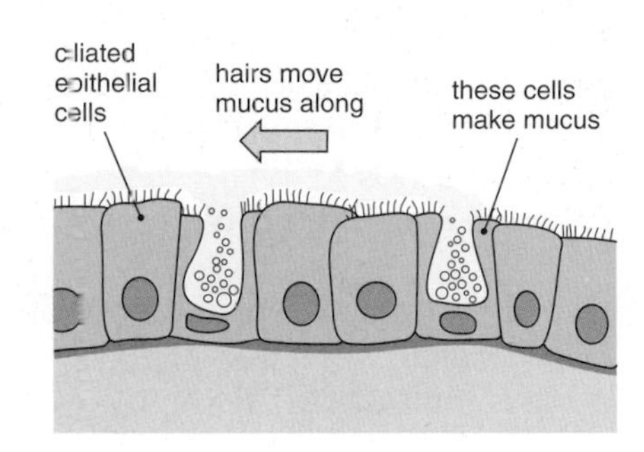

► Two-way trip to your lungs

Before going down your trachea, air enters your **larynx** (voice-box).
This is sometimes called your Adam's apple.
Can you feel it?

Your larynx contains your vocal cords.
When air blows over these you make sounds.
It's a bit like blowing through a mouth-organ.

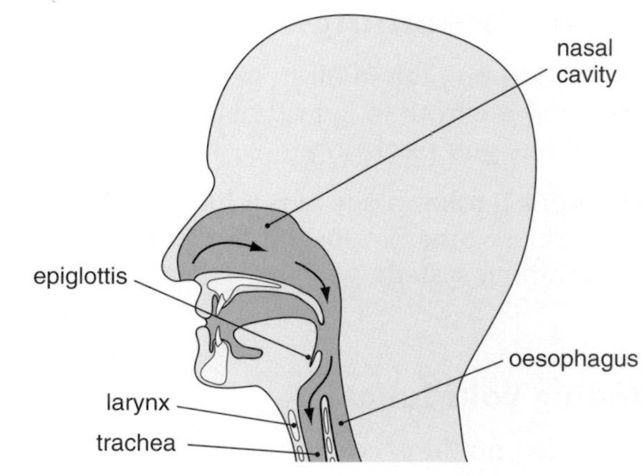

The pathway of air to your trachea

You can't breathe and swallow at the same time.
This is because when you swallow, a flap of skin called the **epiglottis** drops over the opening to your larynx.
This stops any food from going down your trachea.

Air is sucked down your trachea.
So why doesn't it collapse?

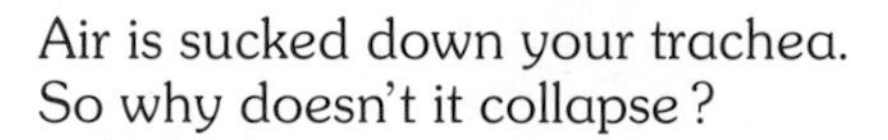

It is kept open by rings of **cartilage**.
The cartilage rings are C-shaped.

Your trachea branches many times, a bit like the roots of a tree.
The branches end up at tiny air sacs called **alveoli** (al-v-o-lee).
It is here that gas exchange takes place.

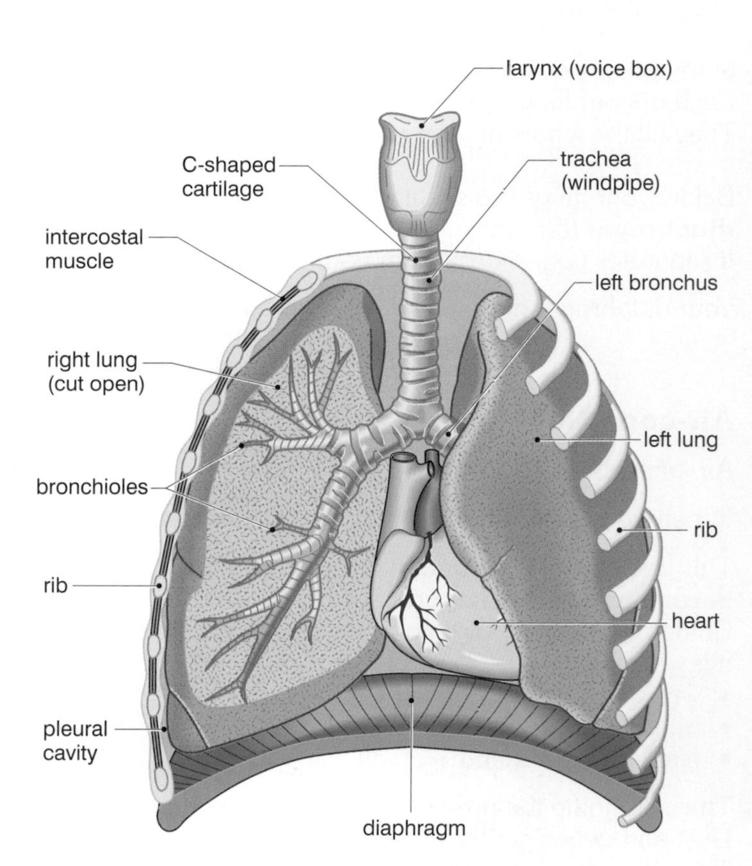

Your lungs are spongy.
They are surrounded by the **pleural membrane**.
This makes a slippery fluid.
How do you think that this helps when your lungs rub against your ribs?

Your ribs protect your lungs.
They also move during breathing.
Can you find the muscles that move your ribs?
They are called the **intercostal muscles**.

Your diaphragm forms the floor of your thorax.
What is it made of?

The diaphragm also moves during breathing.

▶ Breathing

Try putting your hands on your chest.
Breathe gently in and out.
Can you feel your ribs rising and falling?

Your lungs act like a pair of bellows, sucking in air and blowing it out.
But it is the muscles between your ribs and in your diaphragm that work your lungs.

Breathing in

- Your intercostal muscles ***contract***.
  They raise your ribs upwards and outwards.
- The muscle in your diaphragm ***contracts***.
  Your diaphragm flattens.
- These increase the volume of your thorax.
  The pressure inside your thorax ***decreases***.
- Air passes ***into*** your lungs because the external air pressure is greater.

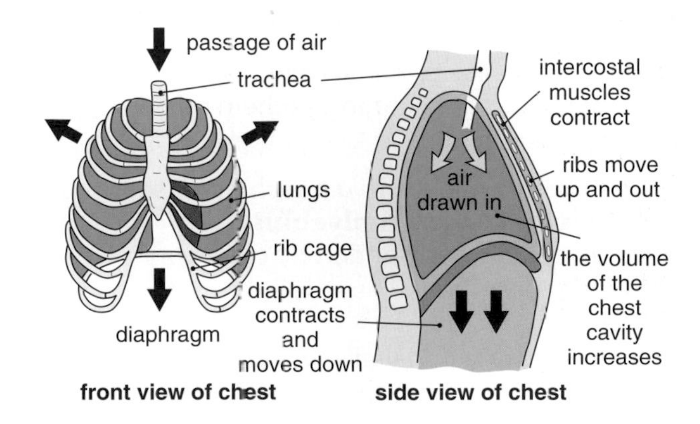

Breathing out

- Your intercostal muscles ***relax***.
  This lowers your ribs downwards and inwards.
- The muscle in your diaphragm ***relaxes***.
  Your diaphragm bulges upwards.
- These decrease the volume of your thorax.
  The pressure inside your thorax ***increases***.
- Air is forced ***out*** of your lungs because the pressure inside them is greater than the external air pressure.

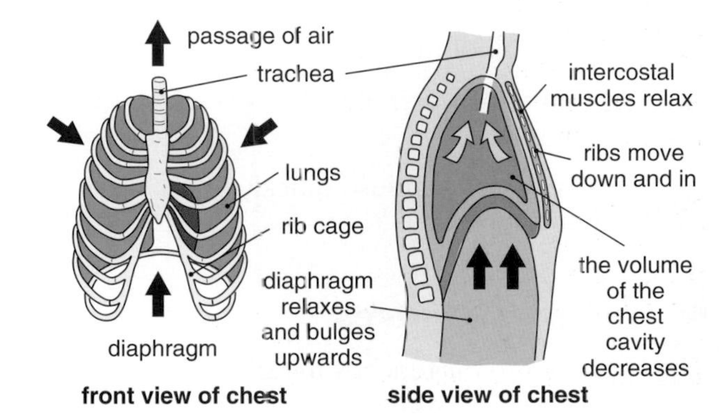

Experiment 5.8 A chest model

Using the model supplied by your teacher:

Pull the rubber sheet down and then push it up.
Do this a few times more.
What happens to the balloons?

- Which part of the model represents:
  a) the lungs b) the diaphragm c) the ribs?
- What is not very good about the model?
- Does it move like the ribs?
- Is there really such a large space around the lungs?

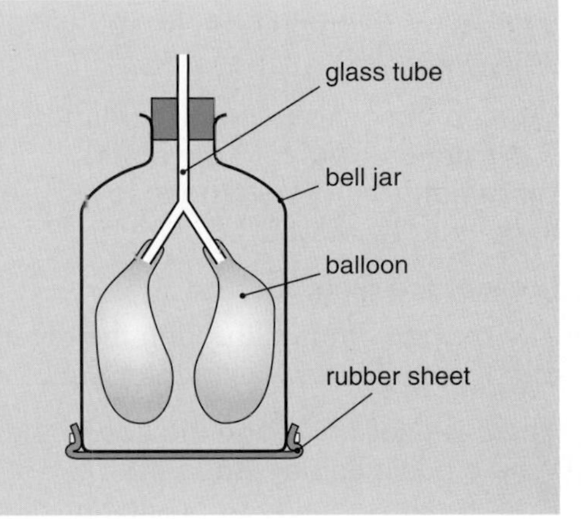

▶ Deeper into your lungs

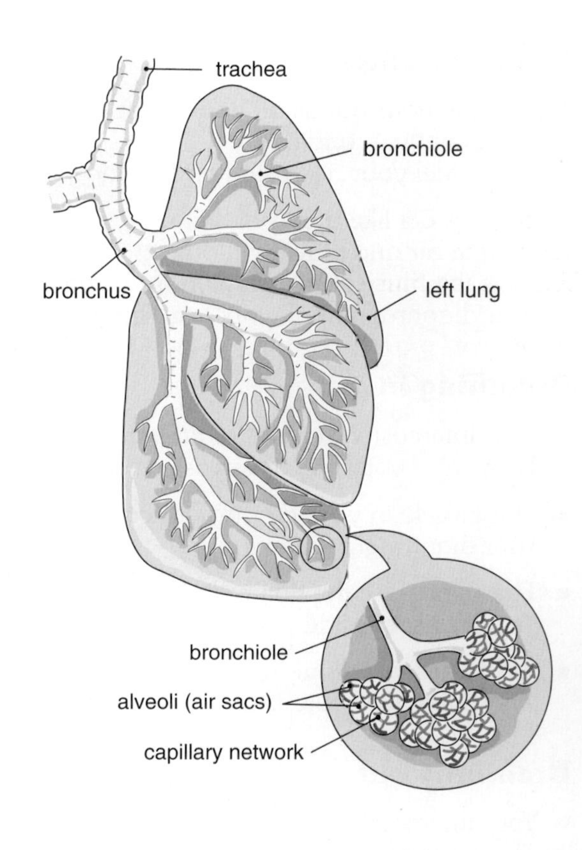

To see how gas exchange takes place we have to look much deeper into the lungs.

Your trachea splits into two.
Each short tube is called a **bronchus**.
One bronchus enters each lung.

Each bronchus divides many times to give lots of smaller branches called **bronchioles**.

Cartilage rings keep the bronchi and the bronchioles open when the pressure inside them drops (when you breath in).

Each bronchiole leads to a bunch of air sacs called **alveoli** (singular **alveolus**).
Each alveolus is surrounded by a network of blood capillaries.

The alveoli have thin walls.
Does this make it easier for gases to get through?

The alveoli are moist.
Do gases have to dissolve before they pass through the wall of the alveolus?

Why do you think each alveolus is so close to a blood capillary?

This allows gases to diffuse quickly into and out of blood.

▶ Swopping gases

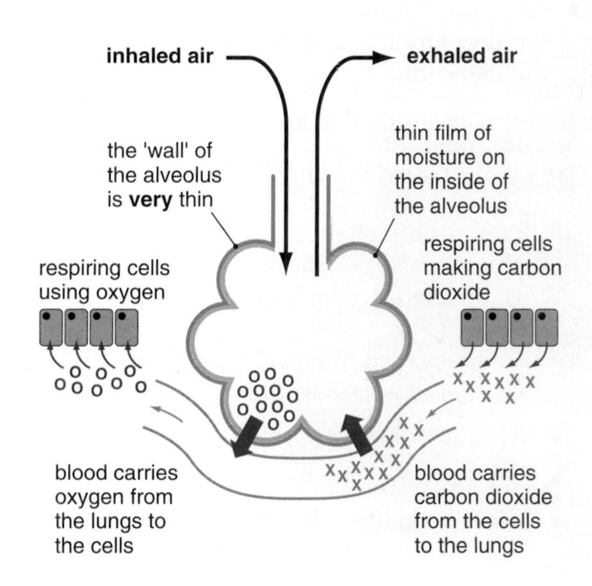

The breathed-in air reaches the alveoli.
It contains a lot of oxygen.
Your blood transports the oxygen around your body, so how does the oxygen get into your blood?

Oxygen dissolves in the water lining each alveolus.
It **diffuses** through to the blood.
What does the oxygen have to diffuse ***through*** to get into the blood?

Look at the diagram:

The oxygen diffuses through the alveolus wall and the capillary wall to enter the blood.

There is a lot of carbon dioxide in the capillary.
Where has it come from?
Does it diffuse in the opposite direction?

► Take a deep breath

An adult can take in about 5 litres of air in their deepest breath.

At rest, about half a litre of air is breathed in and out. During exercise, an extra 3 litres of air can be taken in. Why do you think this is?

Do not attempt the next two experiments if you suffer from asthma or any other respiratory disease.

Experiment 5.9 Measuring your vital capacity

The most air you can breathe out is called your **vital capacity**. You can measure this by using the apparatus in the diagram:

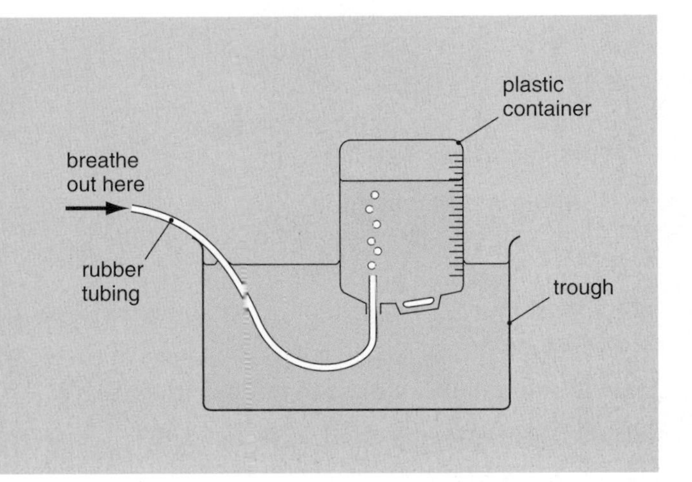

Get someone to hold the plastic container full of water and the end of the rubber tube in position.

Take a deep breath in and breathe out steadily through the rubber tube.

If you find it a strain, stop immediately.

Make sure the levels are equal inside and outside the container before you read off the volume.

You could try comparing your vital capacity with others in your class.

What do you think affects a person's vital capacity?

Is there any difference between males and females? Why do you think this is?

How would age and fitness have an effect?

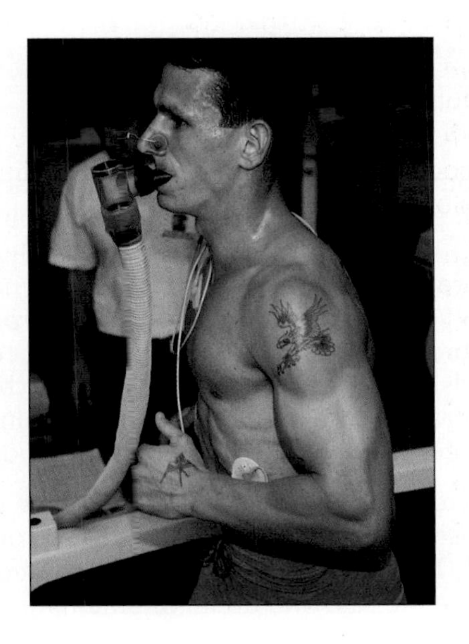

Experiment 5.10 Measuring your tidal volume

You can use the same apparatus to measure your **tidal volume**.
This is the volume of air that you breathe out when you are resting.

Compare your tidal volume with your vital capacity. Why do you think it is so much less?

▶ Breathing and exercise

How many breaths per minute do you take when resting?

It is probably something like 16 breaths per minute.

But what happens to your breathing rate when you exercise?

How does exercise affect breathing?

Investigation 5.11

Plan an investigation into the effects of exercise on your breathing rate.

Try to compare the effects of light and heavy exercise. Step-ups are a good form of exercise to try.

- How much did your breathing rate increase when you exercised?
- Which had the greater effect, heavy exercise or light exercise?
- Did you notice anything about how ***deep*** your breathing was (how big each breath was)?

Why does your rate and depth of breathing increase with exercise?

How does it get more oxygen to your muscles?

Why do your muscles need more oxygen?

How does your rate and depth of breathing get rid of more carbon dioxide from your muscles?

Why do your muscles make more carbon dioxide?

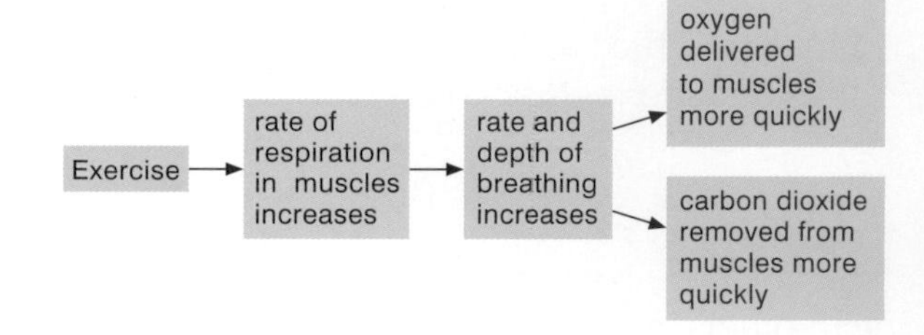

▶ Control of breathing

You don't think about your breathing.
Most of the time it just happens.

So what makes you breathe faster and deeper when you exercise?
Which part of your body controls breathing?

The brain has a special part for controlling breathing.
When you exercise you make ***more carbon dioxide***.
Your brain detects this rise in the blood reaching it.
It sends messages along nerves to your chest muscles.
Your breathing rate and depth of breathing are increased to lower the carbon dioxide in your blood.

An increase in carbon dioxide lowers the pH of the blood. Exercise also increases the temperature of the tissues and blood. These two factors are also detected by the brain and increase the rate and depth of breathing.

► Respiration without oxygen

Do you remember what we called respiration ***with*** oxygen?
Aerobic respiration won't work without oxygen.
But sometimes respiration can occur ***without*** oxygen.
We call this **anaerobic respiration**.

Food from microbes

Fermentation

Many microbes can respire successfully without oxygen.
Yeast can respire with or without oxygen.
When it respires without oxygen it is called **fermentation**.

glucose ⟶ alcohol + carbon dioxide + energy

Can you think of any uses for fermentation?
Yeast is used in wine-making and brewing (see page 351).

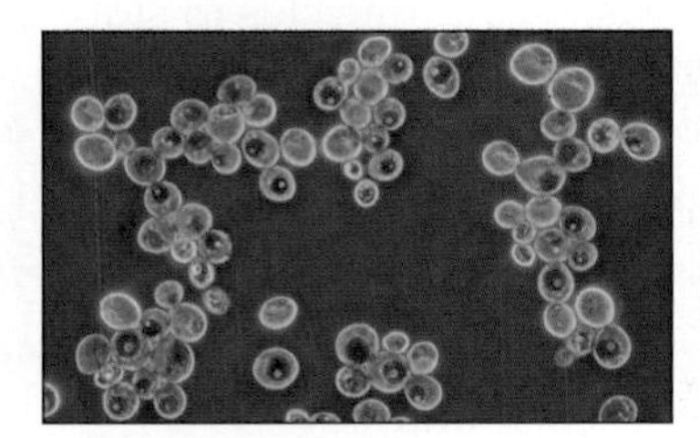

Yeast cells

Experiment 5.12 Fermentation

Make a mixture of yeast and 10 % glucose solution.
Set the apparatus up as shown:

Add a few drops of diazine green indicator.
This turns pink in the absence of oxygen.

tube
liquid paraffin
glucose solution and yeast
hydrogencarbonate indicator

- Why did the hydrogencarbonate indicator turn yellow?
- How long did this take?
- What gas did the paraffin prevent from entering?
- How did the diazine green prove that no oxygen had entered?

Plan an investigation to find out what affects the rate of fermentation.

Fermentation not only puts the fizz into our drinks,
it also makes our bread rise.
Yeast contains enzymes that ferment the sugar in flour.

Experiment 5.13 Making dough rise

Mix 20 g flour and 1 g sugar in a beaker.
Add 20 cm^3 of yeast mixture and stir it to a paste.
Pour the mixture into a measuring cylinder.
Record the volume of the dough every 3 minutes
for 30 minutes.
Draw a line graph to show your results.

- What do you think made your dough rise?
- Describe how your dough rose over the 30 minutes.

Plan an investigation to find out how you could make your dough rise faster.

► Muscles without oxygen

Your muscles need oxygen and glucose to respire aerobically. These are brought to your muscles by your blood system.

During long periods of vigorous activity your muscles become fatigued and they stop contracting efficiently. When this happens, your heart and lungs can not get enough oxygen to your muscles quickly enough. This causes your muscles to start to carry out anaerobic respiration.
Glucose is broken down to **lactic acid**, when there is no oxygen

glucose ⟶ lactic acid + energy

'I wanna repay my oxygen debt'

Lactic acid can slowly poison your muscles.
This causes cramp.
We must get rid of the lactic acid.

Have you noticed that we carry on breathing faster and deeper after vigorous exercise?
The extra oxygen breaks down the lactic acid.
This extra oxygen is called the **oxygen debt**.
Our oxygen debt builds up after we exercise hard.
It has to be 'paid back' straight away.

Sprinters build up lactic acid in their muscles.
They often hold their breath during a 100 metre race.
Afterwards they need about 7 litres of oxygen to get rid of the lactic acid.
They breathe deeply after the race in order to repay their oxygen debt.

Long-distance runners could not stand such a build up of lactic acid.
They run at a much slower speed.
They build up some lactic acid in the early stages of the race, but get rid of this while they are running.

Anaerobic respiration produces less energy than aerobic respiration.
Without oxygen, glucose is only partly broken down into alcohol or lactic acid.
A lot of energy remains in the molecules of alcohol and lactic acid.

	Energy released (kJ/g glucose)
aerobic respiration	16.1
fermentation by yeast	1.2
anaerobic respiration in muscle	0.8

► Biology at work : Training at altitude

In the 1968 Olympics, athletes who usually trained and competed at sea level did not perform as well as expected. This was because the games were held in Mexico City at an altitude of 2242 m.
The athletes who normally lived at a high altitude did well, particularly in the endurance races such as the 10 000 m.

At high altitudes there is less oxygen in the air.
This means that less oxygen can be carried to the muscles by the blood.
The body responds by :

- releasing red blood cells stored in the spleen
- increasing the rate at which red blood cells are made
- making it easier for haemoglobin to give up its oxygen when it reaches the muscle tissue (see page 88).

The amount of haemoglobin circulating in the blood increases by 50–90 %.
This means that the blood is able to carry more oxygen.
At altitudes of 2000–2500 m, it takes about 2 weeks for the body to bring about these changes.

A hypoxic training room

Recent developments have attempted to reproduce the benefits of altitude training at sea level.
These include the use of **hypoxic training rooms**, which have the following benefits:

- reduction in travel costs
- no change in air pressure
- no exposure to higher levels of ozone and UV light
- better oxygen supply to the tissues
- drop in heart-beat rate.

Look at the graph,it shows how the number of red blood cells increased in Himalayan mountain climbers during an expedition lasting 110 days.

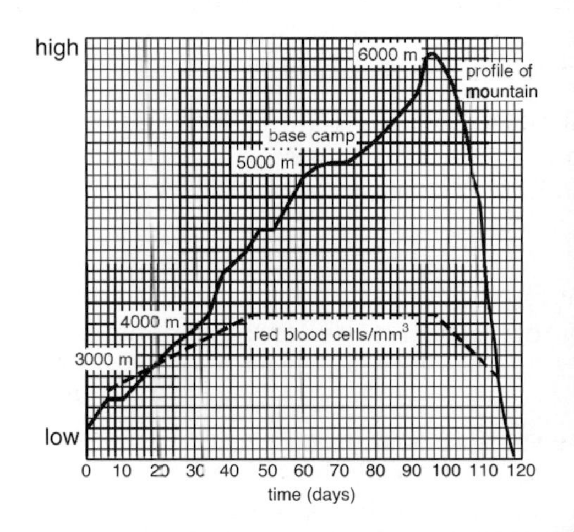

Why is it an advantage to the climbers to increase the number of their red blood cells?

How long did it take for the red blood cells to reach their highest concentration ?

Why do you think that there was no increase in the concentration of red blood cells between 4000 m and 6000 m?

Summary

- Respiration involves the breakdown of glucose to release energy.
- Aerobic respiration uses oxygen to do this.
- Carbon dioxide is made as a waste product and must be removed.
- The rate of respiration can be measured with a respirometer.
- Air entering your lungs is warmed, cleaned and moistened.
- Exchange of gases takes place in the alveoli.
- Your intercostal muscles and diaphragm are used in breathing.
- Your breathing rate is controlled by your brain and increases with exercise.
- Yeast and muscles are able to respire without oxygen.
- Anaerobic respiration in muscle results in an oxygen debt that has to be repaid to oxidise lactic acid to carbon dioxide and water.

► Questions

1. Copy and complete :
Respiration takes place in all our . . . . . The fuel for respiration is . . . . . It is broken down to release . . . . . Also produced are water and the waste gas . . . . When it takes place in the presence of . . . . we call it . . . . respiration. These reactions take place in every living cell, inside tiny structures called . . . . .

2. Look at the apparatus used in this experiment :

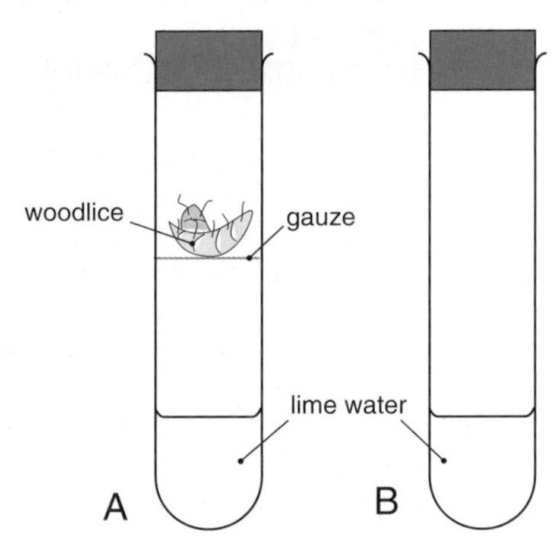

a) Suggest a title for the experiment.
b) After 12 hours the tubes were examined. What results would you expect ?
c) What was tube B for ?
d) What would have happened if the lime water had been replaced by hydrocarbonate indicator ?

3. Give an explanation for each of the following :
a) When you breathe on a cold window, water droplets form.
b) Breathed-out air turns lime water cloudy quicker than breathed-in air.
c) Alveoli (air sacs) are very thin and have a large surface area.
d) Plants give out carbon dioxide in the dark, but take it up in the light.

4. Look at the diagram of the respirometer :

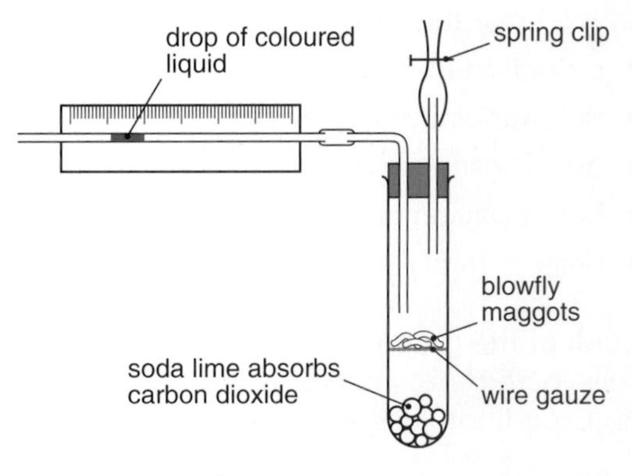

a) In which direction will the drop of coloured liquid move ?
b) What makes this happen ?
c) Why must the spring clip be closed at the start of the experiment ?
d) You are given identical sets of this apparatus. How could you investigate the effects of temperature on the rate of respiration of the maggots ?

5. The diagram shows the human breathing system:

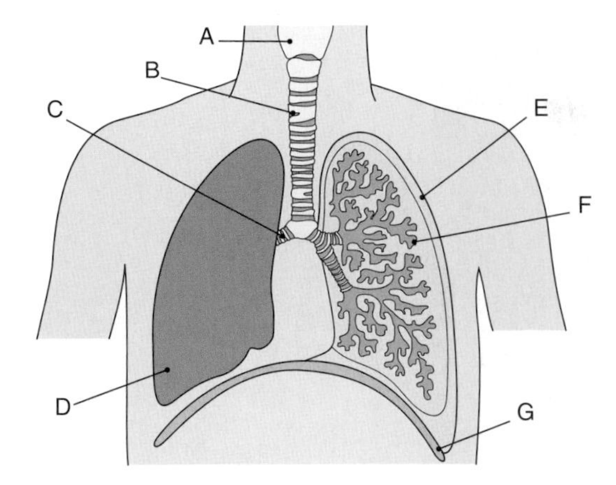

a) Write out letters A to G with the correct labels.

b) Match parts A to G with these descriptions:

i) sheet of muscle forming the floor of the chest
ii) one of these enters each lung
iii) contains the vocal cords
iv) flexible tube kept open by rings of cartilage
v) where exchange of gases takes place
vi) a slippery membrane
vii) made of spongy tissue and found in the chest.

6. The diagram shows some alveoli (air sacs) and a blood capillary in the lung.

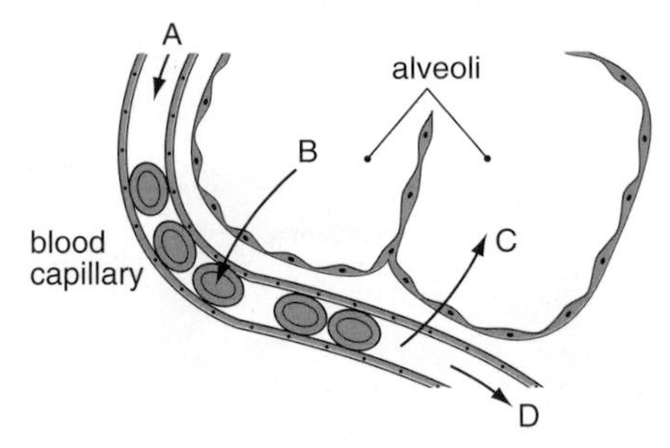

a) Which arrow shows:

i) blood high in oxygen
ii) blood low in oxygen
iii) the diffusion of oxygen
iv) the diffusion of carbon dioxide?

b) Give two features of the alveoli that help gas exchange.

7. Write down a function for each of the following:

a) the C-shaped rings of cartilage in the trachea
b) the epiglottis
c) the pleural membrane
d) the mucus in the trachea
e) the diaphragm.

8. The apparatus was set up as shown:

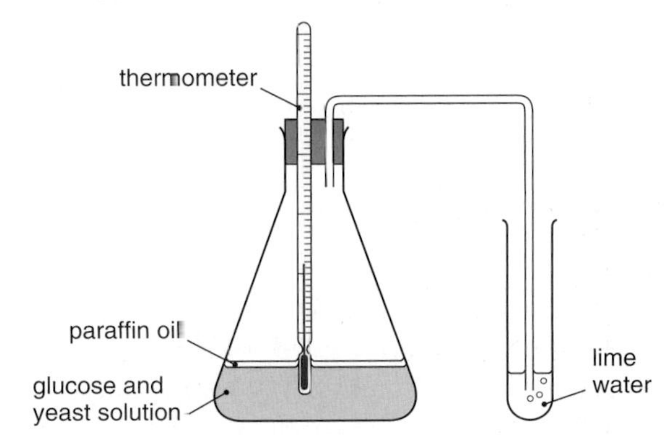

The flask was kept at 35 °C. After 15 minutes the lime water had turned cloudy.

a) What gas was given off?
b) What process produced the gas?
c) Why was the flask kept at a constant 35 °C?
d) What was the paraffin oil for?
e) Suggest a control for this experiment.

9. The table shows the units of lactic acid produced in the leg muscles of an athlete.

Time (minutes)	0	10	20	30	40	50	60	70	80
Lactic acid units	0	1	7	12	9	6	3	1	1

a) Draw a line-graph using the data.
b) When did the lactic acid reach a maximum? Try to explain this.
c) What happened to the lactic acid after this time? Try to explain this.

Further questions on page 171.

BLOOD and CIRCULATION

chapter 6

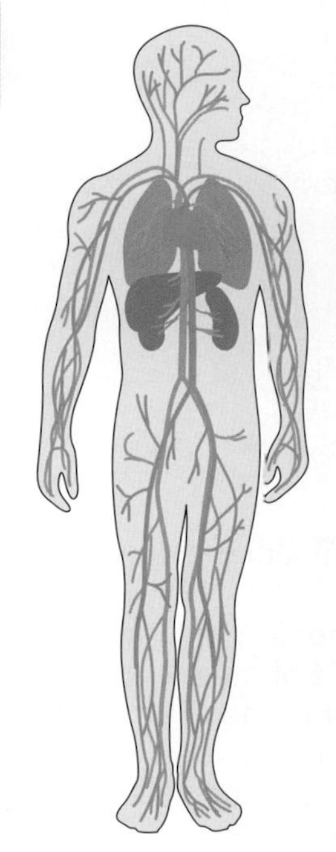

Your blood is carried around your body in tubes called **blood vessels**.
Your heart and blood vessels make up your **blood system**.
Your blood circulates round and round your body in your blood vessels.
So the blood system is often called the **circulatory system**.
What sort of things need to be carried round your body?

Your blood system transports some useful things like:
- oxygen from your lungs to your cells
- food from your gut to your cells.

It also has to remove waste chemicals like:
- carbon dioxide from your cells to your lungs
- waste chemicals from your liver to your kidneys.

Your blood system also transports chemicals like hormones, antibodies and blood proteins to all the cells of your body.

A problem of size

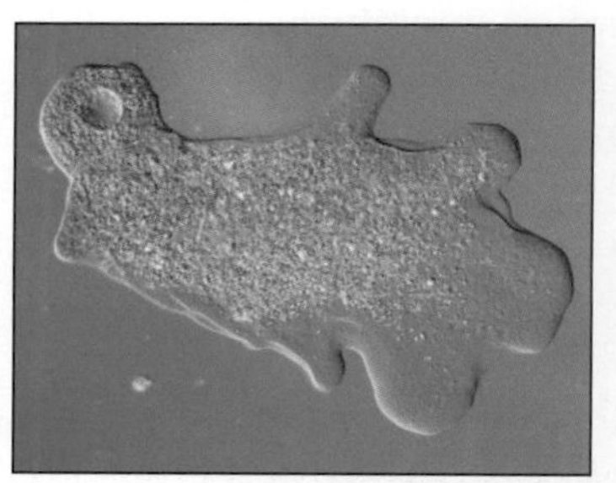

Amoeba

Many small animals do not need a blood system.
Microscopic organisms like Amoeba can get things such as oxygen just by diffusion.
They have a large surface area compared to their volume.
It is easy for things to diffuse in and out.

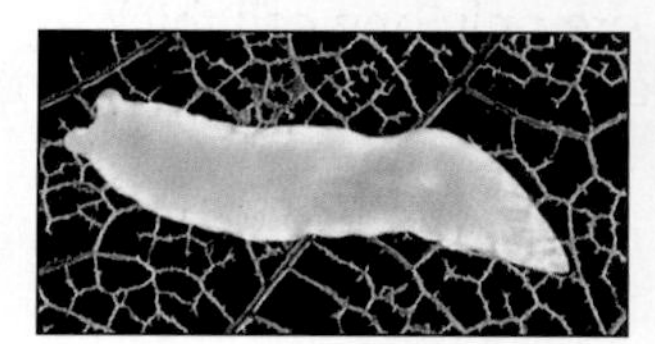

A flatworm

Even larger invertebrates like flatworms do not have blood vessels.
Their bodies are so flat that it is not far for gases and liquids to diffuse in and out.

So why do we need a transport system?
Larger animals can not just rely upon diffusion.
Our bodies are too large for materials to simply diffuse in and out.
It would take a molecule of oxygen days to diffuse from the outside to the centre of your brain!
We have a system of tubes and a pump to carry substances around our bodies quickly.

► Your circulation

At the centre of your blood system is your **heart**.
Its job is to pump the blood around your body.

The rest of the blood system is made up of tubes called **blood vessels**.
There are two main types.
Can you remember what they are called?

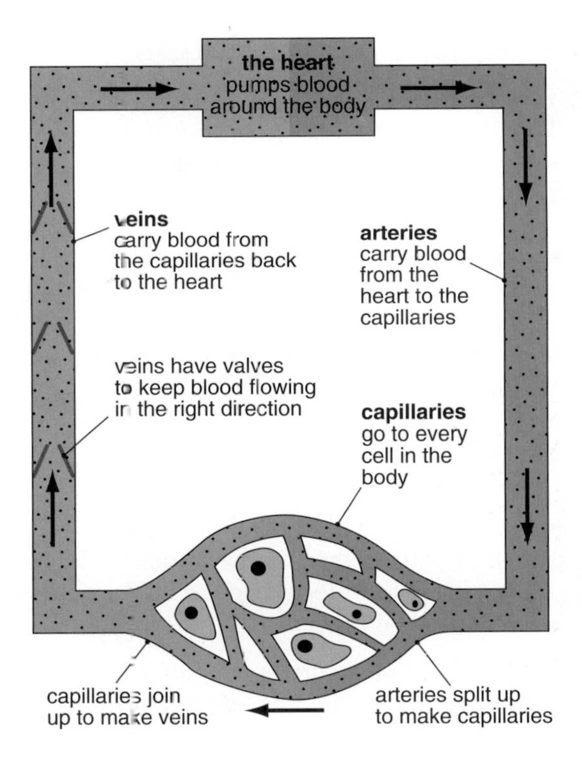

Arteries carry blood away from the heart.

Veins carry blood back to the heart.

When they get to an organ in your body, arteries branch many times.

The smallest branches are called **capillaries**.
The capillaries then join up to form veins.
It is in the capillaries that chemicals like oxygen, food and carbon dioxide pass into and out of the blood.

The circulatory system is like a one-way street.
Blood can only go in one direction.

What happens at capillaries?

The arteries branch many times until the smallest branches form capillaries.
These are very narrow and taper as they reach the body cells.
Here a red blood cell can only just squeeze through.

Blood flows through capillaries very slowly, so this gives time for exchange of materials to take place.
Capillary walls are only one cell thick.
Oxygen and food can easily pass out of the capillary to the cells.
Carbon dioxide and other waste chemicals can easily pass from the cells into the capillary.

It is estimated that there are over 80 000 km of these tiny tubes in your body.
That's a huge surface area for things to pass across!

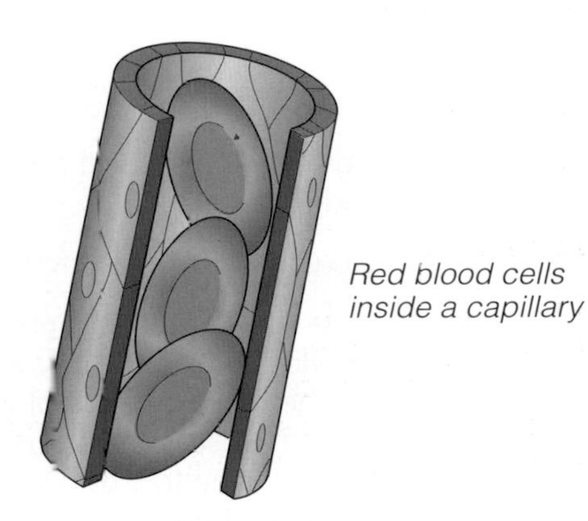

Red blood cells inside a capillary

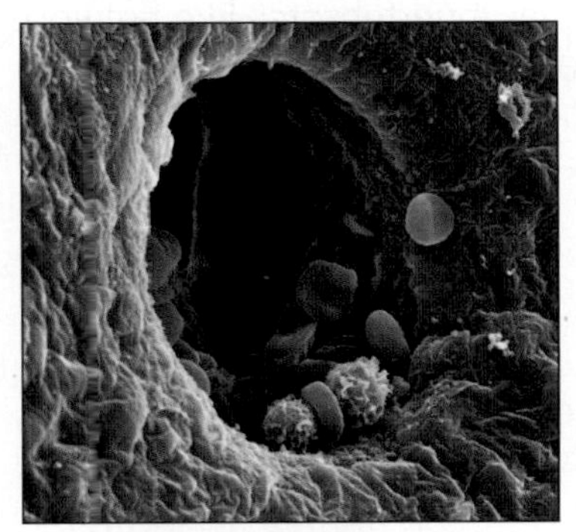

Scanning electron micrograph of red blood cells entering a capillary

▶ A double circulation

Your heart is divided into two halves : the ***right*** and the ***left***.
The blood in the right side does not mix with the blood in the left side.
So your circulation is really in two parts :

- The right side of your heart pumps blood to your lungs and then back to the heart again.
  How does the blood change when it gets to your lungs ?
  What does it pick up ? What does it drop off ?

  In your lungs the blood picks up oxygen.
  We say that it becomes **oxygenated**.
  The blood also gets rid of carbon dioxide.

- The left side of your heart pumps blood to the rest of your body and then back to the heart again.
  How does the blood change when it gets to your body cells ?
  What does it drop off ? What does it pick up ?

  The blood gives up its oxygen to your body cells.
  We say that it becomes **deoxygenated**.
  Carbon dioxide passes into the blood from the body cells.

lungs
right side of heart
left side of heart
the heart
rest of body

Look at the diagram :

How many times does the blood pass through the heart on one circuit of the body ?

That's why it's called a ***double*** circulation.

William Harvey was an English physician.
He used his knowledge of anatomy to make a unique discovery about the circulation of blood around the body.
As a result of careful observation and carrying out experiments, he was able to explain how blood moves around the body in a circle – travelling from the left side of the heart in arteries and then back to the right side of the heart in veins.

In 1623, he published his book *On the Motions of the Heart and Blood*. In it he showed how the evidence from his experiments disproved many of the long-held ideas of the time.

Harvey also predicted that there were thousands of tiny capillaries connecting arteries to veins, despite being unable to see them.

Why was Harvey unable to observe blood capillaries?

Harvey demonstrating the action of valves to a group of physicians in London

▶ Arteries

When your heart muscles contract they force the blood into your arteries.
What do you think the pressure of blood is like in the arteries?
Each beat of the heart pumps the blood along under high pressure.

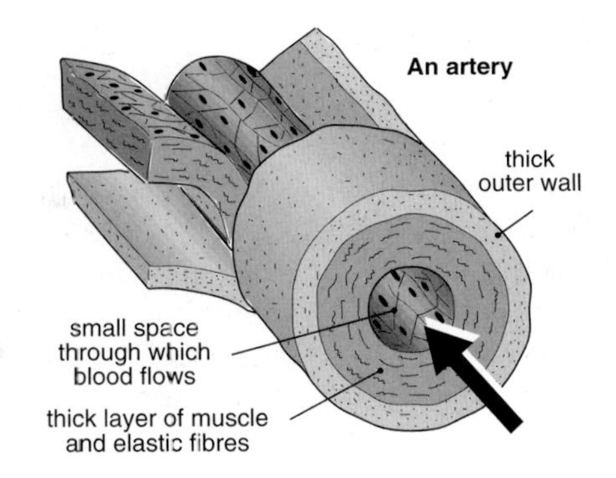

The artery walls are elastic and stretch to take the blood.
Then they contract and bounce back to force the blood along.
This bouncing back can be felt as a **'pulse'** as the blood flows through.

Experiment 6.1 Taking your pulse

Can you feel your pulse?
Try to feel an artery at your wrist or at the side of your neck.

The number of pulses per minute shows how fast your heart is beating.

How does your pulse rate compare with other people's?

What happens to your pulse rate when you exercise?
Plan an investigation into the effect of various types of exercise on pulse rate.

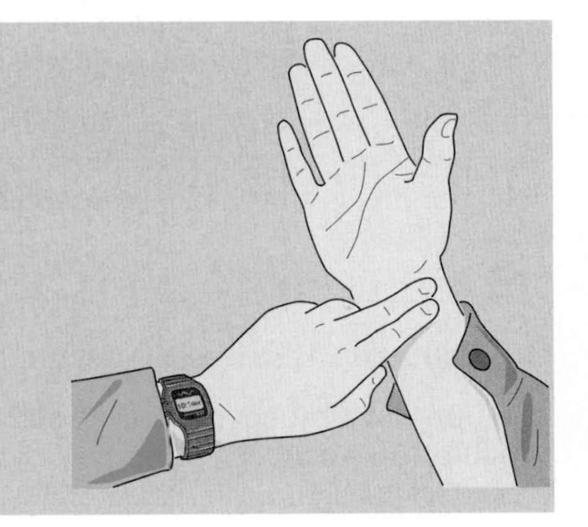

▶ Veins

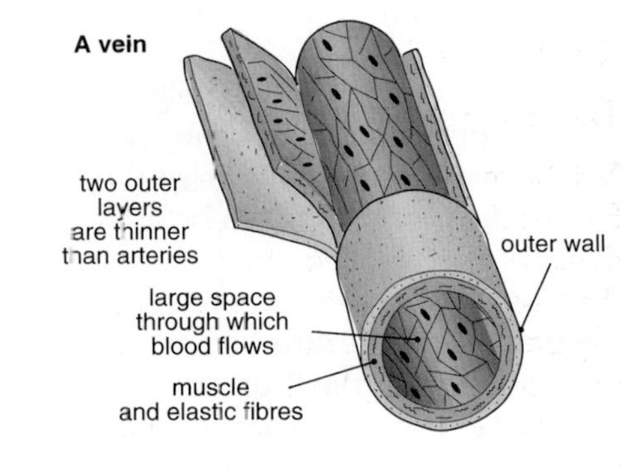

Capillaries join up to eventually form veins.
Veins are wider than arteries and have thinner walls.
The pressure inside veins is much lower.
So the blood flows much more slowly in them.
The blood is often squeezed along by your muscles.

The flow of blood in veins is helped by **valves**.
Valves are like double doors that will only open in one direction.
If you try to go back in the other direction the doors won't open.
Valves stop your blood from flowing backwards.

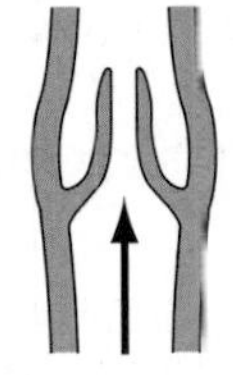

Valves open to let the blood flow towards the heart

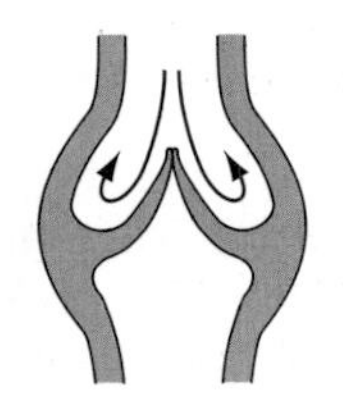

Valves close to stop blood flowing backwards

► Your heart

Your heart is nearly all muscle.
It has a big job to do.
It is the pump that circulates blood around your body.
Your heart beats about 70 times per minute – for a lifetime.
So it is just as well that your heart muscle never tires.

The double pump

Your heart is really two pumps side by side.
The right side of your heart is one pump.
The left side of your heart is another pump.

Each side is kept completely separate.
This way the deoxygenated blood on the right side does not mix with the oxygenated blood on the left side.

On each side of the heart there are two chambers.

The upper chambers are called **atria** (singular **atrium**).
Blood empties into them from veins.
When the atria contract they pump blood in to the lower chambers.

The lower chambers are called **ventricles**.
These have much more muscular walls.
When the ventricles contract they pump the blood out into arteries.

Between each atrium and ventricle is a **valve**.
What do you think that it is for?
The valve prevents the blood flowing back into the atrium when the ventricle contracts.

Why do you think that the ventricles have more muscular walls than the atria?
Do they have to pump the blood the same distance?
Why not?

The left ventricle has a more muscular wall than the right ventricle.
Does it have to pump the blood much further?

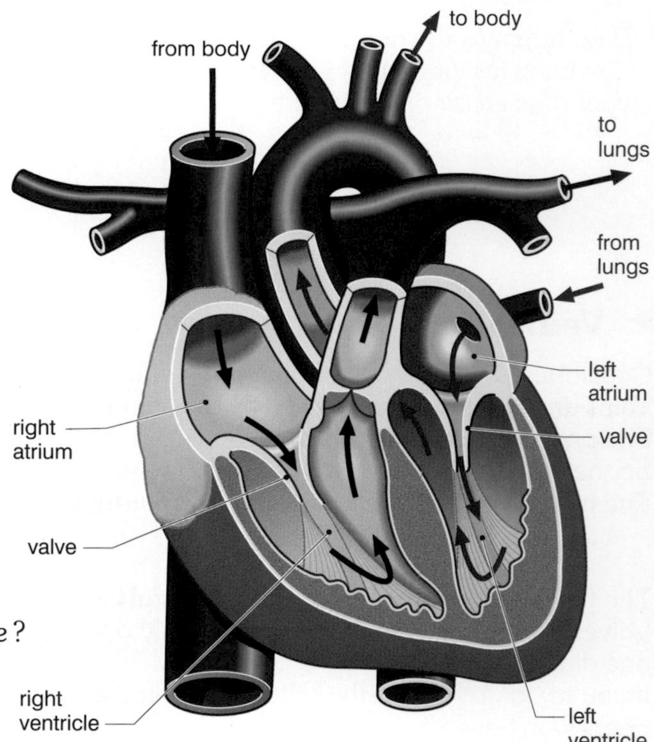

The arrows show how the blood moves through the heart

▶ Heart action

The heart pumps blood when its muscle contracts.

When the muscle contracts the chamber gets smaller and squeezes the blood out.

After each chamber contracts it relaxes.
So it fills up with blood again.

In perfect harmony

The two sides of the heart work together.
The atria contract and relax at the same time.
The ventricles contract and relax at the same time.

Diastole is when the heart muscles are relaxed.
Blood flows into the atria from the veins.

Systole is when the heart muscles contract.

- First the atria contract and force the blood into the ventricles.
  The valves between the atria and ventricles open due to the pressure of blood against them.
- Then the ventricles contract.
  They force the blood out into the arteries.
  The valves close to prevent blood from flowing back into the atria.

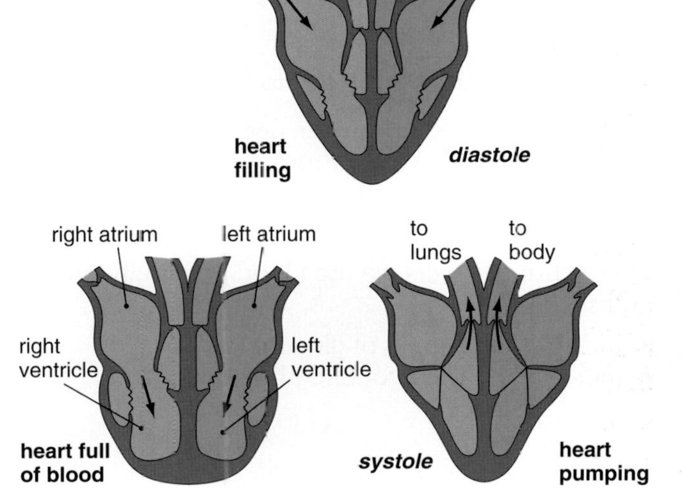

The **right ventricle** pumps blood to the **lungs** in the **pulmonary artery**.

The **left ventricle** pumps blood to the rest of the **body** in the **aorta** (main artery).

Deoxygenated blood returns to the **right atrium** in the **vena cava** (main vein).

Oxygenated blood returns to the **left atrium** in the **pulmonary vein**.

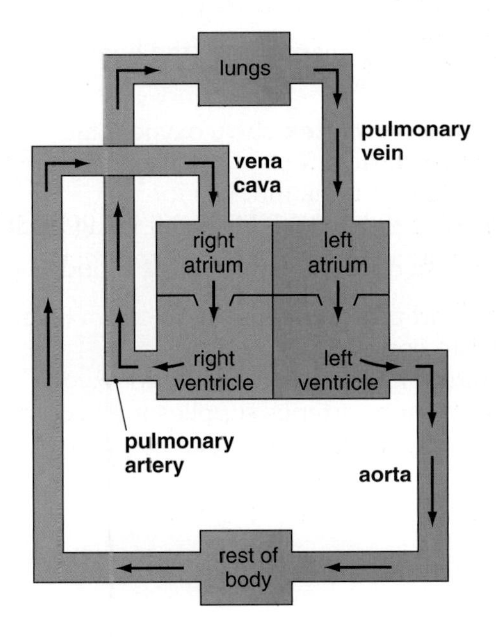

► Control of heartbeat

If the heart was removed from the body it would continue to beat!
What does this tell you about what makes the heart beat?

The beating of the heart is controlled by the **pacemaker**.
This is a group of cells in the right atrium.
The pacemaker sends electrical messages to the heart muscle.
These messages stimulate the heart muscle to contract.

The pacemaker also receives information from the brain.
Some nerves slow down the heart rate, others speed it up.
So the brain is able to adjust the heart rate to the needs of the body.

What might cause your heart to beat faster?

During exercise your muscles need more energy from respiration in order to contract.
So your heart beats faster and the arteries supplying the muscles **dilate** (widen).

These changes increase the blood flow to the muscles and so:

- increase the supply of glucose and oxygen
- increase the removal of carbon dioxide

Regular exercise makes for a healthy heart

The heart's blood supply

Despite being full of blood, the heart needs a blood supply of its own.

Coronary arteries carry oxygenated blood to the heart muscle.

Why does the heart muscle need a good oxygen supply?

What else does it need from the blood to give energy?

The heart muscle needs energy from respiration in order to contract.
Respiration requires glucose and oxygen.
The coronary arteries supplies the heart muscle with both glucose and oxygen.

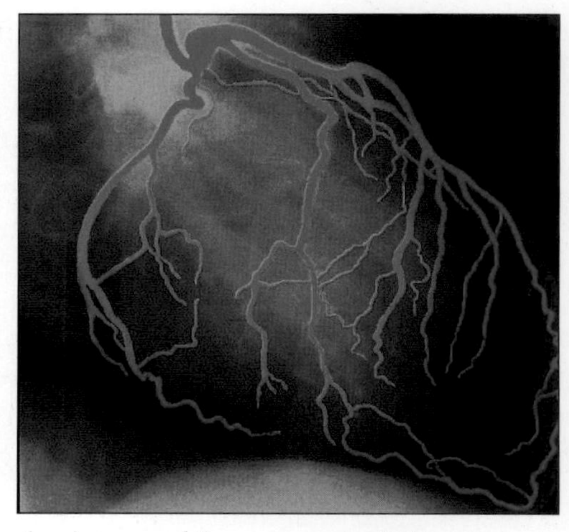

Angiogram of the coronary arteries

▶ Heart disease

What might happen if a coronary artery became blocked?

The oxygen supply to the heart muscle would be cut off.
This could cause a **coronary heart attack**.
If the heart muscle is starved of oxygen then it will die.
If the damage to the heart muscle is extensive, then the person may die.

However, many people survive heart attacks, with treatment followed by adjustment to their lifestyles.

Heart disease causes a quarter of all deaths in Britain.
It is the biggest single killer of middle-aged men in the developed world.

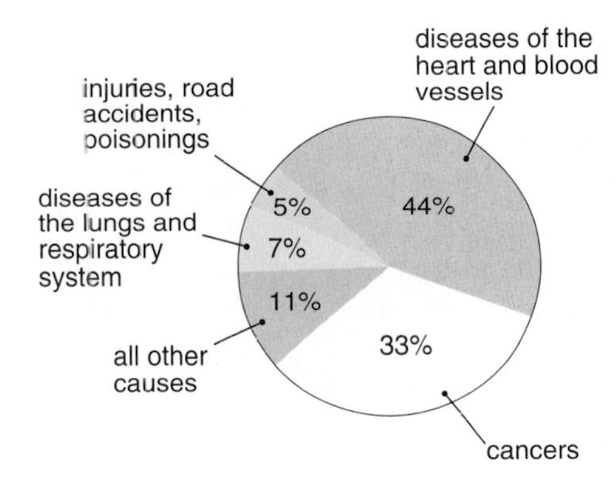

Causes of death in people under 75 in the UK (total deaths = 267 500)

Slowing the flow

Healthy arteries have a smooth lining.
They let the blood flow through easily.

A chemical called cholesterol, made in the liver and found in the diet, can stick to the walls.
This can narrow the artery and slow down the flow of blood.

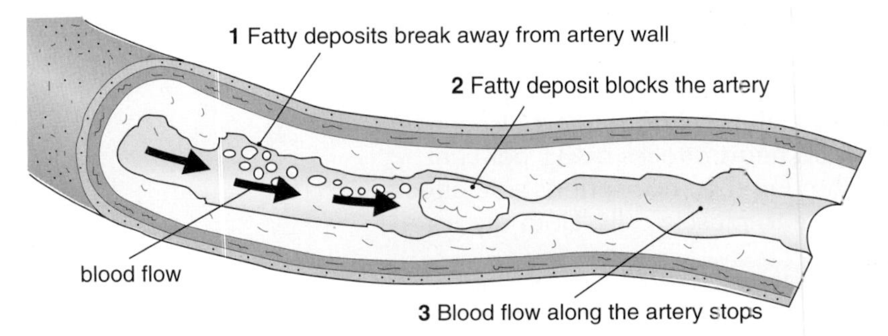

The artery walls can become rough.
This can cause the blood to clot and block the vessel.
The blockage is called a **thrombosis**.

Narrowing of the coronary artery causes serious problems:

- If the coronary artery gets partly blocked it can cause chest pains, especially if activity or emotion makes the heart work harder.
  This is called **angina**.
  It is caused by not enough oxygen getting to the heart muscle.
  Angina should act as a warning to the sufferer.
- A total blockage or thrombosis can cause a heart attack.
  The supply of oxygen is cut off.
  It causes a severe pain in the chest.
  The affected part of the heart is damaged.

The heart may stop beating altogether – this is called **cardiac arrest**.
Death will follow unless the heart starts beating again within minutes.

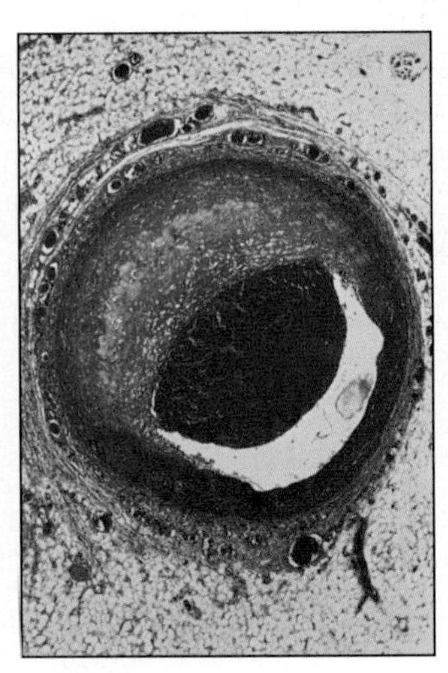

A blocked artery in section

Risk factors

Risk factors are things that are thought to increase the chances of getting heart disease.
Some of them you can't avoid like :

- ***Inherited genes*** – heart disease tends to run in families.
- ***Age*** – the chances of getting heart disease increase with age.
- ***Sex*** – men are more likely to get heart disease than women.

Some of the other risk factors you can do something about are :

- ***Eating fatty foods*** – these can increase cholesterol in the blood.
- ***Being over-weight***.
- ***Smoking.***
- ***Taking little or no exercise***.

Avoiding heart disease

- ***Take care of your diet :***
  - Eat more poultry and fish – they are less fatty.
  - Cut down on fried foods.
  - Eat less red meat.
  - Eat more fresh fruit and vegetables.
- ***Take some regular exercise***.
- ***Do not smoke***.

Statins are heart drugs that were invented 20 years ago. They have been proved to cut death rates from heart disease by 28 per cent and further non-fatal heart attacks by 31 per cent. Their development has been hindered by two serious side effects: irritation of the liver and damage to muscle cells. Both are rare.

Experiment 6.2 Dissecting a sheep's heart

Look at a dissected sheep's heart.
(The heart is cut open by two vertical cuts, one through the left atrium and ventricle, the other through the right atrium and ventricle.)

Notice the differences in the thickness of the walls.

If the blood vessels are still intact, try to find out which is which.

Look for the coronary vessels on the surface.

Look inside for :

- the valves between the atria and the ventricles,
- the valves at the base of the pulmonary artery and aorta.

Try running a stream of water against the valves. Do they open ? How does this help the heart ?

Wash your hands with soap and water when you have finished.

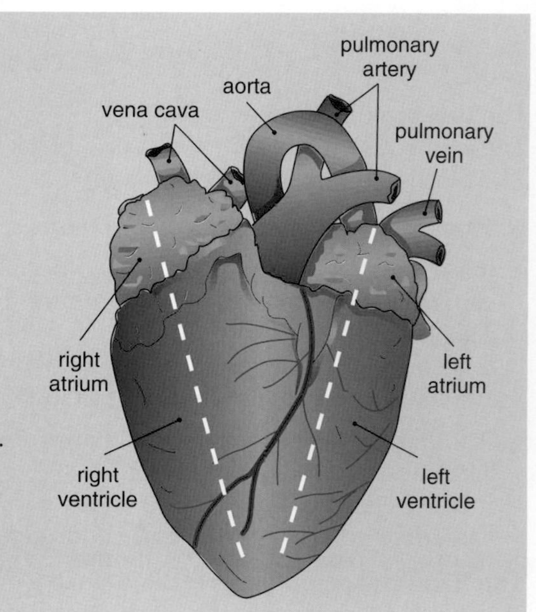

▶ Your blood

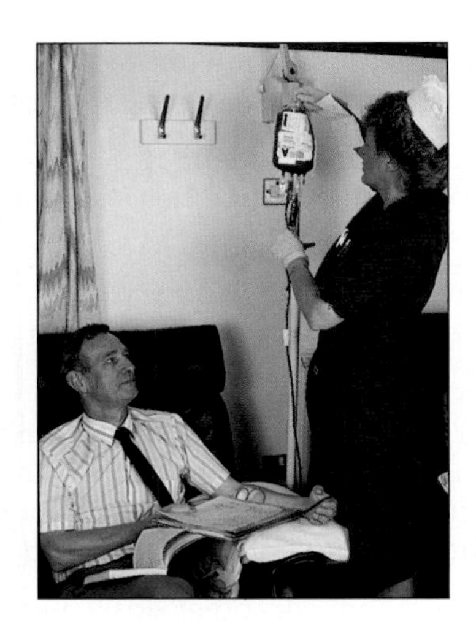

If someone has an accident or a major operation,
they often lose a lot of blood.
The blood is vital for life.
It has to be replaced quickly.
The person has to have a **blood transfusion**.
(For more about blood transfusions see Biology at Work, page 93.)

So why is your blood so important to you?

Your blood does two important things:

- it transports things from one part of your body to another.
- it helps to protect your body from disease.

What's blood made of?

You have about 5 litres of blood in your body.
That's a bucket full.
Blood looks like a red liquid, but there's more to it than that.

What happens if you leave a sample of blood to stand?

Look at the test-tubes:

Can you see it has separated into two parts?

- The yellow liquid is called **plasma**.
  It is mainly water with chemicals dissolved in it.
  Some of these are:
  - Food, such as sugars, amino acids, vitamins and minerals.
  - Chemical waste like urea.
  - Blood proteins like antibodies.
  - Hormones – chemicals that control things like our growth.

- At the bottom of the test-tube the cells
  have settled out.

  There are three main types of blood cells:
  - Red cells have no nucleus.
    They look red because they have a red pigment
    called **haemoglobin**.
  - White cells do have a nucleus.
    There are two main types:
    lymphocytes and **phagocytes**.
    White cells do not have haemoglobin
    so they don't look red.
  - **Platelets** are tiny bits of cells.

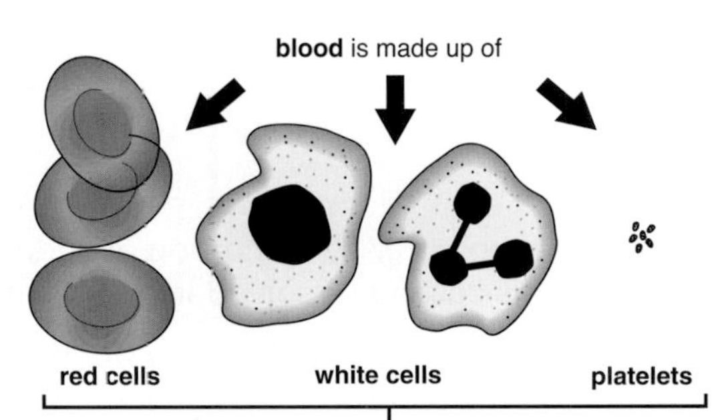

▶ Red cells

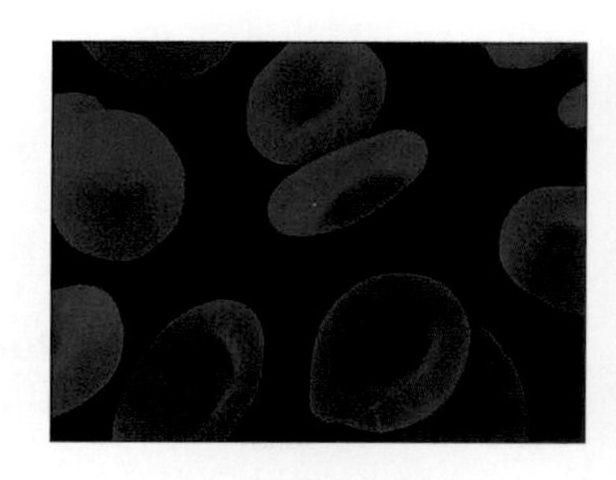

There are about a million red cells in each drop of blood.
They are made in the bone marrow.

Red cells carry oxygen.
How does their shape help them to do this?

Red cells are disc-shaped with the middle pushed in.
They have a large surface area to volume ratio.
This helps them to absorb a lot of oxygen.

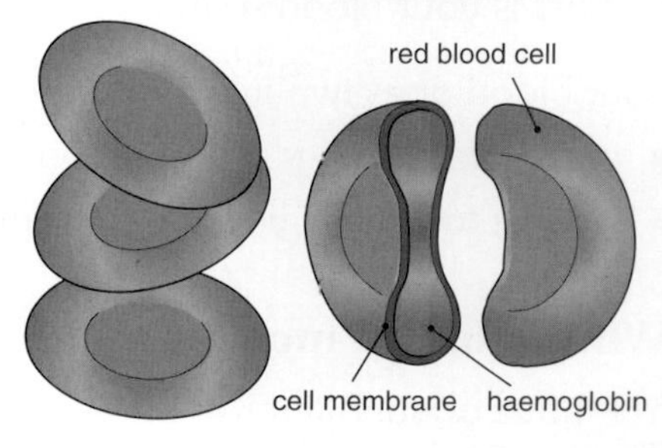

Red cells have no nucleus.
Instead the cell is filled with **haemoglobin**.
This is a special protein that contains iron.
You must have enough iron in your diet to make
enough haemoglobin for your red cells.

Haemoglobin combines easily with oxygen.
It forms **oxyhaemoglobin**.

Haemoglobin + oxygen ⟶ oxyhaemoglobin

Look at the diagram:

Where does oxyhaemoglobin form?
Where does oxyhaemoglobin break down to give
oxygen and haemoglobin?

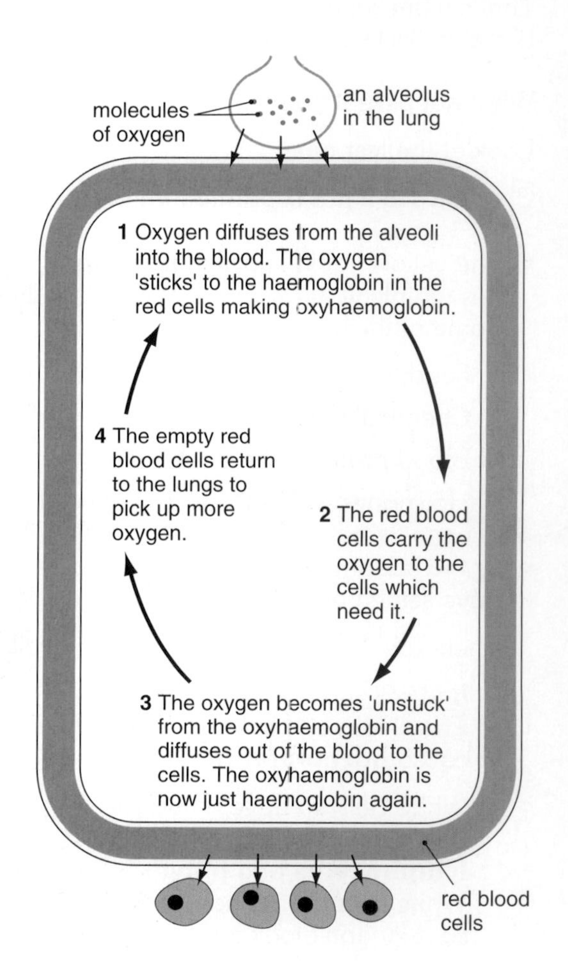

Demonstration 6.3 Transporting gases in the blood

Your teacher will give you some blood that is safe to use.
Pour equal amounts into two boiling-tubes A and B.
Bubble oxygen through tube A and carbon dioxide
through tube B.

- Why does the blood in A go bright red?
- Does the blood in tube B have less oxygen?

Now try bubbling oxygen through the blood in tube B
and carbon dioxide through the blood in tube A.
Try to explain your observations.
Wash your hands with soap and water
when you have finished.

CO_2 too!

The red cells also carry some carbon dioxide.
But most of it is carried dissolved in the plasma.

Where do you think carbon dioxide ***enters*** the blood?
Where do you think carbon dioxide ***leaves*** the blood?

▶ White cells

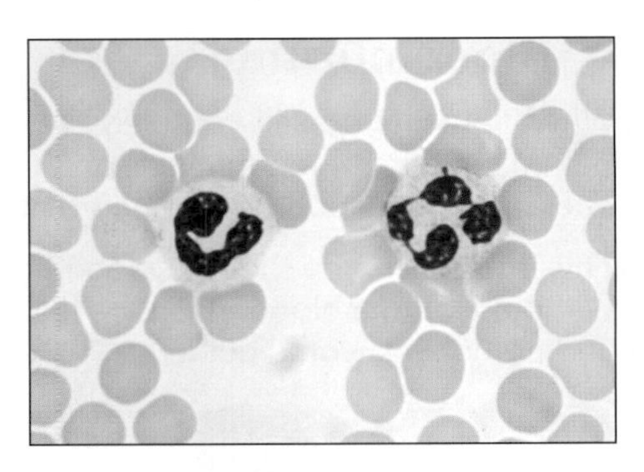

The white cells fight disease.
There are far fewer of them than red cells.
They also look different.
Can you see how they are different?

White cells are not disc-shaped.
They do not have haemoglobin.
They do have a nucleus.

Like red cells, the white cells are made in the bone marrow.
Their job is to protect the body from any pathogens that get into the blood.
The two types of white cells do this in different ways.

Lymphocytes

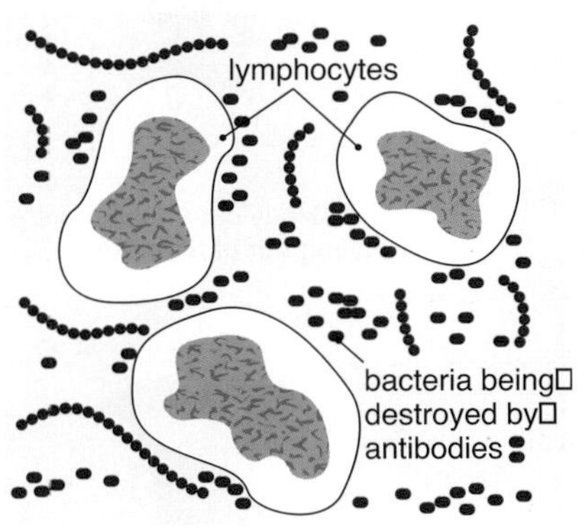

When a bacterium or virus enters the body the white cells recognise that it is 'foreign' and should not be there.
The lymphocytes make chemicals called **antibodies**.
These attack the pathogens in a number of ways:

- They make them stick together.
- They dissolve them.
- They destroy the toxins (poisons) that the pathogens make.

After you have had a disease the antibodies stay in your blood.
They make you **immune** to the disease.
There is a different antibody for each type of pathogen.
You can learn more about immunity in Chapter 10.

Phagocytes

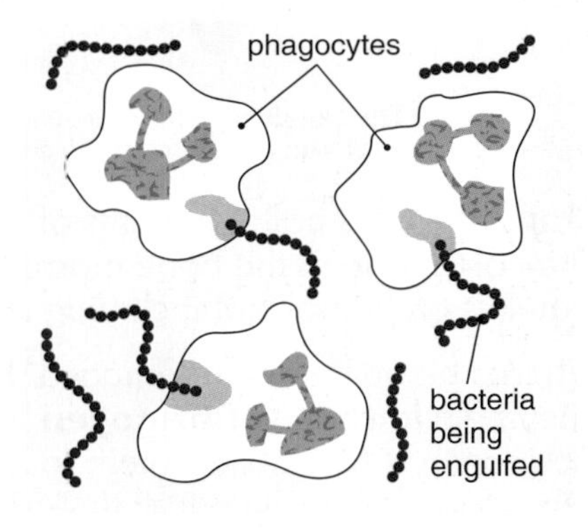

These are the 'cell-eaters'. They engulf or swallow up pathogens and take them into the cell. They then digest them and kill them.

When pathogens invade the body white cells move towards them.
They can squeeze through capillary walls.

Experiment 6.4 Making a blood smear

Your teacher will give you some blood that is safe to use.

Put a few drops on one end of a microscope slide.
Use another slide to draw the blood over the surface.
This gives a **blood smear**.

When it is dry put a few drops of Leishman's stain on the smear. After 5 minutes wash the stain off.

When it is dry, look at your slide under the microscope.
Identify and draw any white blood cells.

When you have finished, dispose of your slide into a beaker of disinfectant.

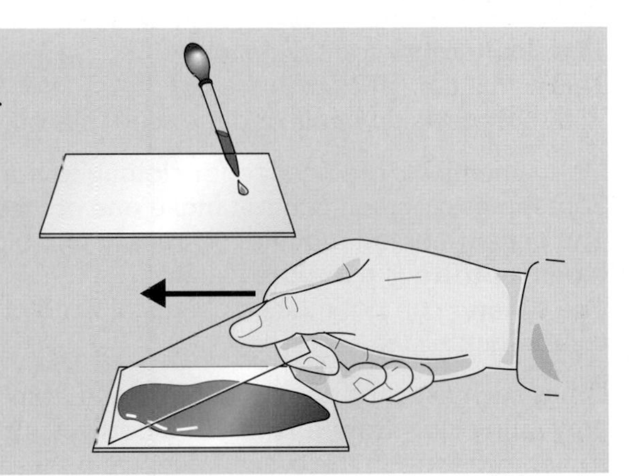

► Blood clotting

When you cut yourself you bleed.
Before long the blood thickens and the bleeding stops.
The thickened blood has formed a **clot**.

This is another way that the blood fights disease.
Without clotting, blood would be lost
and pathogens would get in.

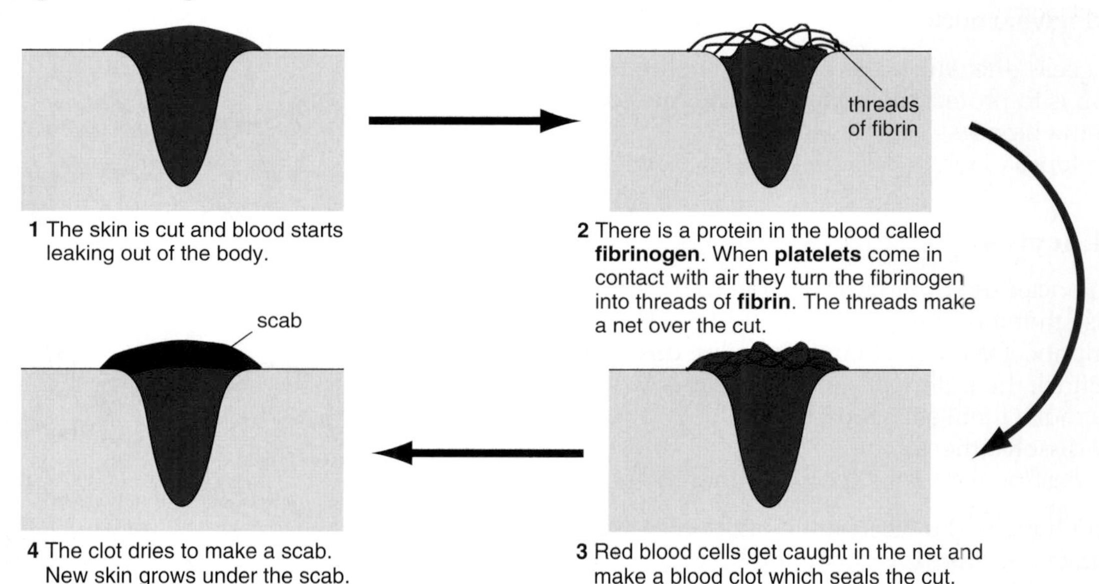

1 The skin is cut and blood starts leaking out of the body.

2 There is a protein in the blood called **fibrinogen**. When **platelets** come in contact with air they turn the fibrinogen into threads of **fibrin**. The threads make a net over the cut.

3 Red blood cells get caught in the net and make a blood clot which seals the cut.

4 The clot dries to make a scab. New skin grows under the scab.

Platelets are small fragments of cells.
They are made in the bone marrow like the other blood cells.
Platelets are important if clotting is to take place.

When a blood vessel is damaged the platelets start work.
They help to change **fibrinogen** to **fibrin**.
Fibrinogen is a soluble protein found in the plasma.
Fibrin forms a meshwork of threads.
Red cells get trapped in the threads to make the clot.

The clot hardens to make a scab.
This keeps the cut clean.
With time the skin heals and the scab falls off.

Many chemicals are needed for clotting to happen.
Sometimes a person can not make one of these chemicals.
The person's blood may not clot easily and blood is lost.
Haemophilia is a disease like this.
The sufferer can not make a chemical needed for clotting called Factor 8.

Drugs such as warfarin and heparin can 'thin the blood' preventing clots from forming in blood vessels. Clots can sometimes form in the case of deep vein thrombosis (DVT).

Red cells caught in fibrin threads

► The circulator

Your blood transports things around your body.
Let's remind ourselves what's carried where :

What it carries	Where it carried it	How it carries it
oxygen	from the lungs to the rest of the body	in the red cells
carbon dioxide	from the body to the lungs	in the plasma
dissolved food	from the gut to the rest of the body	in the plasma
urea	from the liver to the kidneys	in the plasma
hormones	from the hormone glands to the rest of the body	in the plasma
heat	from the liver and muscles to the rest of the body	in all parts of the blood

How do these things get into and out of the blood?

Exchange at the capillaries

The capillaries are the smallest blood vessels.
What else can you remember about them?

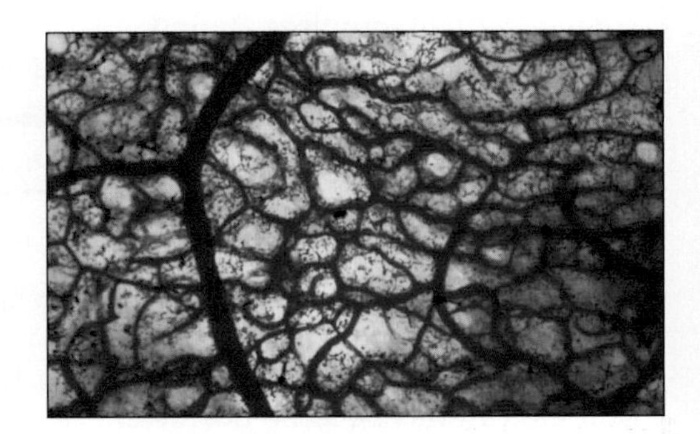

Here are a few things about capillaries :

- they have very thin walls
- they have large a surface area
- body cells are never far from a capillary
- blood flows through them very slowly.

Each of these things helps substances pass into and out of cells easily.
In each case try to explain why.

Tissue fluid

Plasma leaks out through the capillary walls.
It surrounds the body cells.
It is now called **tissue fluid**.
Tissue fluid helps substances to ***diffuse*** into and out of cells.

Useful substances pass from the tissue fluid to the cells.
What do you think these are?

Waste chemicals pass from the cells into the tissue fluid.
What do you think these are?

Most of the tissue fluid then passes back into the blood capillaries.

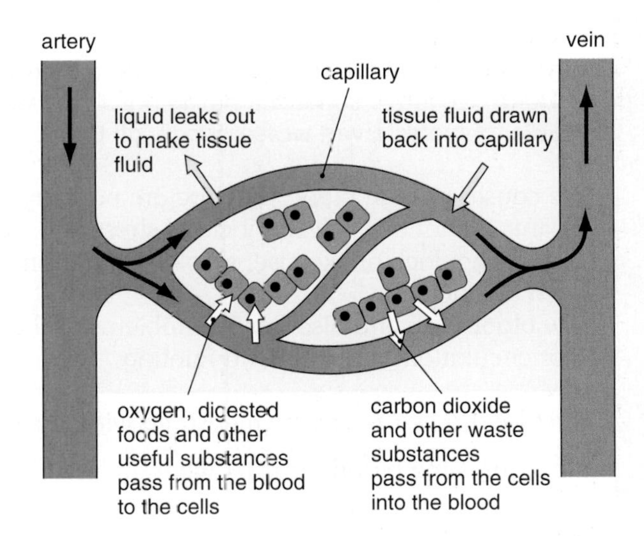

▶ Biology at work : Artificial pacemaker and blood pressure

Artificial pacemaker

Disease and ageing can affect the pacemaker in the heart.
The heartbeat can become too slow.
The artificial pacemaker works by mimicking the natural pacemaker in the heart.

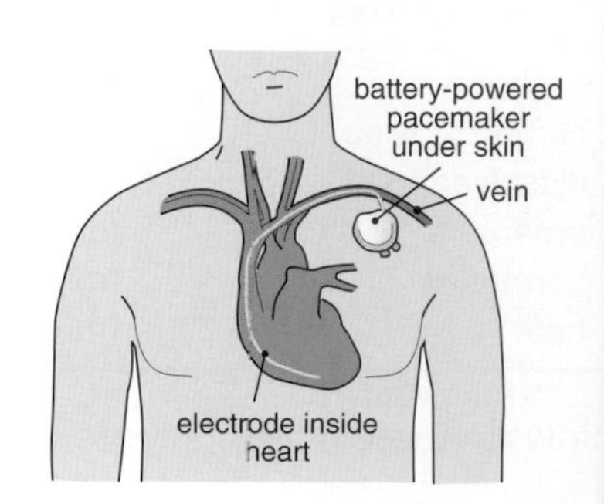

The artificial pacemaker consists of a pulse generator and two leads or electrodes.
It can be implanted under the patient's skin, on the chest wall.
The electrodes are connected to the right atrium and right ventricle through a vein.
Each electrode can sense the electrical activity of the heart muscle.

If the heart misses a beat, the artificial pacemaker generates small electrical impulses.
These stimulate the atria and ventricles telling them to contract.

Blood pressure

The pumping heart produces a high pressure in your arteries.
We call this the **blood pressure**.
It rises if you do anything to make your heart beat faster, or if the arteries become narrower.

Constant high blood pressure is harmful.
It puts a strain on the heart and makes it work harder.
It can also cause an artery to burst open.
If this happens in the brain it can cause a **stroke**.
A stroke can leave someone partly paralysed and unable to speak. Even worse, it can kill them.

The causes of high blood pressure are not fully understood.
But things that can affect it include stress and tension, over-eating, lack of exercise, smoking and drinking too much alcohol.
Low blood pressure also has its problems and can result in poor circulation, dizziness and fainting.

The blood pressure can be measured with this instrument :

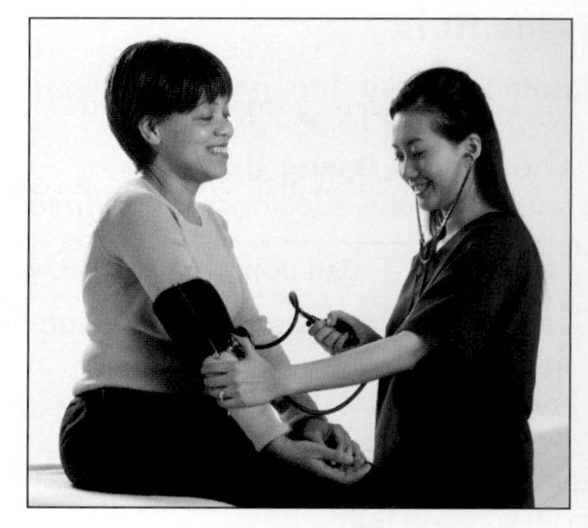

Measuring someone's blood pressure

It measures the blood pressure when the heart contracts and when it relaxes.
The first figure is put over the second to give a fraction.
A healthy young adult's blood pressure is about 120/75 mmHg.

► Biology at work : Blood transfusions

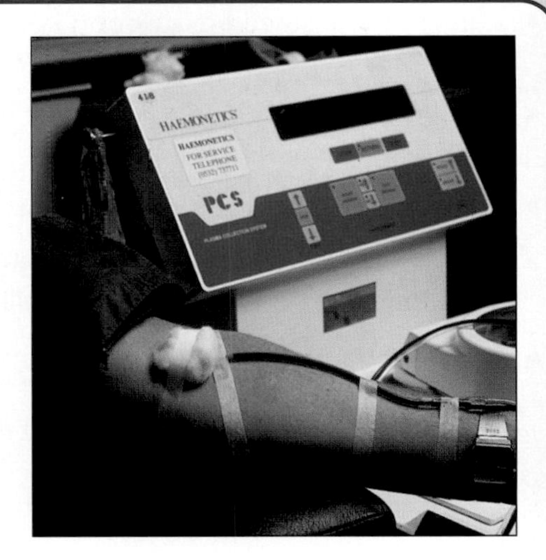

People who are ill or injured may need a blood transfusion.
The blood drains into a vein in the arm from a plastic bag.

But not just any blood will do.
If someone is given blood of the wrong group it may make their red cells stick together.
This can be fatal if blood vessels become blocked.

The main **blood groups** are called **A, B, AB** and **O**.

Your blood group is determined by the **antigens** present on your red cells.

There are two types of antigens : **A** and **B**.

People with blood group **A** have **A** antigens only.

People with blood group **B** have **B** antigens only.

Blood group **AB** has both **A** and **B** antigens.

Blood group **O** has neither **A** nor **B** antigens.

In the plasma there are **antibodies**.
But these antibodies do not attack antigens on their ***own*** red cells.

For instance, the antibodies in blood group A plasma do not attack the A antigens on blood group A red cells, but they will attack B antigens.

The antibodies in group B plasma do not attack the B antigens on blood group B red cells, but they will attack A antigens.

The antibodies in group AB plasma do not attack the A or B antigens on blood group AB cells.

The antibodies in group O will attack both A and B antigens.

The table shows which groups are safe for transfusion :

Group	Can donate to	Can receive from
A	A and AB	A and O
B	B and AB	B and O
AB	AB	all groups
O	all groups	O

To which blood groups can group O donate their blood?
Group O people are called universal donors.

From which blood groups can group AB receive blood?
Group AB people are called universal recipients.

Summary

- Larger animals need a transport system to circulate chemicals around the body.
- Arteries carry the blood to the body cells. Veins return blood to the heart.
- Capillaries link up arteries and veins.
- Chemicals are exchanged between the blood and the body cells across capillaries.
- The heart is our muscular pump that keeps our blood circulating. Both sides of the heart contract and relax at the same time.
- The blood is made up of plasma, red cells, white cells and platelets. Red cells carry oxygen around the body. White cells protect us from pathogens. Platelets are involved in the process of blood clotting. The plasma transports carbon dioxide, dissolved food, urea, hormones and blood proteins.
- Tissue fluid leaks out of the blood at capillaries. It enables exchange of materials to take place efficiently.

▶ Questions

1. Copy and complete :
Blood is pumped around the body by a muscular . . . . .
Blood travels away from the heart in . . . . .
These contract and . . . . the blood along. This can be felt as a . . . . .
Blood returns to the heart in the . . . . . These have . . . . walls than arteries.
Blood is prevented from flowing backwards in them by . . . . .

2. Look at the diagram of the blood :

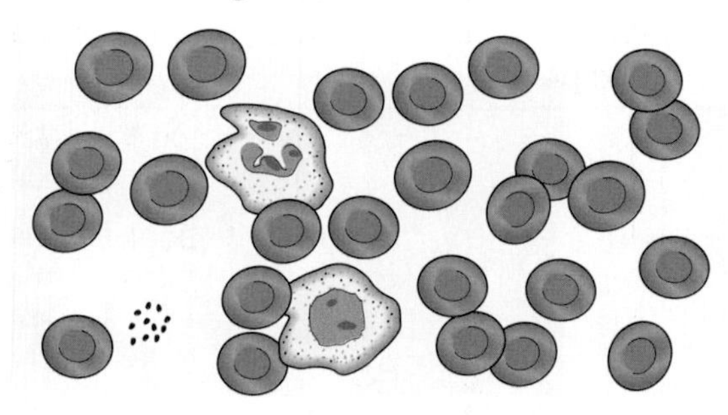

a) Name three ways in which the white blood cells are different from the red blood cells.
b) Name two things about red cells that adapt them for carrying oxygen.
c) What are the two types of white cell? Explain how they act to protect the body from disease.

3. Look at the diagram of the human heart in section :

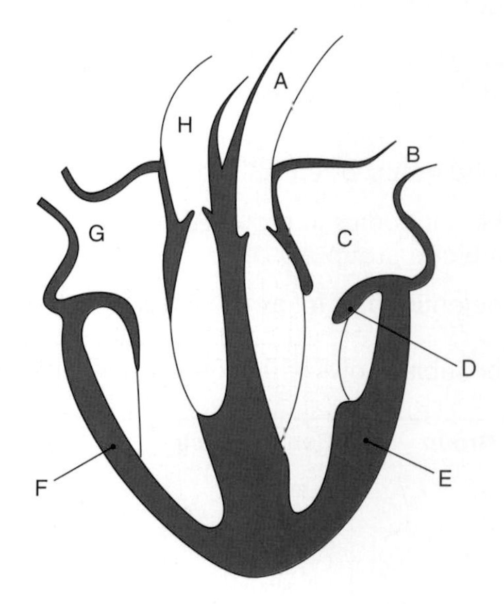

a) Name the parts labelled A to H.
b) Why do you think that E is thicker than F?
c) What is the function of D?
d) Which side of the heart carries oxygenated blood?

4. Look at the diagram of the heart:

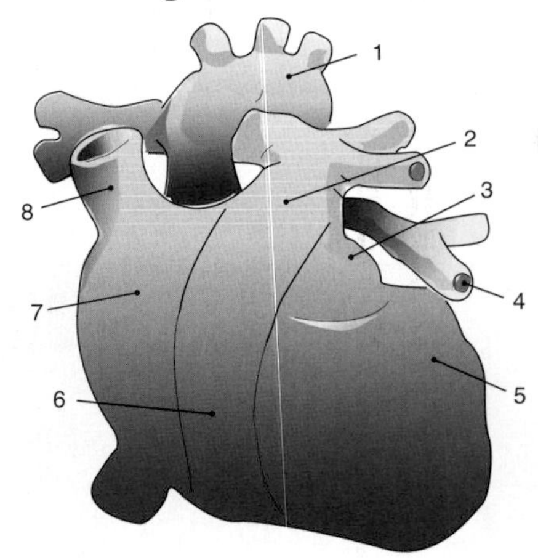

a) Label the parts 1 to 8.
b) Which two blood vessels in the diagram carry oxygenated blood?
c) In which blood vessel is the blood under the greatest pressure?
d) Which part of the heart contracts to send blood to the lungs?

5. a) What happens to the heart during:
i) diastole ii) systole
b) Explain how the heart is able to control the actions in i) and ii) above.

6. The graph shows the change in pressure in the ventricles during a heartbeat.

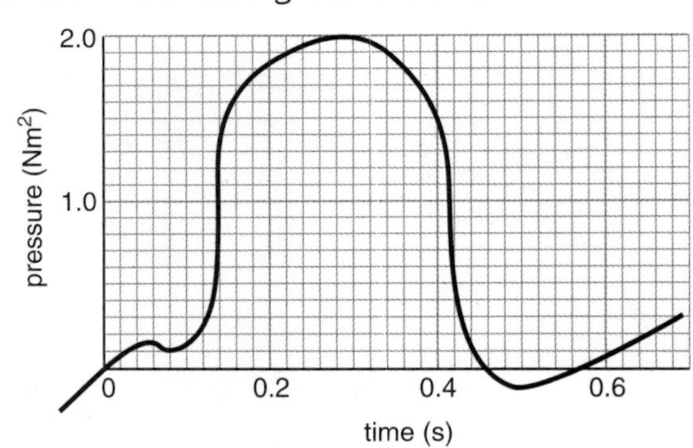

a) What is the maximum pressure in the ventricles?
b) How are the ventricles able to produce this high pressure?
c) Why is this important?
d) At what time is the pressure falling most rapidly?
e) What is causing this drop in pressure?

7. The diagram shows a blood capillary lying next to some muscle cells:

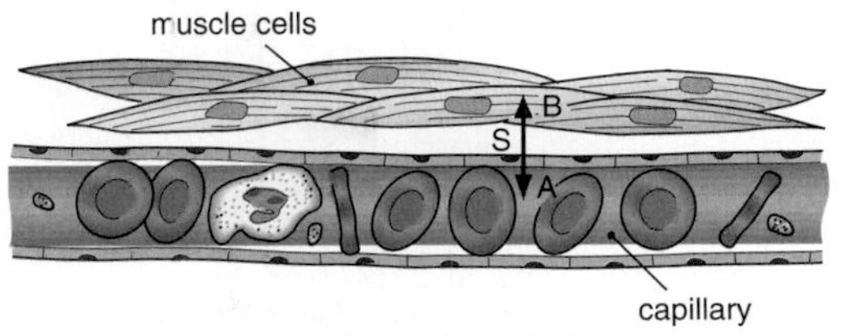

a) What fluid is found in S?
b) Name two substances that would pass from A to B.
c) Name two substances that would pass from B to A.
d) What is the capillary wall like to enable this to happen?

8. Copy and complete the table:

Arteries	Capillaries	Veins
Carry blood .... from the heart	Connect .... and	Carry blood .... the heart
Have a .... wall	Walls are very	Have a .... wall
Blood flows through at .... pressure	Low pressure allows exchange of materials	Blood flows through at .... pressure
No	No	Valves stop backflow of blood

9. At high altitude there is less oxygen in the air. People who live at altitude make more red cells to get what oxygen they can from the air. The table shows the parts of the blood of three people:

	Person A	Person B	Person C
red cells (mm^3)	7 500 000	5 000 000	2 000 000
white cells (mm^3)	5000	6 000	5 000
platelets (mm^3)	250 000	255 000	500

a) Which person lives at high altitude? Give a reason for your choice.
b) Which person is suffering from anaemia (lack of iron)? Give a reason for your choice.
c) Which person has blood that will not clot properly? Give a reason for your choice.

Further questions on page 171.

chapter 7

Homeostasis

Have you ever cooked something in an oven?

You turn the dial to the temperature that you want.
When it reaches that temperature, you put in whatever you are cooking.
You don't have to re-adjust the temperature.
It keeps more or less the same.

How do you think that this happens?

Inside the oven there is a **thermostat**.
It keeps the oven at the temperature you want.

If the thermostat detects that the oven is getting too hot, it switches the heater off.
The oven temperature drops.

If the temperature falls too low then the thermostat switches the heater back on again.
The oven temperature rises again.

This is an example of **negative feedback**.
Information about the oven temperature is fed back to the thermostat.
It acts by either switching the heater on or off.

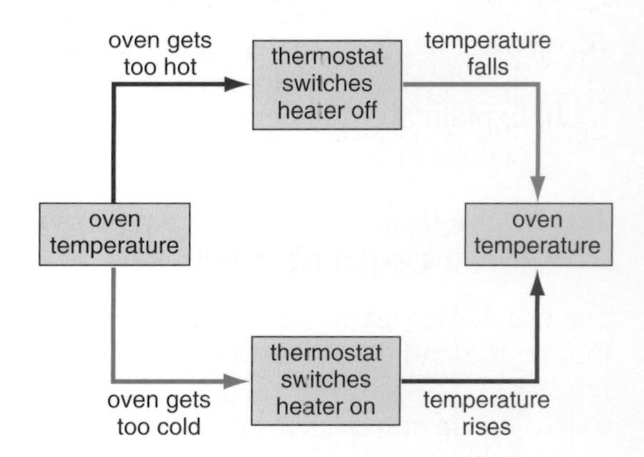

Negative feedback systems are at work in the body.
If conditions in the body change, e.g. your temperature rises, the body reacts to reverse the change, e.g. it brings about a fall in your temperature, returning it to normal.

Keeping things steady

Many chemical reactions are going on inside your body.
Molecules are being built up and broken down in your cells.
Can you remember what controls these reactions?

Enzymes work best in particular conditions.
Can you remember what they are?

Any slight change in the conditions can slow down or stop the enzyme from working.
It is important that things like temperature, pH and water content are kept as steady as possible.

▶ Controlling conditions

Keeping conditions steady inside the body is called **homeostasis**.
Which part of the body do you think acts as the thermostat ?

The brain has overall control of our body processes.
When blood flows through the brain, it checks :

- the temperature
- the concentration of chemicals, such as carbon dioxide.

So what happens if the temperature of the blood reaching the brain is too high ?
It sends out messages along nerves to parts of the body that lower our temperature. For instance, we start to sweat.

Can you guess what happens if we get too cold ?
The brain detects the blood temperature again.
This time it sends out messages along nerves to parts of the body that raise our temperature.
So this time we would stop sweating.

The control of body temperature is an example of homeostasis.
Our blood is providing the negative feedback to our brain.

normal body temperature → blood gets too hot → brain switches on cooling mechanisms → blood temperature falls → normal body temperature

normal body temperature → blood gets too cold → brain switches on warming mechanisms → blood temperature rises → normal body temperature

Exercise makes us sweat

▶ Other control systems

The best temperature for the body is 37 °C.
But what about other conditions ?

- Our ***blood sugar*** level has to be kept constant.
  It has to be carefully controlled by our liver and pancreas.
- Our ***water level*** is controlled by our kidneys.
- The ***pH*** of our blood is kept constant at 7.4.
  Our kidneys control this by getting rid of excess ions.
- The ***carbon dioxide*** concentration of the blood is controlled by our lungs.

All these things rely on negative feedback if they are to be kept constant.

The brain controls many conditions in the body

▶ Controlling blood sugar

Your body cells need glucose for energy.
They need it in controlled amounts.

What happens when you eat a high carbohydrate meal ?
Your blood glucose can go up 20 times.
But it does not stay high.

Special cells in your ***pancreas*** detect the high glucose level in your blood.
The pancreas makes a hormone called **insulin**.
The insulin tells the liver to take glucose out of your blood.
It is changed into **glycogen** in the liver.
So insulin ***lowers*** your blood glucose level back to normal.

A high-carbohydrate meal

What happens when you run a race or carry out some other type of exercise ?
Your muscles use up lots of glucose.
Your blood sugar level falls.
But it does not keep falling.

This time your pancreas makes another hormone called **glucagon**.
When this gets into your blood, it travels to your liver.
Glucagon tells the liver to break the glycogen down to glucose again.
The glucose is released into the blood.
So glucagon ***raises*** your blood sugar level back to normal.

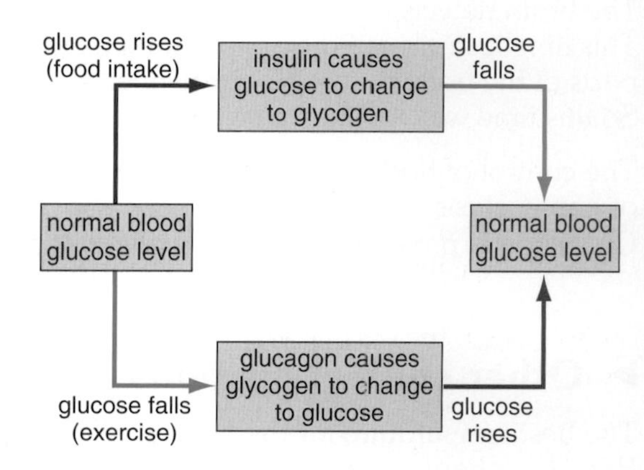

Built-in control

In this case, blood sugar level is controlled by the pancreas.
It ***monitors*** the glucose level in the blood.

As a result of the negative feedback that it gets, it either :

- makes insulin to decrease the blood sugar, ***or***
- makes glucagon to increase the blood sugar.

Insulin and glucagon are important hormones.
They act by switching off or switching on the supply of glucose.

These are pancreas cells.
The ones in the middle make insulin and glucagon.

▶ Biology at work : Diabetes

Some people have a high level of glucose in their blood.
Their pancreas can not make enough insulin.
So they do not convert enough glucose to glycogen.
Their blood sugar level becomes dangerously high.
This can often make them tired and thirsty.
If it goes untreated it can lead to weight loss and even death.

Diabetes can be detected if glucose is found in the urine.
There is so much glucose in the blood that the kidneys can not reabsorb it all.
They have to excrete some of it.

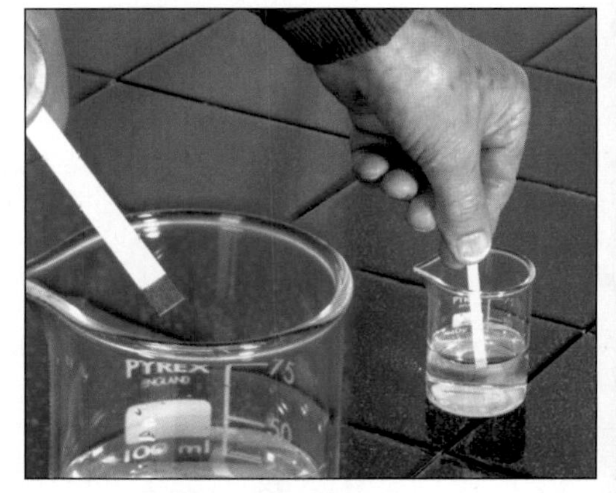

The strip will turn blue if glucose is present in the urine sample.
Is the person a diabetic, or not?

There are two types of diabetes: **type 1** and **type 2**.
Type 1 diabetes, also known as 'early onset diabetes', occurs when the body cannot make insulin. It is often caused by an immune reaction when the body attacks and destroys the cells in the pancreas that make insulin.
This form of the disease usually occurs rapidly and before the age of 20.
Sufferers have this condition for the rest of their lives, but they can be treated with regular measured injections of insulin. At first it is difficult to get the dose of insulin exactly right.
The dosage will depend upon the person's diet and activity.
If too much insulin is injected the blood glucose level can fall too low.
Why do you think this is?
It can cause trembling, sweating and general weakness.
Type 1 diabetics learn to notice these symptoms and eat something sugary to raise their blood glucose level.

Type 2 diabetes, also called 'late onset diabetes', is more common than type 1.
It tends to develop after the age of 40 and is linked to obesity.
Fortunately it is not as serious as type 1 and can usually be controlled by a combination of a low-glucose diet and physical exercise. The cause is usually due to a drastic decrease in the ability of the cells of the pancreas to make insulin.

This boy has type 1 diabetes and has to inject himself with insulin every day.
For many years the insulin used was extracted from pigs or cows. This was slightly different from human insulin and gradually produced an immune reaction in the body reducing its effectiveness.
Now, human insulin is produced by genetic engineering.

▶ Your skin

Your skin has many important jobs :

- it protects your body from damage,
- it stops pathogens getting in,
- it stops too much water loss,
- it lets you feel touch, pain, temperature and pressure,
- it helps keep your body temperature constant.

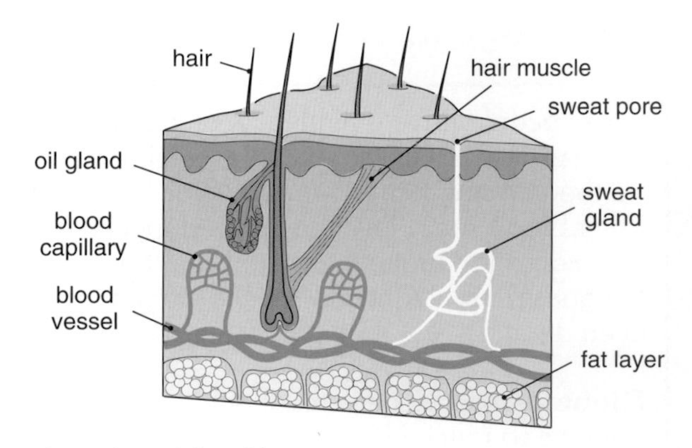

A section of the skin

▶ Hot or cold ?

We are **homiothermic** ('warm-blooded').
This means that we can keep our body temperature constant all the time.
On a cold winter's day or in the hot summer, our body temperature stays around 37 °C.
This is the best temperature at which our enzymes work.

Ectothermic ('cold-blooded') animals like lizards cannot do this.
On a hot day their body temperature is high.
On a cold day their body temperature is low.
Cold-blooded animals are inactive in winter because their body temperature is too low.

Many warm-blooded animals like us have a layer of fat beneath their skin.
This helps to insulate their body.
Animals like seals and polar bears have a very thick layer of fat.
Why do you think this is ?

A hair-raising experience

Many warm-blooded animals have fur or hair.
This traps a layer of air close to the skin.
Air is a poor conductor of heat.
So it cuts down the amount of heat lost.

In cold weather the hairs stand up.
They do this when the hair muscles contract.
This traps a thicker layer of air.
So it cuts down even more on heat loss.

In hot weather the hairs lie flat.
The hair muscles are now relaxing.
Less air is trapped close to the skin.
So more heat is lost by radiation.

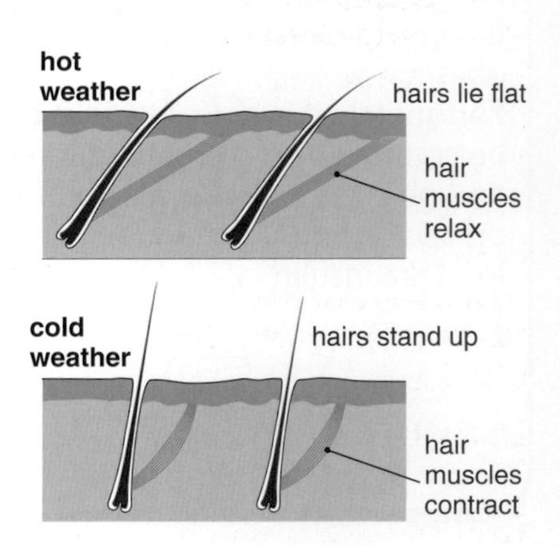

► Controlling body temperature

No matter what the weather is like, your body temperature stays at 37 °C – unless you have a fever.
Your brain monitors the temperature of the blood running through it.
Nerves bring information to the brain about the temperature of your skin.
Your skin helps you to keep your body temperature constant.

When it's hot:

What is your skin like when it is hot?
Why do you sweat and look red-faced?

- **Blood vessels** at your skin surface dilate (widen).
  This process is called **vasodilation**.
  They allow more blood to flow to the surface.
  So more heat is lost by radiation.
- **Sweat glands** in your skin make sweat.
  The sweat evaporates and this cools you down.

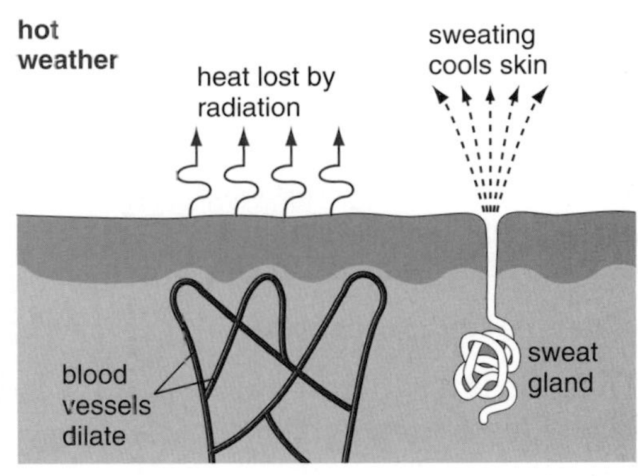

Getting colder:

What is your skin like when it gets cold?
Why do you look pale and shiver?

- **Blood vessels** at your skin surface constrict (get narrower).
  This process is called **vasoconstriction**.
  They cut down the flow of blood to the surface.
  So less heat is lost by radiation.
- **Sweat glands** stop making sweat.
- **Shivering**
  Your muscles start to contract quickly.
  The contraction needs energy from respiration.
  This produces extra heat that warms your body.

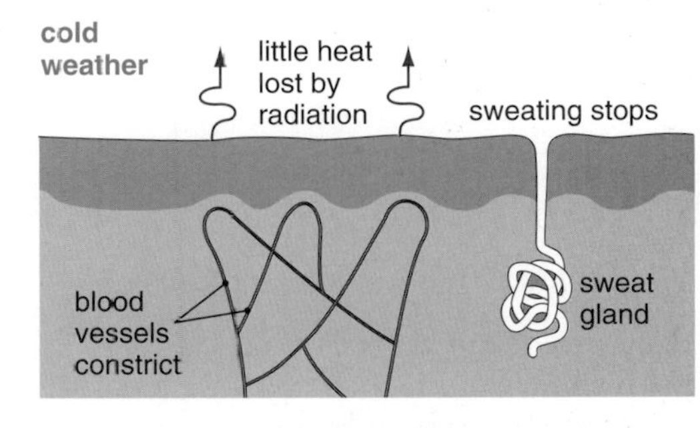

Hypothermia

This is a gradual cooling of the body.
Eventually the temperature deep inside your body will also drop.
A drop of 2 °C starts to affect the brain.
Body movements and speech start to slow down.
The person may go into a coma and eventually die.

Why do you think that babies and old people are particularly at risk?
Why do you think a hot meal and warm clothes would help?

Damp clothes and cold winds can also cause hypothermia.
Why do you think that pot-holers and climbers might be at risk?

Remember also, that high temperatures can cause heat stroke, dehydration, and death.

▶ Excretion

Chemical reactions in your body cells produce waste
This waste includes carbon dioxide and urea.

These chemical wastes have to be removed.
Otherwise they would poison us.

Removing waste made in our cells is called **excretion**.

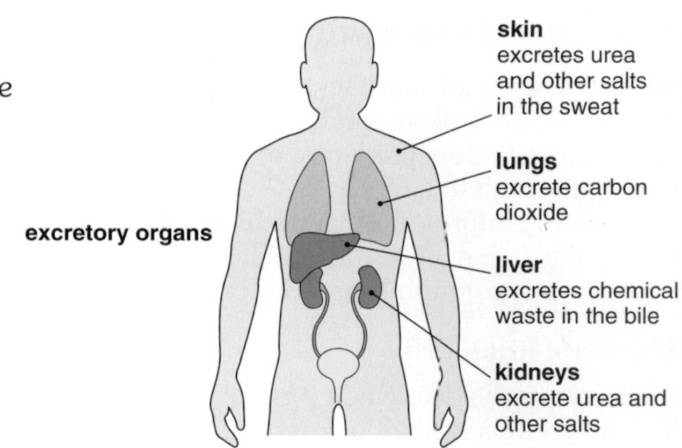

What are the organs that remove carbon dioxide?

If your lungs did not excrete carbon dioxide you would not survive long. Why not?

Your body cannot store excess amino acids.
So they are broken down in the liver to make a waste chemical called **urea**.

This is called **deamination**.

The urea is taken from the liver to the kidneys.
The kidneys excrete the urea.

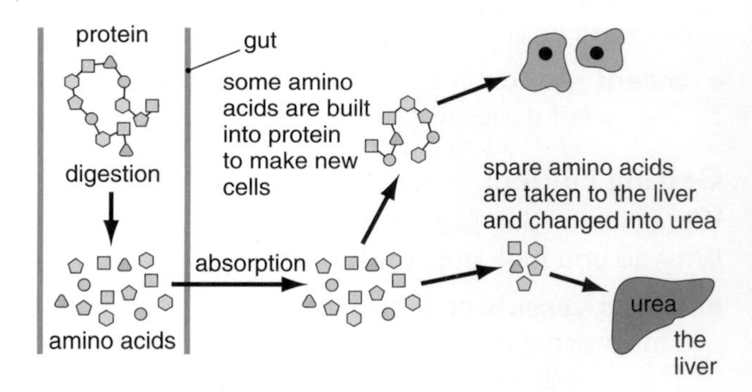

▶ Your kidneys

Do you know where your kidneys are?

They are at the back of your body.
Try putting your hands on your hips.
Your kidneys should be where your thumbs are.

Waste chemicals like urea are carried to your kidneys in the blood.
The kidneys take these chemicals out of the blood as it flows through them.
They are then excreted as **urine**.
So your kidneys 'clean' your blood.

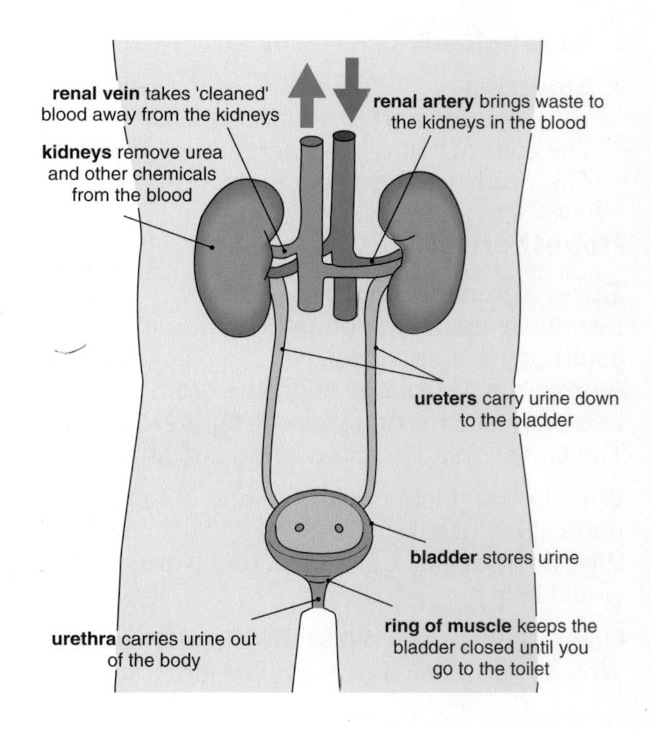

▶ Inside the kidneys

If you cut open a kidney lengthways, you can see what is inside.

You should be able to make out two areas:
a dark outer area – the **cortex**
and a light inner one – the **medulla**.

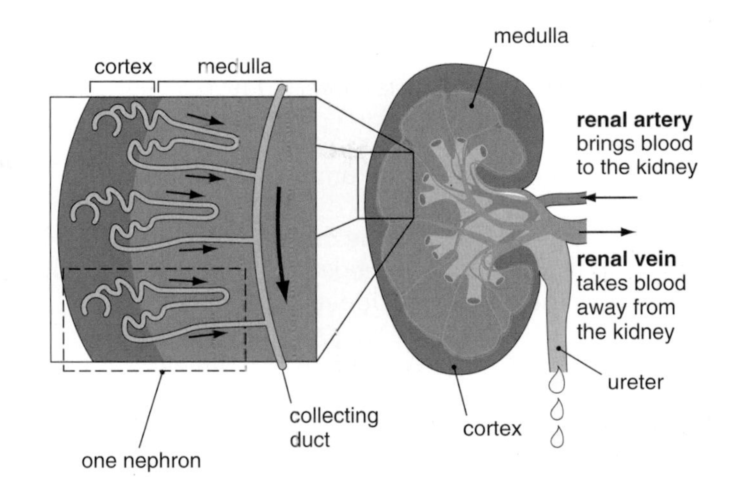

Inside each kidney are thousands of tiny tubes called **nephrons**.
These **filter** your blood and remove waste chemicals.
The filtering is done in the outer area.

The waste chemicals are turned into urine.
This drains down the ureter to the bladder.

▶ How the kidneys work

Blood is brought to each kidney in the renal artery.
It contains a lot of waste chemicals like urea.

The renal artery branches many times.
Each branch ends in a bunch of capillaries called a **glomerulus**.

The glomerulus is inside part of the nephron called the **Bowman's capsule**.

The capillaries then carry blood away from each nephron.
They join up and eventually form the renal vein.

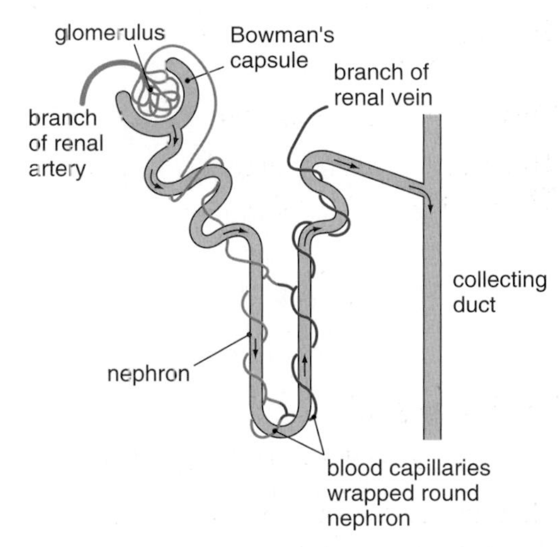

As blood passes through each glomerulus it is filtered.
The filter is like a net with tiny holes in it.
Large molecules, like blood proteins, are too big to pass through the filter.
Small molecules, like urea, glucose, salts and water, pass out of the glomerulus and into the nephron.

All the glucose, some salts and much of the water are needed by the body.
They have to be **reabsorbed** back into the blood from the nephron against a concentration gradient.
This takes place by active transport.
Energy from respiration is needed for reabsorption.

What is left is urea and waste salts dissolved in water.
This is now called urine.
It flows down the ureter to the bladder.

The 'cleaned' blood leaves the kidney in the renal vein.

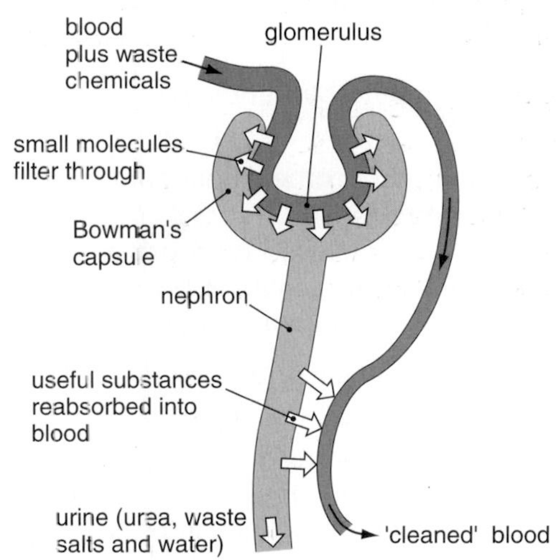

How a nephron works

▶ Controlling body water

You take in water and lose it every day.
Look at the pie-charts:

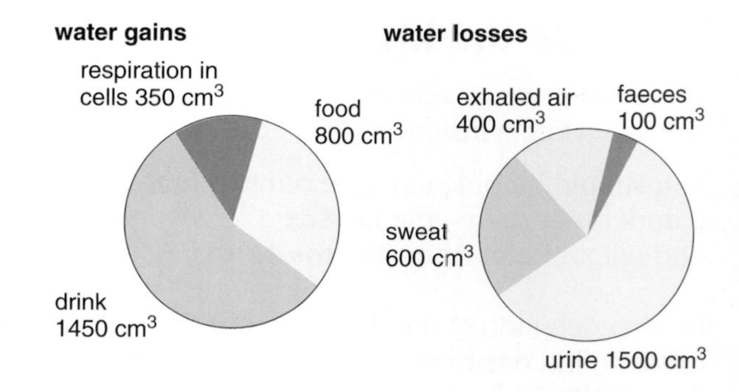

Your body needs a constant amount of water in the cells.
Your body has to balance the amount of water it takes in with the amount it gets rid of.
This is also the job of the kidney.

What happens when you drink a lot of fluids?
Of course, you need to urinate more.

The blood becomes diluted.
Your kidneys remove more water from it.
This extra water makes a lot of dilute urine.

What happens when it is hot and you do not drink much fluid?
You tend to urinate less.

Your blood becomes more concentrated.
Your kidneys remove less water from it.
You make a small amount of concentrated urine.
But how is this all controlled?

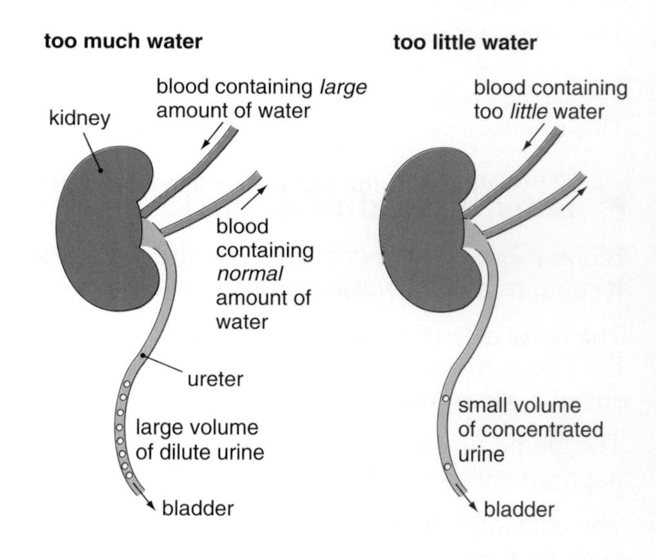

Controlling the kidneys

The brain monitors the water content of your blood.
The amount of water in your urine is controlled by a hormone.
It's called **antidiuretic hormone** – **ADH** for short.
ADH is made by the **pituitary gland** when the brain detects a lowering of the water content of your blood.
It is made when you need to keep water in your body.

Let's imagine that you haven't had a drink for a while:

- your blood becomes more concentrated;
- ADH is produced;
- it tells the kidneys to reabsorb most of the water from the nephrons back into the blood;
- you make a small amount of concentrated urine.

So what happens if you drink lots of fluids?

- your blood becomes dilute;
- no ADH is produced;
- the kidneys don't reabsorb much water from the nephrons back into the blood;
- you make lots of dilute urine.

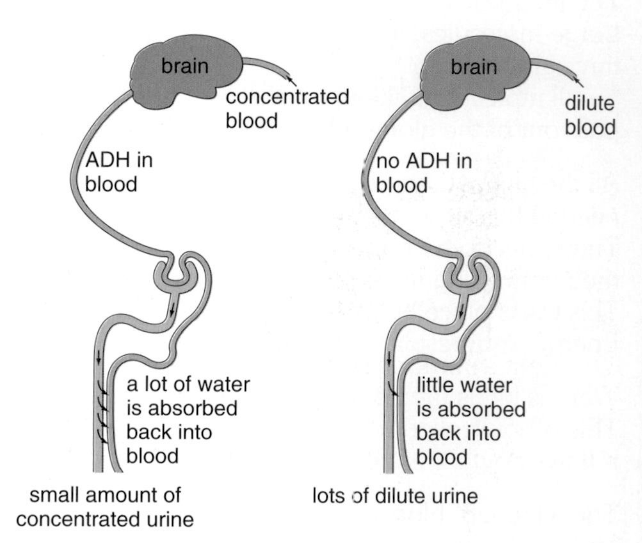

► Biology at work : The kidney dialysis machine and kidney transplants

The kidney dialysis machine

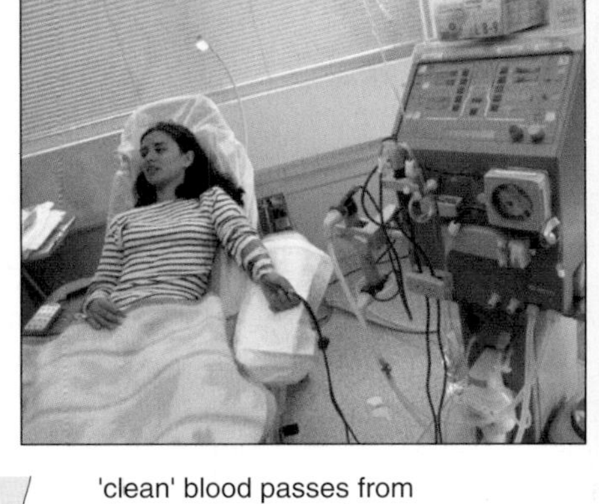

You can survive on one kidney.
But if both kidneys become diseased or damaged, it can be fatal.

Fortunately a kidney dialysis machine can be used to remove the waste chemicals from a patient's blood.
The patient has to use the machine for about 5 hours, two or three times a week.

- First a tube is connected to one of the patient's veins.
- The blood flows along the tube and into the machine.
- Inside the machine the blood is pumped over the surface of a **dialysis membrane**.
  This separates the patient's blood from the **dialysis fluid**.
- Urea diffuses out of the blood, across the dialysis membrane and into the dialysis fluid.
- The dialysis fluid already has sugars and salts in it. So sugars and salts from the blood will not diffuse across into the fluid.
- Urea and other wastes leave the machine in the dialysis fluid.
- The patient's 'cleaner' blood passes back into the vein.

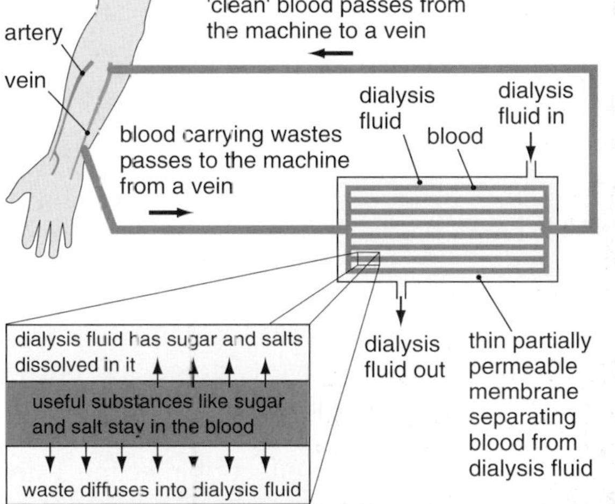

Kidney transplants

A person with failed kidneys may have a kidney transplant. This involves replacing the diseased kidney with a healthy one from a donor.

Sometimes a close relative wants to donate one of their kidneys. A near relative would have a 'tissue-type' similar to the patient. This would reduce the chances of the patient's body rejecting the transplant.

Also to prevent rejection, the bone marrow of the patient is treated with radiation to stop white blood cell production. Along with the use of drugs, this helps to suppress the patient's immune system.

The surgeon attaches the transplant kidney close to the patient's bladder. After the operation the patient has to rest in sterile conditions for some time and is then able to lead a normal life.

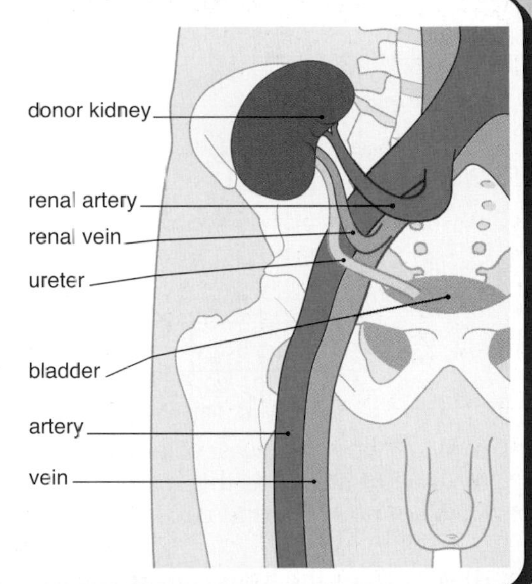

Summary

- Homeostasis means keeping conditions constant inside the body.
- The pancreas produces insulin and glucagon. Insulin lowers blood glucose by converting it to glycogen in the liver.
  Glucagon raises blood sugar by converting stored glycogen back to glucose.
- The brain has a major role in homeostasis.
- The skin is important in keeping your body temperature constant.
  The sweat glands, blood vessels and hairs in the skin are involved.
- The kidneys carry out excretion by getting rid of urea and other wastes.
  The kidney also regulates the amount of water in your blood.
- Kidney failure can be treated by dialysis or by transplants.

▶ Questions

1. Copy and complete:
Keeping conditions steady inside the body is called . . . . .
After a . . . . meal our blood sugar rises. The pancreas produces a hormone called . . . . .
This converts glucose to . . . . and it is stored in the . . . . .
During a race our blood sugar level may get . . . . . The pancreas makes another hormone called . . . . . This converts stored . . . . back to glucose so the muscles can use if for . . . . .

2. The graph shows the effect of injecting 1 unit of insulin into a person.
The concentration of glucose in the blood was measured at regular intervals.

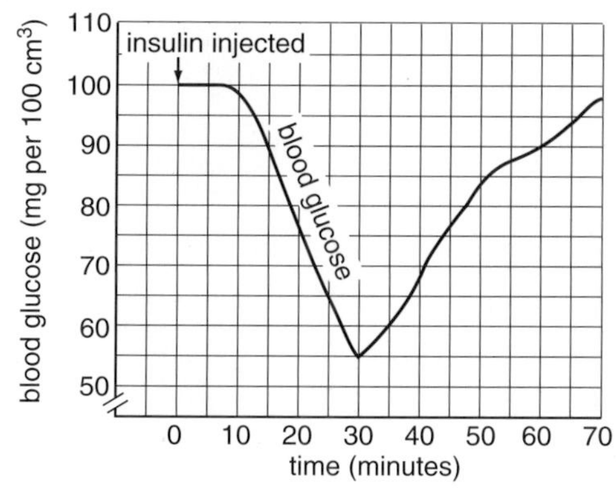

a) What was the lowest value of blood glucose?
b) At what time was this recorded?
c) What happened to cause the blood glucose level to fall?
d) Why does the blood glucose level start to rise again?

3. The graph shows the effect of changing outside temperature on the body temperature of a human (warm-blooded) and a lizard (cold-blooded):

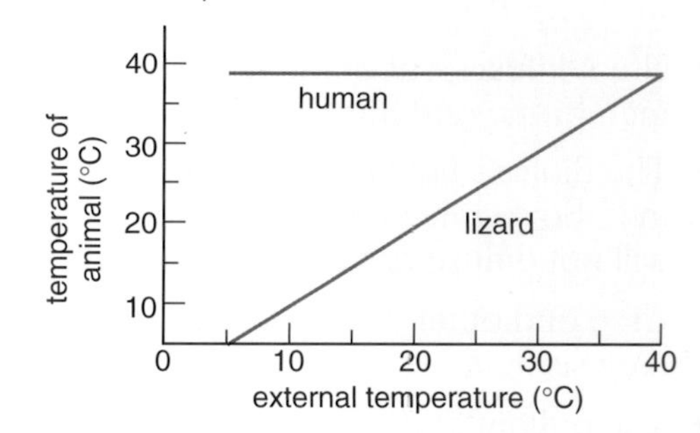

a) What happens to the body temperature of the human as the outside temperature increases? Explain why this happens.
b) What happens to the body temperature of the lizard as the outside temperature increases? Explain why this happens.
c) Why are lizards most active in warm weather?
d) How do you think lizards cope with very hot weather?

4. Look at the diagram of the skin section:
a) Name the parts A to D.
b) What do parts B and D do if you get too hot?
c) What do parts B and D do if you get too cold?
d) Explain how parts A and C react in the cold.

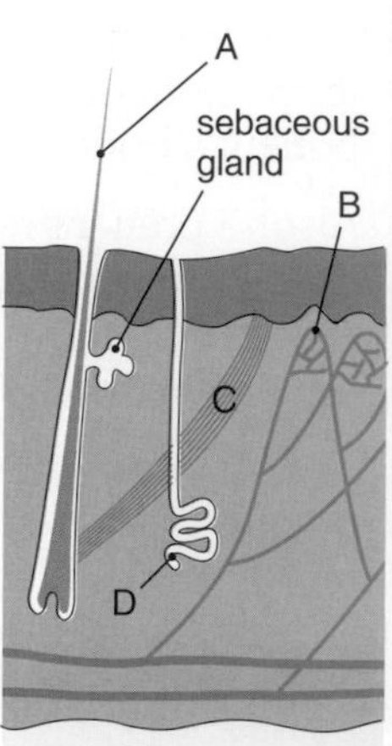

5. a) Which parts of the body lose most heat energy?
b) Which groups of people are most at risk from hypothermia?
c) What advice would you give elderly people about preventing hypothermia?
d) Why are several layers of thin clothing better for keeping you warm than one layer of thick clothing?

6. The diagram shows a simple version of a kidney dialysis machine.
The patient's blood is separated from the dialysis fluid by a partially permeable membrane.

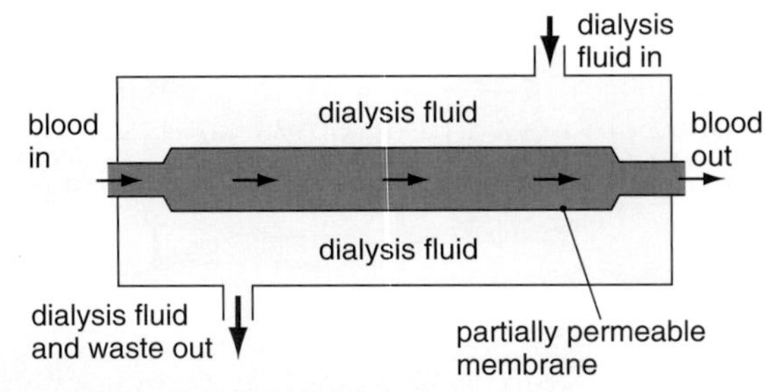

a) By what process do chemical wastes pass from the blood into the dialysis fluid?
b) Why do proteins not pass out of the blood?
c) Why would the presence of protein in the urine indicate kidney damage?
d) Why should the presence of glucose in the urine cause concern?

7. The table shows five substances which are present in the blood supply to the kidney, in the nephron, and in the urine. (All values are in mg per dm^3.)

Substance	Blood entering kidney	Nephron	Urine
urea	0.4	20	20
glucose	1.5	1.5	0
amino acids	0.8	0.8	0
salts	8.0	8.0	16.5
protein	82	0	0

a) Which substances pass from the blood into the nephron?
b) How do they pass into the nephron?
c) Which substances are reabsorbed into the blood from the nephron?
Explain why this happens.
d) Explain the results for protein.

8. a) Name the parts of the excretory system A to D:

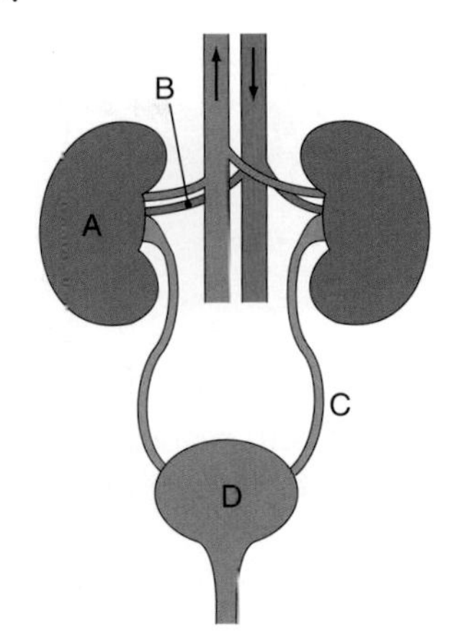

b) Match each part with one of these functions:
1. Stores urine.
2. Filters urea and other waste chemicals out of the blood.
3. Carries blood with a high concentration of urea.
4. Carries urine down to the bladder.

9. The graph shows how the quantities of sweat and urine vary with temperature:

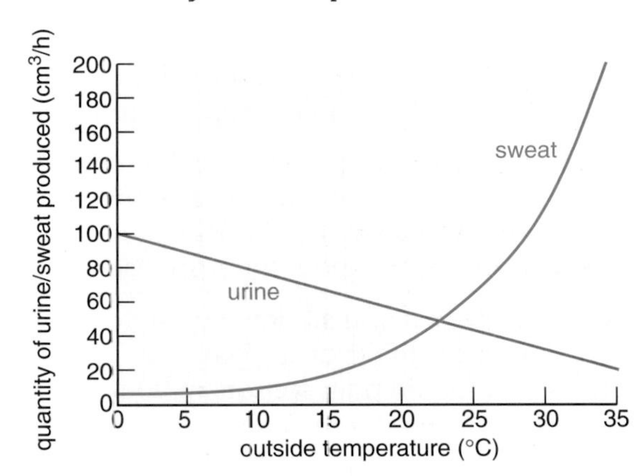

a) At what temperature is the amount of sweat and urine the same?
b) What happens to the amount of sweat as the temperature rises?
Explain why this happens.
c) What happens to the amount of urine as the temperature rises?
Explain why this happens.

Further questions on page 171.

CONTROL & COORDINATION

chapter 8

Things are happening around you all the time.
You have to detect and respond to many changes.
But how does your body do this?

Your body responds to changes in two ways, with your **nervous system** and your **endocrine** or **hormonal system**.

Your nervous system sends electrical messages along nerves to and from different parts of your body.

Your hormonal system sends chemical messages around your body to target organs in the blood.

The electrical messages and the chemical messages tell your body what to do.

Getting a reaction

All our reactions happen in a similar way.
There are always stimuli, receptors and effectors.

- **Stimuli** are changes that can be detected.
  A stimulus is just one of these changes.
- **Receptors** detect the changes.
- **Effectors** bring about the responses.

What happens if you sit down on a drawing pin?
The stimulus is the drawing pin.
The receptors are pain sensors in your skin.
The effectors are the muscles in your legs.
Your response is to get up quickly!

The chain of events is:

stimulus ⟶ receptor ⟶ coordinator ⟶ effector ⟶ response

The coordinator is the part of the body that decides what to do.
What do you think the coordinator is in our example?

This type of action involves the nervous system.
Can you think of some other examples?

▶ Your nervous system

The nervous system ***controls*** your actions.
It ***coordinates*** different parts of your body so that they work together and are able to bring about the correct responses.

Your nervous system coordinates your muscles, so that you can walk, write, read this book or do exercise.

When you smile, the nervous system coordinates the muscles of your face.

Your nervous system also coordinates things that you don't even think about, like swallowing, blinking and breathing.

The main parts of the nervous system are the **brain** and the **spinal cord**.
Together they are called the **central nervous system**.
They are both made of delicate nervous tissue.
The brain is protected inside the skull.
The spinal cord is protected inside your backbone.

The central nervous system is connected to different parts of the body by **nerves**.
Each nerve is made up of lots of **nerve cells** or **neurones**.

Sense organs are our receptors.
They send messages to the central nervous system telling it what has happened.
These messages are sent along **sensory neurones**.

Muscles and glands are our effectors.
The central nervous system sends messages telling them what to do.
These messages are sent along **motor neurones**.

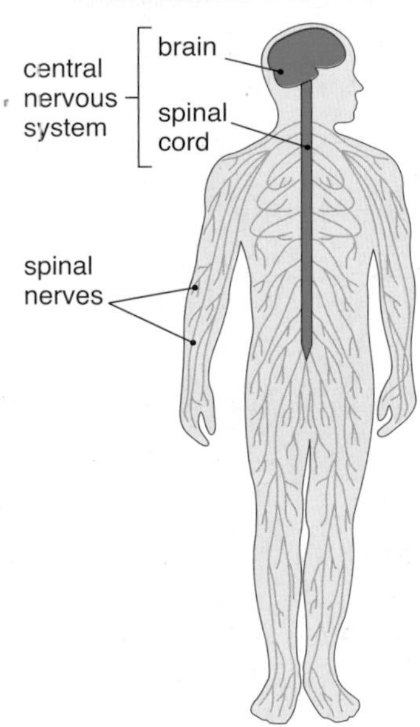

The main parts of the human nervous system

Experiment 8.1. Inside the spinal cord

Hold a slide of a section of the spinal cord up the light.
Can you see two areas ?
The middle area is the grey matter.
Look at this part under the microscope.
Can you see any nerve cells ?

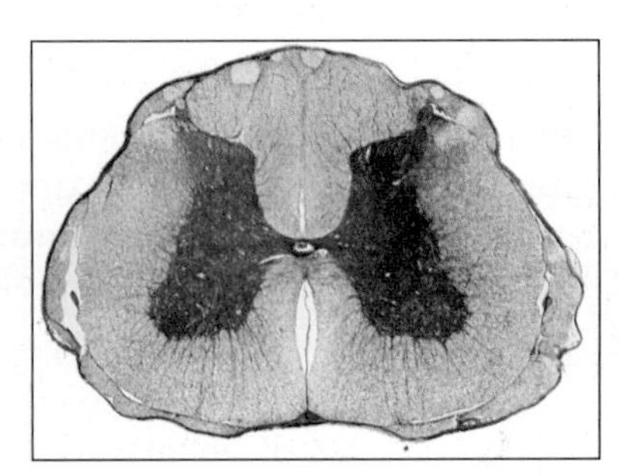

A section of the spinal cord

▶ Neurones

Nerve cells are different from other cells.
They do have a cell membrane, cytoplasm and nucleus, but they are a different shape.
Part of the cell is stretched out to form the **axon**.
The axon can be over a metre long.

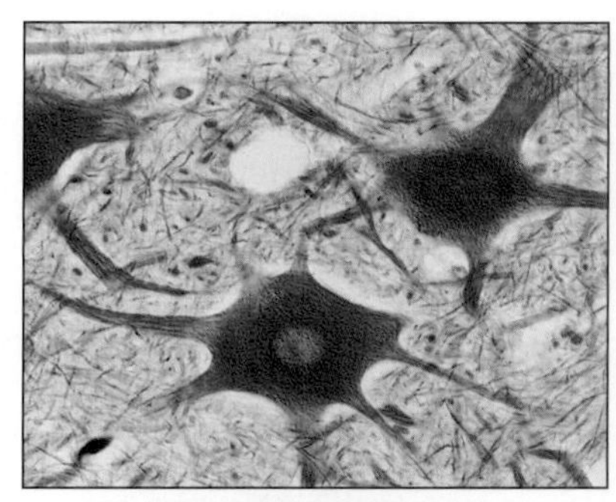

Neurones in the brain

Sensory neurone

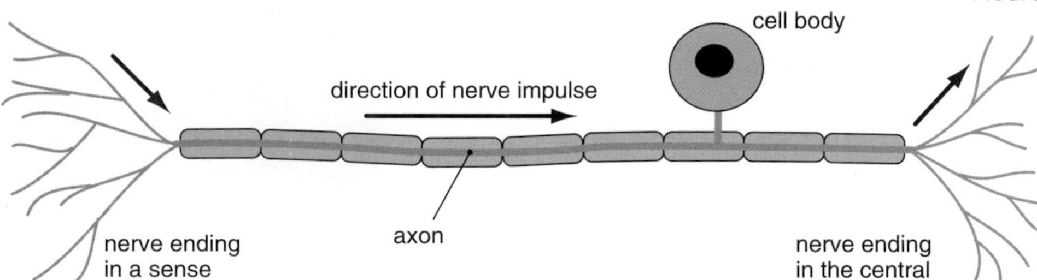

Motor neurone

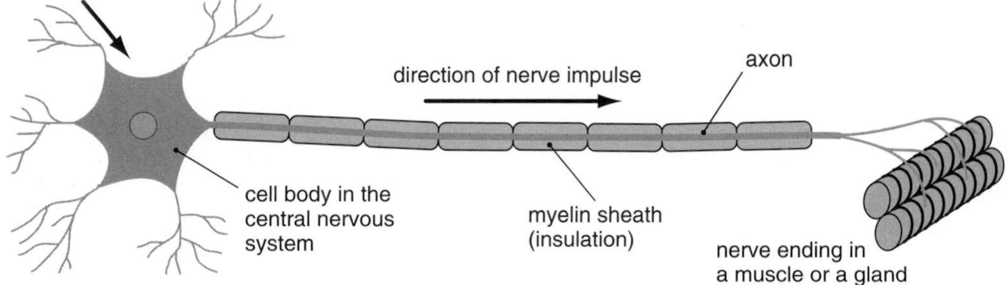

How the messages are carried

The messages that nerves carry are called **nerve impulses**.
They are electrical signals.
They pass very quickly along the axon of the neurone.

An impulse travels along the axon like a train along a track.
Each one is separate from the next.
They travel along one after another.
Some axons have a **fatty sheath** around them.
This insulates the axon and makes the impulse travel along faster.

In **multiple sclerosis** the fatty sheath breaks down.
Impulses slow down or may even stop.
People with this disease gradually lose the use of their muscles because the messages never reach them.

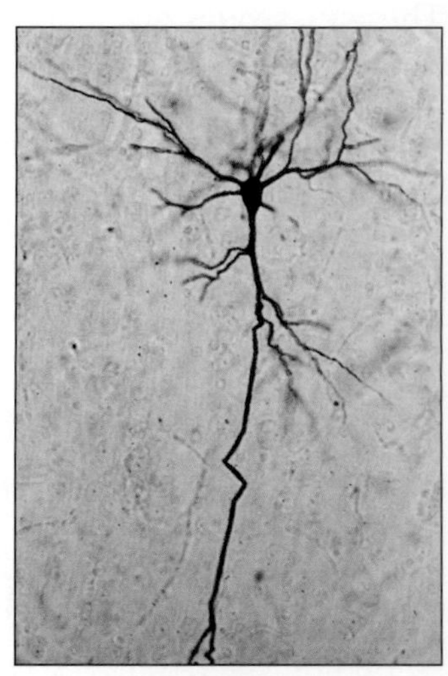

This neurone has a long axon

▶ Coordination

Your nervous system helps you to react to different situations.
Let's use an example to see how this happens.

What happens when you get an itch on your elbow?
Look at the diagram and follow the chain of events:

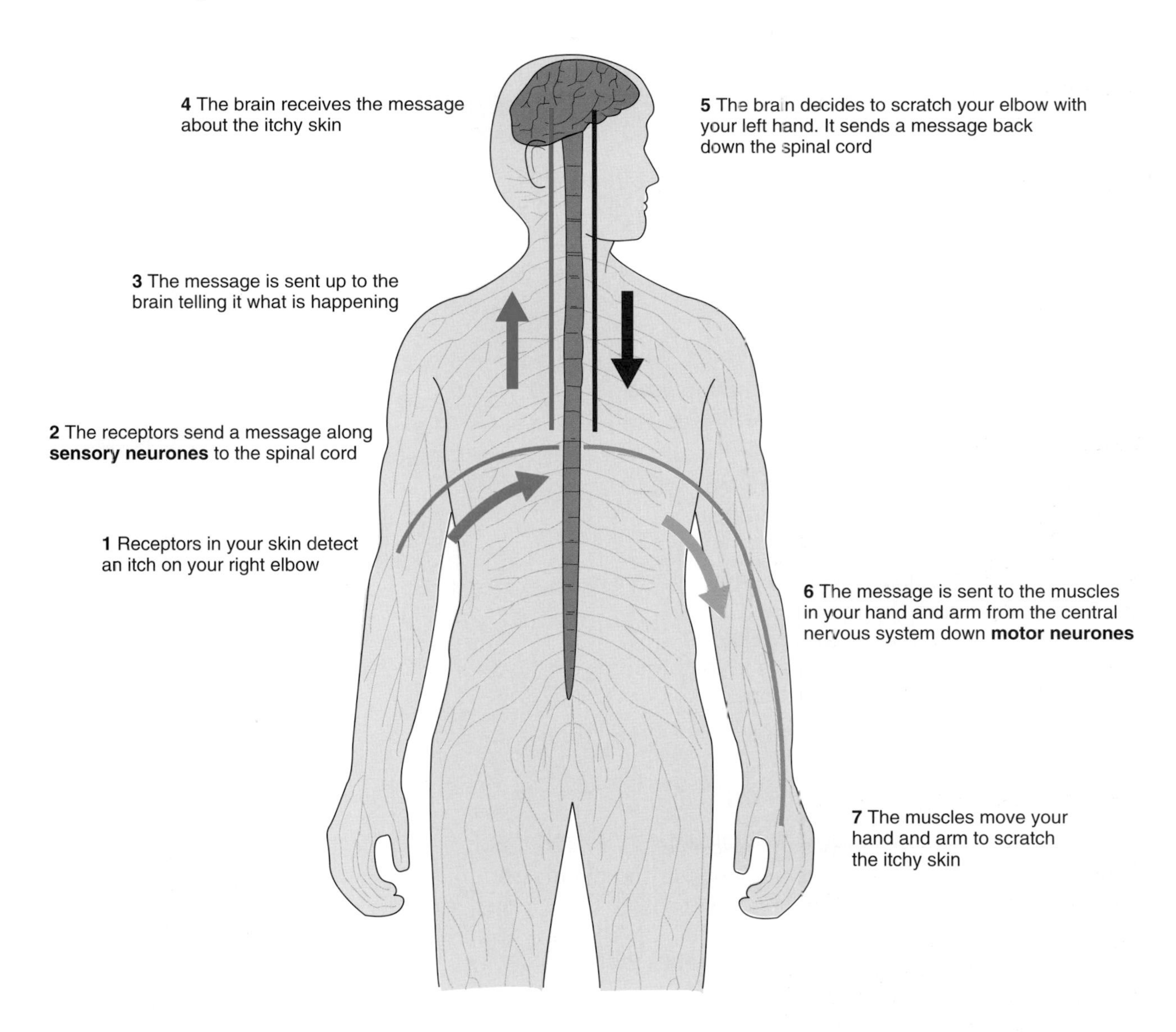

What is the stimulus in this reaction?

What is the response?

Which parts of the body are the receptor, the effector and the coordinator?

▶ Synapses

The end of one neurone is not connected to the next.
There is always a small gap between them.
The gap is called a **synapse**.

When an impulse reaches the end of an axon,
a chemical is produced.
This chemical is called a **neurotransmitter**.
The chemical diffuses across the gap and binds with receptor molecules in the membrane of the next newrone.
It starts off an impulse in the next neurone.

Only one end of a neurone can make this neurotransmitter.
So synapses make sure an impulse can only travel in ***one*** direction.

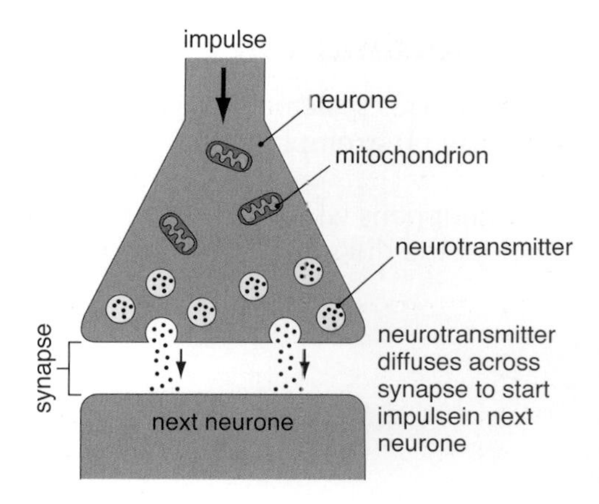

How a synapse works

Synapses have two other functions.
They act as :

- ***a resistor*** – it may take a number of impulses before enough neurotransmitter is made to start the impulse in the next neurone.
- ***a junction box*** – one neurone may pass on its impulse to a number of other neurones.

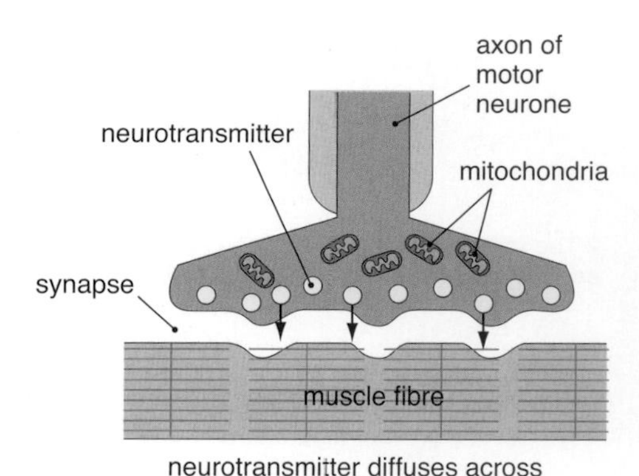

How an impulse reaches a muscle

Our synapses are easily affected by drugs.
Some drugs can block them.
Others can make them work too quickly.
Alcohol is thought to affect synapses in the brain.
This can slow down people's reactions.

To the muscles

We use nerves to control our muscles.
Motor neurones end in synapses in muscle cells.
A neurotransmitter passes across the synapse and the muscle cell contracts.

Motor neurone disease affects the neurones that join with muscles.
The neurones start to break down and can not carry impulses any more.
So the muscles can not contract and the person is paralysed.

Nerve–muscle connections

► Reflex arcs

You take your hand away from a hot object very fast.
You do it automatically – without thinking.
Why do you think this is?

Many reflexes protect you.
They happen very quickly, so you don't harm yourself.

Look at the diagram below.
Try tracing the pathway of the impulse along the neurones.
This pathway is called a **reflex arc**.

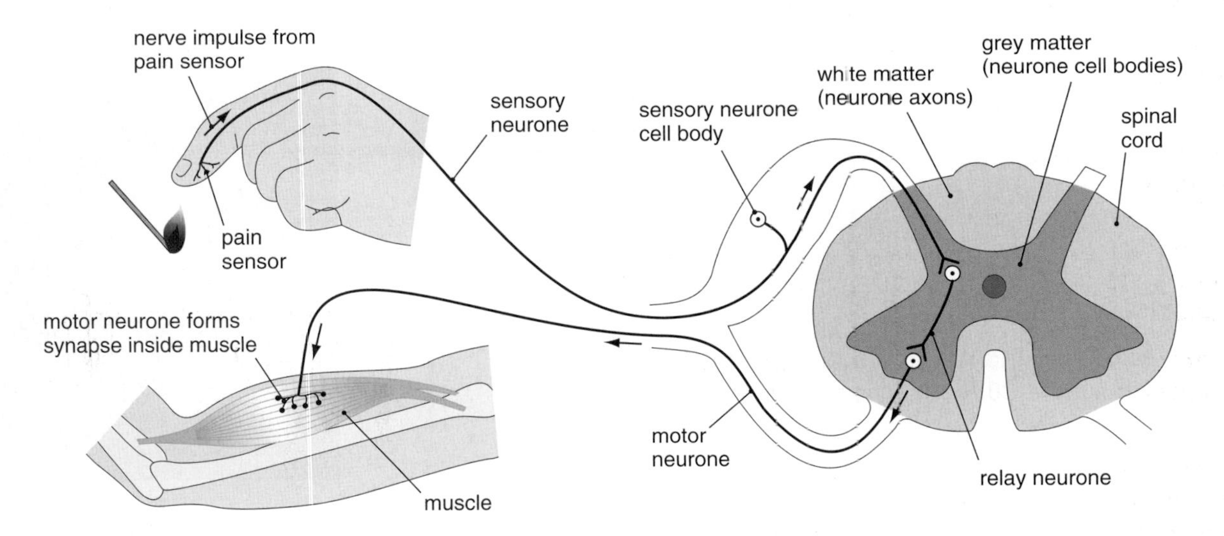

The **stimulus** in our example is the hot flame.

The **receptor** is the heat sensor in the skin.

- The impulse travels to the spinal cord along the **sensory neurone**.
- In the spinal cord the impulse is passed on to the **relay neurone**.
- This passes the impulse on to the **motor neurone**.

The motor neurone carries the impulse to a muscle in the arm. The muscle is the **effector**.

The muscle contracts to remove the hand from the hot object. This action is the **response**.

How many synapses are there in this reflex arc?
There is one between each neurone and one between the motor neurone and the muscle – that makes three!

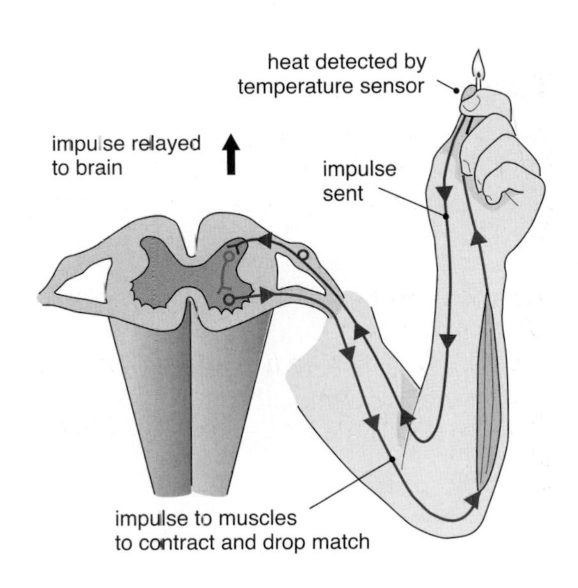

► Your reflexes

- Pulling your hand away from a hot object.
- Blinking when dust gets into your eye.
- Coughing when food goes down the 'wrong way'.
  What have all these reflexes got in common?

Well for one thing you can not stop yourself reacting.
These reflexes are automatic and often protect you.

Experiment 8.2 Testing your reflexes

Try to test some of your reflexes with a partner.
What happens with each of these:
- Sit on the bench with your legs relaxed.
  Your partner taps you just below the knee.
- Look straight ahead.
  Your partner suddenly waves a hand in front of your eyes.
- Kneel on a chair and let your feet hang loose.
  Your partner taps the back of your foot, just above the heel.
- Your partner shines a torch into your eye?

How fast?

Lots of sportsmen and sportswomen need fast reflexes.
What sports do you think need quick reactions?

You can see how quick your reflexes are by measuring your **reaction time**.

Experiment 8.3 Measuring your reaction time

You can measure your reaction time with a falling ruler.
Place your arm on the bench as in the diagram:
Your partner holds the ruler with zero next to your little finger, but ***not*** touching it.
When your partner decides to let the ruler go, try to catch it as quickly as possible.

Read off the scale next to your little finger.
Try the test 10 times.
Record your results in a table.

Now repeat the test but with the ruler touching your hand.

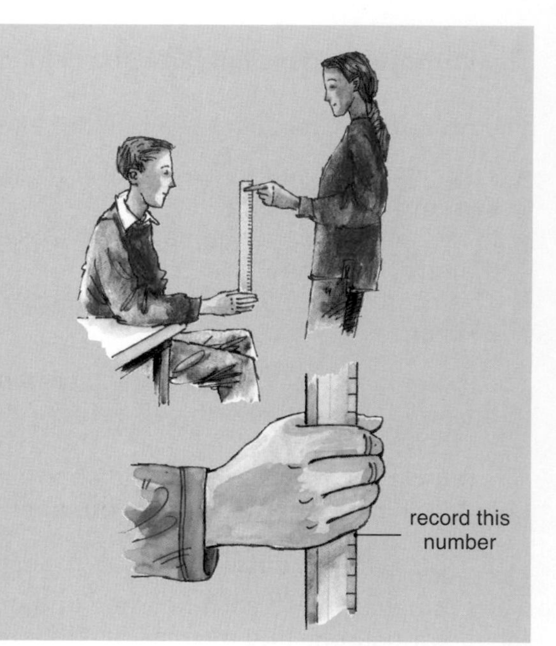

- Does your reaction time improve with practice?
  Why do you think this is?
- Was your reaction time quicker with or without the ruler touching your hand? Why was this?

Try to change the test so that you use only your hearing.

► Your brain

Your brain **coordinates** your actions.
Many of them are complicated.
Riding a bike, dancing or playing soccer, for example.

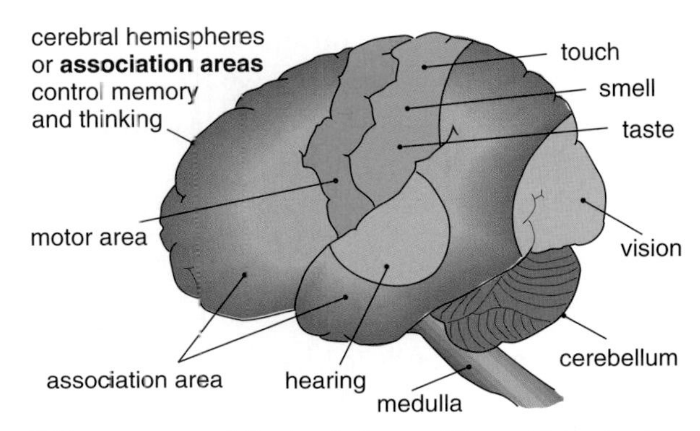

Different parts of the brain have different jobs to do

Your brain is at the top of the spinal cord.
It contains more than ten billion neurones.
These link up to enable you to coordinate incoming and outgoing impulses.
This is how you control your actions.

The brain is very complex.
We still have a great deal to discover about how it works.

Three important parts are :

- The **cerebral hemispheres** control complex behaviour.
  They are responsible for thought, memory and intelligence.
  They link the senses such as seeing and hearing with muscles that bring about movement.
  This front part of our brain is responsible for our feelings and emotions.
  The cerebral hemispheres coordinate our **voluntary** actions.
  We are conscious of voluntary actions and they may involve decision making, e.g. choosing a book in a library.
  Involuntary actions are based on reflexes and do not involve conscious control by the brain.
  You can find more about voluntary actions on page 361.

- The **medulla** is the part that attaches to the spinal cord.
  It controls automatic actions like our heartbeat, breathing and blood pressure.

- The **cerebellum** controls our sense of balance and muscular actions.
  It allows us to make precise movements such as walking, running or riding a bike.

His cerebellum must be working overtime!

Conditioning

Your brain can influence your reflexes.
You make saliva when food is in your mouth.
But other things can make your mouth water.
The smell of food or the bell ringing for lunchtime.
This type of reflex involves the brain.
It is called **conditioning** and is a type of learning.
Can you think of other examples of conditioning?
You can find out more about conditioning on page 363.

▶ Your senses

We are aware of things around us.
Our senses detect stimuli and we respond.

Humans have receptors or **sense organs** :

- The **skin** responds to touch, pressure, pain, heat and cold.
- The **tongue** responds to chemicals in our food and drink. It gives us our sense of taste.
- The **nose** responds to chemicals in the air. It gives us our sense of smell.
- The **ears** respond to sound vibrations and movements. They give us our sense of hearing and also our balance.
- The **eyes** respond to light rays. They give us our sense of sight.

Which senses are being used here ?

▶ Your eyes

Sight is one of your most important senses.
Just think what it must be like to live in darkness all the time.

Each eye lies in a socket in the skull.
It is moved by the actions of 3 pairs of **eye muscles**.
These swivel your eyes in their sockets.

At the front of the eye is the transparent **cornea**.
Light enters your eye through here.
It then passes through the **pupil**.
This is surrounded by the coloured **iris**.

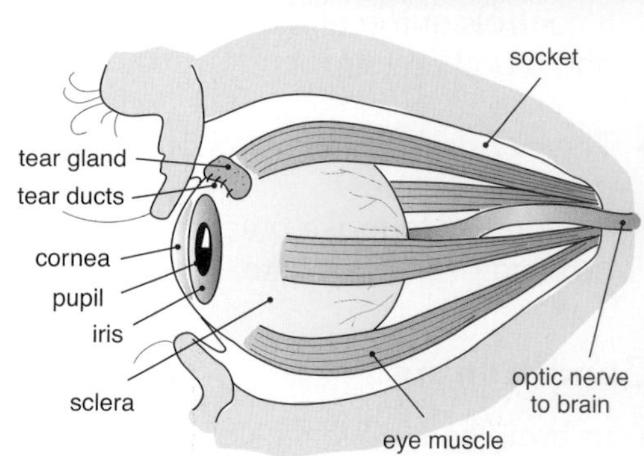

At the front of the cornea is the **conjunctiva**.
This is a delicate, transparent layer.
It is kept moist by the **tear glands**.
These make the tears that wash your eye clean every time you blink.

In humans, both of our eyes point forwards.
But because they are differently placed, each eye views the same visual field from a slightly different angle.
This over-lapping of fields of view is called **binocular vision**.
Animals with binocular vision are much better able to judge distance. Animals need to judge distance accurately, for example, when grasping branches in trees or when striking their prey.

The pupil reflex

If you look in the mirror you will see that there are two sets of muscles in your iris.
The **circular muscles** are arranged around the pupil.
The **radial muscles** run outwards from the pupil like the spokes in a wheel.

The role of the iris and pupil is to regulate the intensity of light that reaches the sensitive **retina**.

In bright light the circular muscles ***contract*** and the radial muscles ***relax***. This constricts (narrows) the pupil and so less light reaches the retina.

In dim light the circular muscles ***relax*** and the radial muscles ***contract***. This dilates (widens) the pupil and so more light is able to reach the retina.

This is an example of a simple reflex arc.
The retina is stimulated by the amount of light reaching it.
It sends off impulses along the optic nerve which are coordinated by the brain.
Impulses then pass to the iris which then alters the size of the pupil.

In dim light

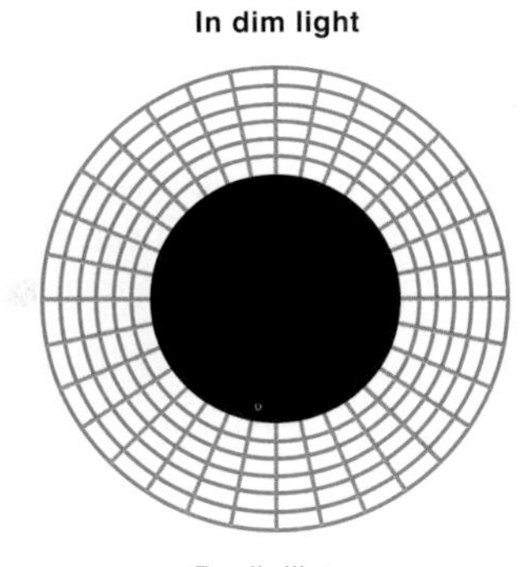

Pupil dilates

Circular muscles relax, radial muscles contract

In bright light

Pupil constricts

Circular muscles contract, radial muscles relax

Inside the eye

choroid
black layer containing lots of blood vessels

vitreous humour
transparent jelly-like substance which supports the back of the eye

ciliary muscle
changes the thickness of the lens when focusing

retina
inner light-sensitive layer
it contains rod cells that work in dim light and cone cells that detect colour and details

conjunctiva

cornea

aqueous humour
watery liquid filling the front of the eye

yellow spot or **fovea**
most sensitive part of the retina

lens
can change its shape to focus light onto the retina

blind spot
point where the optic nerve attaches to the eye
no light-sensitive cells here

iris
controls the amount of light entering the eye

suspensory ligaments
hold the lens in place

optic nerve
carries nerve impulses away to the brain

sclera
tough, white, protective layer

Seeing things

Light enters your eye through the transparent cornea, it passes through the lens and is focused on the retina.

In the retina there are cells which are sensitive to light called rods and cones.

When light stimulates them they send impulses to the brain along the optic nerve. Your brain interprets these impulses to make a picture.

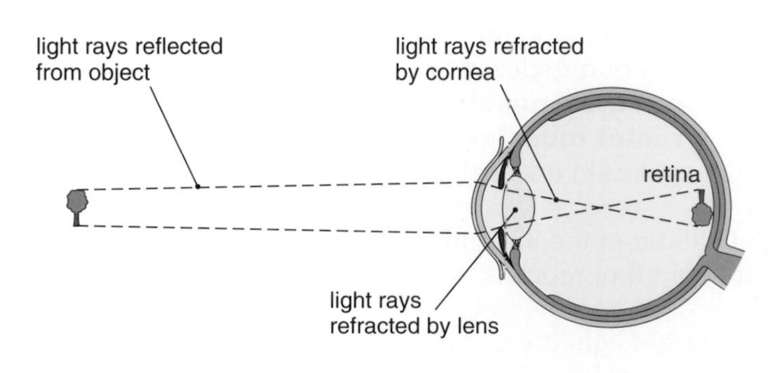

Notice that the image on the retina is ***inverted***. But your brain has learned to turn the picture the right way up.
Rod cells respond to dim light and are located mainly around the periphery of the retina. **Cone cells** detect colour and respond to light of high intensity. Cones are mainly found in the fovea.

Focusing

Most of the refraction of the light rays is done by the curved cornea.
But your lens can bend the light rays slightly.

The shape of the lens is controlled by the ciliary muscles.

looking at a distant object

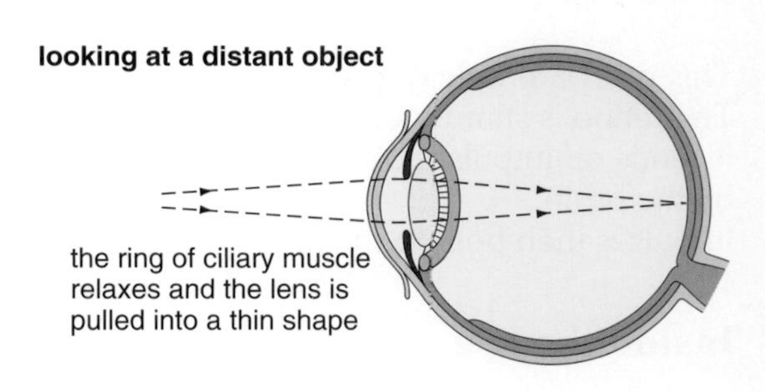

looking at a near object

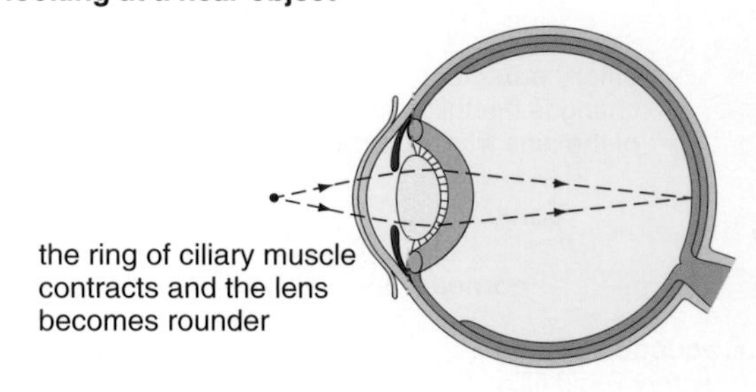

If you are looking at a distant object :

- the ciliary muscles ***relax***
- this ***tightens*** the suspensory ligaments
- so the lens is pulled into a ***thin*** shape.
- The distant object is focused on the retina.

If you are looking at a near object :

- the ciliary muscles ***contract***
- this ***slackens*** the suspensory ligaments
- so the elastic lens goes ***fatter***.
- The near object is focused on the retina.

Experiment 8.5 Finding your blind spot

Hold this book up in front of you at arm's length. Cover your ***right*** eye and keep staring at the magic wand. Move the page slowly towards you until the rabbit disappears.

This happens because the light rays from the rabbit are falling on to your blind spot where there are no light-sensitive cells.

Short sight

A person who can see near objects clearly but can not focus distant objects is **short-sighted**.

This is because either :
- the eye ball is too long, or
- the lens bends the light rays too much (it is too fat even when the ciliary muscles are relaxed).

So the light rays from a distant object are focused ***in front*** of the retina and the image is blurred.

Short sight can be corrected by wearing glasses with a **concave (diverging)** lens.
This will bend the light rays outwards before they enter the eye so they will be focused on the retina.

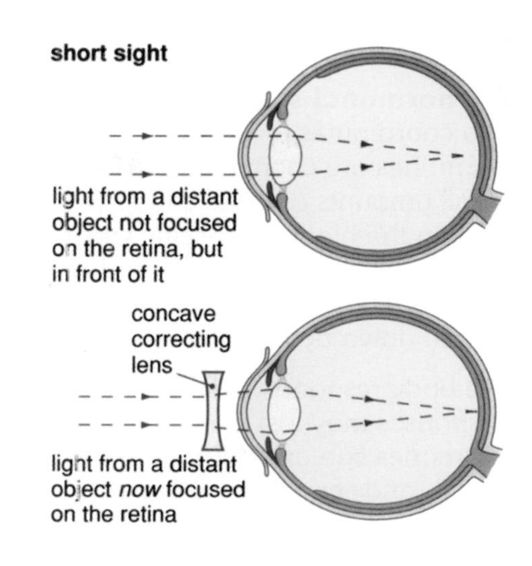

Long sight

A person who can see distant objects clearly but can not focus near objects is **long-sighted**.

This is because either :
- the eye ball is too short, or
- the lens can not bend the light rays enough (it is too thin even when the ciliary muscles are contracting).

So the light rays from a near object are focused towards a point ***behind*** the retina and the image is blurred.

Long sight can be corrected by wearing glasses with a **convex (converging)** lens.
This will bend the light rays inwards before they enter the eye so they will be focused on the retina.

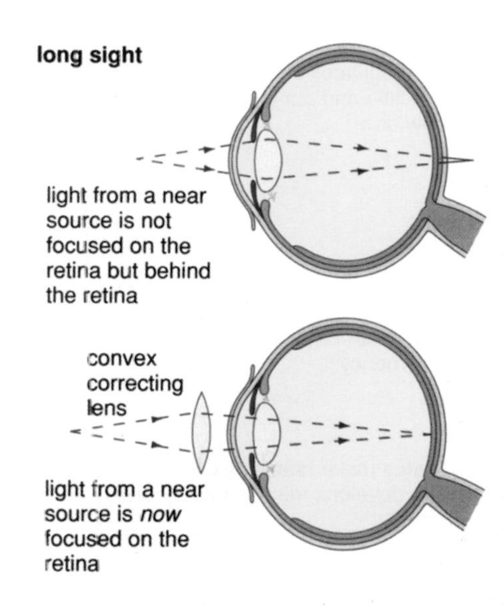

New techniques have made it possible to use laser surgery to operate on the cornea. This means that a person can do without glasses and contact lenses.
For people with short-sightedness, for instance, the laser is set to reduce the thickness of the cornea.
This enables the eye to bring images into focus properly.

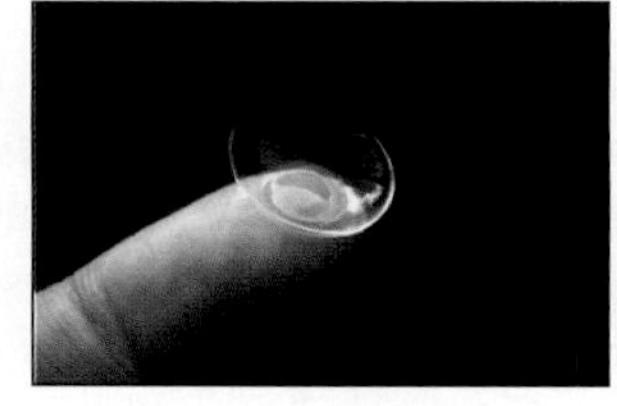

Contact lenses are a popular alternative to glasses

Some elderly people find it difficult to focus properly.
This is because, with time, the lens becomes less elastic.
The lens can also become cloudy forming a **cataract**.
This makes it difficult to see clearly.
Operations can now be carried out to successfully replace the natural lens with a plastic one.

▶ Hormones

The **hormonal system** or **endocrine system** also coordinates the body.
Hormones are chemicals produced by **endocrine glands**.
Small amounts of these chemicals are carried around the body in the blood to specific **target organs**. These target organs recognise a particular hormone and respond to it.
After they have performed their functions, hormones are broken down by the liver.

The body responds to these hormones.
Responses may last a few minutes or go on for years.
Hormones can affect things like the rate of metabolism, growth and sexual development.

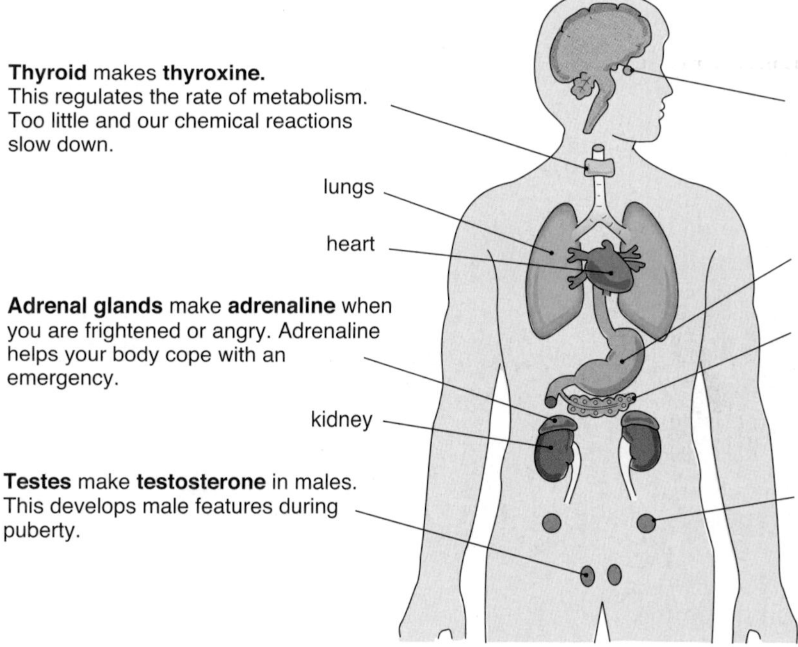

Hormones are involved in homeostasis.
Hormonal glands are affected by negative feedback.
If the level of hormone in the blood is too high the gland detects it and makes less hormone.

Sometimes things can go wrong.
A gland may make too much or too little of a hormone.
For instance, too much pituitary growth hormone can make a person become a giant, too little can make a person become a dwarf.

What happens if too little insulin is produced by the pancreas?
How is diabetes treated?

Adrenaline

Adrenaline is produced by the adrenal glands which are located above each kidney.
Adrenaline is released during times of excitement, fear or stress.
Often called the 'flight or fight' hormone, adrenaline helps the body prepare for action in the following ways :

- Glycogen is converted to glucose in the liver, so more glucose reaches the muscles as a source of energy for the rapid contractions needed for sudden action.
- Heart rate increases so that more glucose and oxygen are delivered to the muscles for energy release.
- The bronchioles widen so more air reaches the lungs.
- Blood vessels to the brain and muscles widen, so more glucose and oxygen are delivered to these organs.
- Blood vessels to the gut and other organs narrow, allowing blood to be diverted to more life-saving organs.
- Hairs are raised ('goose pimples' in humans). This makes furry animals look larger to deter attackers.

The production of adrenaline has evolved to protect us and other animals from danger.
If too much adrenaline is produced, as a result of prolonged stress, constant high blood pressure and heart disease may result.
Beta-blockers are drugs that combine with adrenaline and so reduce its effects.

Other hormones

Hormones are covered in other chapters of this book:

Insulin and **glucagon** control blood sugar levels (page 98).

ADH controls the level of water in your body (page 104).

Look at the table to see how the nervous system and the endocrine system work together to control the activities of our body.

Nervous system	Endocrine system
information passes as electrical impulses along neurones	information passes as chemical messengers in the blood
effects are rapid and short-lived	effects are usually slow and longer lasting
affects particular organs	affects the whole of the body
often involves reflexes	controls growth, development, metabolism and reproduction

▶ Adolescence

You are born with a complete set of sex organs.
But they only become active later in life.

Between the ages of about 10 and 14, the testes start to make sperm and the ovaries start to make eggs.
This time of development in your life is called **puberty**.

Girls usually develop earlier than boys do.
But how early varies from person to person.

What do you think starts these changes off?
The answer is 'hormones'.

The **pituitary gland** at the base of the brain starts to make hormones.
These make the sex organs active.
The sex organs start to produce sex hormones which develop our **secondary sexual characteristics**.

The testes start making **testosterone**.
This hormone brings on other changes in boys:
- the testes start to make sperm
- hair starts to grow on the face and body
- the voice deepens
- the muscles develop.

The ovaries start making **oestrogen**.
This hormone brings on other changes in girls:
- the ovaries start to release eggs
- hair starts to grow on parts of the body
- the breasts develop
- the hips widen
- periods start.

You become an **adolescent** when puberty starts.
Adolescence finishes when you stop growing at about 18 years.
Adolescence can be an emotional time.
Hormones can bring about mood changes and increase sexual urges.
Most people cope well and develop into responsible young adults.

▶ Ovulation and the menstrual cycle

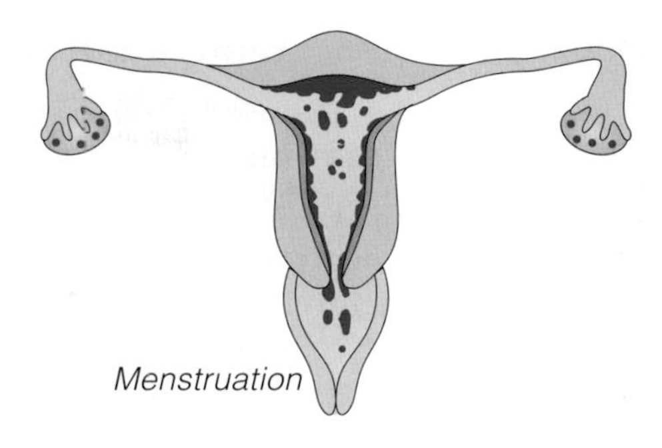
Menstruation

One change that happens to girls at puberty is that they start to have periods. This usually happens when a girl is between 8 and 15 years old.

During a period the lining of the uterus breaks down and a small amount of blood and cells passes out of the vagina.
This is called **menstruation**.

As soon as the girl's period has finished a new egg starts to develop in the ovary.

It grows inside a fluid-filled ball called a **follicle**.

As the follicle gets bigger it moves to the edge of the ovary.

Eventually the follicle bursts releasing the egg into the oviduct.
This is **ovulation**.

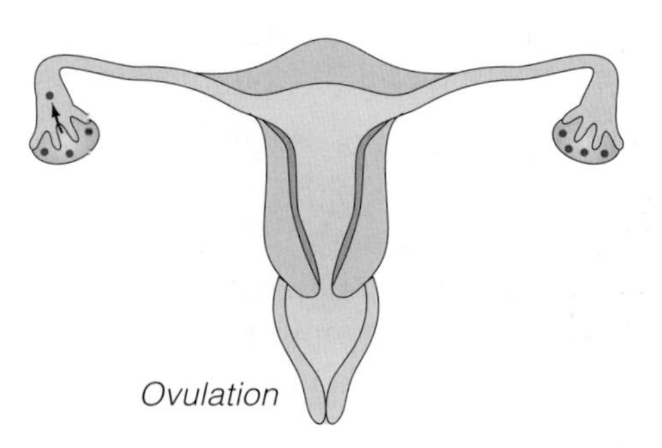
Ovulation

The empty follicle forms the **yellow body**.

While the egg is developing in the ovary the lining of the uterus starts to thicken.
In the week after ovulation it has a thick lining of blood vessels and glands.
If fertilisation occurs the fertilised egg **implants** in the thick uterus lining.
The woman is pregnant.

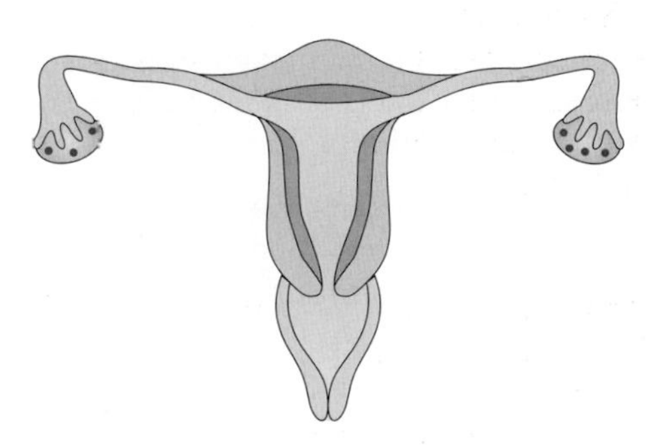
Uterus ready for implantation

If fertilisation does not occur the egg dies and passes out of the vagina.

The yellow body also breaks down in the ovary.

The thick lining of the uterus breaks down and is lost during menstruation.

The cycle now begins again.

What happens to the lining of the uterus if a pregnancy does occur?

Why does a thickened lining of the uterus help the embryo develop?

Between the ages of 45 and 55 years a woman's periods stop. This is called the **menopause**.

Ovulation and menstruation are controlled by hormones.

► Control of the menstrual cycle

Hormones from the **pituitary** control the cycle.

A pituitary hormone called **FSH (Follicle Stimulating Hormone)** starts the cycle off. It tells the ovary to make an egg.

The follicle and egg start to develop. This gives a signal to the ovary telling it to make **oestrogen**.

Oestrogen causes the lining of the uterus to thicken and prevents more eggs developing.

Oestrogen passes to the pituitary in the blood. It stops the pituitary from making any more FSH.

Instead it gives the signal for another pituitary hormone to be produced. This is called **LH (Luteinising Hormone)**.

LH makes the ovary release an egg (ovulation). It also turns the empty follicle into a **yellow body**.

The yellow body starts to make **progesterone**. Progesterone makes the uterus lining thicken even more.

Both oestrogen and progesterone make sure the lining of the uterus is ready for implantation of the fertilised egg.

If pregnancy occurs these two hormones continue to be produced. They make sure that the lining of the uterus stays thick and they stop the woman's menstrual cycle.

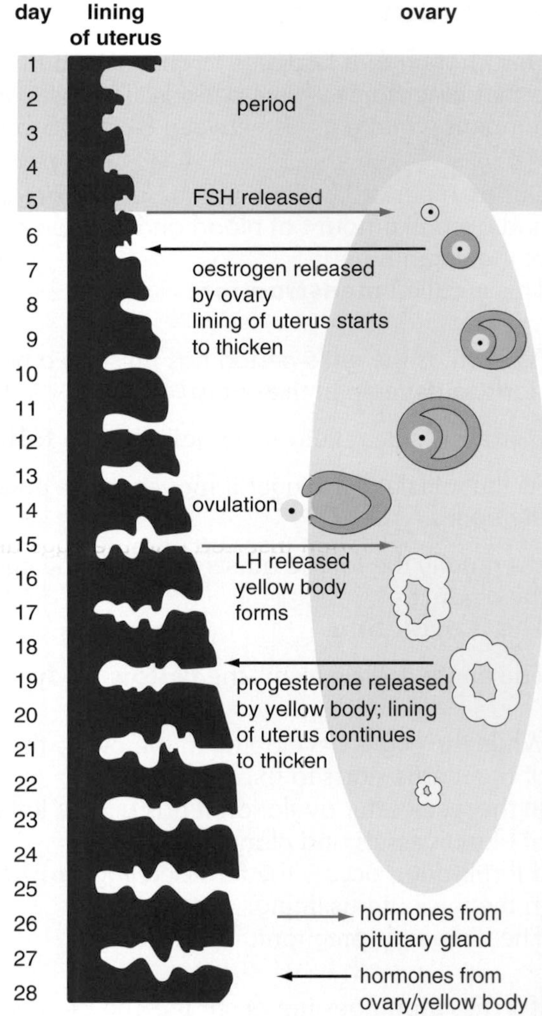

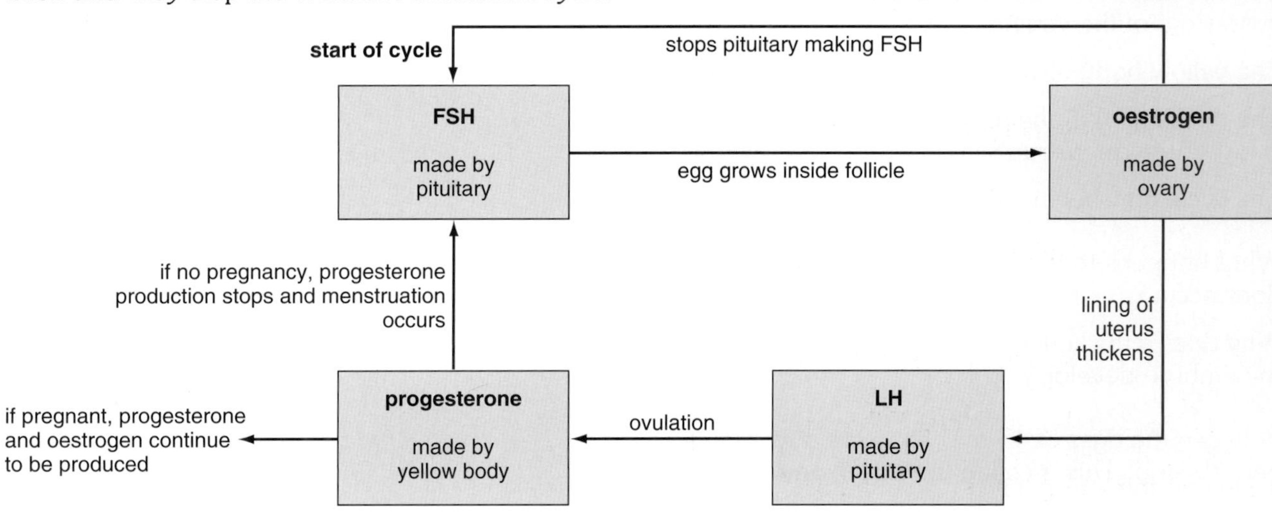

How hormones control ovulation and menstruation

▶ Biology at work : In vitro fertilisation

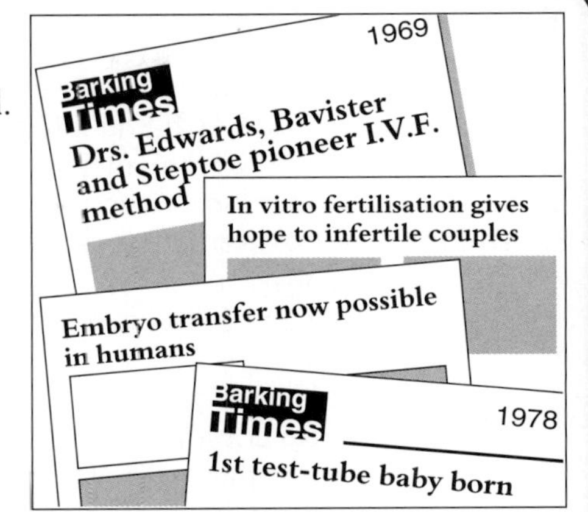

Some couples are unable to have children.
This may be because the man can not make enough sperms.
Another reason may be that the woman's oviducts are blocked.
Both these problems prevent sperms and eggs from meeting.

In vitro fertilisation (often abbreviated to IVF) can often help these couples.
'In vitro' means 'in glass'.
It involves fertilisation of a human egg outside the body.
This used to be called making 'test-tube babies'.

First the woman is injected with FSH.
This makes her produce eggs.
The doctor makes a small incision in the body wall.
A fine tube is then inserted and the eggs are sucked out.

The eggs are kept alive in a solution containing food and oxygen.
Some semen from the father is mixed with the eggs.
The fertilised eggs are kept in the solution for a few days.
They are watched under the microscope as they develop into embryos.

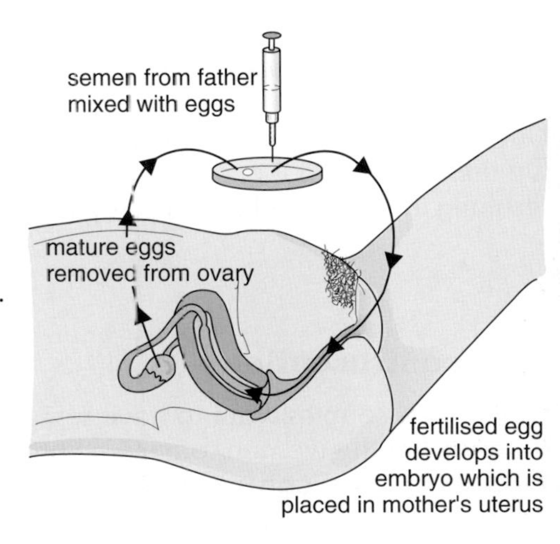

The doctor then places an embryo into the mother's uterus.
The embryo develops normally into a baby.

Why do you think the eggs were placed into a solution containing food and oxygen?

Why do you think that fertilised eggs are left for a few days before implanting them into the uterus?

Sometimes more embryos form than can be used.
Many people think that it is wrong to destroy these extra embryos.
What do you think?

Sometimes these extra embryos have been frozen.
They can then be used later if the first embryos do not grow.
Do you think that it is right to do this?

▶ Biology at work : Controlling fertility

Fertility drugs

Some couples want to have children but can not.
Couples are regarded as being infertile if they have had regular, unprotected sexual intercourse for 12 months without a pregnancy occurring.
Often the cause of infertility is that the woman's ovaries do not release eggs.
This is due to a lack of FSH production by the pituitary.

Treatment for this type of infertility involves regular injections of a **fertility drug** containing FSH.
The FSH stimulates the ovaries to release eggs.
Other treatments involve tablets that make the pituitary insensitive to oestrogen.
Remember that oestrogen inhibits the production of FSH.
So if oestrogen production is blocked by the drug, then the pituitary continues to release FSH and ovulation occurs.

Unfortunately fertility treatment does not always work.
On the other hand it can work too well; too many eggs may be released resulting in twins, triplets, quadruplets or even more !

Oral contraception

Quite often couples want to have sexual intercourse but do not want the woman to become pregnant.
Oral (by mouth) **contraceptives** contain oestrogen which inhibits the production of FSH by the pituitary.
As a result, no eggs mature to be released by the ovaries and so pregnancy can not occur.
The woman has to take a pill every day.
For many couples the pill is a very reliable and convenient method of contraception.

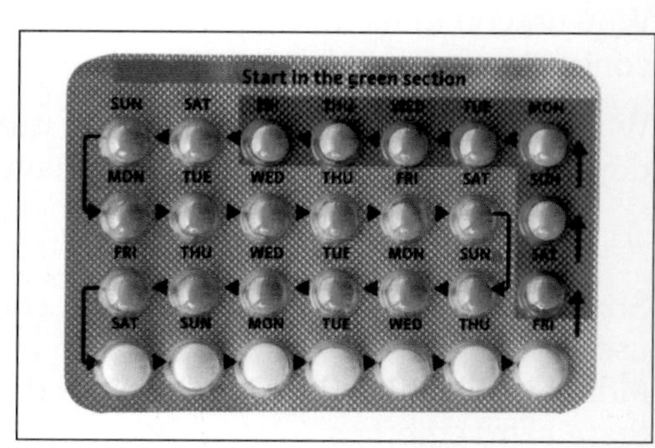

Contraceptive pills

Drawbacks are that failure to take the pill regularly can result in a pregnancy.
Also, side effects such as headaches and feeling sick can occur in some women.
In a very small number of women, the pill can be the cause of heart and circulation problems.

Summary

- Sense organs (receptors) detect stimuli and bring about responses in effectors.
- The nervous system and hormonal system control and coordinate your actions.
- Neurones carry nervous impulses around your body.
  Between two neurones is a gap called the synapse.
- A reflex arc is a nerve pathway.
  Reflexes are automatic, fast and often protective.
- The brain is the controlling centre of the nervous system.
- Senses include touch, taste, smell, sight, hearing and balance.
- Receptors send impulses to the brain along sensory neurones.
- Impulses are carried to effectors along motor neurones.
- The eye can convert light rays into nerve impulses.
- Hormones, like adrenaline, are made in glands, like the adrenals, and are carried around the body to target organs in the blood.
- Secondary sexual characteristics develop due to oestrogen (in girls) and testosterone (in boys).
- The menstrual cycle is controlled by hormones produced by the pituitary and the ovaries.

► Questions

1. Copy and complete :
The brain and .... make up the central nervous system.
The brain is protected by the .... and the spinal cord by the .... column. Impulses are carried to the spinal cord by the .... neurones. Inside the .... matter of the spinal cord the impulses are passed on to .... neurones. The impulses leave the spinal cord along .... neurones. There is a gap between two neurones called a .....

2. a) What is meant by :
i) a stimulus ii) a receptor iii) a response ?

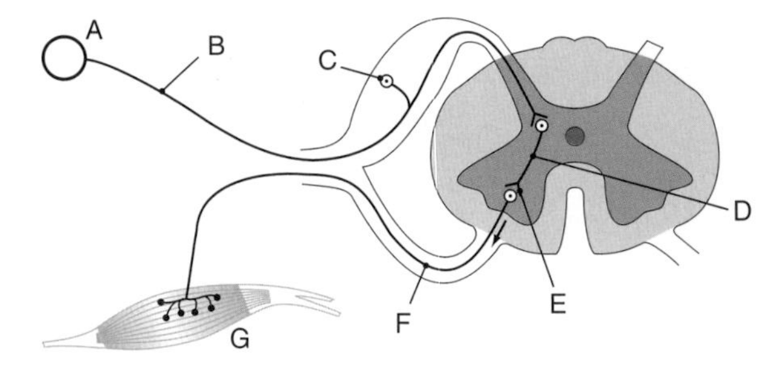

b) Name the parts labelled A to G.
c) Explain what is happening at the points A to G.

3. Look at the diagram of the motor neurone :
a) Name the parts labelled A to D.
b) Give the functions of parts B, C and D.

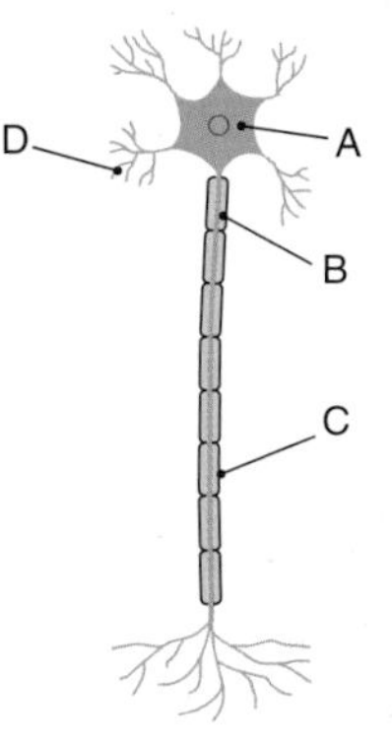

4. Match each of the following in column A with their function in column B :

Column A	Column B
• synapse	• carries impulses from the spinal cord to a muscle
• cerebellum	• controls learning and memory
• sensory neurone	• a gap between neurones
• cerebral hemispheres	• controls balance
• motor neurone	• controls heartbeat, breathing and blood pressure
• medulla	• carries impulses from a sense organ to the spinal cord

5. a) What is meant by a reflex action?
   b) Which reflex action happens when you:
      i) get dust into your trachea
      ii) have a bright light shone into your eye
      iii) see or smell some nice food
      iv) stand out in a cold wind?
   c) How does each of these reflexes help you?

6. a) Name four ways in which the hormonal system is different from the nervous system.
   b) Which hormone:
      i) prepares the body for action
      ii) reduces the amount of glucose in the blood
      iii) controls the rate of chemical reactions in the body
      iv) is produced in the testes of the male
      v) is produced in the ovaries of the female?

7. a) What is the female hormone produced by the ovaries during puberty?
   b) What changes does this hormone make in a girl's body?
   c) What is the male hormone produced by the testes during puberty?
   d) What changes does this hormone make in a boy's body?

8. An egg is released from a woman's ovary on 7th March.
   a) Over which days would fertilisation be most likely to occur?
   b) The egg was not fertilised. How soon after 7th March will the woman's period start?
   c) How long does a period usually last?
   d) When is the next egg likely to be released?

9. Give the proper biological names for each of these parts of the eye:
   a) Light-sensitive layer.
   b) Controls the amount of light entering the eye.
   c) Delicate, transparent layer at the front of the eye.
   d) Tough, white, outer layer of the eye.
   e) Jelly-like substance that keeps the eye in shape.
   f) Carries nerve impulses to the brain.
   g) Black middle layer.
   h) Controls the shape of the lens.
   i) Attaches the lens to the ciliary muscles.

10. The diagram shows a section through the human eye:

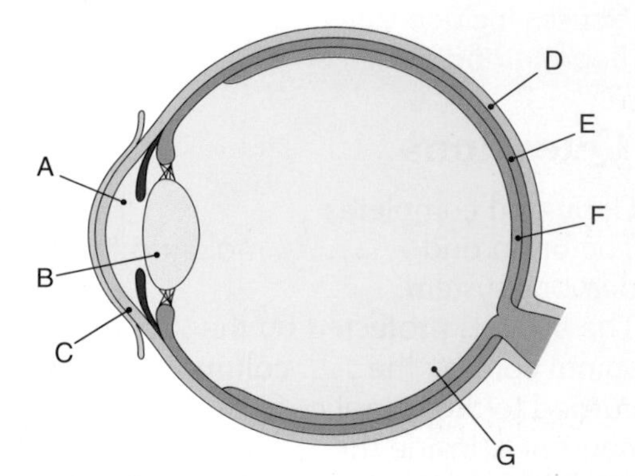

   a) Name the parts labelled A to G.
   b) Which of these parts help in the focusing of light on to F?
   c) Write out the sequence to show the pathway of light from C to F:
   d) How are nerve impulses carried away from the eye to the brain?

Further questions on page 171.

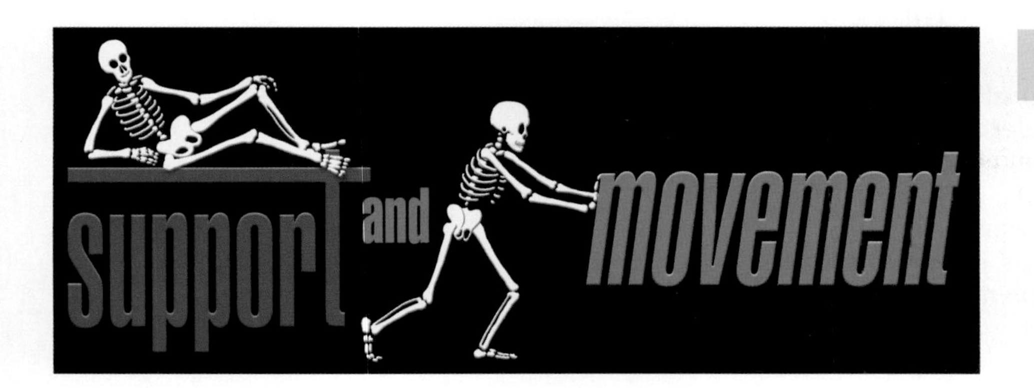

chapter 9

All animals need to support their bodies.
They also need to move about.
Most animals need a supporting framework – they need a **skeleton**.

Skeletons are used for :

- ***Supporting*** the body and giving it shape.
- ***Protecting*** soft parts of the body.
- ***Moving*** the body with the help of muscles.

► Liquid skeletons

Some animals don't seem to have a skeleton at all.
Look at the jellyfish in the photograph :

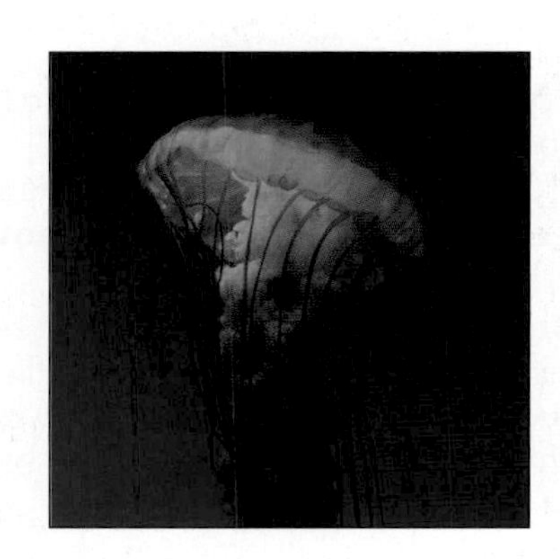

How does it support its body and move about?

Its soft body is filled with water.
It moves its muscles against the water.
This opens and closes its umbrella.
So it propels itself along.

Worms also have a liquid skeleton.
The liquid is trapped in spaces inside the body.
The muscles squeeze against the liquid.
This keeps the body firm.

Muscles can squeeze in different parts of the worm's body.
This changes its shape and helps it to move along.

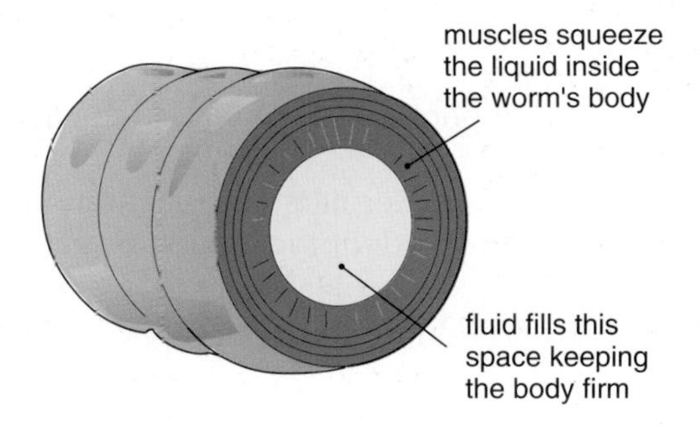

▶ Exoskeletons

Many animals have a skeleton on the ***outside***.
This is called an **exoskeleton**.
Can you think of an animal with an exoskeleton ?

All the arthropods have exoskeletons.
Arthropods include insects, spiders and crabs.
They have an exoskeleton made out of **chitin**,
a complex carbohydrate.

Look at the crab in the picture :

Its exoskeleton is like a suit of armour.
There are flat plates to protect the body.
Hollow tubes form the limbs and allow
movement at **joints**.

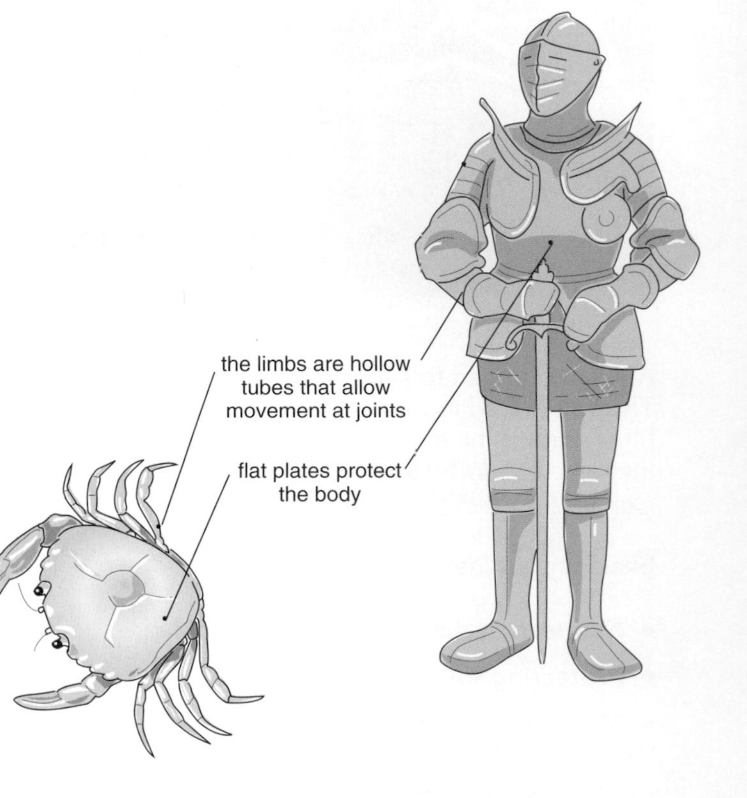

Exoskeletons give good support and protection,
just like armour does.
But also, like armour, they can be very heavy
to carry around.
Animals with exoskeletons never grow very large.
If they did their exoskeletons would become too
heavy for their muscles to move.

The soft parts of these animals are ***inside***
the skeleton.
But an exoskeleton can not grow as the rest of
the body does.
Every so often the hard covering is shed and
a new one grows. This is called **moulting**.

Metamorphosis is the change in body-form as an animal grows.
In insects such as butterflies, blowflies or the dragonfly in the photo,
the young are called **larvae**. They do not look like the adult.
Each time the larva moults it gets bigger until it forms a resting
stage called a **pupa**.
Eventually the adult emerges from the pupa and flies off.
This dramatic change from young to adult is called **complete metamorphosis**.

In metamorphosis, the young and the adult have different food
sources.
For example, caterpillars eat vegetation whilst butterflies eat nectar.
How is this an advantage to the insect?

Young and adult insects often have different habitats.
This also would reduce competition for scarce resources.

A dragonfly larva moulting its exoskeleton

▶ Endoskeletons

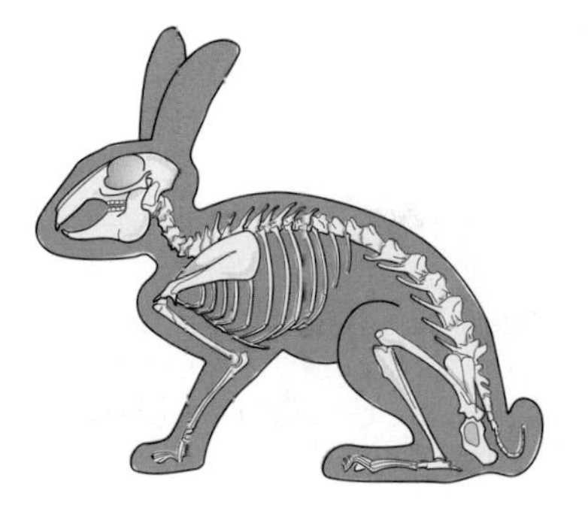

Your skeleton is ***inside*** your body, so it is called an **endoskeleton**.
It is made of hard bone and cartilage.
Having an internal skeleton provides a strong framework for muscles and means that it can grow with the body.

Fish, amphibians, reptiles, birds and mammals all have endoskeletons.
They are all **vertebrates**.
Some fish, like sharks, have an endoskeleton made only of cartilage.

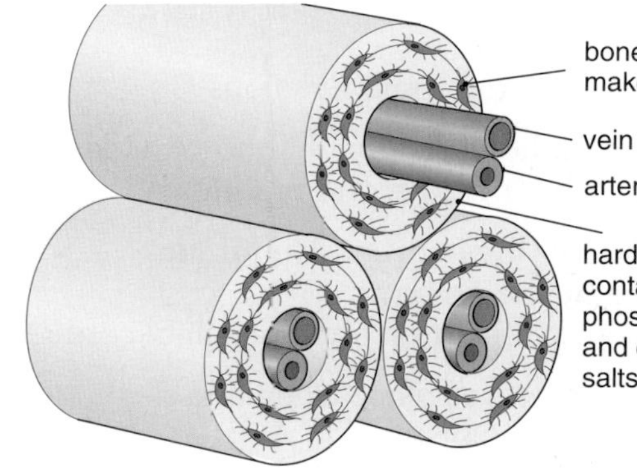

Look at the drawing of a section of bone under the microscope :

Can you see cells in the bone ?

Bone and cartilage are both ***living*** tissues.
So the skeleton can grow as the rest of the animal does.
The living cells are also able to repair broken bones.
So if we fracture a bone, it will heal up, providing that it is set in plaster. Elderly people are more prone to fractures due to soft bones.
This condition, known as **osteoporosis** is caused by a lack of calcium in the diet.

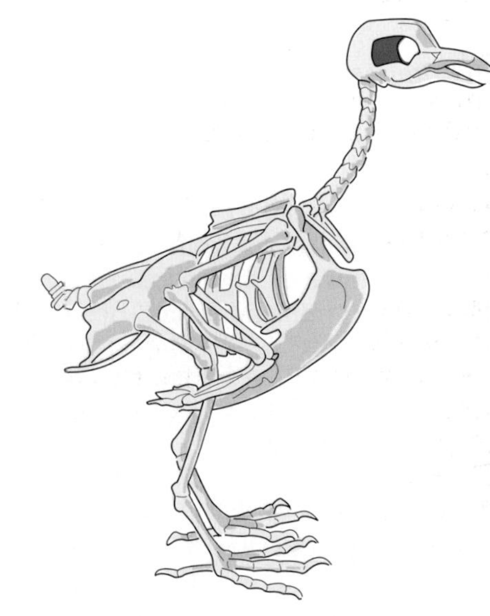

All vertebrate skeletons have the same basic parts :

- A **skull** which contains and protects the brain.
- A jointed **backbone** made up of small bones called **vertebrae**.
- A **rib-cage** protecting the thorax.
- **Limbs** (arms and legs) and **limb girdles** (shoulders and hips).

Look at these two skeletons.
See if you can pick out the basic parts in each one.
Which animal does each skeleton belong to ?

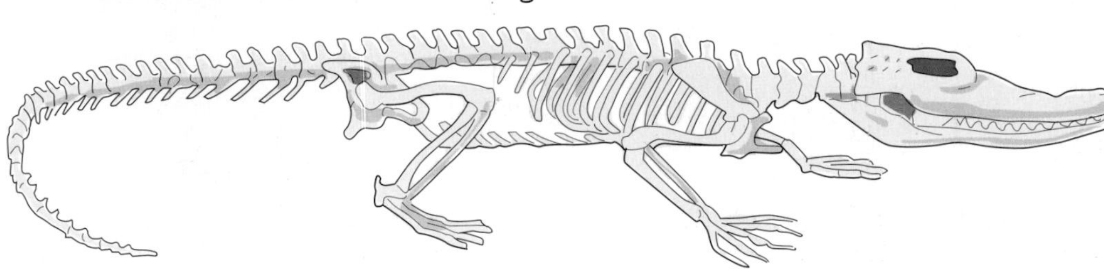

► The human skeleton

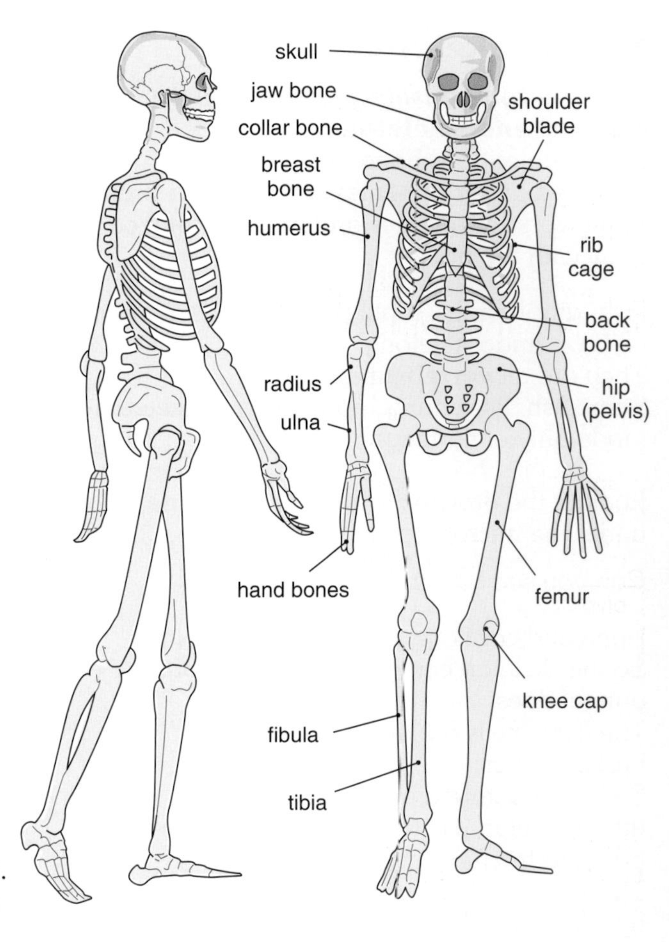

Your skeleton is made up of more than 200 bones.

Look at the diagram :

Can you pick out the four basic parts of the vertebrate skeleton :

How many of these bones can you name ?

How is ***this*** skeleton different from the ones on the previous page ?

Our skeleton has four main functions :

- **Support** – it holds us upright and provides a framework for tissues and organs.
- **Protection** – the heart and lungs are protected by the rib-cage. What protects the brain and the spinal cord ?
- **Movement** – takes place when muscles move bones at joints.
- **Making blood cells** – red and white blood cells are made inside the bone marrow.

In humans, the skeleton starts off as being cartilage.
It is then slowly replaced by the addition of calcium and phosphorus.
This process is known as **ossification**.
Scientists can determine whether a person is still growing by the amount of cartilage present in their skeleton.
Can you think of any parts of your body that are made only of cartilage ?
How about your outer ear, nose or the ends of your long bones ?

Experiment 9.1 Parts of a skeleton

Look closely at the different bones of a human skeleton.

- How is the skull attached to the backbone ?
- How are the ribs attached to the backbone ?
- How are the limbs attached at the shoulders and hips ?
- Can you find a common pattern to the bones of the arm and the bones of the leg ?
- The long bones are hollow. Why do you think this makes them lighter and stronger than solid bones ?

▶ Joints

Joints occur where two bones meet.
Joints allow movement to take place.

Some joints allow more movement than others.
Some don't allow any movement at all.

Look at the different types of joint in the X-rays :
Then look at the table to see how they move.

Joint	Where found in body	Type of movement
hinge	elbow, knee, finger	in only one plane – like the hinge on a door
ball-and-socket	hip and shoulder	in all directions
pivot	neck	nodding or turning
fixed	skull and pelvis	no movement
gliding	backbone	slight movement

Synovial joints

Most movement occurs at **synovial joints**.
Hinge and ball-and-socket joints are both types of synovial joint.

Movement at these joints could cause friction.
A synovial joint is built to cut down friction :

- The ends of the bones are covered with **cartilage**. This acts as a shock-absorber and stops the two bones rubbing together.
- The **synovial membrane** encloses **synovial fluid**. This lubricates or oils the joint and makes movement easy.
- The bones are held together at a joint by tough **ligaments**.
- Muscles are connected to the bones by **tendons**. When muscles work, they pull on tendons and move the bone.

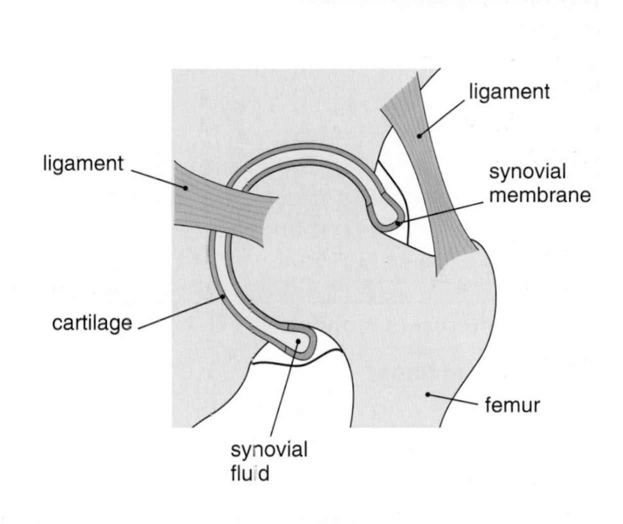

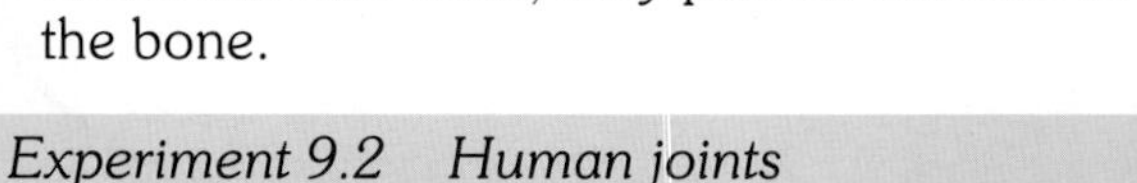

Experiment 9.2 Human joints

Look carefully at a model of the human skeleton.
Try to find the different types of joints shown in the table above.

► Muscles at work

Your muscles provide the force needed to move bones at joints.
Muscles can not ***push*** – they can only ***pull***.

When a muscle **contracts** it gets shorter and fatter.
When a muscle is not contracting it returns to its normal size – we say that it **relaxes**.

Muscles like your **biceps** and **triceps** work in pairs.
When one contracts, the other relaxes.
They form an **antagonistic pair** of muscles.

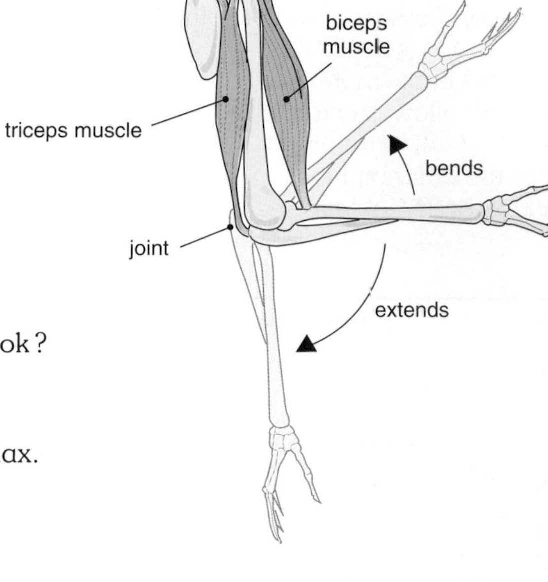

What happens to your muscles when you pick up a book?

Nerves carry impulses from your brain to the muscles in your arm.
They tell your biceps to contract and your triceps to relax.
As your biceps shortens it pulls on the tendon that pulls up your lower arm.
Your arm bends at the hinge joint at the elbow.

What do you think happens to your arm muscles when you put the book back onto the table?
This time your triceps contracts and your biceps relaxes to straighten your arm.

Experiment 9.3 Testing your finger strength

Set up the clamp stand as shown:
Place your hand flat on the table and put your middle finger through the elastic band.
Now move your finger down to touch the table.
Count the number of finger movements that you can do ***continuously*** for 2 minutes.
Record the number of finger movements for each 20-second period in a table like this:

Time interval (seconds)	0–20	20–40	40–60	60–80	80–100	100–120
Number of finger movements						

Plot a line-graph with axes like this:

Try to explain your results.

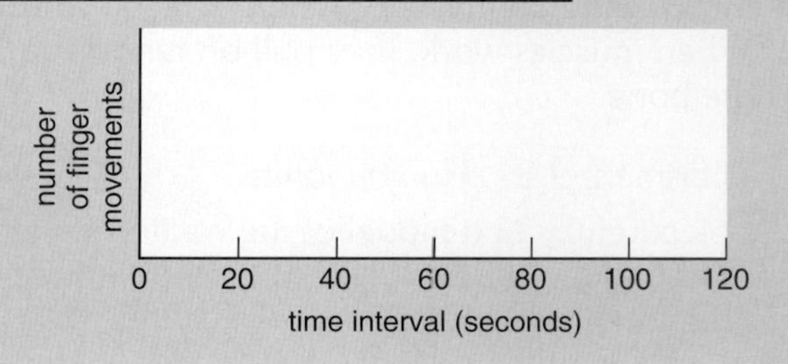

▶ Biology at work : Sports injuries

Many sportsmen and sportswomen run the risk of injury.
The commonest injuries occur to muscles, ligaments, bones and joints.
These sorts of injuries often happen early in the season when training sessions start.

A dislocated shoulder

Pulled muscle

This happens when a muscle is over-stretched.
Some of the muscle fibres may tear causing the muscle to contract.
The muscle swells up due to internal bleeding.

Sprains

Ligaments join the bones together at joints.
If a joint bends beyond its normal limits the ligament can tear.
A strain like this needs rest and the pain can be eased by an ice-pack and a supporting bandage.
If many ligaments tear, a bone can come out of place.
We say that the bone is **dislocated**.
A doctor can put the dislocated bone back in place.

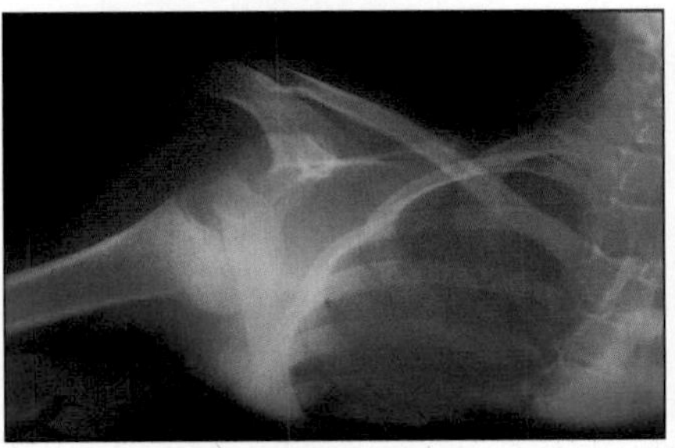
Can you see the dislocation in the X-ray?

Displaced cartilage

The knee has to withstand a lot of strain.
There are two pads of cartilage in the knee joint that act as shock-absorbers.
One of these may become damaged or pushed out of place if the knee is suddenly twisted.
Soccer players sometimes have to have an operation to remove a displaced cartilage.

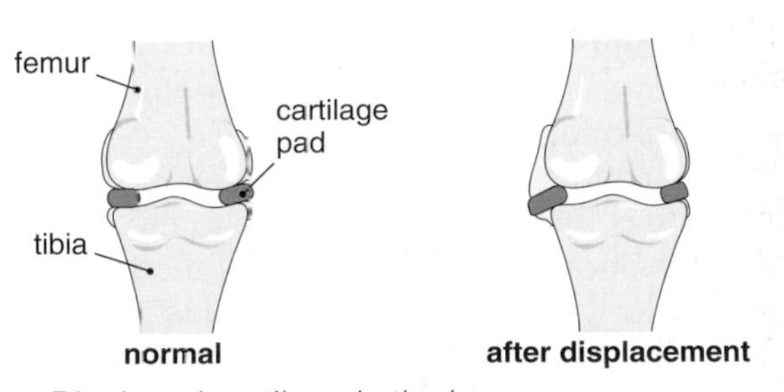

Displaced cartilage in the knee

Fractures

Bones can become broken or fractured.

- A **simple fracture** is when the bone breaks cleanly in two.
- A **greenstick fracture** is when the bone breaks on one side only.
- A **compound fracture** is when there is more than one break.
- An **open fracture** is when the broken bone pierces the skin.

Fractures are treated by resetting the bone.
After checking with an X-ray, the injury is put in a splint or a plaster cast.

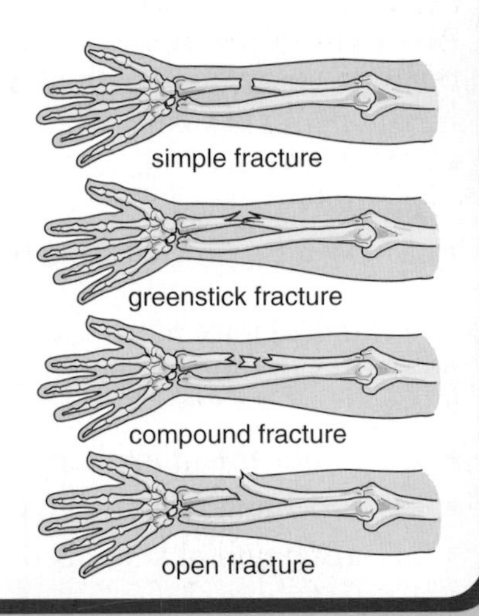

▶ Biology at work : Arthritis and joint replacement

As we get older our joints don't work as smoothly.
Sometimes they rub and grind against each other.
This friction causes pain and makes it difficult to move.
Arthritis is a disease that can make things worse.

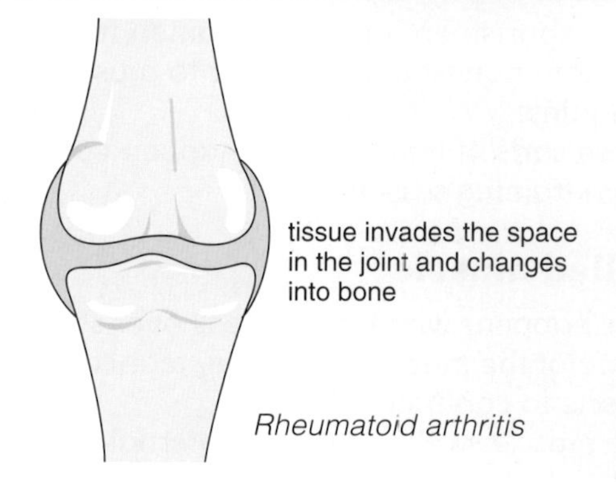

Rheumatoid arthritis

Rheumatoid arthritis is when the smaller joints of the body become inflamed.
Tissue grows across the joint and makes movement difficult.
The joint can become permanently fused so there is no movement at all.
The disease is usually inherited.
The rate of cartilage destruction is very variable, taking many years in some people, but as little as a few months in others.

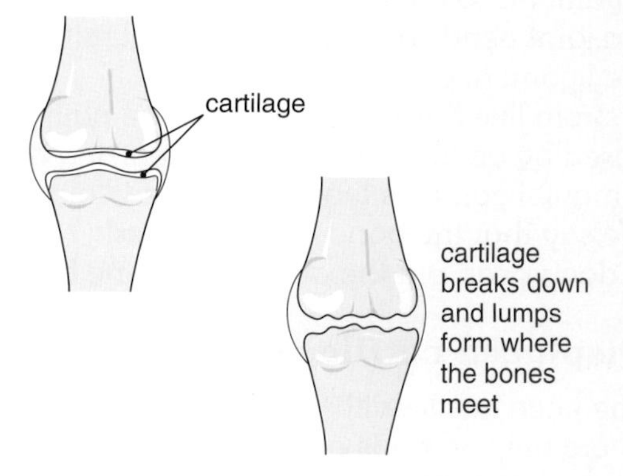

Normal joint (left); osteoarthritis (right)

Osteoarthritis usually affects older people.
The cartilage at the end of the bones becomes worn away.
The cartilage acted as a shock-absorber.
Without it there is a lot more friction so movement of the joint can be very painful.
Sometimes the diseased joint is replaced by an artificial one.
Osteoarthritis is not caused by genetic factors.
Obesity is thought to contribute to the disease.
A large body mass puts a much greater strain on joints, particularly the knee, hip and ankle joints.
This increases the rate at which the cartilage is eroded.

An **artificial joint** can be used to replace the ball-and-socket joint at the hip.
It is made up of two parts.

- a stainless steel ball which replaces the head of the femur bone, and
- a plastic cup in which the ball swivels.

The artificial joint must have all the important properties of the real one.
It must :

- allow movement in all three directions
- be lubricated to cut down friction
- be strong and able to absorb knocks.

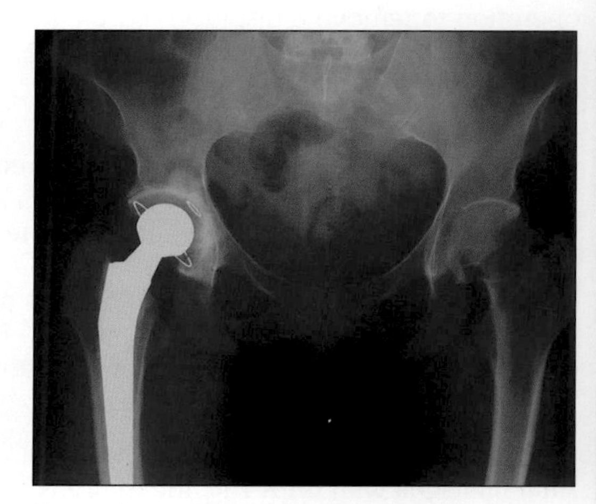

X-ray of an artificial joint

Summary

- Most animals need a skeleton for support, protection and movement.
- Exoskeletons give good protection but are heavy and cannot grow with the rest of the body.
- Vertebrates have an endoskeleton made of bone and/or cartilage which can grow as the rest of the animal does.
- The backbone is supported by muscles and protects the spinal cord.
- A joint occurs where two bones meet. Different types of joint allow different amounts of movement.
- Bones are held together at joints by ligaments. Muscles are attached to bones by tendons.
- Synovial joints contain synovial fluid to lubricate the joint. The ends of the bones are covered with cartilage which acts as a shock-absorber and stops the bones rubbing together.
- Muscles do work by contracting.
- Muscles often work in antagonistic pairs – when one contracts the other relaxes.
- Bones that are fractured can be re-set and supported in a splint or plaster cast.
- Arthritis can occur if the cartilage at the end of the bones at a joint becomes worn away.
- Artificial joints can be used to replace hip and knee joints.

▶ Questions

1. Copy and complete:
A joint occurs where two .... meet. At a joint two bones are joined together by ..... Movement is brought about at a joint by ..... When a muscle .... it shortens and thickens. When a muscle .... it returns to its original shape. Muscles often occur in pairs. When one muscle contracts the other ..... These are called .... muscle pairs.

2. Look at the diagram of the arm:

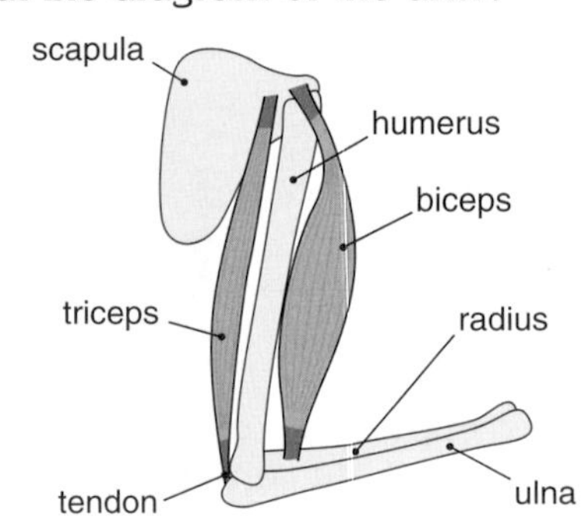

a) Which muscle contracts to raise the arm?
b) Which muscle contracts to lower the arm?
c) Why are the biceps and the triceps known as an antagonistic pair of muscles?

3. a) What are the functions of a skeleton?
b) What is the difference between an exoskeleton and an endoskeleton?
c) Why does an exoskeleton restrict the size to which an animal can grow?
d) Why do animals moult their exoskeleton as they grow?

4. Match the bones in column A with the descriptions in column B:

Column A	Column B
humerus	Protects the brain.
pelvis	Helps us to breathe in and out.
skull	The largest bone in the body.
femur	There are many of these in the backbone.
vertebrae	Upper arm bone.
ribs	Attaches the lower limb bones to the backbone.

5. Which structures:

a) attach bones to bones
b) attach muscles to bones
c) act as shock-absorbers at the ends of bones?

6. Look at the diagram of the synovial joint:

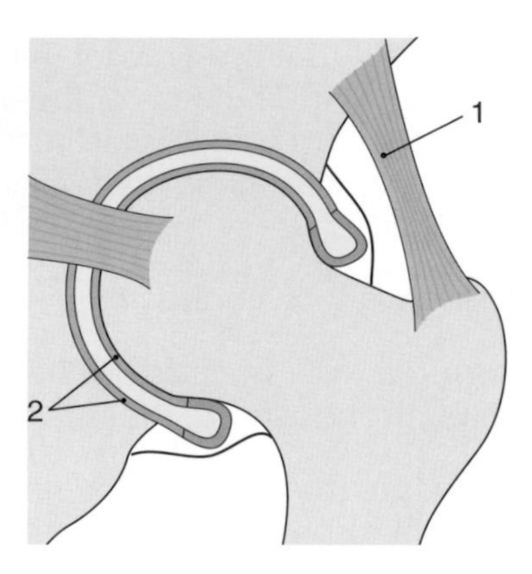

a) What is this type of synovial joint called?
b) Where is it found in the body?
c) What sort of movement does it allow?
d) What is the name of the structure labelled 1 and what job does it do?
e) What is the name of the structure labelled 2 and what job does it do?
f) Why is there fluid in this joint?

7. Look at the diagram of the bones of the human right hand:

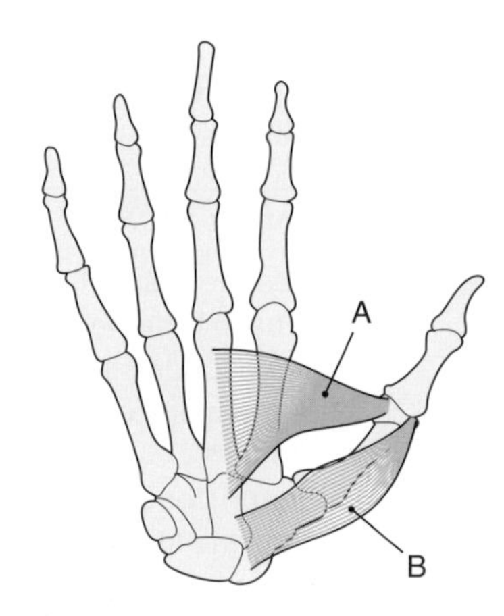

a) Which of the muscles (A or B) moves the thumb towards the fingers?
b) What does the other muscle do while this is happening?
c) Explain why there are two muscles attached to the thumb?

8. a) What are the advantages of having a backbone made up of many separate vertebrae?
b) Where would you find these joints in the body and what type of movement do they give:
i) fixed joints
ii) pivot joints
iii) gliding joint?
c) Why do you think birds have hollow bones?

9. The diagram shows the skeleton and some muscles of a human arm.

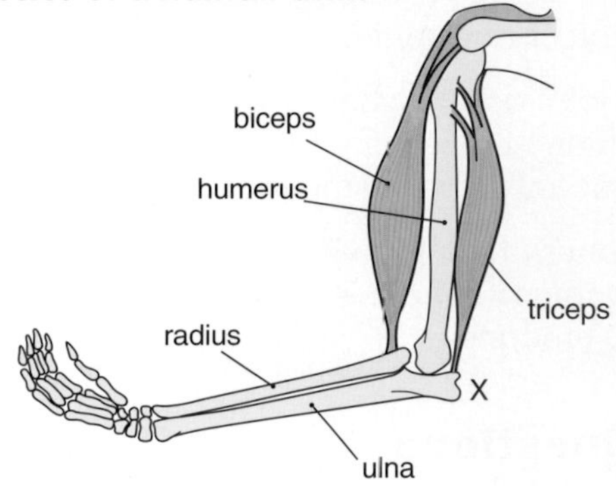

a) Which labelled part bends the arm?
b) Explain, using names given in the diagram, how the bent arm could be straightened again.
The diagram below shows a simplified synovial joint similar to the one found at X.

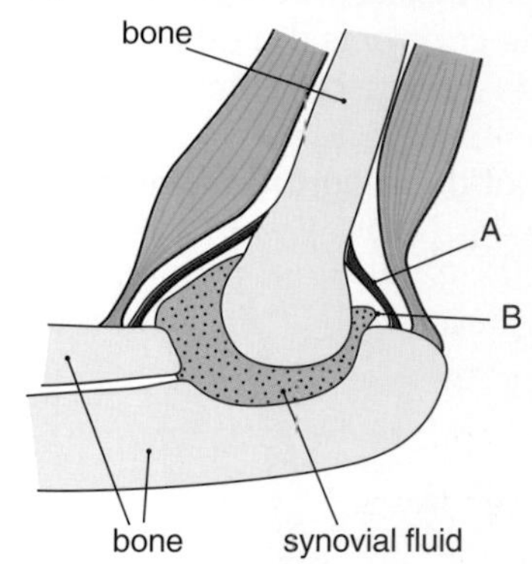

c) i) On a copy of the diagram draw the position of the cartilage.
ii) What is the function of the cartilage?
iii) Name the parts labelled A and B on the diagram.
iv) Suggest what might happen if the synovial fluid was not there.

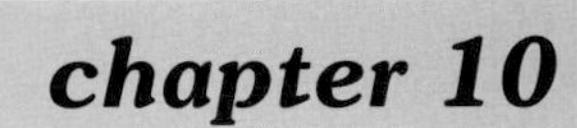

▶ Microbes and disease

In the 19th century **Louis Pasteur** showed that microbes made food go bad.
He thought that microbes could also caused disease.
He was able to show that infectious disease was caused by cholera in hens and by anthrax in sheep.

About the same time, **Robert Koch** was able to prove that diseases such as tuberculosis were caused by microbes. Pure cultures of microbes when injected into healthy animals brought about the symptoms of the disease.

Pasteur and Koch could not have imagined that one day not only a particular disease organism would be identified, but that we could vaccinate against it and even eradicate it from the world,as in the case of smallpox.

Louis Pasteur

Robert Koch

What are pathogens?

Bacteria, viruses and fungi are all microbes.
Not all of them are harmful. Some are useful and help us to make bread, cheese and wine.
The microbes that cause disease are called **pathogens**.

(*Remember* : not ***all*** diseases are caused by microbes, for instance, diabetes is a disease caused by the pancreas not being able to make enough insulin.)

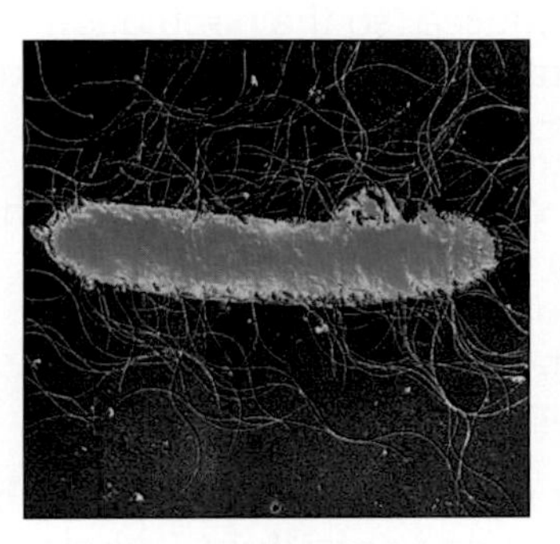

A bacterium found in the gut

Bacteria

Bacteria are cells that are big enough to be seen under the light microscope.
Bacteria are found everywhere – in the air, in water and in the soil.
They can also be found inside living organisms.
Some bacteria are useful, but others can cause diseases such as pneumonia, scarlet fever and tuberculosis.

The basic structure of a bacterial cell is shown here:

Can you see the differences between this cell and an animal cell or a plant cell?

The bacterial cell has a cell wall,but not made out of cellulose as in plant cells.
There is no proper nucleus, just a loop of DNA.
Many of the structures found inside other cells such as mitochondria, are missing in bacteria.
Bacteria often have additional loops of DNA inside their cytoplasm called **plasmids**.

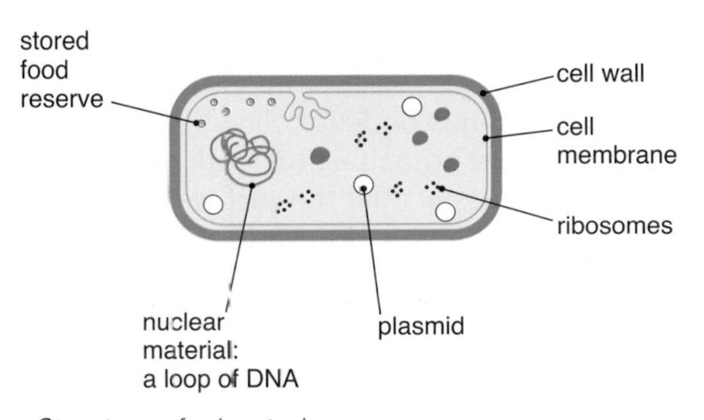

Structure of a bacterium

Bacterial growth

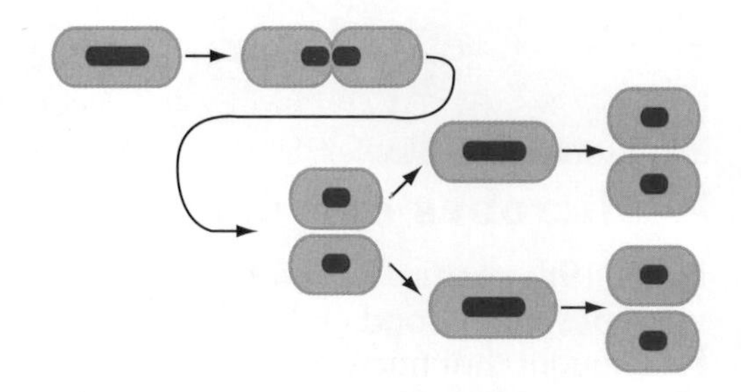

Bacteria can be grown in sterile conditions in the laboratory (page 348).
A colony of bacteria starts with just one cell.
In the right conditions, the cell divides to give two cells, two cells become four, four become eight, eight become 16, and so on.
Bacteria can multiply very quickly to form a **colony**.

If you look at the graph you can see four main phases in the growth of a bacterial colony :

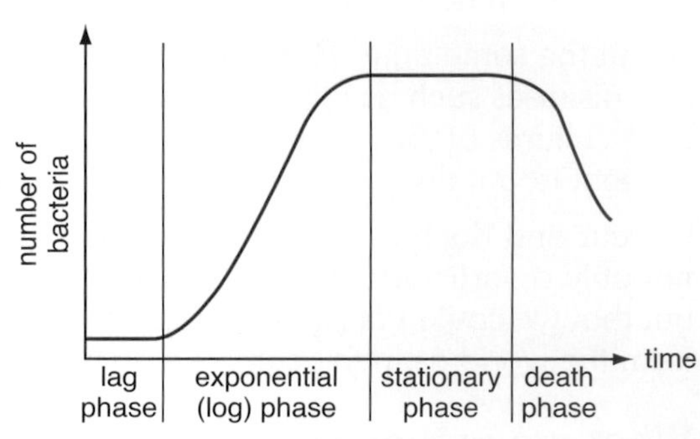

- The **lag phase** when little growth occurs since the cells are taking up water and starting to make enzymes.
- The **log phase** when the population is increasing rapidly. The population increases by doubling and there is no shortage of food or water.
- The **stationary phase** when bacterial cells are dying at the same rate at which they are being produced. This may be because of shortage of food or because waste products are building up.
- The **death phase** when more cells are dying than are being produced, so the population declines. Cause of death may be lack of food, shortage of oxygen or a build up of toxic waste products.

Bacteria which cause disease can survive harsh conditions such as heat, cold and drought.
They can rest for a long time as **spores**.
When good conditions return, they germinate and multiple rapidly again.

There are three main shapes of bacteria – **bacillus** (rods), **coccus** (spheres) and **spirillum** (spirals).

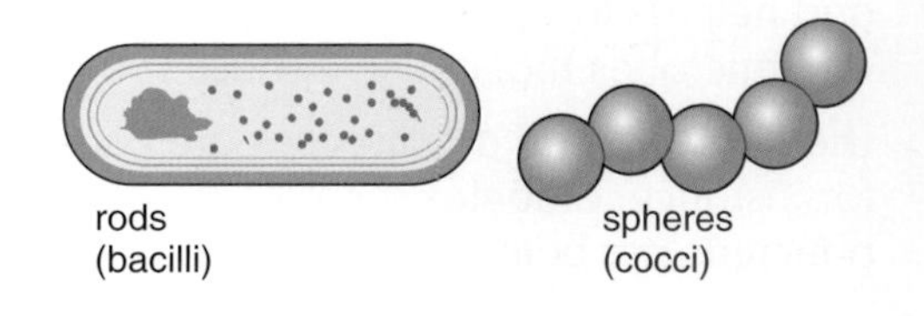

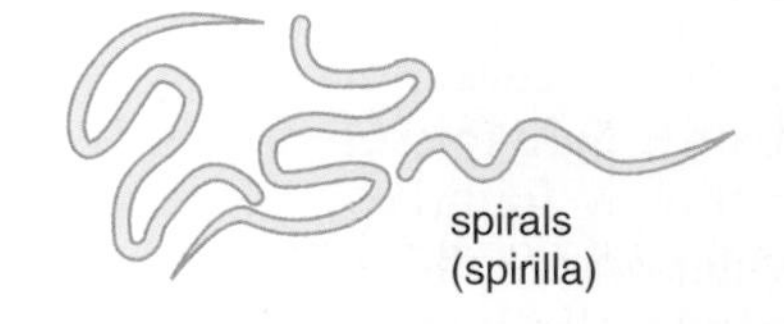

Fungi

Some fungi can also cause disease such as athlete's foot and ringworm.
Fungi are not plants since they do not have chlorophyll.
The main fungus body is called the **mycelium.**
It consists of a branching network of threads or **hyphae.**
The hyphae grow over the surface of their food source.
They release enzymes which digest the food outside the fungus.
The digested food is then absorbed by the hyphae.
Fungi reproduce by making spores that can be carried to infect another person or animal.
Fungi are visible under the light microscope and the spread of fungal disease increases in poor hygiene conditions.

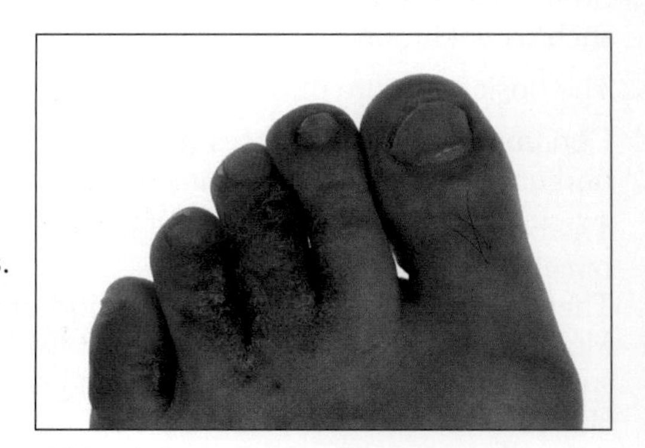

Athlete's foot

Viruses

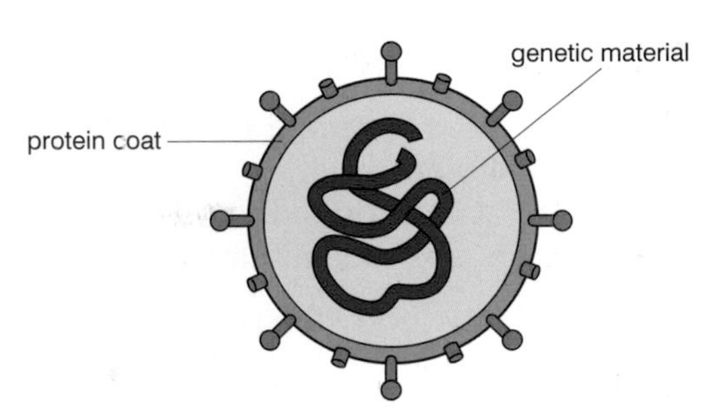

Structure of a virus

Like some bacteria and fungi, viruses are pathogens.
This means that they can cause disease.
Viruses are **parasites** – this means that they rely upon the cells of another organism (the **host**) for food and to be able to reproduce.

Viruses are extremely small, far smaller than bacteria or fungi.
They are only visible under an electron microscope.

A virus consists of a **protein coat** which surrounds a core of either DNA or (less often RNA).
In fact, viruses are not proper cells at all.
They have no cell membrane and no nucleus.
So how do they exist and reproduce?

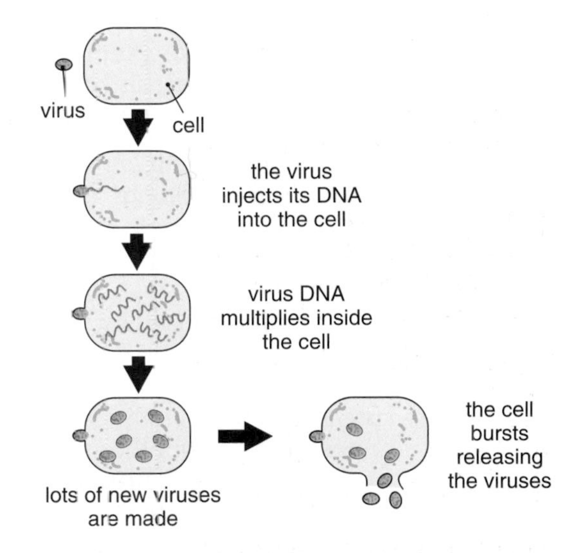

Viruses can only exist ***inside*** living cells.
Once they enter the host cell, they hijack its enzymes and use them to make new viruses.
This takes place as follows:

- The virus enters the body.
- The viral DNA is injected into the host cell.
- The viral DNA instructs the enzymes in the host cell to make new virus protein coats.
- The viral DNA also multiplies inside the host cell.
- The new viral DNA and protein coats join together to make new viruses.
- The host cell bursts releasing the new viruses.
- The new viruses are now free to infect other cells.

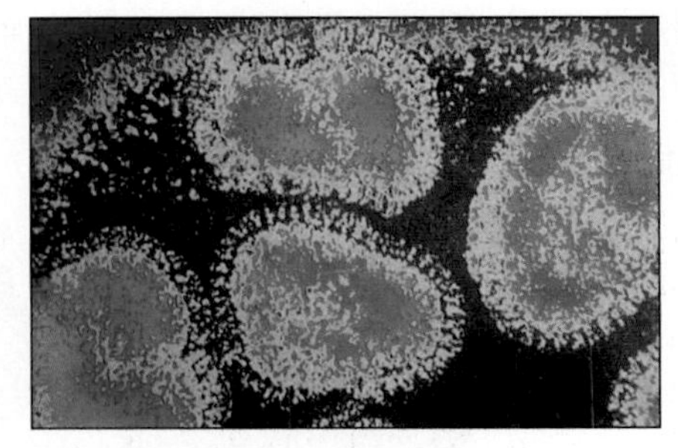
Influenza viruses

Viruses can be very harmful and are the cause of many diseases because they reproduce so quickly.
They do not respond to antibiotics and are constantly changing to produce new resistant strains.

Diseases caused by viruses include influenza, the common cold, measles, chickenpox and AIDS.
An **epidemic** is when an infectious disease spreads rapidly through a population, such as the epidemics of new strains of influenza that can occur.
A **pandemic** occurs if the disease spreads over a wide area, such as a continent or the whole world. TB and AIDS are pandemic diseases.

► How do pathogens affect us?

Pathogens have to enter our body before they can do us any harm.
They can get in through the nose and mouth and through any cuts in our skin.

Once inside the body the pathogens start to multiply.
Conditions inside our body are just right for them and numbers can increase rapidly.
But it takes some time before we start to feel ill.
This early stage of the disease is called the **incubation period**.

So how do pathogens affect us?

Pathogens can cause disease in two ways:

- They destroy living tissue, for example, lung tissue can be destroyed by tuberculosis bacteria.
- They make poisonous waste called **toxins**, for example, salmonella bacteria make the toxins that cause food poisoning.

The **symptoms** of a disease are the effects that it has on the body.
These symptoms are often caused by the toxins that the pathogens make.

Diseases are spread when the pathogens from one person are passed on to another person.
A person who has the disease is **infectious**.
They may pass the disease on to other people.

Can you think of any ways in which diseases are spread?

Death toll rises in food bug outbreak

Five people have died of food poisoning in Britain's worst case of *E. coli bacteria* contamination.

A hospital has been closed to all GP-arranged admissions except suspected cases of the *E. coli 0157* food poisoning outbreak.

The butcher's shop thought to be the source of the outbreak announced yesterday that it was temporarily closing.

Seven members of staff linked to the food poisoning outbreak in Scotland are infected.

Thirty-two adults and a child were being treated yesterday in the hospital, where the Lanarkshire Infectious Disease Unit is based. The number giving cause for concern rose from ten to 15 over the weekend, and the number showing symptoms rose from 189 to 209.

high temperature

headache

loss of appetite

sickness

All these symptoms are caused by the body trying to fight, or resist, the microbes causing the infection

► How are pathogens spread ?

Here are some ways in which people can be infected with pathogens.

In the air
Pathogens can enter our body in the air we breathe. The pathogens can stick to dust floating in the air.

The bacteria causing diphtheria can be spread in this way.

What happens when an infected person sneezes or coughs ?

Tiny drops of liquid are showered into the air. This is why you should cough or sneeze into a handkerchief.

Viruses that cause flu and the common cold are spread in this way. So is tuberculosis, when active TB bacteria are coughed or sneezed into the air.

By touching
You can pick up some pathogens by touching an infected person.
You can also become infected by touching things that an infected person has used such as towels, combs or cups.

The fungus that causes athlete's foot is spread by walking on wet floors after infected people.

A disease that is spread by touch is **contagious**. Very few diseases are contagious.

In food and water
Food and drink can be infected with pathogens.

Typhoid and cholera are spread when infected faeces get into drinking water.

Infection can be passed onto food by a person with dirty hands.
This is why you should always wash your hands after going to the toilet and before you have a meal.

Some food products that come from animals contain bacteria which are only destroyed by cooking thoroughly.
Salmonella bacteria are found in some poultry products.

By animals
Many animal pests can carry pathogens that they pick up from faeces.
Flies will settle on animal dung.
If they crawl over uncovered food they will spread the pathogens from the faeces like the dysentery bacterium.
Food should be covered up or in a fridge to avoid this.

Mosquitoes can spread malaria if they bite an infected person.
They carry the pathogens to the next person that they bite and so the disease is spread.
Insects that carry disease in this way are called **vectors**.

The housefly is a major vector of dysentery

By infected needles
Drug addicts should never share needles.
If an infected person uses a needle the disease can be passed on to anyone else who uses it.

Viruses causing diseases such as AIDS and hepatitis can be passed into the blood in this way.

Preventing infection

Good hygiene is often the key to preventing the spread of disease :

- Wash your hands
  - before meals,
  - after going to the toilet, and
  - before handling food.
- Wash your hair regularly – special shampoos can get rid of dandruff and head lice.
- Have a regular bath or shower especially in hot weather.
- Clean your teeth at least twice a day – first thing in the morning and last thing at night.
- Thoroughly wash any cuts or scratches. A plaster will help to stop microbes getting in.
- ***Food*** should be covered to keep flies away. Cook food thoroughly and eat it straight away or keep it in the fridge or freezer. Keep cooked food away from raw food.
- ***Water*** should be boiled (or chemically sterilised) before drinking if there is any risk of contamination.

How many ways of spreading disease can you find here ?

▶ Destroying pathogens

If something is **sterile** it is free from pathogens.
Can you think of any ways of killing pathogens ***outside*** the body?

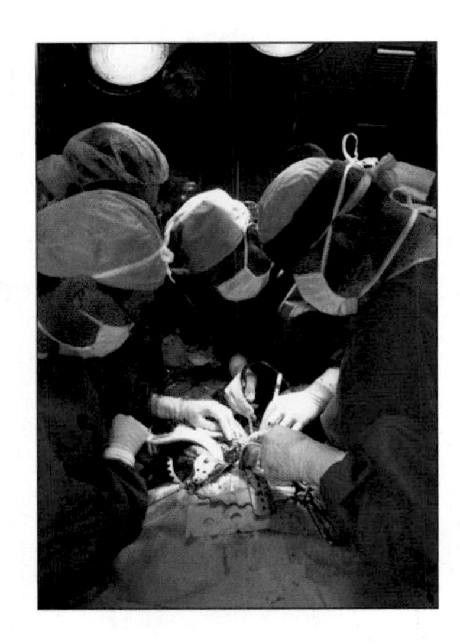

- **Heating** is one way of sterilising.
  Hospitals use heat to sterilise instruments.
  They are heated to 120 °C in a type of pressure cooker called an **autoclave**.

- Dressings can be treated with **radioactivity** to kill all microbes.

- **Disinfectants** are chemicals that kill pathogens.
  They are often used on non-living surfaces.
  Disinfectants are used on kitchen work surfaces and in toilets.

- **Antiseptics** are chemicals that kill pathogens on living tissue.
  They are weaker than disinfectants which would damage our cells.

In the 1860s the British surgeon **Joseph Lister** used the first antiseptic.
Lister noticed that patients' wounds often went bad or **septic** after operations.
He concluded that the pathogens entered the wounds from the air.
Lister sprayed wounds with an antiseptic called **carbolic acid** during the operation.
He also washed scalpels and dressings with it.
Far fewer patients died from infected wounds.

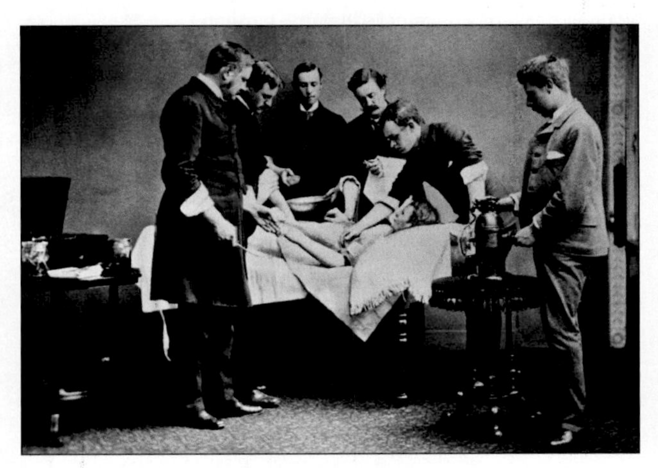

Joseph Lister performing an operation using the first antiseptic

The ***MRSA*** bacterium is of great concern to experts in infectious diseases.
There is an increasing possibility that if you go into hospital for an operation or if you develop an open wound, the MRSA superbug will be there, ready and waiting to cause infection and delay healing.
The bacterium was 95 % controlled by **penicillin** in the 1940s, but now less than 10 % responds to penicillin.
Patients are treated with a combination of strong antibiotics.
But MRSA should be prevented by medical personnel washing their hands between patients and by introducing a stricter programme of cleanliness in hospitals.

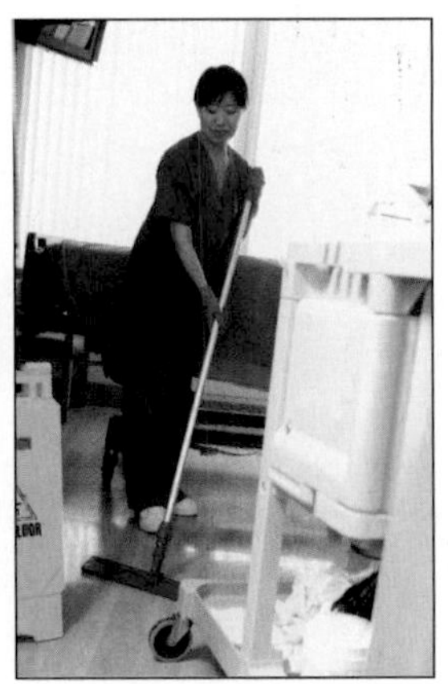

Cleanliness fights MRSA in hospitals

Barriers

How does your body defend itself from pathogens?

Your body has a number of ways of stopping microbes from getting in.

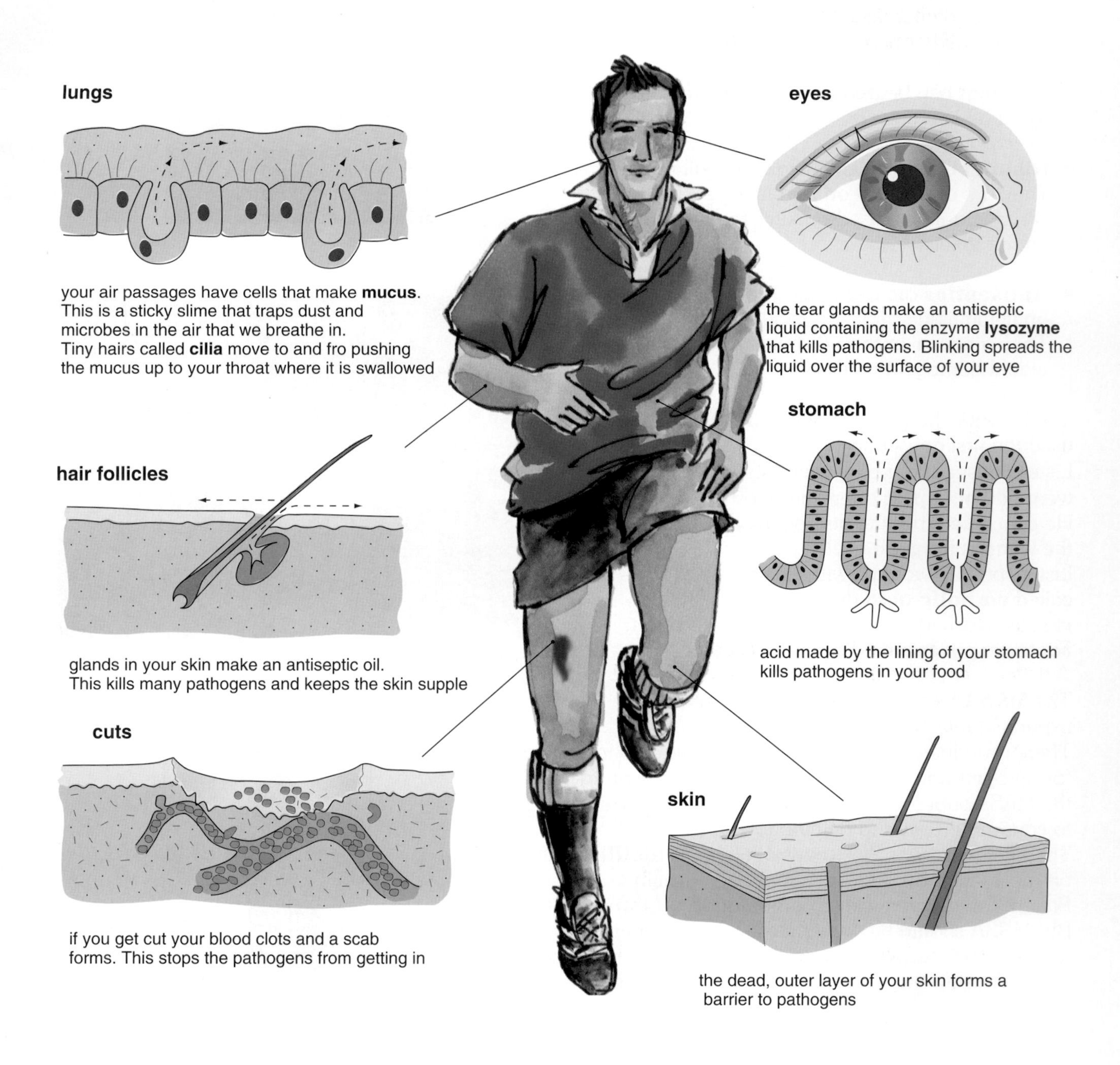

▶ Immunity

Do you know how pathogens are killed ***inside*** the body?.

All pathogens have chemicals on their surface called **antigens**.
These chemicals are largely made of protein.
When you catch a disease like measles your body makes chemicals called **antibodies**.
These antibodies stick to the antigens on the surface of the pathogen.
Antibodies make the pathogens stick together.
White blood cells are then able to attack and destroy them more easily.

Each type of pathogen has a different antigen.
So each kind of pathogen can only be destroyed by a certain kind of antibody.
Once you have made a particular antibody it stays in your blood for a long time.
It is ready to kill any more pathogens if you get the same disease again.
You are now **immune** to that particular disease.

White blood cells can also make chemicals called **antitoxins**.
These destroy the toxins (poisonous wastes) made by the pathogens.

You don't have to catch a disease to become immune to it.
You can be **immunised** with a **vaccine**.
A vaccine contains dead or inactive pathogens.
These pathogens still have antigens and they stimulate your white cells to make antibodies.
These antibodies will now destroy the antigens.

Once you have been **vaccinated**, your immune system will be able to react very rapidly if you are infected by the same pathogens again.
Antibodies will be made, and the antigens destroyed possibly without you having any symptoms.

This is called **active immunity**.

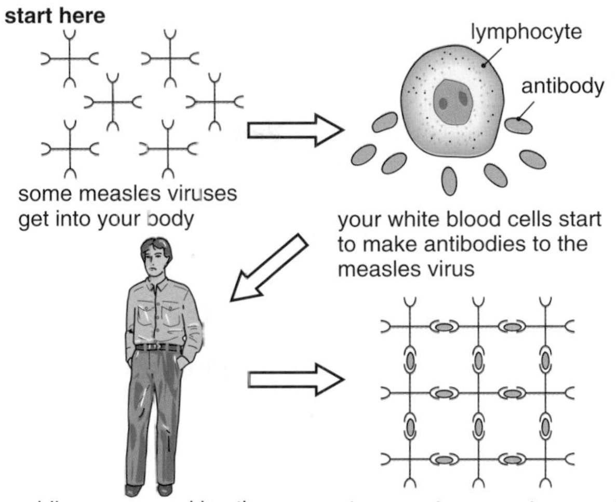

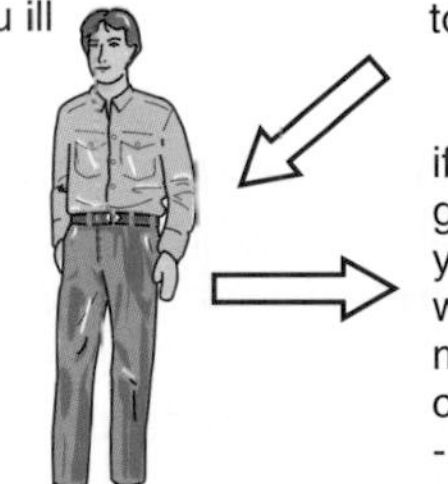

A rubella vaccination

Passive immunity

With **passive immunity** you are not injected with weakened pathogens but with antibodies themselves. This treatment is used to give rapid protection against particularly dangerous pathogens.
A good example is the disease **rabies** which you might catch if bitten by an infected dog.

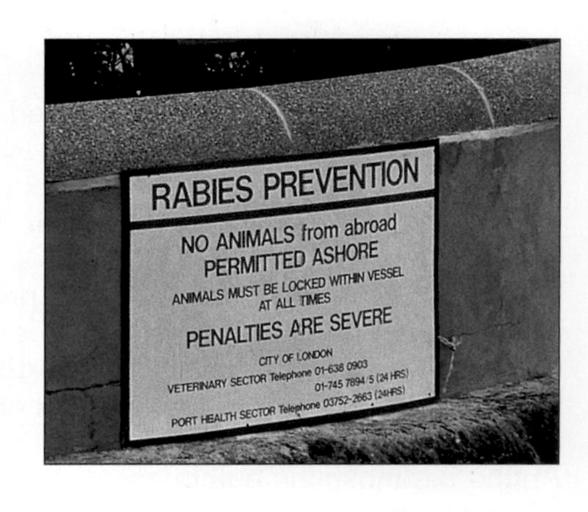

How does the immune system work?

Two types of white blood cells (**lymphocytes**) are involved in giving us immunity.
They are called **T cells** and **B cells**.

The T cells recognise the antigens on the surface of the pathogens.
To do this they have special **receptors** on their surface.
These receptors allow the T cells to attach to the antigens, and they can then destroy them.

T cells also have another important job.
They stimulate the B cells to multiply.
The B cells produce **clones** (genetically identical copies) of themselves.
These cells are then able to produce antibodies against any specific antigens.

There are as many as 10 million different B cells.
So for every antigen that enters the body, there will almost certainly be a B cell to produce antibodies against it.

Some B cells are known as **memory B cells.**
These don't actually make antibodies but they are still very important.

They live in the blood for a long time and they ***remember*** particular antigens.
This means that the next time you pick up a particular infection your immune system can respond to it very rapidly.

These B cells give us what is called an **immunological memory.**

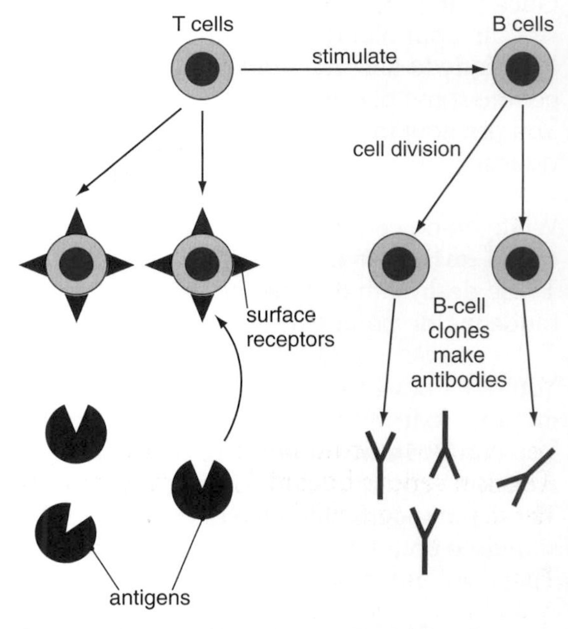

The production of lymphocyte T and B cells

► Vaccines

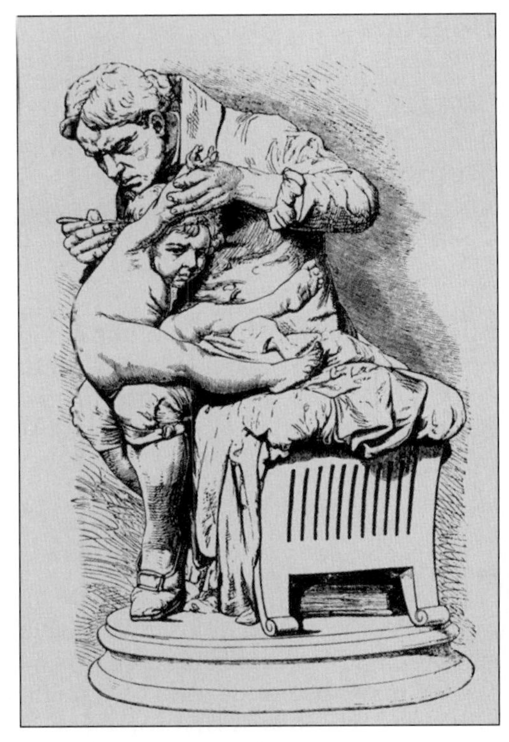

Jenner vaccinating his son

About 200 years ago smallpox was a deadly disease.
Edward Jenner was a doctor in Gloucestershire.
He noticed that people who caught cowpox were immune to smallpox.
Cowpox is a mild disease which can be caught from cattle.

Jenner scratched the skin of a young boy.
He then rubbed in pus from a person suffering from cowpox.
The boy caught cowpox but soon recovered and was immune to the disease.

Then he inoculated the boy with pus from a smallpox victim.
The boy did not catch the deadly smallpox.
The boy had become immune to smallpox because the virus had similar antigens to the cowpox virus.

Poliomyelitis ('polio' for short) is a virus that destroys nerve cells.
It damages the spinal cord so much that victims become paralysed.

In 1953 **Jonas Salk** made a vaccine to prevent polio.
He was able to kill samples of the virus.
Injecting the dead virus into people gave them immunity to the disease.
Polio has now disappeared from developed countries.

Epidemic feared after meningitis claims two adults

In 1999 the UK became the first country to use a new vaccine against ***Meningitis C***.
This is a serious bacterial disease responsible for many deaths amongst children.

First used in Britain in 1988, the combined ***MMR*** vaccine gives protection against three diseases: measles, mumps and rubella (German measles).
It was controversial because some people wrongly feared that the vaccine would make their children more susceptible to a condition called **autism** (a mental condition impairing responses).

What other diseases are vaccines available for?

Have you been inoculated against tetanus, whooping cough, measles, diphtheria, rubella, mumps or influenza?

Boosters

There are some diseases that vaccines can not be made for.
If there is an outbreak of the disease people need protection quickly.
They can be injected with ready-made antibodies.
These antibodies have been made in the body of another person or animal.

But antibodies that we have ***not*** made inside ourselves do not always last very long.
A further dose or 'booster' may need to be given.
Boosters are needed to protect against typhoid and cholera.

▶ Antibiotics

Some chemicals can be used to relieve the symptoms of a disease but they don't kill pathogens.
For instance, aspirin is used as a painkiller.
Other chemicals like **antibiotics** relieve the symptoms by killing the pathogens.

Alexander Fleming at work in his laboratory

The first antibiotic was discovered by **Alexander Fleming** in 1928.
He was growing bacteria on agar plates.
But he left one of the plates open by accident.
A mould started to grow on the surface.

Fleming noticed that the mould was stopping the bacteria from spreading.
It seemed to be making a substance that killed the bacteria.
The mould was called ***Penicillium notatum***.

Ten years later **Howard Florey** and **Ernst Chain** discovered how to extract large quantities of the active substance found in the mould.

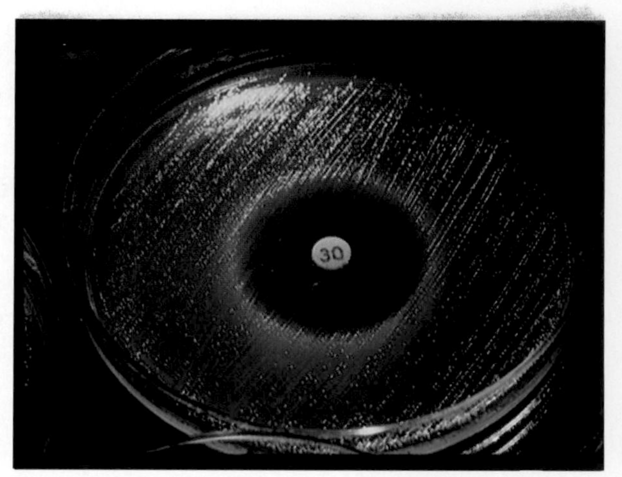

No bacteria are growing around the penicillin disc at the centre

This substance was called **penicillin** and was the first antibiotic. It was quickly put to good use in treating soldiers' wounds in the Second World War.

Today when we talk about penicillin we are referring to a large group of antibiotics. These are produced by a variety of different strains of the penicillium fungus. (See Resistance to antibiotics, page 268.)

▶ Clinical trials

Some diseases can be treated with medicines that contain useful drugs. But before they can be used any new medical treatment has to be extensively tested and trialled.
Clinical trials are used to determine whether new drugs and treatments are both safe and effective. New therapies are tested on people, but only after laboratory and animal studies show promising results.

All clinical trials are based upon a set of rules called a **protocol**.
A protocol sets out what types of people will participate in the trial, along with the schedule of tests, procedures, medications and dosages and the length of the study.

Thalidomide was a drug found to relieve morning sickness in pregnant women. But it had not been fully tested for its use. Many babies born to mothers who took the drug were born with severe limb abnormalities.

In a clinical trial the participants are seen regularly by the research staff, who monitor their health and determine the safety and effectiveness of the treatment.

Clinical trials of new medications go through four phases :

- Phase 1, when the researchers test a new drug on a small group of people (20–80) to evaluate its safety, determine a safe dosage range and identify any side effects.
- Phase 2, when the drug or treatment is given to a larger group of people (40–100) to see if it is effective and evaluate its safety.
- Phase 3 involves giving the drug to large groups of people (more than 200) to further determine effectiveness, monitor any side effects and compare it with commonly used treatments.
- Phase 4 studies are carried out after the drug or treatment has been marketed. These studies continue assessing the drug or treatment to collect information about the effects on various populations and any side effects associated with long-term use.

A **placebo** is an inactive substance that has no treatment value. In clinical trials experimental treatments are often compared with placebos to assess the treatment's effectiveness.
A **blinded study** is a study where the participants do not know whether they are being given the experimental treatment or a placebo.
A **double-blind study** is a study where neither the participants nor the study staff know which patients are receiving the experimental treatment and which ones are receiving a placebo. These studies are performed so that neither the patients' nor the doctors' expectations about the experimental drug can influence the outcome.

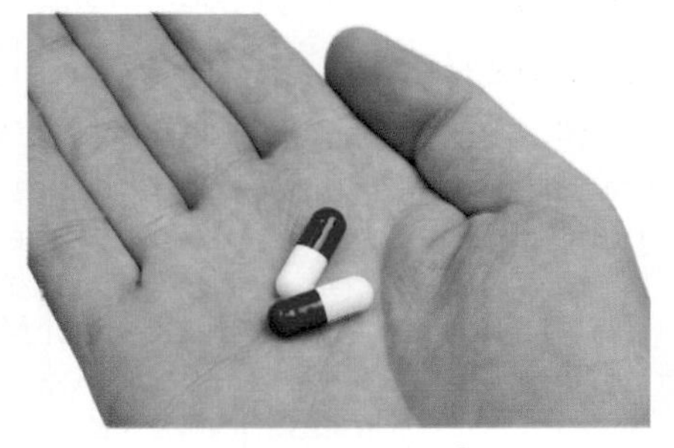

Which one is the placebo ?

▶ Tuberculosis (TB)

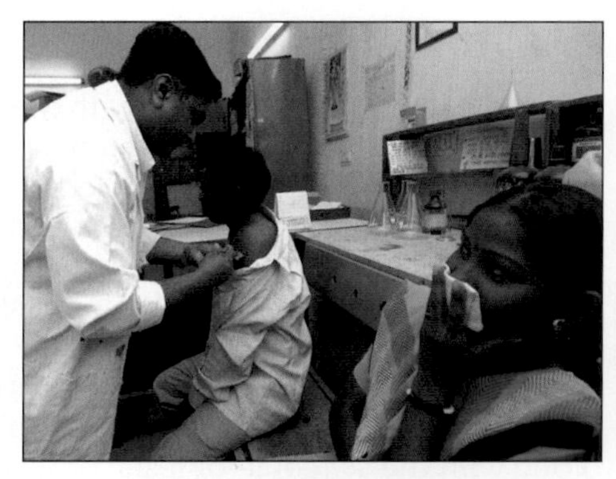

A TB patient covers her mouth in an attempt to stop the spread of the disease

Tuberculosis (TB) is an infection caused by the bacterium *Mycobacterium tuberculosis*. It usually affects the lungs but can go on to affect other parts of the body.

TB bacteria are coughed or sneezed into the air by people who have active TB disease. They are carried in the air in tiny water droplets. If a person breathes these in then the bacterium may multiply in the lungs.

Most people who are in good health do not develop active TB disease, if they breathe in TB bacteria. This is because their immune system kills or inactivates the bacterium before it can spread.

Active TB occurs in 1 in 20 people who breathe in TB bacteria. The bacteria multiply in the lungs and cause a bad cough that lasts longer than 2 weeks, chest pains and coughing up of sputum or blood. TB is most likely to affect people that are already in poor health, for example malnourished children in developing countries.

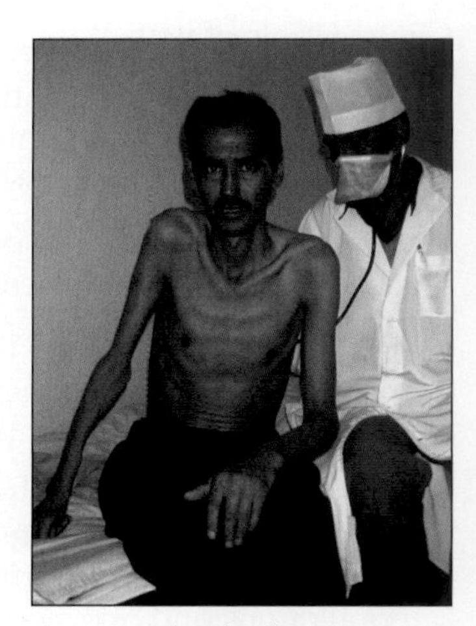

A nurse checks the progress of a TB patient, who has lost much of his bodyweight

But some people develop active TB months or years after a minor infection has been halted. Some bacteria can remain dormant (inactive) for many years. These TB bacteria may start to multiply if the body's immune system fails later in life. People most at risk are the elderly or frail, the malnourished and people suffering from diabetes or AIDS.

You normally need close contact and 'heavy exposure' with an affected person to catch TB. The spread of TB is more common in poorer areas of the world with overcrowding, poor sanitation and poor housing increasing the risk.

TB can almost always be cured but normal antibiotics do not kill TB. You need to take a combination of three or four special antibiotics. With treatment people can make a full recovery, but it is vital that the medication is taken correctly for the full course.

Multi-drug resistant TB (MDR-TB) is a type of TB that is resistant to some antibiotics. This can occur if patients do not take their medicine as prescribed. The TB can become resistant to certain antibiotics that no longer kill the bacterium. MDR-TB is a serious problem and very difficult to treat.
The increased incidence of TB in the UK is thought to be due to the reactivation of a previous TB infection which was at first controlled by the immune system.

Migrants not responsible for spread of TB in UK

Research has been presented to show that migrants are not responsible for the increasing incidence of tuberculosis (TB) in the UK.
Investigators from the University of Surrey fingerprinted the DNA of the different strains of TB in the UK. They found that the DNA of TB-infected individuals born in the UK was 'markedly different from that in patients born overseas'.

▶ Malaria

Malaria is a disease spread by the bite of the female *Anopheles* mosquito.

It is an example of a disease caused by neither a virus nor bacteria, but a protozoan. The microbe responsible is a tiny single-celled parasite called ***Plasmodium.***

When a mosquito bites an uninfected person, *Plasmodium* passes into the blood together with saliva.
It then invades the red blood cells and liver cells.
In these cells it multiplies producing many more parasites.

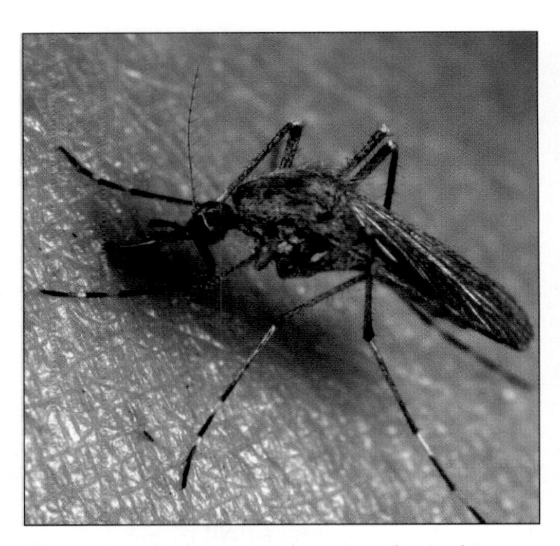

The mosquito has mouthparts adapted to pierce skin

What are the symptoms of malaria?

Malaria victims tend to suffer from regular bouts of fever accompanied by chills and heavy sweating. These bouts are associated with the bursting of red blood cells and the release of more parasites.

The most dangerous form of malaria involves the red blood cells sticking together. This blocks the blood supply to important organs like the brain and can cause death.

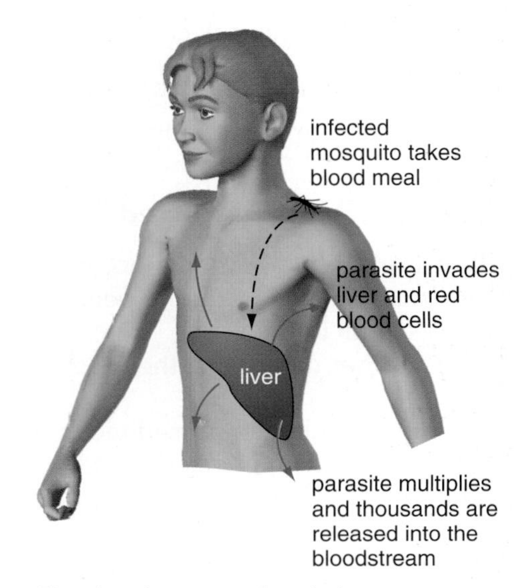

The development of malaria

How can malaria be prevented?

Most effort goes into destroying the mosquito and so preventing its transmission.
Some examples of control measures are :

- using insecticides to kill mosquito larvae in ponds
- stocking ponds with fish that eat the larvae
- draining the ponds that the mosquitoes use as breeding areas
- surrounding beds with nets treated with insecticide.

Other methods of control involve dealing with the humans rather than the mosquito :

- use of anti-malarial drugs, like quinine, which prevent the parasite from spreading throughout the body
- development of vaccines
- use of insect repellents on the skin.

Healthworker fumigates homes to remove mosquitoes

▶ AIDS (Acquired immune deficiency syndrome)

Most people have heard of **AIDS**.
But how many know exactly what it is?
AIDS is actually a collection of diseases which result from a weakening of the immune system.

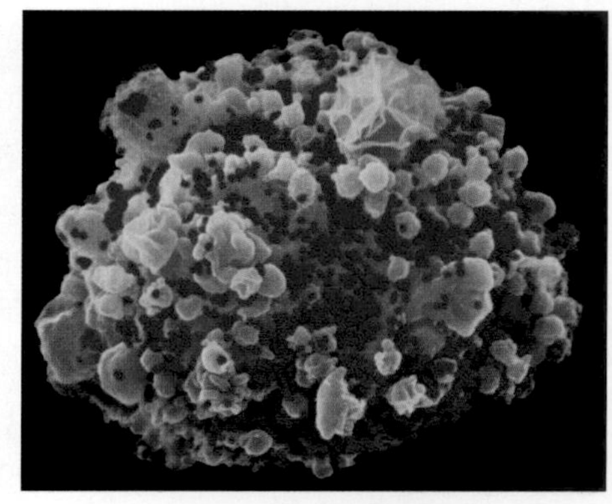

A white blood cell infected by the HIV virus (shown in red)

AIDS is caused by a virus called **HIV**.
HIV (human immunodeficiency virus) attacks and destroys the white blood cells that help us to fight infection.
This reduces the body's ability to fight disease.

The early symptoms of AIDS are very much like flu, with swollen glands and a high temperature.
Later symptoms might include weight loss, various types of cancer and a decrease in brain function.

Catching HIV does not necessarily result in AIDS.
Some people simply remain as carriers, with no symptoms at all.

How is HIV transmitted?

HIV is transmitted in the blood or semen.
The virus can pass from one person to another during sexual intercourse.
Either partner may infect the other.

The HIV virus can be passed via dirty needles

The virus can also be passed via hypodermic needles contaminated with infected blood.
In this way, HIV has spread very quickly amongst drug addicts.

Unborn babies are also at risk from HIV.
This is because the virus can pass across the placenta to the fetus.

How can AIDS be prevented?

Although there is no cure for AIDS and as yet no vaccine for HIV, there are precautions that can reduce its spread. These include :
- the use of condoms during sexual intercourse
- setting up free needle exchanges to reduce the use of shared needles amongst drug users
- careful screening of donated blood used for transfusions.

A government leaflet warning about the dangers of AIDs

► Biology at work : Antibodies and pregnancy testing

As we have seen earlier in this chapter, antibodies play an important role in our immune system. They also have a wide range of other uses, e.g. in pregnancy testing and the inactivation of poisons.

To use antibodies in this way, scientists have found a way of creating pure samples called **monoclonal antibodies**.

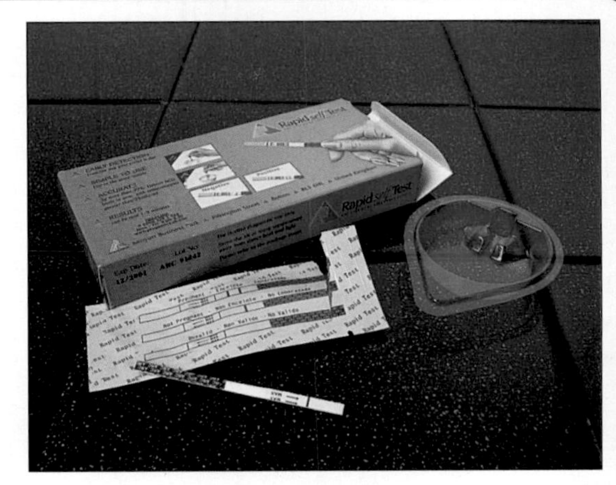

A commercial pregnancy testing kit

How are these monoclonal antibodies produced?
Firstly, scientists take lymphocyte B cells that produce a specific antibody.
Then they combine them with a type of rapidly dividing tumour (cancer) cell.
These cells with fused nuclei are called **hybridoma cells**.
They undergo repeated cell division to produce identical hybridomas.
Each hybridoma produces the specific antibody originally coded for by the B lymphocyte cell.

In pregnancy testing kits, these antibodies can be used to detect the presence of a hormone called **human chorionic gonadotrophin (hCG)**.
This is found in the urine of women in the early stages of pregnancy.

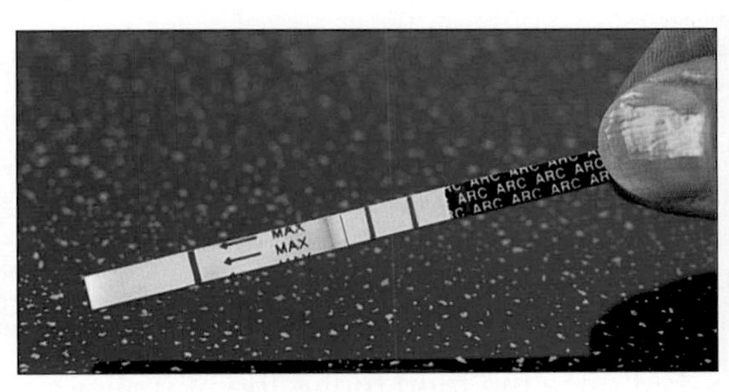

Test stick showing a positive result

The test kit has a dipstick, which has a band of the antibodies on its surface.
When this stick is dipped in a urine sample these antibodies will bind with any molecules of hCG that are present.

This combination of hormone and antibody then moves up the stick.
Eventually it reaches another band of antibodies which also bind to hCG, and at this point the combination of antibodies and hCG will show up as a coloured line.

If this line is seen on the dipstick then the test is positive, the woman is pregnant.

▶ Biology at work : Preserving food

Fancy these grapes ?

Do you know what makes food go off ?

Bacteria and fungi get into the food from the air.
They attack the food and make it taste bad.
Some of these microbes can make us ill.

To stop food going bad we can **preserve** it.

To do this we must :
- kill the microbes in the food, and
- stop them from growing again.

What conditions do you think stops food from going bad ?

- **Heating** food to a high temperature sterilises it.
  It can then be sealed in clean ***cans*** or ***bottles***.

- **Pasteurisation** kills the bacteria in milk.
  It was invented by **Louis Pasteur**.
  The milk is heated to 72 °C for 15 seconds, then cooled quickly.
  This kills most of the bacteria and does not affect the flavour.

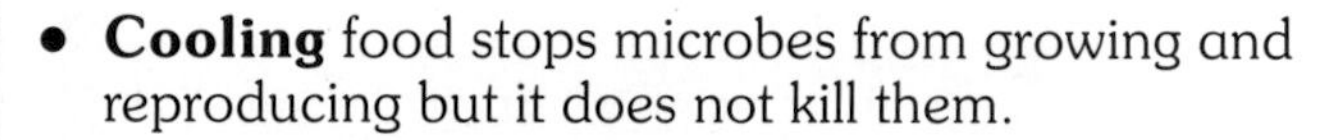

- **Cooling** food stops microbes from growing and reproducing but it does not kill them.

  A refrigerator keeps food at about 5 °C.
  This will keep food fresh for a few days.

  A freezer preserves food at below −18 °C.
  This stops all microbe activity and food can be preserved for many months.
  But once the food thaws the microbes start to grow again.

  Frozen food should be fully defrosted before it is thoroughly cooked, otherwise the microbes will just be warmed by the cooking and will multiply quickly.

► Biology at work : Preserving food

- **Drying** is a way of preserving foods like fruit, vegetables and some meats.
  The microbes can not live without water.
  Some foods like coffee and soups are **freeze-dried**.
  The food is frozen and the ice is drawn off in a vacuum before sealing in packets.

Freeze-dried foods

- **Chemicals** can kill microbes in food.
  Many **food additives** act as preservatives, including sulfur dioxide, nitrates and nitrites.
  Each one is given an **'E number'**.

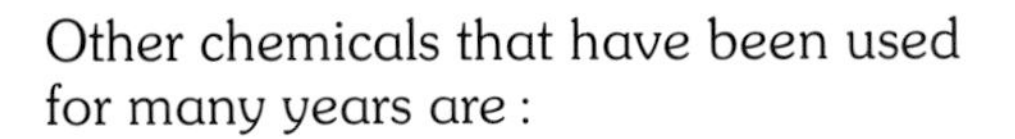

Other chemicals that have been used for many years are :

Pickling foods in vinegar makes it too acid for microbes to live.

Adding **salt** takes water out of the food by osmosis so the microbes die.

The **sugar** in preserved jams also makes microbes lose water by osmosis.

Fish like kippers and salmon are preserved by **smoking**.
The smoke kills the microbes in the foods.

How are each of these foods preserved ?

- **Irradiation** kills the bacteria and fungi that cause food spoilage.

  The food is exposed to gamma radiation.
  This kills the microbes but does not denature enzymes in the food.
  So the ripening and texture of fruit and vegetables is not affected.
  Food cannot be sold for a period of 24 hours after irradiation.
  In the past there has been resistance to this technique.

  Think about arguments for and against food preservation by :

  – irradiation

  – chemical preservatives.

Summary

- Pathogens are microbes that cause disease. They include bacteria, fungi and viruses.
- The symptoms of a disease are caused by the toxins made by the pathogens.
- Pathogens can be spread in the air, by touch, in food and water, and by animals.
- Good hygiene is the best way of preventing the spread of disease.
- Disinfectants and antiseptics help to prevent the spread of infection.
- The body's own defences include skin, blood and mucus lining the air passages of the lungs.
- When you catch a disease your body makes antibodies that give you immunity.
- A vaccine is a dead or harmless sample of a disease microbe.
- Antibiotic drugs have been very successful in the treatment of disease.
- Clinical trials are used to determine whether new drugs and treatments are both safe and effective.
- Tuberculosis, malaria and AIDS are very different diseases caused by very different pathogens and spread in different ways.

▶ Questions

1. Copy and complete:
Pathogens are . . . . that cause disease. Human diseases are caused by . . . ., bacteria and . . . . . The early stage of a disease is called its . . . . period. The symptoms of a disease are caused by the . . . . made by the pathogens. If something is microbe-free we say that it is . . . . . Pathogens are killed on work surfaces by . . . . . Pathogens are killed on living tissues by using . . . . . Your air passages have cells that make . . . . . This traps dust and . . . . and tiny hairs called . . . . carry the mucus up to the throat.

2. Explain why you should:
a) Always wash your hands before handling food.
b) Never share a towel with someone.
c) Always wash your hands after going to the toilet.
d) Never let a dog lick your face.

3. a) What does it mean when you are immune to a disease?
b) How is immunity brought about?
c) What is a vaccine?
d) How does a vaccine work?

4. The apparatus below was used in an experiment to find out the conditions which cause milk to decay.

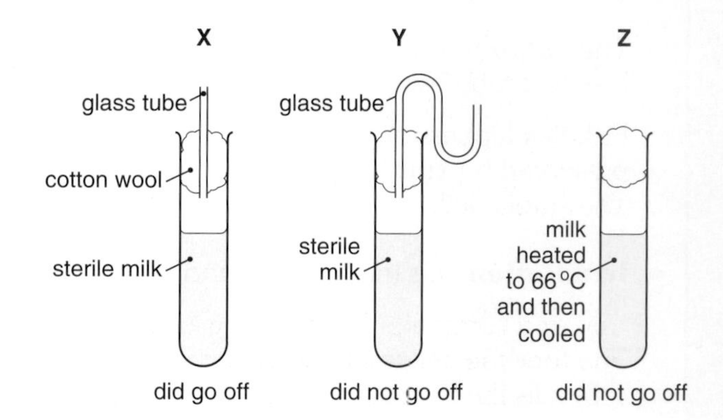

The milk in test-tubes **X** and **Y** was sterilised by boiling.
a) What kind of organisms make food go bad?
b) Explain why the milk in test-tube **X** went off but the milk in test-tube **Y** did not.
c) Milk is often preserved by the treatment in test-tube **Z**.
Why is it better to use this method rather than boiling the milk?

5. Look at the graph. It shows a patient's temperature when suffering from a bacterial disease.

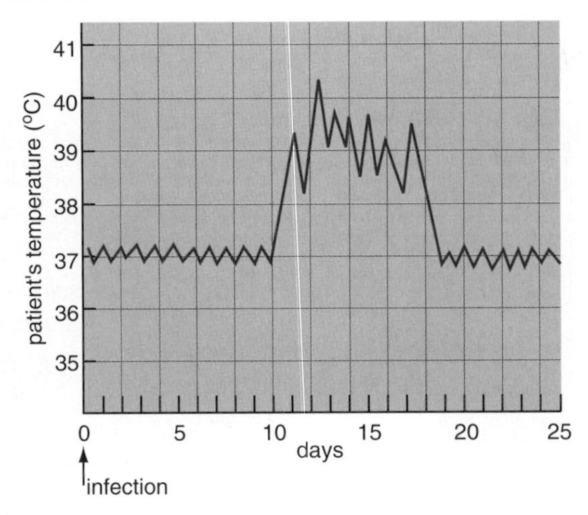

a) What symptom of the disease is shown on the graph?
b) How long was the incubation period? What was happening during this time?
c) What caused the fever and how long did it last?

6. a) What is an antibiotic?
b) How was the first antibiotic discovered?
c) In the 1960s American soldiers in Vietnam were treated for syphilis with the antibiotic penicillin. But some of the syphilis pathogens became resistant to the penicillin. How do you think this could happen?

7. Copy and complete the following table to show how the diseases are spread.

disease	how spread
tetanus	
cold/flu	
cholera	
tuberculosis	
plague	
syphilis	
malaria	
athlete's foot	

8. Some antibiotics kill bacteria whereas others prevent the bacteria from dividing. Bacteria were grown in three tubes. Equivalent doses of different antibiotics were added to each tube. The number of living bacteria was counted every hour for 10 hours. The following graph shows the results.

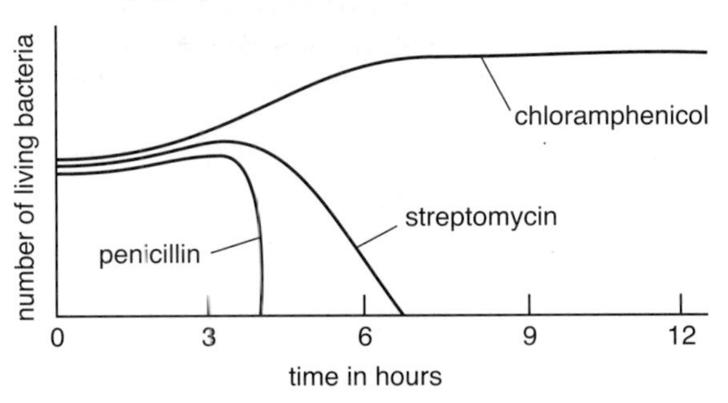

a) Which antibiotic killed the bacteria fastest?
b) Explain your answer to a).
c) Which antibiotic had little, if any, effect on the number of bacteria?
d) Explain your answer to c).
e) Why are antibiotics useful even if they only stop bacteria dividing?

9. The following graph shows the number of people in the UK who have had tuberculosis (TB) and the number of sufferers who have died from the disease.

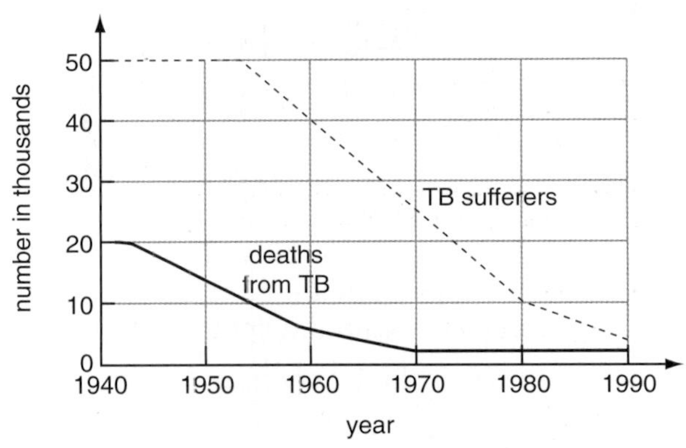

a) Suggest which year vaccinations against TB began.
b) From the graph determine:
   i) the number of sufferers in 1960
   ii) the number of deaths in 1960
   iii) calculate the percentage of sufferers that died in 1960.

Further questions on page 171.

chapter 11

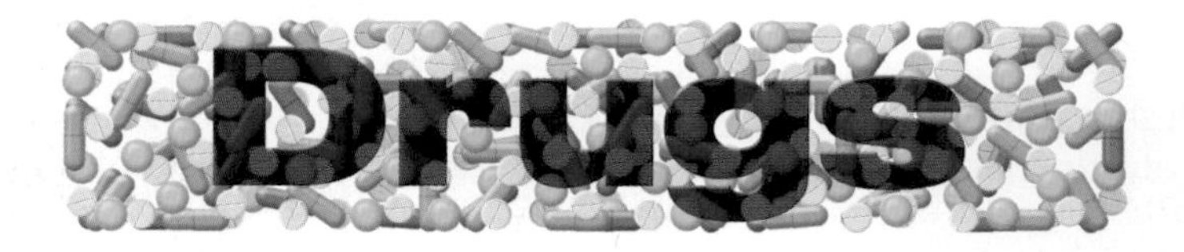

Aspirin, cannabis, alcohol, paracetamol and heroin.
These are all **drugs**. So what exactly is a drug?

A drug is a chemical that affects the way in which your nervous system works.

Piriton Tablets (chlorpheniramine maleate 4mg)
Fast relief from nettle rash, hives, heat rash, prickly heat or dermatitis; reactions to food, medicines or insect bites; hayfever symptoms of the eyes and nose
INGREDIENTS Active: chlorpheniramine maleate. Also contains: lactose, maize starch, magnesium stearate, colour: yellow iron oxide (E172)
DOSAGE Adults: Take one tablet every four to six hours (maximum 6 in one day). **Children aged 6-12:** Half a tablet every four to six hours (maximum 6 halves in one day). Not recommended for children under 6
If symptoms persist consult your doctor
DO NOT TAKE PIRITON TABLETS IF YOU ARE TAKING MAOI DRUGS
Please read the enclosed information leaflet carefully before use
KEEP ALL MEDICINES OUT OF THE REACH OF CHILDREN

WARNING: May cause drowsiness. If affected do not drive or operate machinery. Avoid alcoholic drink.

P

PL10949/0106 Piriton is a Glaxo trade mark © 1994
Glaxo Pharmaceuticals UK Ltd, UB11 1BT, England Store below 30°C

Drugs can be beneficial or harmful.
Many medicines contain useful drugs such as antibiotics and painkillers.

Medicines contain at least one drug. That's why you should be very careful when you use them.
Some medicines are only available on prescription but can be dangerous if you exceed the prescribed dose.

But there are other drugs that are not useful.
Some like tobacco are legal, but others like cannabis and ecstasy are not.
Alcohol and tobacco are the two commonest drugs.
They are easily available but can cause serious health problems.

There are many different drugs and solvents.
Different drugs have different effects on people.
The strength of the drug also affects what it does to you.

Some people take a drug without knowing what's in it or how powerful it is.
This makes taking the drug even more dangerous.

Britain has strict laws against people who possess, sell or pass on certain drugs.
Breaking these laws can mean a fine, caution or maybe a prison sentence.

In the UK drugs are legally classified, class A being the most dangerous with the heaviest penalties and class C being the least dangerous with the lightest penalties.

HERALD
MUM'S DRUGS ANGUISH!

The Record
ECSTASY -ONE TABLET CAN KILL!

THE GAZETTE DAILY
LOCAL BOY IN DRUG FATALITY

Class A drugs include: cocaine, heroin, LSD, methadone, morphine, opium, ecstasy and cannabinol, except where it is contained in cannabis or cannabis resin.

Class B drugs include amphetamine, codeine (in concentrations above 2.5 %), Ritalin and barbiturates. Class B drugs become class A drugs if they are prepared for injection.
In May 2008, cannabis was reclassified from a class C to a class B drug.

Class C drugs include mild amphetamines (like slimming pills), tranquillisers (e.g. Valium) and anabolic steroids.

▶ How do drugs work ?

Drugs can be put into different categories according to their general effects :

- **Stimulants** are drugs that speed up the nervous system and shorten a person's reaction time.
  They increase the speed of transmission of impulses across the synapse.
  Caffeine is a mild stimulant found in coffee, tea and cola.
  Amphetamines and cocaine are far more powerful stimulants.
  Ecstasy tablets are stimulants that some people take to make them feel as if they have more energy.
  Some young people have died through taking ecstasy.

- **Depressants** are drugs that slow down the nervous system and lengthen reaction time.
  They act by reducing the rate at which nerve impulses pass across the synapses.
  Depressants (or sedatives) include barbiturates and heroin.
  Benzodiazepines, like Temazepam, have now replaced barbiturates for most medical purposes – they are known as tranquillisers.

Many medical drugs can be dangerous if taken in an uncontrolled way and are available only on prescription from a doctor.

- **Painkillers** such as aspirin and paracetamol can help to relieve painful conditions such as headache, migraine, neuralgia, influenza and rheumatic pain.
  Painkillers act by blocking nerve impulses at the synapse, as does morphine.
  As with any medicinal drug, it is very important not to exceed the stated dose of paracetamol.
  Immediate medical help must be sort in the case of an overdose, even if a person feels well, because of the risk of delayed, serious liver damage.

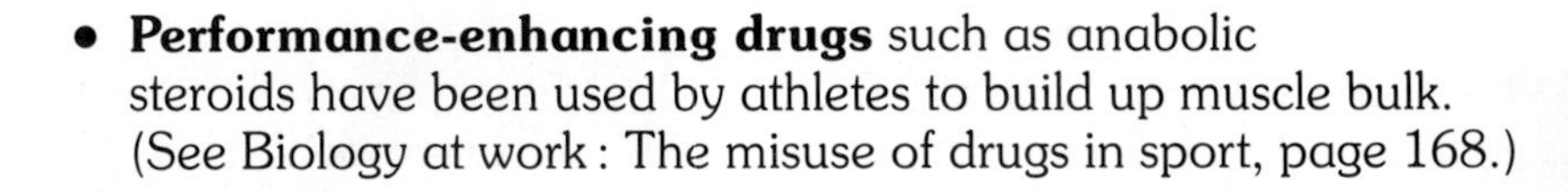

- **Performance-enhancing drugs** such as anabolic steroids have been used by athletes to build up muscle bulk.
  (See Biology at work : The misuse of drugs in sport, page 168.)

- **Hallucinogens** are a group of drugs that can produce sensations of false identity and distort what is seen and heard. As the name suggests they induce hallucinations.
  They include cannabis and the more powerful hallucinogen LSD (lysergic acid diethylamide).
  LSD fuelled the psychedelic rock and art movements of the late sixties.
  (See page 356 for the importance and medicinal value of drugs produced by plants.)

'Disraeli Gears' by Cream

Drug abuse

Some hard drugs can be extremely harmful and can lead to severe health problems particularly to the body's nervous system, liver and kidneys.
Offences involving hard drugs, like heroin and cocaine, are about 10 % of all drug offences.
This can be compared with cannabis (76 %) and amphetamines (12 % of all drug offences).

Injecting a drug is the most dangerous way of taking it.
It is easy to 'overdose' and sharing needles spreads hepatitis and HIV, the virus that causes AIDS.

The body gets used to some kinds of drugs. To get the same effect a person has to take an increasing amount of the drug.
The body has developed a **tolerance** to it. A person can become **dependent** on the drug if they start to have to take it regularly.
Addiction means that the person has become so dependent on the drug that it is doing them serious harm.

If a person stops taking a drug they have become addicted to, they develop **withdrawal symptoms**. But if the drug is not taken these effects can fade after 2 or 3 weeks **rehabilitation**.

Cannabis plants

Cannabis and opiates

Cannabis is less addictive than tobacco and alcohol, but smoking it may cause psychological problems to develop.
Heavy users can display aggressive behaviour if their supply suddenly stops.
A government report found that use of cannabis is not associated with major health or sociological problems, but it may be a 'gateway' drug to more harmful substances, like heroin and cocaine.
Cannabis has a higher tar content than tobacco so smoking it presents the same risks of bronchitis, emphysema and lung cancer.

Confusion over the laws on cannabis could increase if plans to reintroduce tougher laws on stronger varieties of the drug go ahead.
'Skunk weed' is a super-strength form of the drug and is said to be up to ten times stronger than conventional cannabis. Medical research has shown that skunk cannabis can trigger serious psychotic behaviour, such as hallucinations and paranoid delusions.

Cannabis has been widely known for its medicinal use in pain relief from a number of serious conditions :

- cancer : cannabis can suppress nausea brought on by chemotherapy
- AIDS : it can increase appetite and reduce weight loss
- glaucoma (an eye condition) : it can relieve eye pressure
- multiple sclerosis: it can alleviate spasms, pain and tremors.

Opiates are a group of drugs derived from opium in poppies.
They include morphine which is often used as a pain-reducing drug for terminally ill patients.

Queen Victoria was given cannabis to ease her period pains

▶ Solvents

Solvents are everyday products like glues, dry-cleaning fluid, aerosols and lighter fuel. They give off fumes that **sniffers** breathe in. Solvents contain dangerous chemicals that can kill you.

Solvent abuse is a growing problem among youngsters aged 12 to 16. It is against the law for shopkeepers to sell solvents to people under 18 years of age. But many of the solvents are easily available around the home.

Solvent fumes are absorbed by the lungs and soon get to the brain. They slow down breathing and heartbeat rate. Repeated or deep breathing can cause loss of control and unconsciousness. Solvents can cause damage to the liver, lungs and brain.

Solvent abuse claims more deaths than heroin and cocaine put together. Some people die immediately after inhaling some chemicals like aerosols, cleaning fluids and butane gas. These 'sudden sniff' deaths are often due to heart failure.

Suffocation can occur if sniffers inhale from large plastic bags.

Aerosol sprays squirted into the mouth can freeze the air passages causing suffocation.

THE DAILY SKETCH

15TH FEBRUARY 1996

SOLVENT ABUSE NEW DANGERS

The dangers of solvent abuse were graphically illustrated today as the teenage daughter of a prominant local business man was admitted to hospital near to death. Rosie Simmons (14) was taken to Gloucester Royal Infirmary after collapsing in her ... after inhaling an

girls also present were taken under observation but later released without treatment.

Rosie's father, Giles Simmons (44) the owner of a local chain of newsagents claimed that the sale of solvents to young people was to blame."

Sniffers can appear to be drunk.

They run the risks linked with being drunk, like :

- falling from a building or being involved in a road accident,
- passing out and choking on their own vomit.

There is also a risk of fire because many solvents are flammable.

The best advice is ***never inhale solvents***.

Describe the harmful effects of solvents and tobacco on the body and the dangers of contracting HIV and hepatitis when injecting drugs.

► Alcohol

Alcohol is a socially acceptable drug.
It is a part of many people's social lives.

Alcohol is made when yeast is added to a sugary solution such as grape juice.
The yeast breaks down the sugar to make alcohol and carbon dioxide gas.
This is called fermentation.

Alcohol is a **depressant** – it slows down your body's reactions.
As with many other drugs it can be **abused**.
Alcohol does not often kill – a person usually loses consciousness before they can take a fatal amount.

Some people become dependent upon alcohol.
Their bodies develop a tolerance and they need to take greater amounts to get the same effect.
People that become addicted to alcohol can not face life without a drink
They are called **alcoholics**.

Alcohol is absorbed through the gut and carried to the brain in the blood.
From there it affects the nervous system.
Many people find a little alcohol relaxing.
Increasing amounts make them dizzy.
Their judgement and reactions become affected.
For this reason a person should not drink and drive.

With greater amounts of alcohol people lose control of their muscles and their speech becomes slurred.
A person in this state is more likely to get into a fight or have an accident.
Their coordination becomes so poor that they can not walk and end up passing out.

Look at the diagram :

How many units of alcohol are there in :
- a double whisky
- a pint of beer ?

All these drinks contain 1 unit of alcohol

Different brands of alcoholic drinks have different strengths of alcohol.
Why are spirits served in smaller glasses than beer ?
Some lagers are much stronger than others.
The strength of alcohol is shown on the label as percentage volume of alcohol.

Long-term effects of alcohol

Drinking large amounts of alcohol over a number of years can have serious effects on health.
It can lead to stomach ulcers, heart disease and brain damage.

The liver is the part of the body that breaks down alcohol.
Alcohol abuse over a number of years can lead to **cirrhosis** of the liver.
The liver tissue becomes scarred and its healthy cells become replaced with fat, or fibrous tissue.
The liver becomes less able to carry out its job of removing the toxins from the blood.

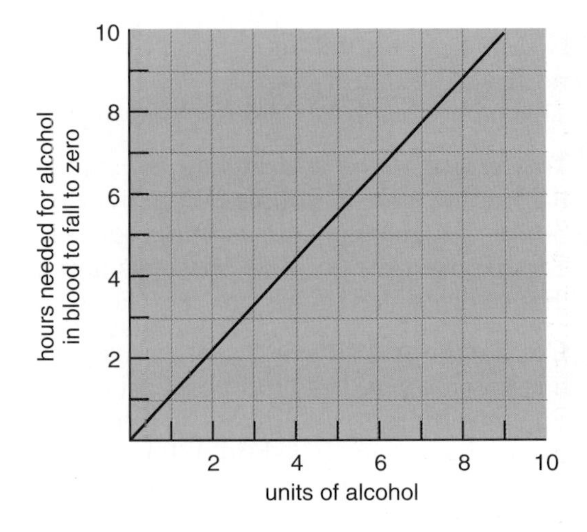

Even a healthy liver takes time to break down alcohol and make it harmless.
It takes about ***one hour*** to remove ***one unit*** of alcohol from the blood.
So depending upon the strength and quantity of the drink, it may take several hours before the body is free from alcohol.

Different drinks contain different amounts of alcohol.
Also a 'safe' amount of alcohol will depend upon age, sex, body size and metabolic rate.
The safe amount for a woman is about two-thirds of that for a man of the same weight.

Why do you think there are legal limits for the level of alcohol in the blood and breath for drivers and pilots?

Like many other drugs alcohol is habit-forming.
A social drinker can turn into a problem drinker.

Many people who become dependent on alcohol do not think that they are.
They try to convince themselves that they do not have a problem.
They feel tense and irritable and find it hard to cope with everyday problems without a drink.

Alcoholics can cause their families pain and misery.
They can become aggressive after drinking and spend a lot of money on drink.

Organisations like Alcoholics Anonymous can help alcoholics.

▶ Smoking and health

Smoking can damage your health.
It can cause diseases of the lungs and heart.
It is estimated that every cigarette shortens a smoker's life by 14 minutes.
Most heavy smokers die from diseases caused by smoking.

Toxic chemicals

Tobacco smoke contains lots of chemicals.
Many of these are harmful:

Nicotine is a drug.
It acts upon the brain and nervous system.
Smokers become addicted to it.
That's why they find it so hard to give up.
Nicotine makes the heart beat faster and narrows the blood vessels.
This can cause heart disease and high blood pressure.

Tar collects in the lungs when the smoke cools.
It contains over a thousand chemicals.
Some of these can cause cancer (are **carcinogenic**).
Tar also irritates your air passages and makes them narrower. It gives you 'smoker's cough'.

Carbon monoxide is a poisonous gas.
It is taken up by the blood instead of oxygen.
So carbon monoxide stops the blood carrying as much oxygen as it should. If a woman smokes during pregnancy there may not be enough oxygen in the blood for the baby to develop properly. Due to this the baby may have a smaller birth weight and is sometimes premature.
Particulates are small burnt fragments of tobacco.
They can accumulate in the lung tissue.

Diseases caused by smoking

Bronchitis is when the air passages become inflamed.
The cilia on the cells lining your air passages stop beating.
So the mucus, dirt and bacteria stay in your lungs.
The bacteria start to breed resulting in chronic bronchitis and 'smoker's cough'. Large amounts of **phlegm** (a mixture of mucus, bacteria and white blood cells) are produced, which the sufferer attempts to cough up.

Emphysema is when chemicals in tobacco smoke weaken the walls of the alveoli.
Coughing can burst them damaging the lung tissue.
Your lungs can not take in enough oxygen and you get breathless.

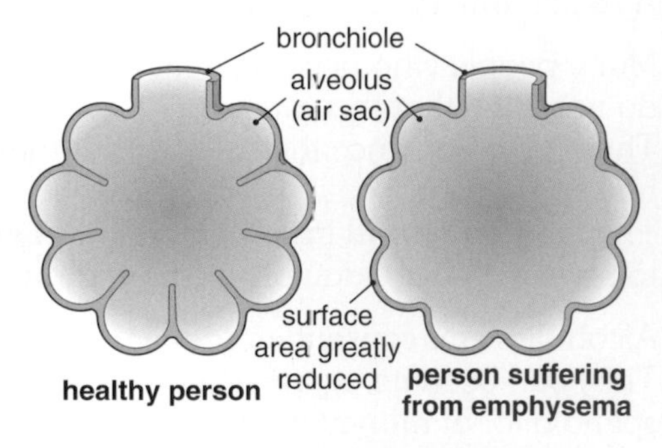

Someone with emphysema can get very short of breath. Their alveoli have less surface area. So there is less gas exchange,

Heart disease

Nicotine and carbon monoxide make the blood clot more easily. This can block the arteries to the heart especially if they already have fat deposits lining them. Blocked arteries reduce the supply of oxygen to the heart and this damages the heart muscle.

Lung cancer

Ninety percent of lung cancer occurs in smokers. Tar is thought to be the main cause.
Tumours form in the lung and if they are not discovered quickly they can spread round the body. Cancers can also originate in the mouth, throat and oesophagus.

Look at the graph:
It shows the number of deaths from lung disease in England and Wales from 1916–1960.

What has happened to the number of deaths from bronchitis and tuberculosis over this time? Can you explain this?

What has happened to the numbers of deaths from lung cancer over this time? Can you explain this?

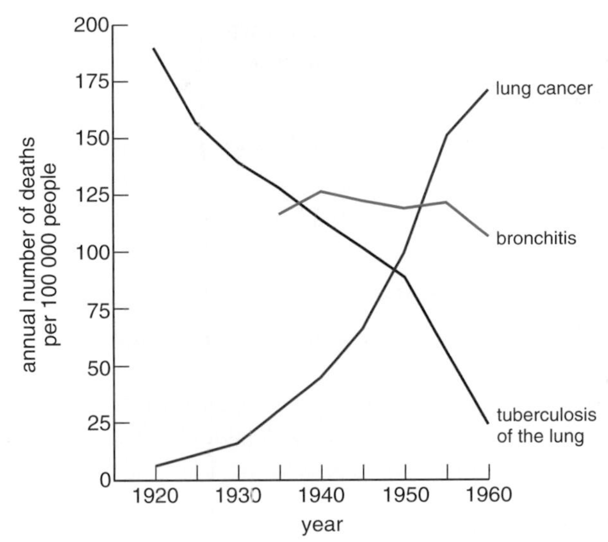

Demonstration 11.1 A smoking machine

First set up the apparatus without the cigarette.

Turn on the suction pump for 5 minutes.

Look at the temperature, the colour of the glass wool and the colour of the lime water.

Repeat the experiment with the cigarette.

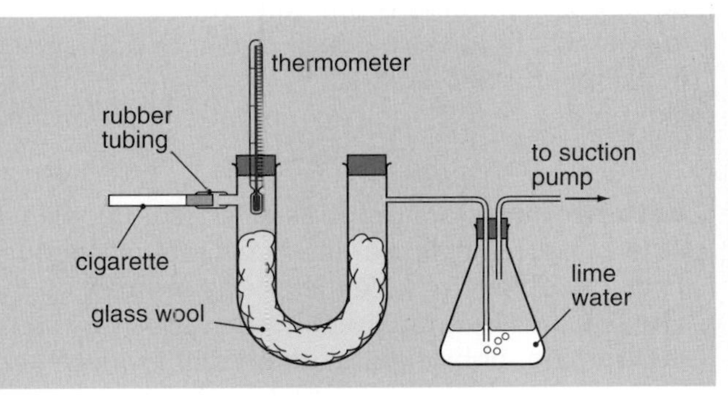

Other people's smoke

Many non-smokers are affected by other people smoking. It can irritate their eyes and give them headaches and sore throats, particularly if they suffer from asthma or hay fever.

People who live and work with smokers can be affected by smoking diseases including lung cancer.

People are becoming increasingly intolerant of **passive smoking**.
Because of this smoking is being banned from more and more public places.
In the UK, smoking is now banned inside all public places.

It is always worth giving up if you do smoke.
The risk of getting lung cancer and other diseases falls after smokers give up.

► Biology at work : The misuse of drugs in sport

Some sports people take drugs to improve their performance.
They do this because:

- Media pressure is put on them to be successful.
- They think that their sporting successes will make them rich.
- They think everyone else is doing it.
- They do not think that they will get caught.

Performance-enhancing drugs have been banned by the International Olympic Committee (IOC) to ensure that competition in sport is fair and to protect the health of sports people.

Ben Johnson won the 100 m title at the 1988 Olympics but was disqualified for taking drugs

Types of drug

Anabolic steroids are substances similar to the male sex hormone testosterone.
They work by mimicking the protein-building effects of this hormone.
The result is muscle growth, which gives the athlete increased strength and endurance.

There are a number of harmful side-effects resulting from the excessive use of anabolic steroids.
In men, use of these drugs can bring about increased aggression, impotence, baldness, kidney and liver damage and even the development of breasts.
In women, there is a development of male features, facial and body hair and irregular periods.

Canadian snooker player Bill Werbeniuk took beta-blockers to steady his aim

Beta-blockers are drugs used to treat people with heart problems.
When taken, they lower the heart rate and reduce blood pressure.
They are able to reduce the effects of stress on the body.
The IOC has banned them in such sports as archery, shooting, ski-jumping, bobsleigh, biathlon and modern pentathlon.

Stimulants, such as amphetamines and cocaine, can give the athlete a lift, keeping them awake and competitive.
They speed up the reflexes and reduce the feeling of fatigue.

They can be harmful to the body since they increase heart rate and blood pressure and reduce the feelings of pain.
They can also be addictive and give rise to panic attacks and increased aggression.

Narcotic analgesics include methadone, codeine and heroin.
These drugs act as pain killers that are able to mask an injury.
The problem is that if the athlete continues to compete, the injury may become much worse or even permanent.
Some narcotic analgesics can be highly addictive.

Diane Mohdahl successfully proved that she was innocent of drug-taking

Summary

- A drug is a chemical that affects the way in which your nervous system works.
- Some drugs are beneficial, but others can be harmful.
- Different categories of drugs include depressants, stimulants, painkillers and hallucinogens.
- Hard drugs such as cocaine and heroin are extremely addictive and can lead to severe health problems.
- Smoking cannabis may cause psychological problems to develop.
  Cannabis and opiates have been used in relieving the pain of some patients.
- Solvents affect behaviour and can damage the lungs, liver and brain.
- Alcohol can slow down reactions and may lead to a lack of self-control, unconsciousness or even coma.
- The long-term effects of alcohol on the body can result in liver and brain damage.
- Tobacco smoke contains toxic chemicals such as nicotine, tar, carbon monoxide and particulates.
- Smoking-related diseases include bronchitis, emphysema, lung cancer and diseases of the heart and blood vessels.
- Some sports people have taken performance-enhancing drugs such as anabolic steroids which increase muscle growth.

▶ Questions

1. Copy and complete:
A drug is a .... that affects the way in which your .... system works. Depressants .... the nervous system and lengthen .... time ....
.... speed up the nervous system and .... reaction time. Cocaine and .... are examples of hard drugs and are extremely ...., doing serious damage to .... Some people become .... to alcohol. Their bodies develop a .... to it and they may end up becoming ....
Tobacco smoke contains toxic chemicals including ...., tar and .... Smoking-related diseases include ...., lung cancer and .....

2. Drugs like barbiturates and heroin are called depressants.
Drugs like amphetamines and cocaine are called stimulants.
a) Explain how depressants act on the nervous system.
b) How would amphetamines and cocaine affect the nervous system?
c) What is meant by the following terms:
i) tolerance ii) addiction iii) withdrawal symptoms iv) rehabilitation?

3. The diagrams show a small part of the lung from a healthy person and from a person suffering from emphysema. Both are drawn to the same scale.

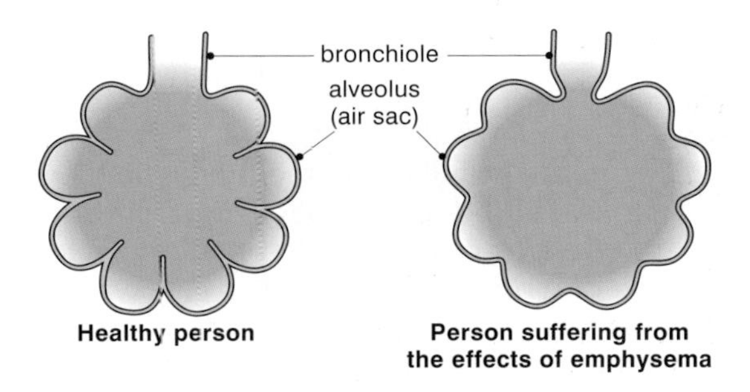

a) What is the function of the alveolus (air sac)?
b) Describe two ways in which a healthy alveolus is adapted to carry out its function.
c) Describe two differences, visible in the diagrams, between the healthy lung and the diseased lung.
d) Explain how each of the differences that you have described, would affect the functioning of the diseased lung.

4. Which row of the table shows two drugs, both of which can seriously damage the liver?

	Drugs	
A	alcohol	barbiturate
B	barbiturate	caffeine
C	caffeine	paracetamol
D	paracetamol	alcohol

5. Before going to lunch at 1.00 p.m., Dennis had a glass of sherry. During lunch he had 2 glasses of wine and a brandy. He returned to work at 2.00 p.m. and worked until 5.30 p.m. On leaving work Dennis drank 2 pints of beer and at 8.00 p.m. caught a taxi home.

The graph shows the level of alcohol in Dennis' blood from lunchtime onwards.

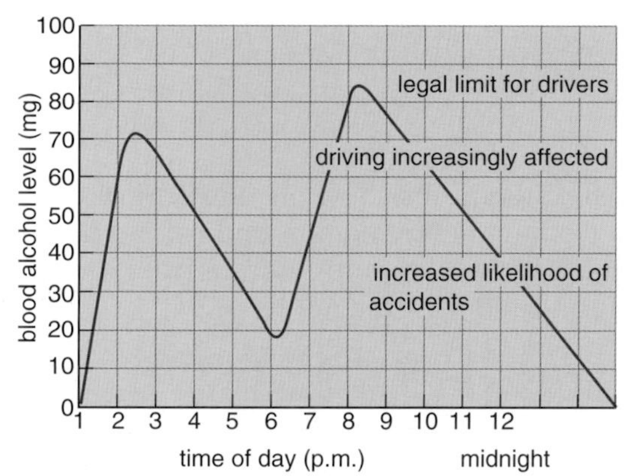

a) From the graph, state the time when:
   i) the blood-alcohol level was highest.
   ii) he was most likely to have an accident at work.

b) If Dennis had not drunk any beer, when would his blood-alcohol level probably have returned to zero?

c) At what time could he have driven his own car home legally?

d) When would his blood have had no alcohol in it?

6. Explain why the following are ***not*** true:

a) Drinking beer is less harmful than drinking spirits.

b) Alcohol is a stimulant drug.

c) It is safe to drive if you are below the legal limit.

d) Drinking heavily for many years does you no harm because your body gets used to it.

7. The following table shows the number of deaths in 1983 from smoking-related diseases.

Disease	Number of deaths		
	men	women	total
lung cancer	33 000	10 000	40 000
heart attack	103 000	77 000	180 000
bronchitis and emphysema	12 000	4500	16 500

a) Draw a bar chart to show the total number of deaths for each disease.

b) Divide each bar into the relevant proportions to show the number of deaths in men and women.

c) Explain how smoking causes:
   i) emphysema
   ii) heart disease
   iii) lung cancer
   iv) bronchitis.

8.

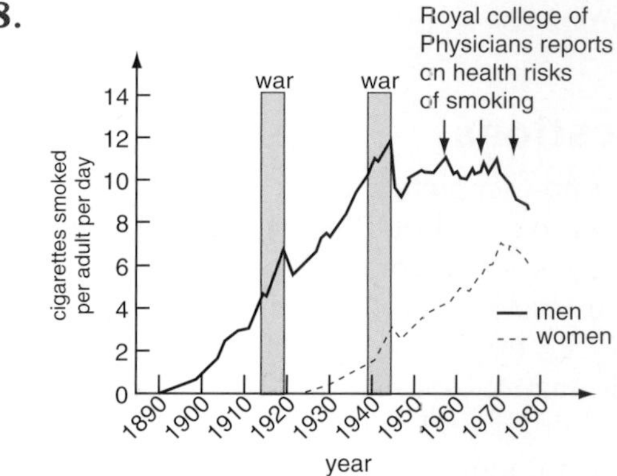

a) i) When did men start smoking?
   ii) When did women start smoking?

b) Describe the pattern of cigarette smoking shown by the whole population.

c) i) Describe the effect of the 1914–18 war on smoking habits.
   ii) Suggest an explanation for your answer.
   iii) Describe the effect of the 1939–45 war on smoking habits.
   iv) Suggest an explanation for your answer.

d) What effect did the Royal College's reports have on the smoking pattern in:
   i) men
   ii) women?

e) Suggest and explain reasons for a downward trend in deaths due to lung cancer.

Further questions on page 171.

► Food and digestion

1. Neil goes to a 'well man' clinic for a check up. His doctor weighs Neil and measures his height. He then calculates Neil's Body Mass Index. He tells Neil he is overweight and must go on a diet.

a) Neil weighs 86 kg.
His height is 1.68 metres.

i) Use the table to calculate Neil's Body Mass Index. *[1]*

Weight in kg (columns); Height in cm (rows)

Height in cm	54	59	64	68	73	77	82	86	91	95	100	104	109	113
137	29	31	34	36	39	41	43	46	48	51	53	56	58	60
142	27	29	31	34	36	38	40	43	45	47	49	52	54	56
147	25	27	29	31	34	36	38	40	42	44	46	48	50	52
152	23	25	27	29	31	33	35	37	39	41	43	45	47	49
158	22	24	26	27	29	31	33	35	37	38	40	42	44	46
163	21	22	24	26	28	29	31	33	34	36	38	40	41	43
168	19	21	23	24	26	27	29	31	32	34	36	37	39	40
173	18	20	21	23	24	26	27	29	30	32	34	35	37	38
178	17	19	20	22	23	24	26	27	29	30	32	33	35	36
183	16	18	19	20	22	23	24	26	27	28	30	31	33	34
188	16	17	18	19	21	22	23	24	26	27	28	30	31	32
193	15	16	17	18	20	21	22	23	24	26	27	28	29	30
198	14	15	16	17	19	20	21	22	23	24	25	27	28	29
2003	13	14	15	17	18	19	20	21	22	23	24	25	26	28

Key: underweight, healthy weight, over weight, obese

ii) Which weight category does Neil belong to? *[1]*

iii) Determine how much weight Neil would have to lose in order to have a healthy weight. *[1]*

b) Explain why Neil's doctor calculates his Body Mass Index, rather than just weighing Neil, to find out if he is over weight. *[2]*

c) In some areas of the world people are starving.
It is important that people eat enough protein. The recommended daily allowance of protein can be determined by using the following formula.
Recommended Daily Allowance of protein in grams = 0.75 × Body Mass in kg

i) Calculate how much protein Neil should eat each day. *[1]*

ii) Neil has a teenage son.
Suggest why Neil's son should eat more protein than Neil. *[1]* (OCR)

2. The diagram shows the main regions of the digestive system in a human.

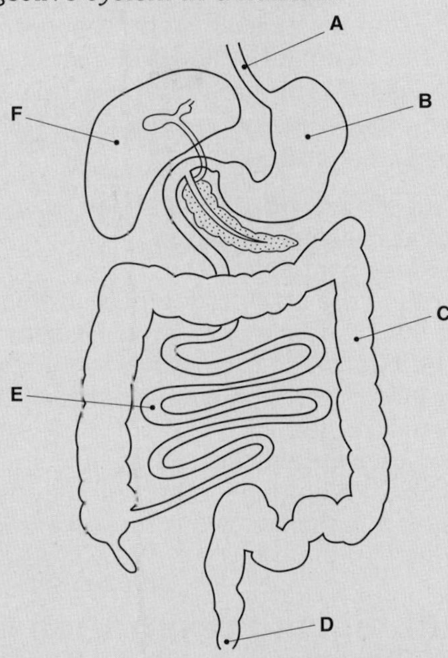

a) Name the parts labelled **A**, **B**, **C**, **D**, **E** and **F** on the diagram. *[3]*

b) In which of these structures

i) are fatty acids and glycerol absorbed *[1]*

ii) is most water absorbed *[1]*

iii) does egestion take place? *[1]* (OCR)

3. The table below gives some information about the nutritional content of a traditional beefburger and of a similar non-meat vegetable burger. Vegetable burgers are made from a mycoprotein, coloured and flavoured to taste like beef.

Contents per 100 g	Beefburger	Vegetable burger
energy	1192 kJ	970 kJ
protein	15.0 g	18.5 g
carbohydrate	3.7 g	11.7 g
fat	23.8 g	12.7 g
sodium**	0.5 g	1.3 g
fibre	0.4 g	4.5 g

**mostly as sodium chloride

a) i) Which 'burger' has the higher protein content per 100 g? *[1]*

ii) How much protein is present in 120 g of beefburger? *[1]*

iii) In which organ of the body are carbohydrates stored? *[1]*

iv) Name the carbohydrate which is stored in this organ. [1]

b) State **two** reasons why a person who is anxious to eat a healthy diet might choose the vegetable burger rather than the beefburger. Give an explanation for the choice in each case. [4] (OCR)

4. Food substances need to be digested before they can pass into the blood.
Many foods contain fat.

a) What are the products of fat digestion? [1]

b) The liver produces a chemical substance called bile which is added to food during digestion. Explain how bile helps in the digestion of fat. [3]

c) Describe **one** effect of eating too much food rich in animal (saturated) fat and explain the problems this may eventually produce in the body. [2] (EDEX)

▶ Breathing and respiration

5. a) Explain, as fully as you can, why respiration has to take place more rapidly during exercise. [2]

b) During exercise the process of respiration produces excess heat. Explain how the body prevents this heat from causing a rise in the core (deep) body temperature. [4]

c) In an investigation four groups of athletes were studied. The maximum rate of oxygen consumption for each athlete was measured and the mean for each group was calculated. The athletes then ran 10 mile races and the mean of the best times was calculated for each group. The results are shown in the table below.

Group of athletes	Maximum rate of oxygen consumption (cm^3 per kg per min)	Best time in 10 mile race (minutes)
A	78.6	48.9
B	67.5	55.1
C	63.0	58.7
D	57.4	64.6

i) What is the relationship between maximum rate of oxygen consumption and time for a 10 mile race? [1]

ii) Suggest an explanation for this relationship. [3] (AQA)

6. The diagram shows the breathing system of human.

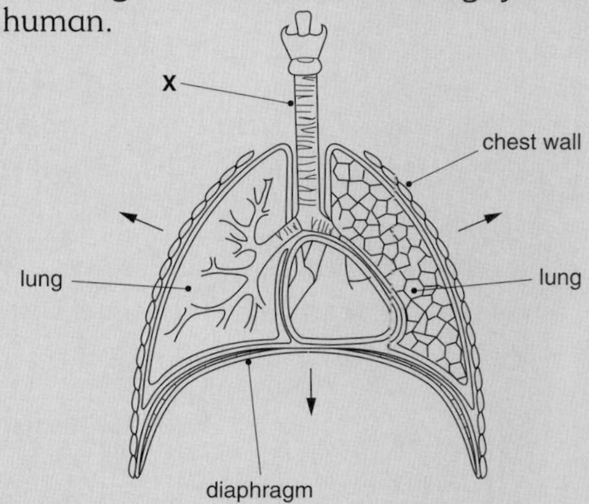

a) Name the tube **X**. [1]

b) Explain how tube **X** is kept open. [1]

c) Why is it necessary to keep tube **X** open? [1]

d) Explain what would happen to the ***volume*** and ***pressure*** of air inside the lungs when the chest wall and diaphragm are moved in the direction shown by the arrows. [2]

e) What makes the diaphragm move in the direction shown? [1]

f) The volume of air breathed during three different activities is shown on the graph.

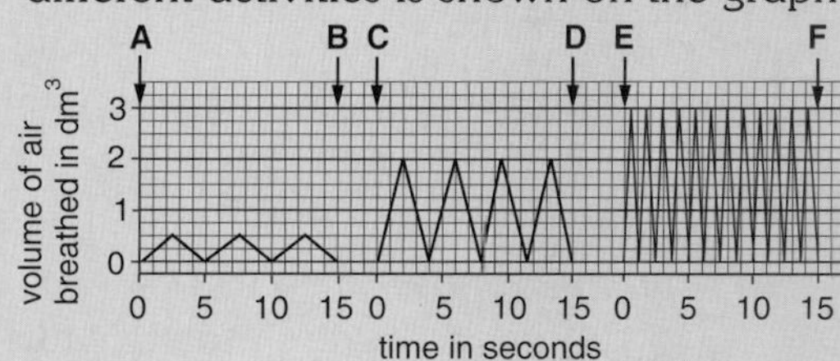

i) What was the number of breaths per minute during the activity between **C** and **D**? [1]

ii) What was the volume of air exchanged per breath during the activity between **E** and **F**? [1]

iii) Copy and complete the table by selecting from the list below the most appropriate activity.

running hard, **resting**, **jogging**

Activity between	Activity
A and **B**	
C and **D**	
E and **F**	

[3] (OCR)

7. The information below was found on a cigarette packet.

Warning : SMOKING CAN CAUSE FATAL DISEASES

a) Name **two** respiratory diseases which could be caused by cigarette smoking. *[2]*

b) The diagram below shows an alveolus (air-sac).

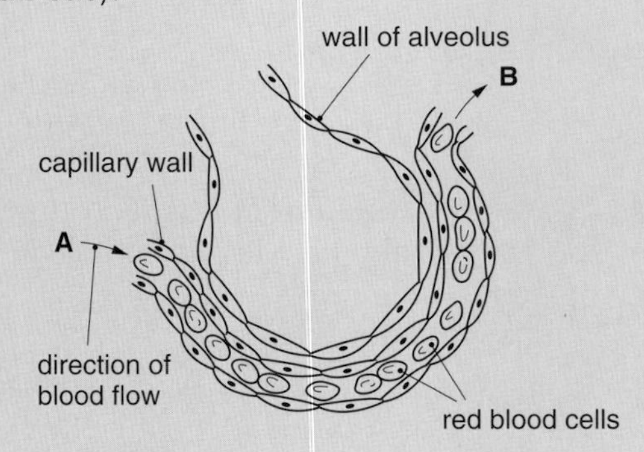

i) Through how many cell layers must oxygen pass to leave the air in the alveolus and reach a red blood cell? *[1]*

The table below shows the relative concentrations of gases dissolved in the blood at the ends of the capillary shown in the diagram.

Gas	End A	End B
Carbon dioxide		
Oxygen	low	

ii) Copy and complete the table using the words **high** and **low**. *[2]*

c) i) Name a type of blood cell **not** shown in the diagram. *[1]*

ii) Explain how the cell named in c) i) is involved in the body's defence against disease. *[1]* (OCR)

▶ Blood and circulation

8. The diagram below represents a smear of blood on a microscope slide.

a) i) How many red blood cells can be seen on the slide ?

ii) How many white blood cells can be seen on the slide ? *[2]*

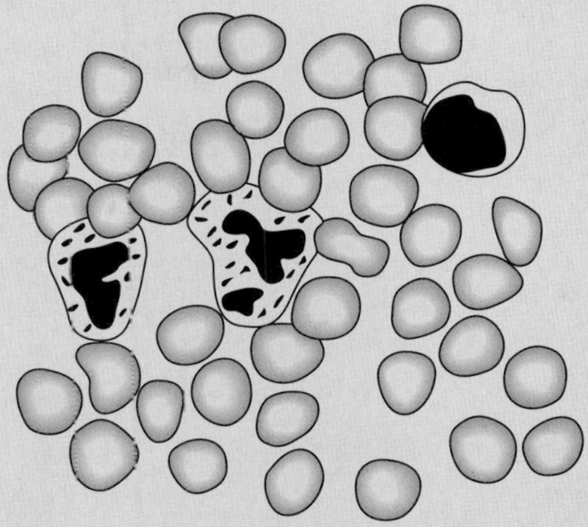

b) i) What is the function of the red blood cells ? *[1]*

ii) Give **two** ways in which red blood cells are adapted to carry out this function. *[2]*

c) Explain how carbon monoxide affects the way in which red blood cells function. *[1]*

d) Red blood cells survive on average about 100 days. New cells have to be produced in the bone marrow.

i) Why are red blood cells not able to reproduce ? *[1]*

ii) 1 mm^3 of blood contains 5 million red blood cells.
How many red blood cells does 1 cm^3 (1000 mm^3) contain? *[1]*

iii) An adult has 5000 cm^3 of blood. How many red blood cells have to be made on average each day in the bone marrow? Show your working *[2]*

e) In some people the bone marrow is diseased and unable to produce enough red blood cells. These people may need a transplant of bone marrow from another person.
Explain how each of the following may help to prevent the rejection of the transplanted bone marrow.

i) Use bone marrow from a brother or sister of the patient. *[2]*

ii) Giving the patient drugs which stop the activity of the white blood cells. *[2]*

f) After the transplant operation the patient has to be isolated from other people for some time. Explain why. *[2]* (AQA)

9. Doctors think that there is a link between heart disease and the level of cholesterol in the blood.
Healthy levels of cholesterol are below 5 units.
The table below shows the percentage of adults whose cholesterol level is above 5.

Age	Percentage of men	Percentage of women
15–24	22	26
25–34	48	42
35–44	66	56
45–54	74	68
55–64	78	86
65–74	74	88
75 and over	68	86

a) Use the information in the table to construct a bar chart to display the data. *[2]*

b) Describe how the pattern for the percentage of men with high cholesterol changes with age. *[2]*

c) Describe how the level of cholesterol in woman, changes and compares with men over 50 years of age.
Suggest a reason for your answer. *[3]*

d) High levels of cholesterol can block coronary arteries.
   i) Explain what this will do to the flow of blood through these arteries. *[1]*
   ii) Suggest why this can be harmful to the heart. *[2]* (OCR)

10. Damaged hearts can be replaced.
Some patients have an artificial heart.
Others have a real heart.

a) Use the following words to describe the **advantages** and **disadvantages** of using an artificial heart.
drugs   power supply   rejection   size *[4]*

b) When a donor heart becomes available, most of the heart patients who need it cannot have it transported.
Explain why. *[3]*

c) There is a shortage of real hearts from donors.
Some people always carry a donor card.
Some people think that everyone should be made to carry a donor card by law.
Other people do not agree with them.
   i) Explain with reasons, the arguments for and against carrying donor cards. *[2]*
   ii) Some doctors think that they should be able to use organs from dead bodies without permission unless the person carried a card saying they did not wish to donate organs.
   Explain with reasons whether you think this point of view should be made into law. *[2]* (OCR)

11. Three pupils were asked to find out who was the fittest. They decided to do this by measuring their pulse rates.
This is what they did.

1. They counted their pulse rates when sitting down.
2. They then exercised for three minutes in different ways:
   Peter ran up and down the stairs;
   Margaret did step-ups;
   John ran on the spot.
3. They counted their pulse rates as soon as the exercise stopped.
4. They counted their pulse rates three minutes after the exercise stopped and again six minutes after the exercise stopped.

Their results are shown on the graph below.

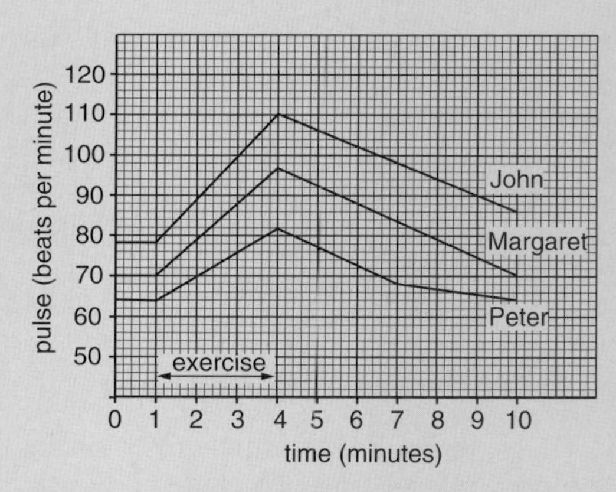

a) What was Margaret's pulse rate three minutes after exercise? *[1]*

b) They concluded that Peter was the fittest person.
Give one reason why they reached this conclusion. *[1]*

c) Suggest two ways they could have improved their investigation. *[2]* (AQA)

▶ Homeostasis

12. The regulation of body temperature is achieved by balancing energy release against energy loss. Energy release is greater during exercise.

a) The rate of metabolism changes during exercise. Describe how this influences energy release. *[2]*

b) Explain why, during exercise, the body attempts to lose more energy. *[2]*

c) What role does **negative feedback** play in regulating body temperature? *[1]*

d) During rest, excess sugar is stored. How is this achieved? *[2]*

e) The graphs below show how the blood glucose and the concentration of hormone involved in glucose storage vary over a 12 hour time period.

i) Using these graphs explain why a single daily dose of hormone would not adequately control blood glucose concentration in diabetics. *[2]*

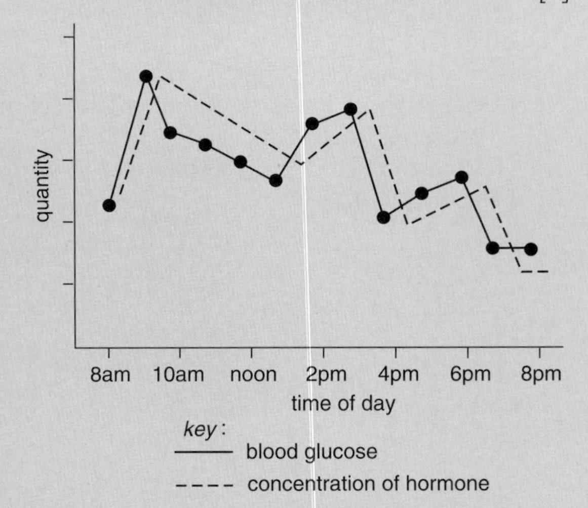

ii) Explain how physical exercise would influence the production of the hormone involved in glucose storage. *[2]* (OCR)

13. The diagram shows the mean daily input and output of water for an adult.

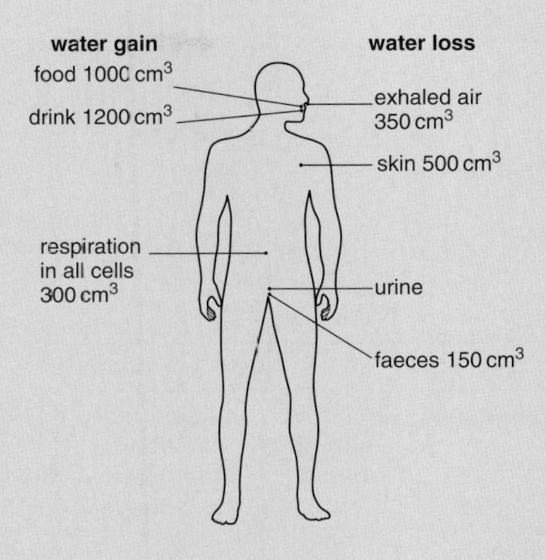

a) Respiration is a source of water.
Copy and complete the equation for respiration

sugar + ... → water + ... + energy *[2]*

b) The kidneys keep the water content of the body constant by controlling the volume of water passed out in the urine.

i) Use data from the diagram to calculate the mean daily output of water in the urine. Show your working. *[2]*

ii) Describe how the amount of water in the body is controlled by the kidneys. *[3]*

c) Sometimes kidneys fail. Two ways of treating kidney failure are the use of a kidney dialysis machine and kidney transplants.
Describe what happens to the composition of a patient's blood as it passes through a dialysis machine. *[3]*

d) In the treatment of kidney failure:

i) Give **two** possible advantages of using a kidney transplant rather than a dialysis machine. *[2]*

ii) Give **two** possible disadvantages of using a kidney machine rather than a dialysis machine. *[2]* (AQA)

14. The kidneys remove waste materials from the liquid part of the blood. The table below shows the concentration of certain substances:
- in the liquid part of the blood
- in the liquid that has just been filtered from the blood in the kidneys
- in the solution in the bladder.

a) i) Which **one** of these substances does **not** pass into the liquid that is filtered in the kidneys ? *[1]*

	Concentration (%)		
Substance	**in liquid part of blood**	**in liquid that has been filtered in the kidneys**	**in liquid in the bladder**
protein	7.0	0	0
salt	0.35	0.35	0.5
glucose	0.1	0.1	0
urea	0.03	0.03	2.0

ii) Suggest **one** reason why this substance does **not** pass out of the blood. *[1]*

b) Explain why the concentration of urea in the liquid in the bladder is much greater than the concentration of urea in the liquid that is filtered in the kidneys. *[1]*

c) i) Describe how a kidney dialysis machine works. *[3]*

ii) Use the data in the table to suggest the concentration that the salt in the dialysis fluid should be. Explain your answer. *[2]* (AQA)

15. The diagram at the top of the next column shows the effect of a change in the water content of the blood.

a) i) What type of substance is ADH? *[1]*

ii) What is the stimulus which causes the pituitary gland to produce ADH? *[1]*

iii) Precisely how is the ADH transported to the kidney? *[1]*

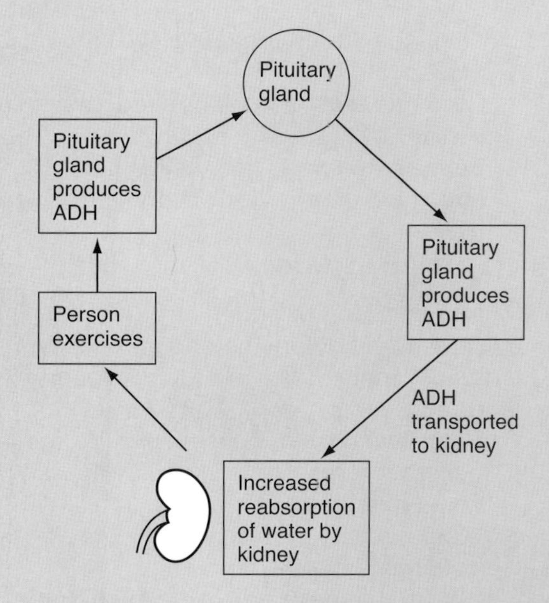

b) i) Using information from the diagram describe and explain the sequence of events when the person stops exercising and drinks a pint of water. *[5]*

ii) Explain why the response to this change would take 20 minutes. *[1]* (AQA)

► Control and coordination

16. The diagram shows a finger touching a hot object.
It also shows neurones **A**, **B** and **C**, which pass electrical impulses from touch receptors to muscle effectors.
Neurones **D** and **E** pass impulses to and from the brain.

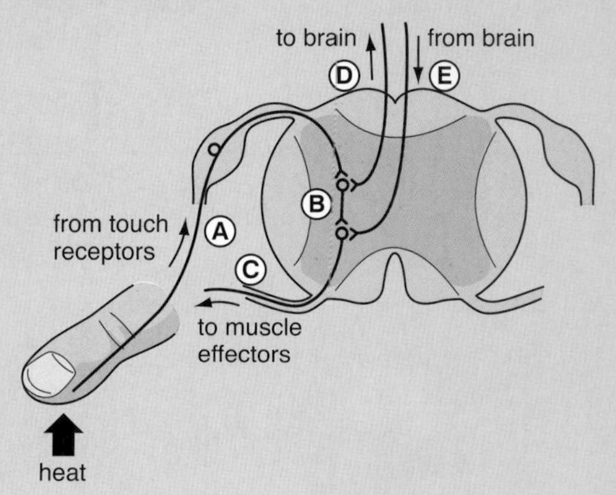

a) Name the pathway of electrical impulses along neurones **A**, **B** and **C**. [1]

b) What is the response of the muscle effectors? [1]

c) Neurones **D** and **E** are **not** involved in the response of the muscle effectors. What is the advantage of this? [1]

d) If one of the neurones **A**, **B**, **C**, **D** or **E** is cut, it may affect the ability to respond if you touch a hot object, or the ability to know that you have touched it. Copy and complete the table by putting the correct letter in each box.

Information about neurone	Letter of neurone
If this neurone is cut, you can remove your finger from a hot object, but you will not know that you have touched it.	....
If this neurone is cut, you cannot remove your finger from a hot object even though you know you have touched it.	....
If this neurone is cut, you cannot remove your finger from a hot object, and you will not know that you have touched it.	....

(3) (EDEX)

17. The table shows the levels of the sex hormones oestrogen and progesterone in the blood stream of a woman during one complete menstrual cycle.

	Level of hormone in blood stream (arbitrary units)	
Day	**oestrogen**	**progesterone**
0	50	46
7	54	40
14	66	58
21	52	112
28	50	46

a) i) Plot the data for the hormones oestrogen and progesterone **as line graphs** on one grid and join the plots. [3]

ii) How many units of oestrogen are in the blood stream on day 18 ? [1]

iii) I) State which of the hormones is responsible for ovulation. [1]

II) Use the information in your graph and the table to help you explain your answer to part I) above. [2]

b) State **two** medical uses of sex hormones in humans. [2] (WJEC)

▶ Disease

18. a) The diagram shows a bacterial cell.

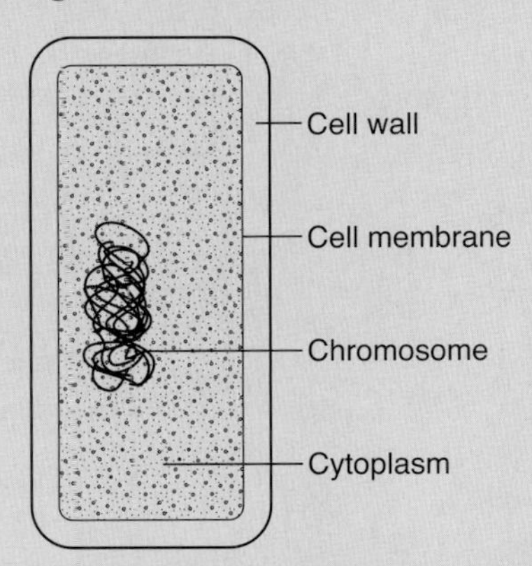

A bacterial cell is smaller than a human cell. Give **two** other ways in which the bacterial cell is different from a cell in the human body. [2]

b) Describe and explain **two** natural defences which help to prevent bacteria entering and harming the human body. [2]

c) The table shows changes in resistance to the antibiotic penicillin in one species of bacterium between 1991 and 1996.

Years	Percentage of cases where bacteria were resistant to penicillin
1991–92	7
1993–94	14
1995–96	22

A doctor was asked to treat a patient who had a sore throat.

i) How does penicillin help to treat infection? [1]

ii) Use the data in the table to suggest why the doctor should not prescribe penicillin. [2] (AQA)

19. a) State which pathogen causes each of the following diseases.
Choose from the following list.

bacteria   fungus   protozoa   virus

i) influenza
ii) cholera
iii) dysentery
iv) athlete's foot

b) The human body has various ways of defending itself against pathogens. Look at the diagram of the body and explain how each labelled part helps to protect us from disease. *[4]* (OCR)

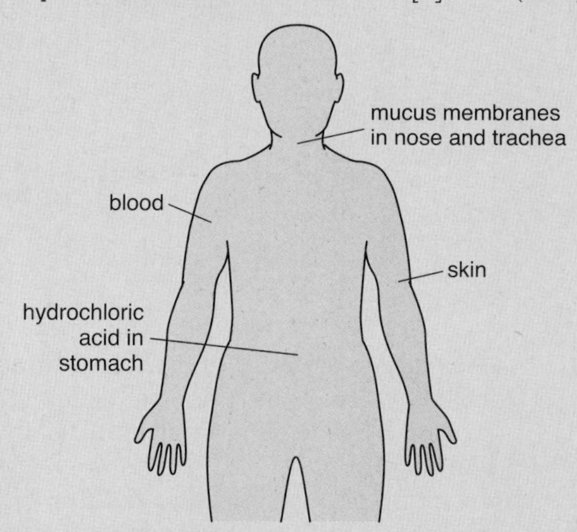

20. In the eighteenth century, surgeons did not wear special clothing or wash their hands before operations. Many of their patients died from infections.

a) Suggest why patients often died from infections after operations. *[1]*

b) In the nineteenth century, Joseph Lister told surgeons to use sprays of carbolic acid in operating theatres and to wash their hands.
The graph at the top of the next column shows the effect that using Lister's instructions had on the number of patients who died from infections after surgery.
Describe how Lister's instructions affected the number of patients dying from infections after surgery. *[2]*

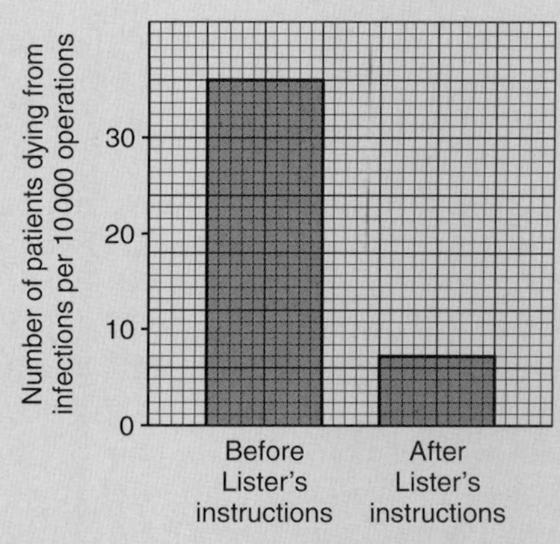

c) Kidney transplants were introduced in the twentieth century as one way of treating patients with kidney failure.

i) Give **one** other way of treating kidney failure. *[1]*

ii) The patient's body may reject a transplanted kidney unless doctors take precautions.
Some of these precautions are listed below.
- A donor kidney is specially chosen.
- The recipient's bone marrow is treated with radiation.
- The recipient is treated with drugs.
- The recipient is kept in sterile conditions.

Explain how each of these precautions may help the patient to survive. *[4]* (AQA)

21. a) The conversion of proteins to amino acids can be represented as shown below.

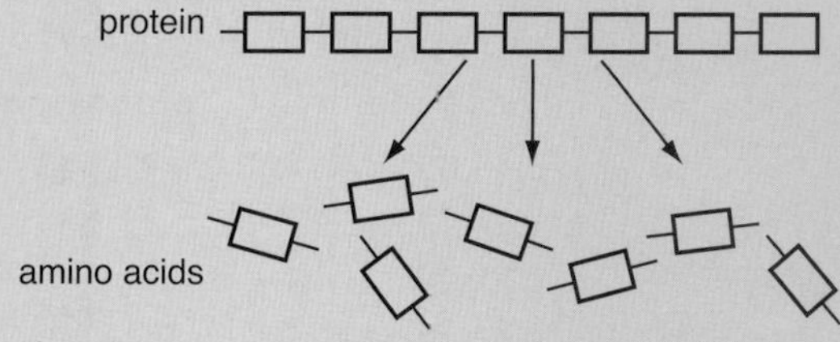

i) What name is given to the breaking down of proteins into amino acids in the body ? *[1]*

ii) State **one** use of amino acids in the body. *[1]*

b) Antibodies are proteins produced in the blood by the immune system when the body is infected.

i) Which part of the immune system produces antibodies ? [1]

ii) The effectiveness of a person's immune system can be reduced by the use of drugs. State **one other** way this can happen. [1]

iii) If a person has a kidney or other organ transplant, drugs are given to reduce the effectiveness of the immune system. Explain the reason for this. [2]

c) **Active** immunity is a permanent type of immunity gained as a result of the body reacting to an infection. **Passive** immunity is a temporary type of immunity where antibodies are given to the body, often by injection.
A baby may acquire passive immunity **other than** by means of an injection. State **one** way. [1]

d) A graph of a person's immunity is shown below.

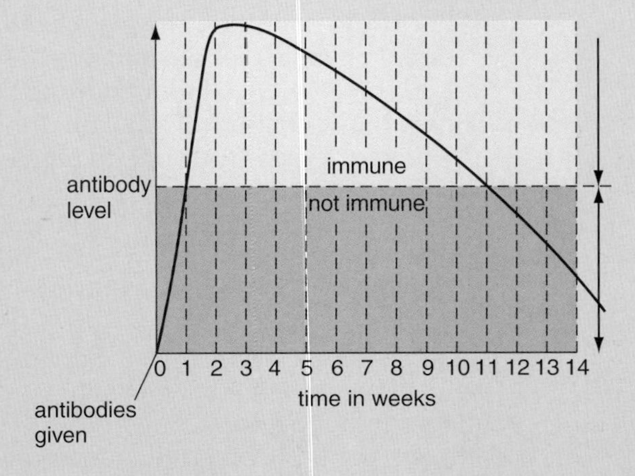

i) For how long was the person immune ? [1]

ii) Does the person to whom the graph refers have active or passive immunity ?
Explain the reason for your answer. [2] (AQA)

▶ Drugs

22. a) Scientists are constantly developing new drugs. All drugs need to be tested in the laboratory and tried out on healthy human volunteers before use with patients.
Thalidomide was developed as a sleeping pill. Unfortunately, many babies were born with limb abnormalities to mothers who took Thalidomide to relieve morning sickness during pregnancy.

i) Explain why a new drug is given to healthy human volunteers in a drugs trial. [1]

ii) Explain why the results of the Thalidomide drug trial did not identify its side effects. [2]

b) Some people think that smoking cannabis can relieve the symptoms of the disease multiple sclerosis. Explain, using scientific and ethical reason, why most doctors would not advise their patients to smoke cannabis for this purpose. [5] (AQA)

23. The table gives information about the amounts of alcohol consumed and the number of deaths from liver disease in some countries.

County	**Mean amount of alcohol consumed** per person per year (litres)	**Number of deaths from liver diseased** per 100 000 people per year
England	8	4
France	17	34
Germany	13	27
Iceland	4	1
Spain	15	22
Sweden	6	12

a) Draw a bar chart to show this information.

b) Alcohol causes harm to the liver. Explain how the information provides evidence of this. [1]

c) The mean alcohol consumption is lower in Germany than in Spain. However, the death rate from liver disease is higher in Germany than in Spain. Suggest one reason for this. [1] (AQA)

Further questions on Humans as organisms

24. Emphysema and tuberculosis are lung diseases. The bar charts on the next page show the link between cigarette smoking and these diseases.
Look at the charts.

a) How does cigarette smoking affect each of these two lung diseases?

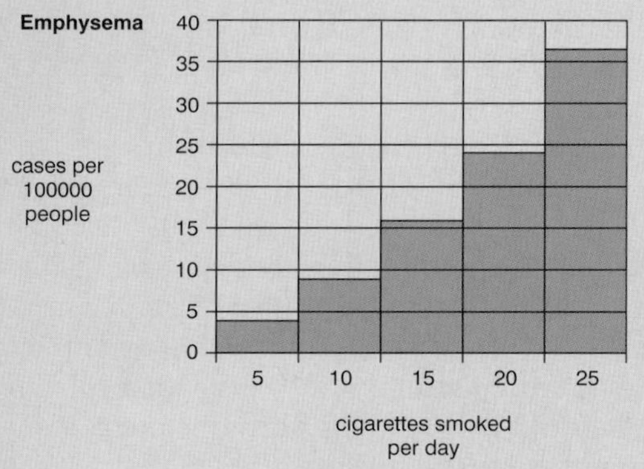

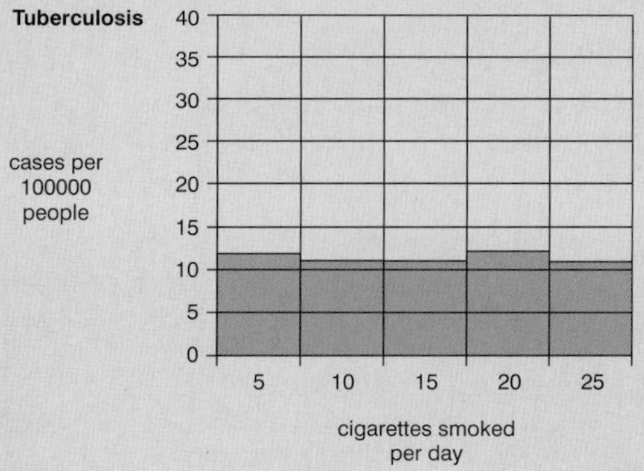

Emphysema
cases per 100000 people
cigarettes smoked per day

Tuberculosis
cases per 100000 people
cigarettes smoked per day

b) Smoking can cause other diseases.
Look at the list of diseases:

athlete's foot **cancer** **diabetes**
heart disease **influenza (flu)**
sickle cell anaemia

Write down two diseases which can be caused by smoking.
Choose your answers from the list.
[2] (OCR)

25. The table at the top ofd the next column shows the relationship between alcohol consumed and blood alcohol level for males and females of different body mass.

a) i) What is the relationship between the amount of alcohol consumed and the blood alcohol level? *[1]*

Alcohol consumed per hour	Blood alcohol level in mg per 100 cm^3			
	Male 45 kg	Female 45 kg	Male 90 kg	Female 90 kg
3 units	37	45	19	22
6 units	75	90	37	45
12 units	150	180	70	90
24 units	300	360	150	180

ii) With people who consume the same amount of alcohol, what is the relationship between their blood alcohol level and body mass? *[1]*

iii) With people of the same body mass who consume the same amount of alcohol, what is the relationship between their blood alcohol level and their sex? *[1]*

b) i) Plot a graph of the data for the 45 kg male on the grid provided. On the same graph, plot the data for 90 kg male. Join the points with straight lines. *[5]*

ii) In certain countries, the legal limit for driving is 80 mg of alcohol per 100 cm^3 of blood. From your graph, how many units of alcohol per hour would a 45 kg male drink to reach the legal limit? *[1]*

iii) What is the difference in the blood alcohol level of the 45 kg male and the 90 kg male after drinking 20 units of alcohol per hour? *[1]*

c) The table below shows how increasing levels of blood alcohol can result in changes in behaviour. Copy and complete the table by naming the part of the brain that would be affected. One box has been completed for you.

Blood alcohol level in mg per 100 cm^3	Behaviour change	Part of brain affected
50	Less able to make decisions	Cerebral hemispheres
100	Loss of balance	
200	Double vision	
400	Respiratory failure	

(3) (EDEX)

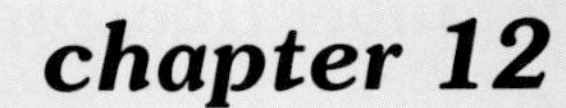

Feeding in Plants

What's the most common colour in nature?

Most of the green we see comes from leaves.
Why are they this colour?

If you look at some leaf cells under the microscope what do you see?
Lots of round, green structures called **chloroplasts**.
What do you think they are used for?

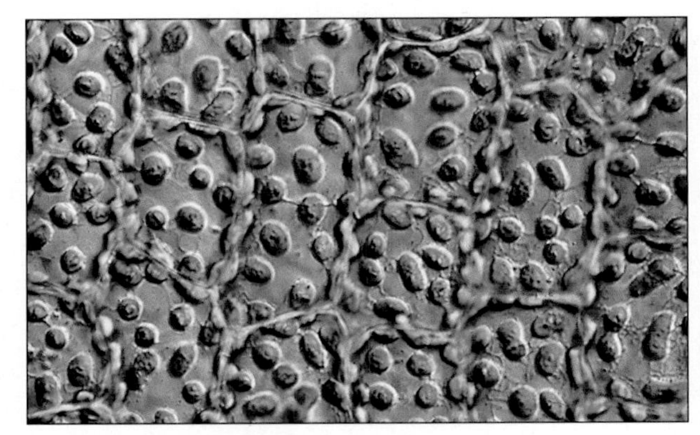
Chloroplasts in moss cells

We call green plants the **producers**.
Why do you think this is?

Green plants are able to make their own food from simple raw materials around them.
This process is called **photosynthesis**.

Energy is needed for photosynthesis.
This energy comes from sunlight.

Chlorophyll is a substance that absorbs sunlight.
Chloroplasts contain lots of chlorophyll.

The light energy is used to convert carbon dioxide and water into sugar (glucose).
The sugar is the plant's food.
Oxygen is made as a by-product.

During photosynthesis the energy from sunlight becomes converted into the chemical bond energy in the glucose.

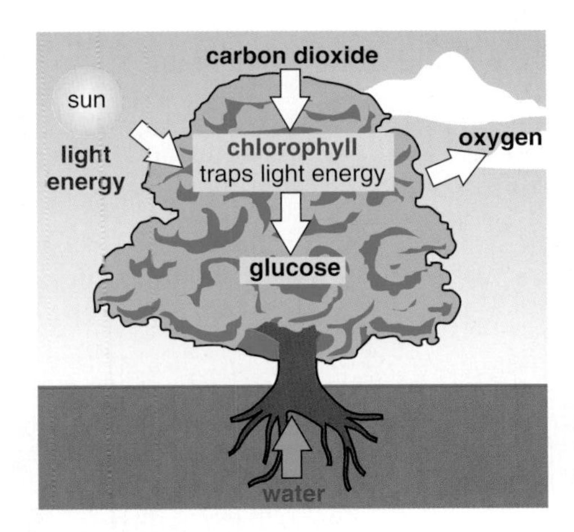

Photosynthesis is not a simple reaction.
It takes place in a number of small stages.
This is the equation for the whole process:

carbon dioxide + water	light and chlorophyll	glucose + oxygen
$6\,CO_2$ + $6\,H_2O$	⟶	$C_6H_{12}O_6$ + $6\,O_2$

▶ Investigating photosynthesis

Green plants make food from simple substances.
We can see from the equation on the previous page that glucose is made.

Experiment 12.1 Testing a plant for glucose

eye protection

Put a piece of raw onion in a pestle and mortar. Grind it up with a little sand and 10 cm^3 of water.

Filter the liquid into a test-tube.

Heat the liquid with 10 drops of Benedict's solution on a water bath.

Did the liquid turn orange?

Starch grains provide an insoluble store of food

If too much glucose is dissolved in the cell sap it would make a strong solution. This would draw water in from other cells by osmosis.
Starch is insoluble and does not cause this problem.
This is why insoluble substances like starch are used for storage in plants.

Experiment 12.2 Testing a leaf for starch

Dip a leaf into boiling water for about a minute to soften it.

Turn off the Bunsen burner.

Put the leaf into a test-tube of ethanol. Stand the test-tube in a beaker of hot water for about 10 minutes.

Wash the leaf in cold water.

Spread the leaf out flat on a Petri dish and cover it with iodine solution.
If the leaf goes blue–black, starch is present.

eye protection

ethanol is flammable

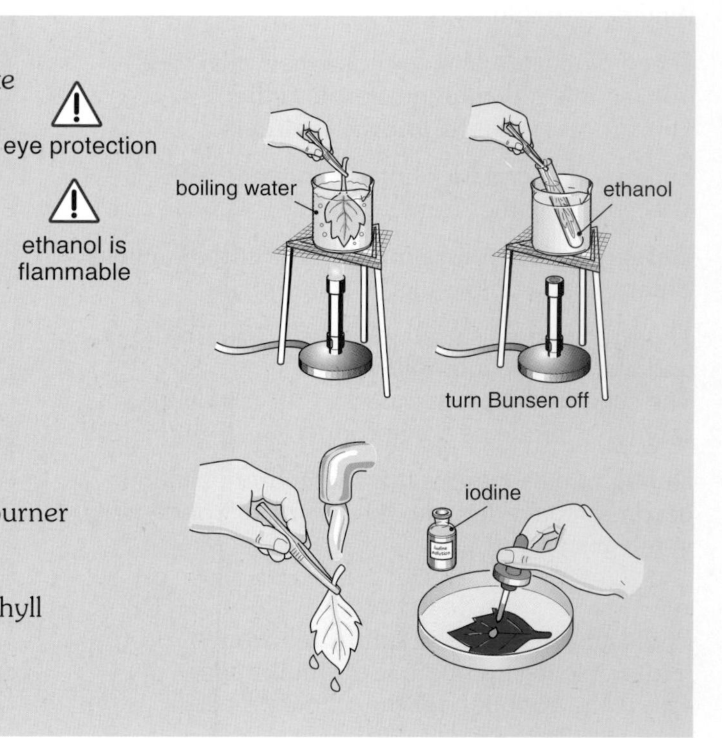

- Why is it important to turn off the Bunsen burner when you were heating the ethanol?
- Why was it necessary to extract the chlorophyll before you tested for starch?

▶ Raw materials for photosynthesis

What do plants need for photosynthesis?

We have already said that light energy is needed to power the process.
If you look back at the equation on page 181 you will see what else is needed.

- **Chlorophyll** absorbs the light energy. Chlorophyll is in the chloroplasts of the leaf.
- **Carbon dioxide** diffuses into the leaves from the air.
- **Water** is absorbed by the roots from the soil.

We can carry out experiments to show that these raw materials are needed for photosynthesis.
We simply give the plant all the things that it needs ***except*** for the one factor that we are investigating.

If the plant is unable to carry out photosynthesis it will not make starch.
But we must make sure that the plant has no starch to begin with.
We can **de-starch** as plant by leaving it in the dark for 24 hours.

Help, I'm being de-starched!

Experiment 12.3 Is chlorophyll needed for photosynthesis ?

Take a de-starched, variegated geranium plant.
(Variegated means some parts of the leaves are white because there is no chlorophyll there.)

Place the plant in sunlight for a few hours.

Draw one leaf to show the white and green parts.

Now test this variegated leaf for starch.

⚠ eye protection

- Did only the green parts of the leaf go blue–black? Why did this happen?
- Why didn't you extract chlorophyll from the leaf and then see if it could carry out photosynthesis?

Variegated geranium leaves

From air and water

How could you prove that a plant needs **carbon dioxide** to make its own food?

Provide it with everything it needs for photosynthesis ***except*** carbon dioxide. Then test to see if it has made starch.

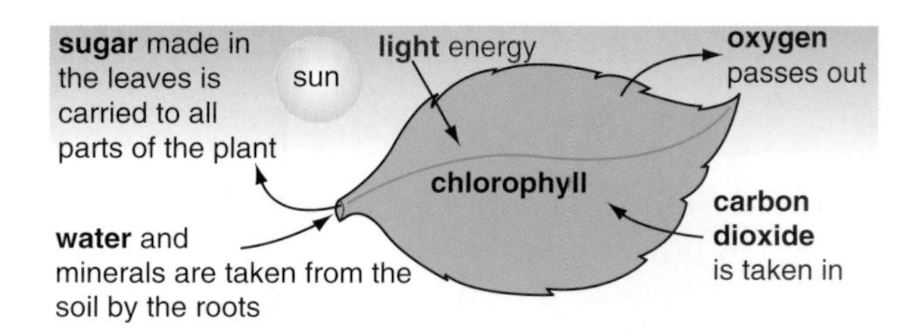

Experiment 12.4 Is carbon dioxide needed for photosynthesis?

Take a de-starched geranium plant.

Enclose it in a plastic bag with a chemical that absorbs carbon dioxide.
(**Soda lime** absorbs carbon dioxide.)

Leave the plant in sunlight for a few hours.

Test a leaf for starch.

⚠ eye protection

- Does the leaf contain starch? Why not?
- Has the plant carried out photosynthesis?
- What would be your **control** plant?
  A control plant should have everything it needs for photosynthesis ***including*** carbon dioxide.

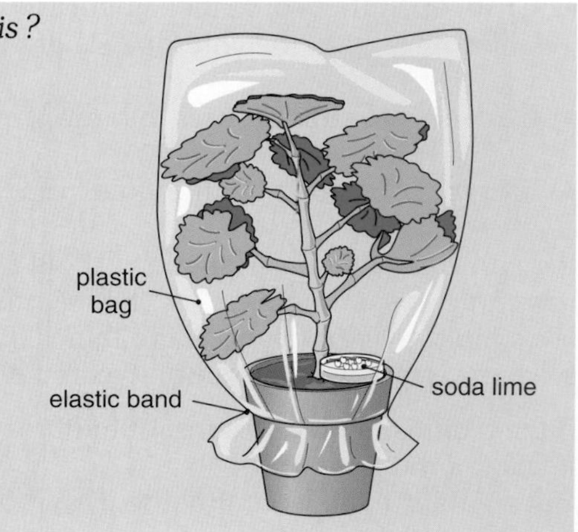

Experiment 12.5 Is sunlight needed for photosynthesis?

Take a de-starched geranium plant.

Cover part of the leaf with some tin foil (this prevents light getting through).

Leave the plant in sunlight for a few hours.

Test the leaf for starch.

⚠ eye protection

- Which parts of the test leaf go blue–black?
- Why do the parts that were covered ***not*** contain starch?

Plants also need water for photosynthesis.
Can you think up a simple experiment to prove this?
It's not easy is it?
If you remove all the water the plant will shrivel up.

Scientists can give plants a special form of water called 'heavy water'.
They can trace this water and see where it goes.
They can show that it is taken up and used in photosynthesis.

▶ Products of photosynthesis

Let's remind ourselves of the photosynthesis equation :

$$\text{carbon dioxide} + \text{water} \xrightarrow[\text{chlorophyll}]{\text{sunlight}} \text{glucose} + \text{oxygen}$$

So how are the products of the reaction useful ?

Most photosynthesis takes place in the leaves.
So most of the food is made there.
But ***all*** parts of the plant need food.
Dissolved food is carried around the plant in its transport system.
What happens to it then ?

- Some of the **glucose** is used in respiration to give the plant energy.
- Some of the glucose is changed to starch and stored in the roots for future use.
- Some of the glucose is used to make **cellulose**. This is needed for plant cell walls.

Glucose can also be converted to other substances :

- Plants get nitrogen by absorbing nitrates from the soil. Glucose and nitrogen can form **amino acids**. Proteins are built up from amino acids. Plants need **proteins** for growth and cell repair.
- **Fats** and **oils** are used for storage in seeds.

Oxygen is also a product of photosynthesis.
This replaces the oxygen that is used up in respiration.

Photosynthesis makes food

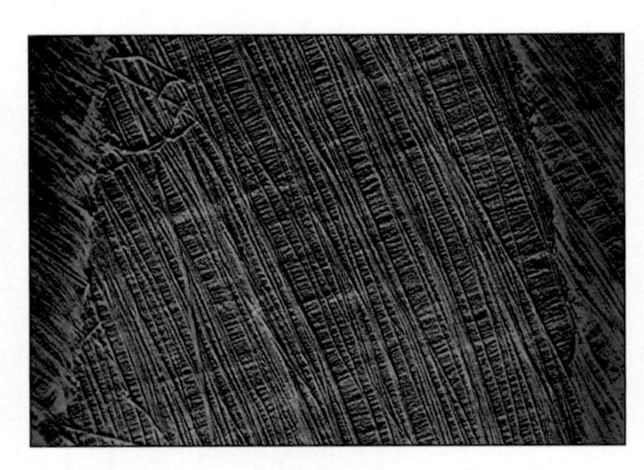

Cellulose strands in a plant cell wall

Experiment 12.6 Oxygen produced in photosynthesis

Set up the apparatus to collect bubbles of gas given off by the pondweed.
Dissolve a little sodium hydrogencarbonate in the water.
Place the apparatus in the light.

Test the gas for oxygen with a glowing splint.

- Why was hydrogencarbonate added to the water ?
- Why is it important to leave a gap between the beaker and the funnel ?

Water rich in carbon dioxide circulates to the pondweed and increases the rate of photosynthesis.

- Why is it essential that a water plant like Canadian pondweed is used in this experiment ? (***Hint***: Think about how the gas is collected.)
- Why is the gas collected unlikely to be pure oxygen ?

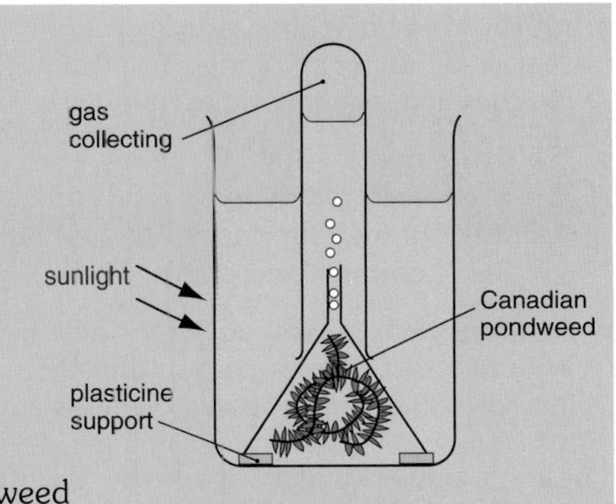

► Why is photosynthesis important?

Think about the food you've eaten in the last 24 hours.
How much of it came from plants?

How about rice, potatoes, corn flakes and peanuts for a start?

And what about the steak or the beefburger?
Where did they come from?
From animals that have eaten plants.

Then there are things like cooking oil and low-fat margarine.
They are made from parts of plants.
Without plants we would soon get pretty hungry!

Investigation 12.7 Food plants

Look at some food plants like the ones shown here:

Try to say what ***parts*** of plants they are.
For instance, celery is a leaf stalk.

Draw some parts of the plants that we eat.
Write a note to say what each part does in a living plant.

Carry out some food tests on different plant parts.

Try testing carrot, onion, potato and different seeds.
Test for sugar, starch, protein and fat.
(See Experiments 4.1, 4.2, 4.3, 4.4, pages 43–5)

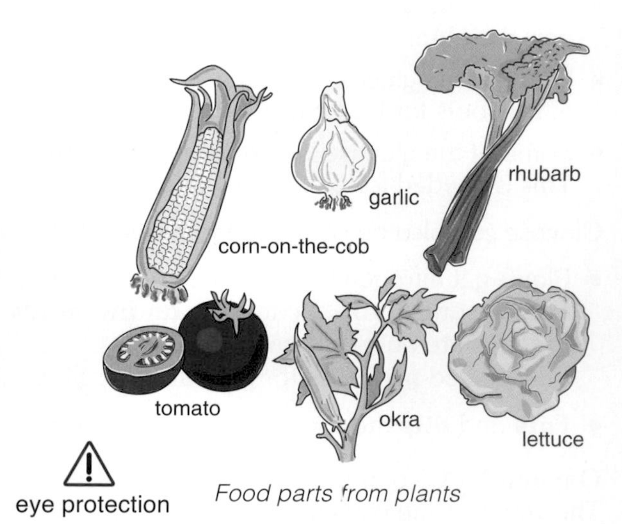

Food parts from plants

- **Medicines** have been extracted from hundreds of species of flowering plants. Tropical rainforests are the main source of these plants.
- **Habitats** are provided by plants.
  The rainforests make up only 6% of the Earth's land surface. But they support more than half the world's species of animals and plants.
- **Atmospheric gases** are kept stable by photosynthesis. Without green plants, carbon dioxide in the air would increase and oxygen would decrease.

These are powerful reasons why the destruction of tropical rainforests should be stopped.

- Plants also provide us with building materials like wood. Fuels like oil, coal and peat have come from fossil plants.

▶ Rate of photosynthesis

Rate always involves time.
The rate of photosynthesis could be measured by how much glucose is made in a given time.

So why are people interested in this?
Well, the faster photosynthesis takes place, the more food is made and the bigger the plant will grow.
Scientists try to increase the rate of photosynthesis to increase the **yield** of a crop.

What sort of things would affect the rate of photosynthesis?

Sugar cane is a crop that grows well in the tropics.
Does the climate affect the rate of photosynthesis?

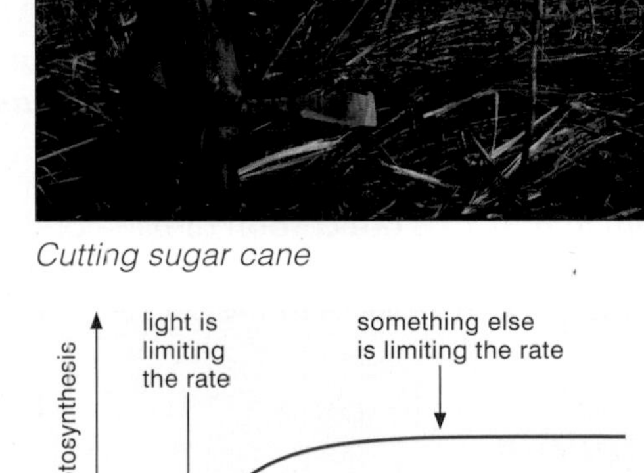

Cutting sugar cane

Light

Photosynthesis increases when light gets brighter – but only up to a point.
When a certain light intensity is reached the rate of photosynthesis stays constant. It can't go any faster even if the light intensity continues to rise.

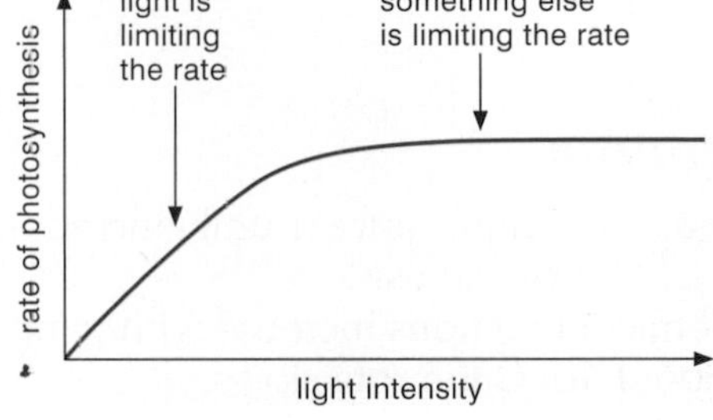

Experiment 12.8 Photosynthesis and light intensity

You can use this apparatus to measure the effects of light intensity on the rate of photosynthesis:

Cut a piece of Canadian pondweed about 5 cm in length.
You can weigh down the other end with a paper clip.

Count the number of bubbles released with the lamp at different distances away from the plant.

- Did the number of bubbles increase when the lamp was nearer to the plant?
  Why do you think this was?

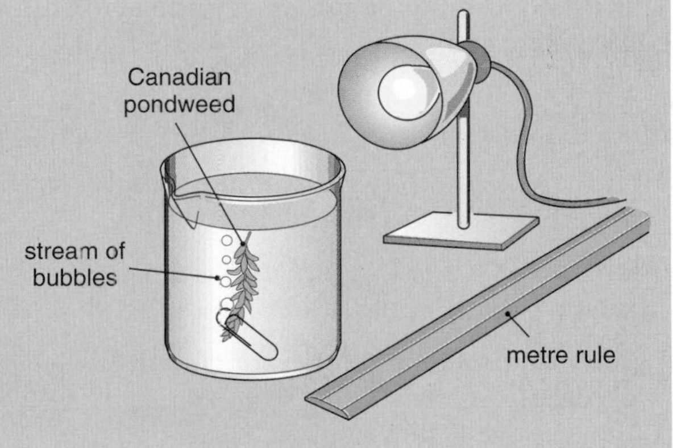

Many plants spread their leaves to catch as much light as as they can.

But light that is too strong can damage the chloroplasts.

Some woodland plants prefer dim light.
We call them **shade plants**.
They are able to make use of the limited amount of light that penetrates the tree canopy and reaches the woodland floor.

Bluebells

▶ Limiting factors

Things like light intensity can affect the rate of photosynthesis – we call them **limiting factors**.

It doesn't matter if the plant has lots of carbon dioxide and water and a nice warm temperature.
If light is in short supply, then light will ***limit*** the rate of photosynthesis.

Let's say light intensity is limiting photosynthesis.
The only way to increase the rate is to ***increase*** the limiting factor – in this case, light intensity.

Other limiting factors are carbon dioxide and temperature.
But only **one** factor can limit the rate at any one time.
It depends on which one is in the shortest supply.

Glasshouses can control limiting factors

Temperature

An increase in temperature usually increases the rate of photosynthesis.
Most chemical reactions increase with temperature.
But at about 40 °C the rate slows.
At temperatures above this, the rate drops quickly.
This is because the ***enzymes*** in photosynthesis are being destroyed.

Investigation 12.9 Plan an investigation into the effect of temperature on the rate of photosynthesis

(***Hint***: You could try the apparatus in Experiment 12.8 using different water baths.)

Remember that other factors like light intensity and carbon dioxide concentration must be kept constant.

Check your plan with your teacher before you start.

Why do you think that crops like grapes and melons grow better in a glasshouse?

The warm conditions inside the glasshouse increase their rate of photosynthesis.
In this way we can grow plants that would not normally grow in the UK.

Different types of plants have different temperatures at which they grow best.
Each has an **optimum** temperature for growth.

Carbon dioxide

The more carbon dioxide you give plants, the more photosynthesis they carry out.
It is not possible to do this with crops outdoors.
The air usually contains about 0.04 % carbon dioxide.

Why do you think that carbon dioxide is often added to glasshouse crops ?

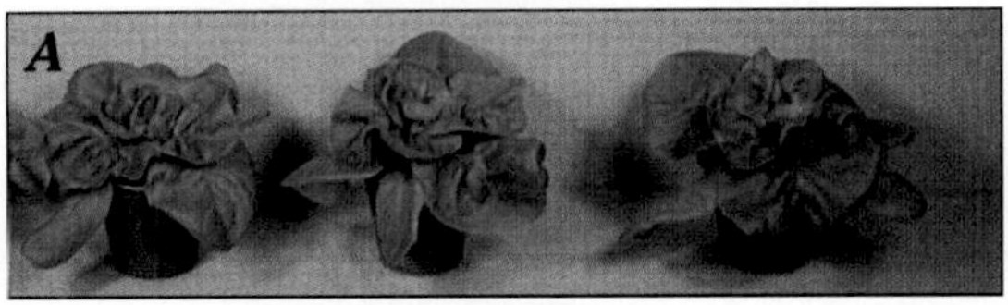

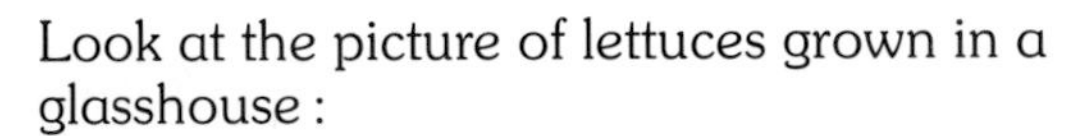

Look at the picture of lettuces grown in a glasshouse :

Those in A are growing in air which has more carbon dioxide than those in B.

Which would sell for the best price ?
Why are these lettuces bigger ?

Investigation 12.10 What is the effect of carbon dioxide on the rate of photosynthesis ?

How could you change Experiment 12.8 to find out the effects of carbon dioxide ?
(***Hint*** : Adding sodium hydrogencarbonate to water increases the concentration of carbon dioxide.)

Remember, other factors like light intensity and temperature must stay constant.

Check your plan with your teacher before you start.

These factors can **limit** the rate of photosynthesis :

- light intensity
- temperature
- carbon dioxide concentration

These are called **limiting factors**.

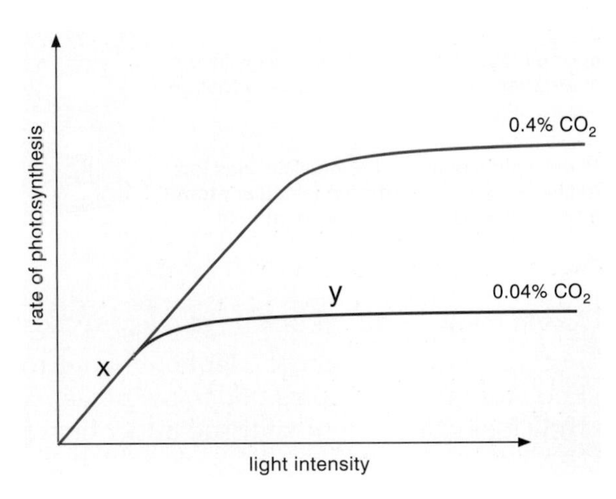

So if we provide more carbon dioxide, photosynthesis will be able to work at a faster rate.

There is not very much carbon dioxide in the atmosphere,only about 0.04 %.
Look at the graph :
What is the limiting the rate of photosynthesis at point X ?
What is the limiting the rate of photosynthesis at point Y ?
What happens to the rate of photosynthesis if the carbon dioxide concentration is increased from 0.04 % to 0.4 % ?

Once again, this means more food can be made.

▶ Leaves

What words would you use to describe a leaf? Flat? Thin? Green?

The leaf is where photosynthesis takes place. It is very well adapted for this job.

Leaves have:
- ***a large surface area*** – to absorb light rays
- ***a thin shape*** –so gases can diffuse in and out easily
- green ***chlorophyll*** – to absorb light
- ***veins*** – to support the leaf surface and to carry substances to and from all the cells in the leaf.

Experiment 12.11 Looking at leaves

Look closely at each surface of a leaf with a lens.

- Is the upper surface glossy? Why is this?
- Which surface is the darker green? Does most light get to this surface?

On the inside

To find out how a leaf works we need to look at a thin slice under the microscope.

cuticle : waterproof layer that also cuts down the water lost by evaporation

upper epidermis : single layer of cells with no chloroplasts.Light goes straight through

palisade layer : the palisade cell contains lots of chloroplasts. Most photosynthesis occurs here

spongy layer : more rounded cells with lots of **air spaces** between them. Gas exchange occurs here

lower epidermis : no thick cuticle. Has lots of tiny holes called **stomata** (singular **stoma**) These allow gases to diffuse in and out

vein : contains tubes called **xylem** that bring water and salts to the leaf and tubes called **phloem** that take dissolved food away

Experiment 12.12 Looking at a leaf section

Put a slide of a section of a leaf on the microscope.
Look for these structures under low power.
Now look at each type of tissue under high power.

▶ Stomata

Stomata are small holes on the underside of the leaf that let gases diffuse in and out.
(The singular of stomata is stoma.)

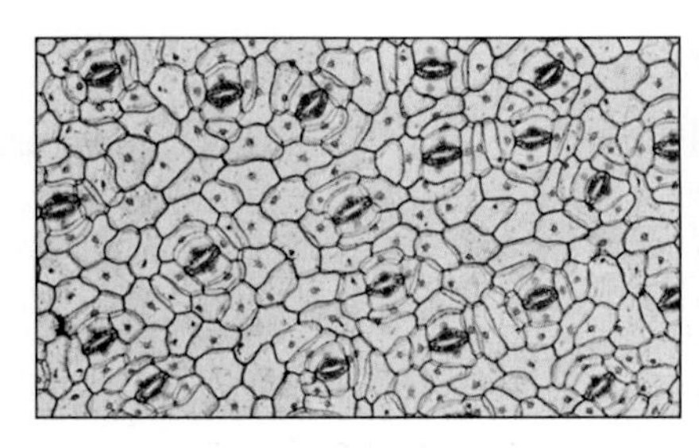

- Carbon dioxide diffuses in for photosynthesis.
- Oxygen made in photosynthesis diffuses out.
- Water vapour diffuses out.

Experiment 12.13 Where are the stomata?
Try dropping a leaf into a beaker of boiling water.
From which surface do bubbles appear?
What is the air coming out of?

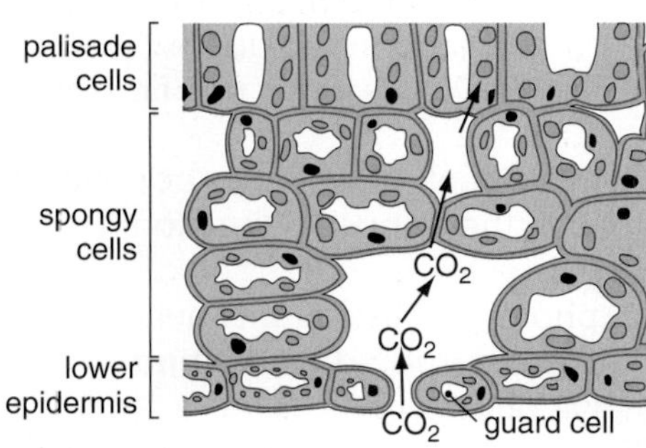

Carbon dioxide diffuses into the leaf for photosynthesis

Why are most stomata on the underside of the leaf?
What might block them on the upper surface?
Would more water be lost by evaporation if they were on the upper surface facing the sun or on the shaded lower surface?

Opening and closing

Stomata can be opened and closed by **guard cells**.

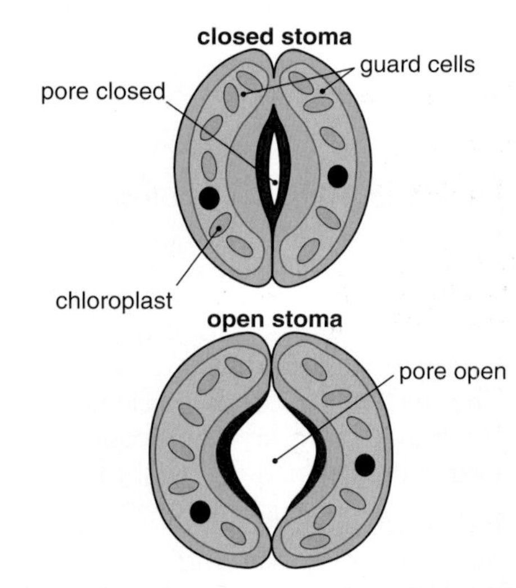

Stomata usually open during the day.
Water passes into the guard cells by **osmosis**.
This makes them bend so the stoma opens.
Carbon dioxide diffuses into the leaf for photosynthesis.

The stomata close at night.
Water passes out of the guard cells by osmosis.
They straighten up so the stoma closes.

The stomata also close in hot dry weather.
Why do you think this is?
Would the plant stay upright if it lost a lot of water?

Experiment 12.14 Looking at stomata
Paint a small square (1 cm × 1 cm) on the underside of a leaf with nail varnish.
The nail varnish makes an imprint of the leaf surface.
Wait for the varnish to dry completely then peel it off.
Put it on a slide with a drop of water and cover-slip.
Observe and draw two or three stomata at high power under the microscope.
Repeat for the upper surface of the leaf.

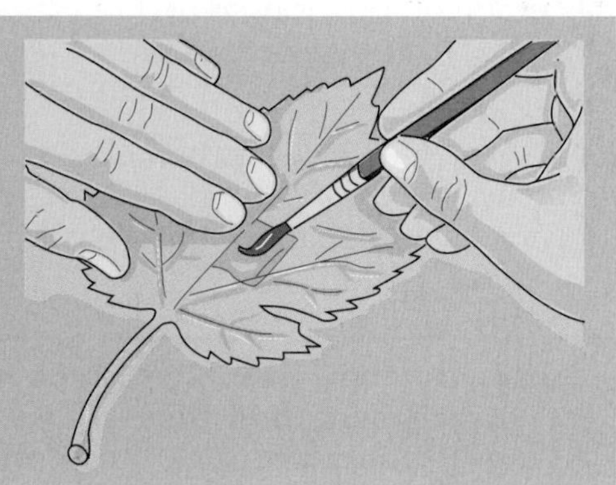

▶ Gas exchange

All living things, including plants, carry out respiration.
What gas do they need for this?
What gas do they get rid of?

For respiration plants need to:
- take in oxygen, ***and***
- give out carbon dioxide.

Respiration takes place ***all the time***.

Can you think of when carbon dioxide and oxygen move in the opposite direction?

For photosynthesis plants need to:
- take in carbon dioxide, ***and***
- give out oxygen.

Photosynthesis only takes place ***in the light***.

These gases pass into and out of leaves through the stomata.

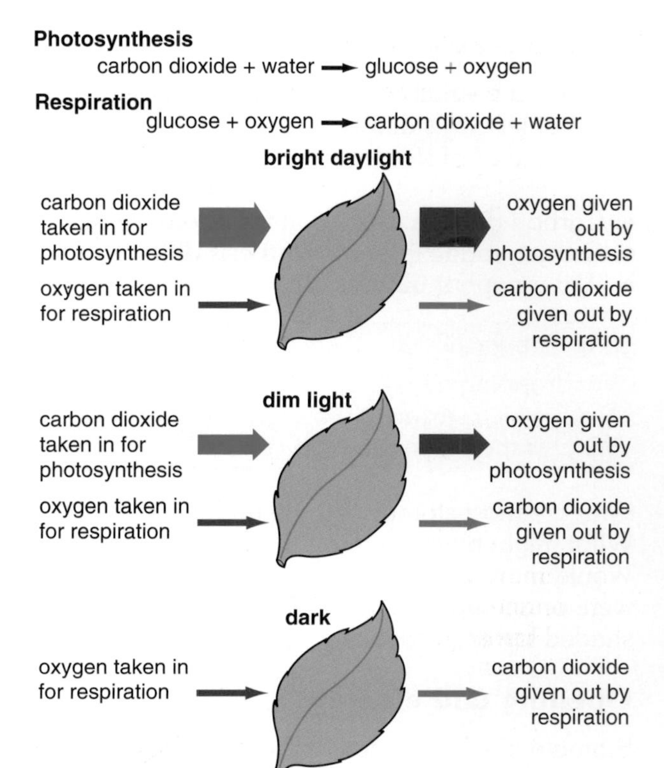

Experiment 12.15 Photosynthesis and respiration

Set up three boiling-tubes as shown here:

Put 5 cm^3 of hydrogencarbonate indicator into each tube.
Put a leaf in tubes 1 and 2 so that each is supported by the wall of the tube.
The underneath of the leaf should face inwards.
Put leaf 1 in darkness by covering the tube with tin foil.
Leave the tubes near a light for 2 to 3 hours.

If carbon dioxide is added to the air, the hydrogencarbonate indicator will turn yellow.
If carbon dioxide is used up from the air, the hydrogencarbonate indicator will turn purple

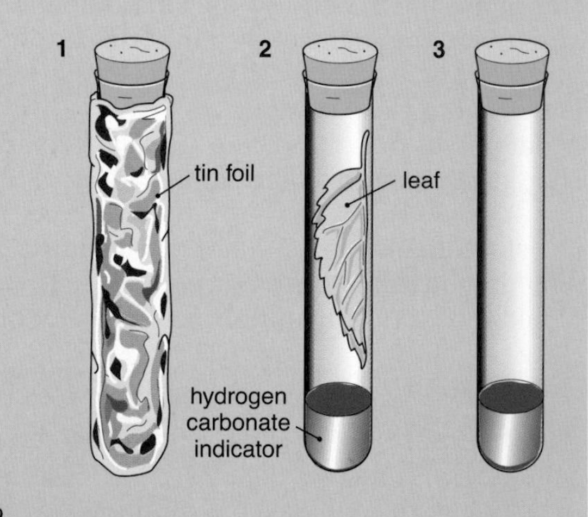

Look at your results.
- In which tube was carbon dioxide released by the leaf?
- In which tube was carbon dioxide taken up by the leaf?
- What was the purpose of tube 3?

During daylight plants produce *more* oxygen by photosynthesis than they use up in respiration.
At night plants produce *only* carbon dioxide by respiration.

▶ Plant nutrients

Have you seen bottles of 'plant food' for sale?
What do you think these contain?

Plants need more than carbon dioxide and water for healthy growth.
They also need **mineral salts** or **nutrients**.
These are usually found in the soil.
Nutrients are taken up in small amounts by the roots.

Can you remember why plants need nitrates?

They need the nitrogen to make proteins.
So nitrogen is one nutrient needed for growth.

Magnesium is used to make chlorophyll.
What would leaves look like if magnesium was lacking in the soil?
Leaves without enough magnesium look yellow.
We say the plant is **deficient** in magnesium.

A shrub lacking magnesium

Experiment 12.16 The effects of nutrients on growth

You can use **water cultures** to find out why plants need different nutrients.

Set up some test-tubes as shown here:

Each solution lacks a certain nutrient except tube 1 which has all of them.

Leave the apparatus in good light for 6 weeks.

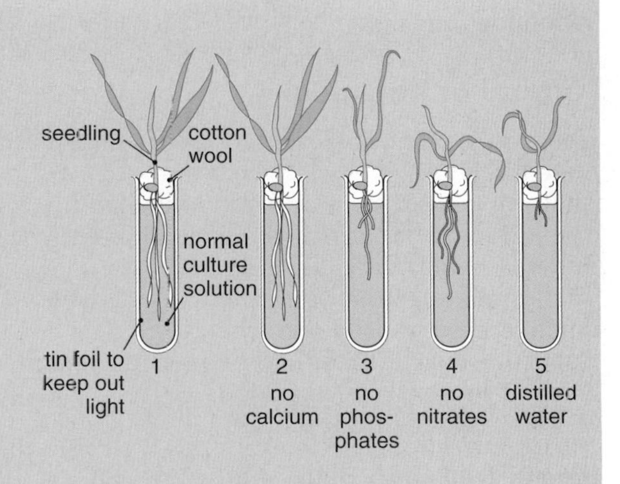

- What sort of things would you look for in the plants after 6 weeks?
  How about colour and size of leaves?
  How about length of stems and roots?
- How would you measure any changes?
- Why do you think the tubes were covered with tin foil?
  Does this stop other plants growing in the water?

Symptoms shown by plants deficient in nutrients include:

- **Lack of nitrate – stunted growth and yellow older leaves.**
- **Lack of phosphate – poor root growth and purple younger leaves.**
- **Lack of potassium – yellow leaves with dead spots.**

▶ Fertilisers

What happens if the soil does not contain enough nutrients?

The farmer or gardener adds more as **fertiliser**.
Fertilisers replace the missing nutrients.

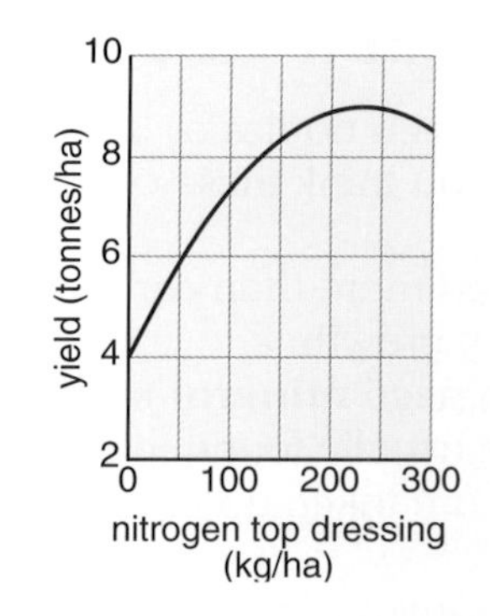

The graph shows the yield of winter wheat with different amounts of nitrogen fertiliser:

What is the yield with no nitrogen fertiliser?
What amount of fertiliser would you use?

NPK fertilisers contain:

- Nitrogen (N) for growth of leaves and stems
- Phosphorus (P) for healthy roots
- Potassium (K) for healthy leaves and flowers.

Both phosphorus and potassium help the reactions in photosynthesis and respiration to work.

The proportions of nitrogen, phosphorus and potassium (N : P : K) are shown on the fertiliser bag.

This fertiliser is called 25 : 0 : 16.
What does this mean?

Natural or chemical?

Chemical or artificial fertilisers are used in huge amounts.
They are easy to store and add to the land.
The farmer knows exactly how much of each nutrient there is in the fertiliser.
The farmer has to be very careful about how much fertiliser is used and when.
Rain can wash fertiliser into rivers and streams where it causes water pollution.
(This is covered in Chapter 20.)

Natural fertilisers include farmyard manure and composts.
Some farmers prefer these because they add **humus** to the soil.
Humus improves the structure of the soil.
Natural fertiliser rots down and releases nutrients more slowly.
There is also less threat to the environment.
The problem for the farmer is that the amount of each nutrient in the fertiliser is not known.

Make a table of the advantages and disadvantages of natural and chemical fertilisers.

▶ Biology at work : Hydroponics

Hydroponics is the growth of plants without soil.
Most tomatoes, cucumbers and sweet peppers are grown this way.

Peat culture

Have you seen tomatoes growing in gro-bags?
This is known as **peat culture**.
It is not used much by commercial growers.
Peat is acid and does not contain many nutrients.
So the peat has to be treated before it can be used.

It is very popular with gardeners.
But this has meant digging up peat bogs and damaging the environment.

Cucumbers grown in artificial media

Nutrient film technique

Plants grown using this technique are supported in sterile sand or rockwool.
A solution is circulated to the roots of each plant.
The solution has:

- oxygen bubbled through it – so the roots can respire
- the correct type and amounts of nutrients
- the best pH for growth.

It is easy to alter the amounts and types of mineral salts.
This will be different for different crops and for different stages of development of the plants.

This technique has been trialed by the Desert Development Centre in Egypt.

Tomatoes grown by nutrient film technique

Biology at work: Glasshouse production

Growers try to improve the yield of their crops.
They try to give them the best possible conditions for photosynthesis to take place.

Conditions inside a glasshouse allow plants to:

- grow earlier in the year
- grow in places where they would not normally grow well.

Ventilator flaps operate automatically

How are these conditions provided?

- **Temperature**
  Sunlight heats up the inside of the glasshouse.
  The glass stops a lot of this heat from escaping.
  Electric or paraffin heaters can be used in cold weather.
  Ventilator flaps can be opened to cool the glasshouse if it gets too hot.

- **Light**
  The glass lets in sunlight.
  Artificial lighting can be used to grow plants when sunlight gets too low.
  Blinds can shade out very strong light.

- **Carbon dioxide**
  Growers can pump carbon dioxide into glasshouses to increase the rate of photosynthesis.
  Sometimes paraffin heaters are used.
  These increase both the temperature and carbon dioxide because when paraffin burns it releases carbon dioxide.

- **Water**
  Many glasshouses have automatic watering systems.
  When needed, sprinklers and humidifiers come on.

Water misting of cabbages

All these factors may be controlled by computer.
Sensors are used to detect each factor.
The feedback is processed by the computer.

Growth in plants

In animals, cell division and growth takes place in all parts of the body.

In plants, growth is restricted to particular growing regions. Cell division and growth takes place mainly at the root tips and the shoot tips.

How can we estimate plant growth?
Well you could measure root length or plant height.
You could also use a **quadrat** to estimate the area covered by the plant.
If you harvest the plant material within the quadrat, heat it in an oven to drive off the water, then you have a measure of the **dry weight** of the sample (see page 288).

Control of growth

If you cut off a shoot tip the shoot stops growing.
But if you put the shoot tip back on it starts to grow again.

The shoot tip makes a hormone called **auxin**.
The auxin stimulates the shoot to grow.
The auxin causes the cells to elongate.

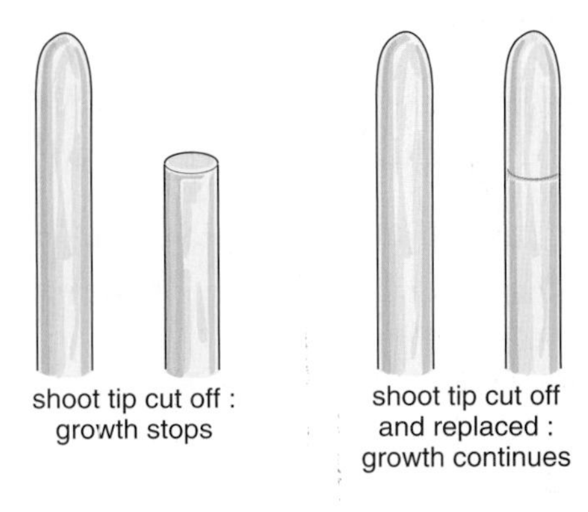

Plants respond to things like light, gravity and water.
Parts of the plant either grow towards them or away from them.
These slow growth responses are called **tropisms**.

How light affects growth

Look at the photograph of the cress seedlings:

They have been put in a window for some time.
The shoots have grown towards the light.

How is this controlled?

- When a shoot only gets light from one side most auxin is found on the shaded side.
- The auxin makes the shoot grow more on the shaded side.
- The shoot bends towards the light.

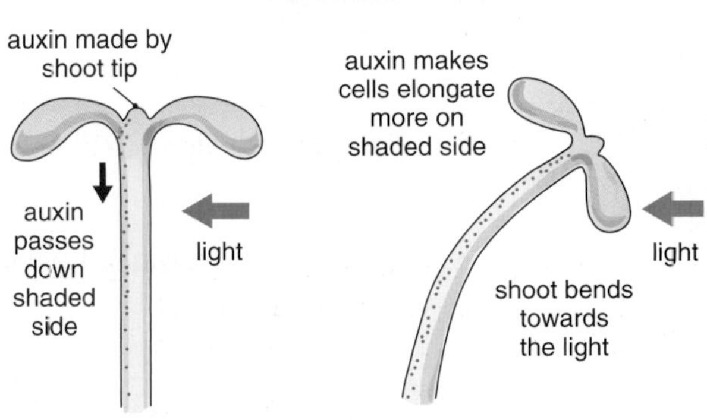

This sort of response is called a **phototropism**.
Because shoots grow ***towards*** the light we say that they are **positively phototropic**.

What is the advantage to the shoot of growing towards the light?

How gravity affects growth

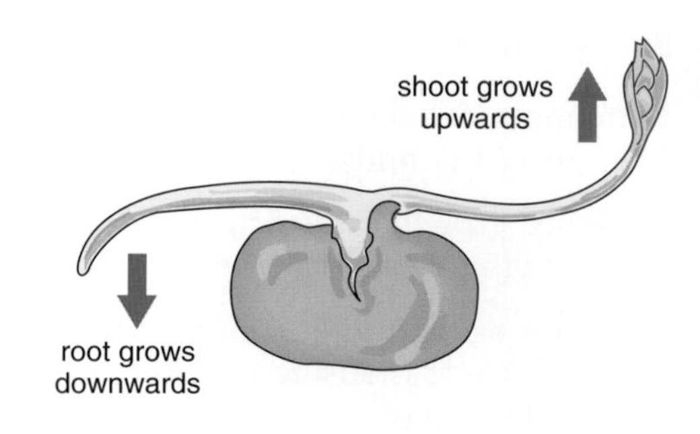

Why is it that whichever way a seed is planted, the root always grows down and the shoot always grows up?

The stimulus in this case is gravity.

Shoots grow up, away from gravity.
Roots grow down, towards gravity.
Again auxin controls this growth.

If a plant is put on its side the auxin builds up on the lower side of the shoot and root.

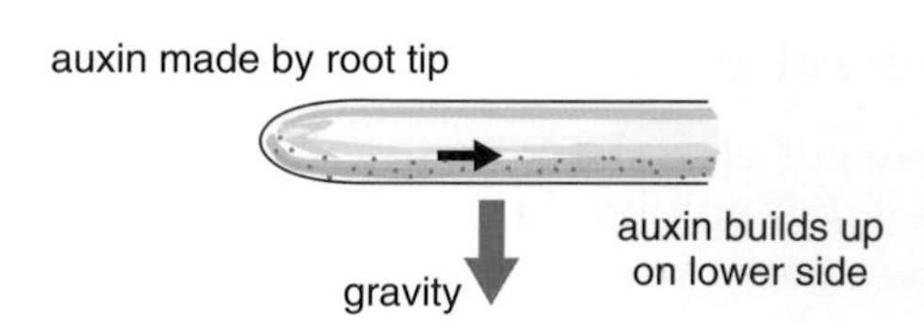

- In the shoot the auxin stimulates it to grow more on the lower side.
- This causes the shoot to bend upwards.
- In the root the auxin also builds up on the lower side.
  But auxin ***slows down*** growth in a root.
- So the upper side of the root grows quicker than the lower side.
- The root bends downwards.

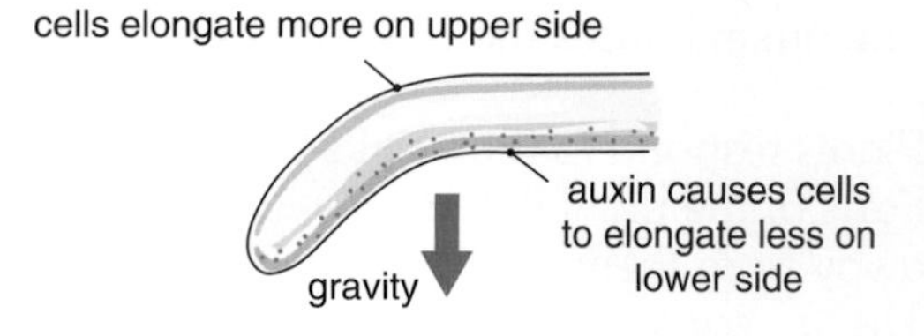

A growth response to gravity is called a **geotropism**.

Explain why we say that
- roots are **positively geotropic**, and
- shoots are **negatively geotropic**.

What is the advantage to the plant of its shoot growing away from gravity and its root growing towards gravity?

Auxin also has other effects on plant growth.
As it passes back from the tip of a stem, auxin prevents side-shoots forming.

What do you think would happen if the tip of the stem was removed?
The auxin will no longer be made so the side-shoots start to grow.

Why does hedge clipping produce a much bushier hedge?

▶ Biology at work : Plant hormones

Rooting powder contains synthetic auxins.
A cutting is dipped into the rooting powder.
The powder stimulates the cut shoot to grow roots.

Carnations and chrysanthemums are grown in this way.

Synthetic auxins are also used as selective **weed-killers**.
They kill the weed by making it grow too fast.
The auxins are sprayed on the leaves, so broad-leaved weeds are affected.
Narrow-leaves grasses and cereals are not affected.

Auxins control **ripening** by telling the ovary to develop into a fruit.
They are normally made by the developing embryo.

Some growers spray synthetic auxins on unpollinated flowers of tomato plants and pear trees.
Fruits form without fertilisation.
So these fruits have no pips!

Have you ever eaten seedless grapes or seedless satsumas?
These have been grown with the help of synthetic plant hormones.

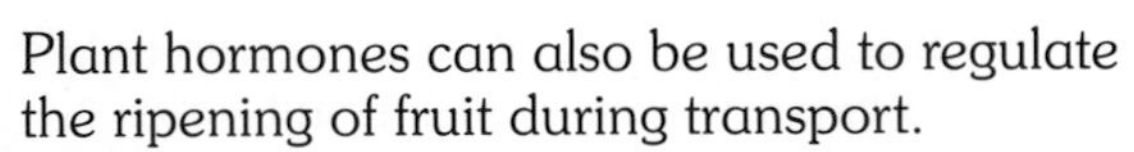

Plant hormones can also be used to regulate the ripening of fruit during transport.

Ethene is made by many fruits.
It causes the fruit to ripen.
Bananas are picked when they are unripe and transported in ships.
During storage ethene is used to make them ripen.
So when they arrive for sale they have changed from green to yellow!

Summary

- Green plants use sunlight to make food by photosynthesis.
  Chlorophyll inside chloroplasts is used to absorb the light.
  Carbon dioxide and water are needed for photosynthesis.
  Sugars are produced in photosynthesis and can form other carbohydrates, amino acids, proteins and fats.
  Oxygen is released as a waste product during the process.
- Plants are important for food, medicines, habitats and controlling the amounts of carbon dioxide and oxygen in the air.
- The rate of photosynthesis can be limited by light intensity, carbon dioxide and temperature.
- Leaves are well adapted for absorbing light and gas exchange.
- Stomata control exchange of gases and water loss.
- Photosynthesis takes place in light but respiration occurs all the time.
- Mineral salts are important for healthy plant growth.
- Plant growth and development is controlled by hormones.
  These hormones can be used commercially to produce seedless fruit, to act as a rooting powder and as selective weed-killers.

▶ Questions

1. Copy and complete :
Green plants make their own food by . . . . .
Green . . . . in the chloroplasts of the leaves traps the sun's . . . . . Raw materials for this process are carbon . . . . and . . . . . Sugars are made in the leaves and are soon changed to . . . . . The waste product of this process is the gas . . . . .

2. The graph shows the effect of increasing the amount of carbon dioxide on the rate of photosynthesis of a pond weed.

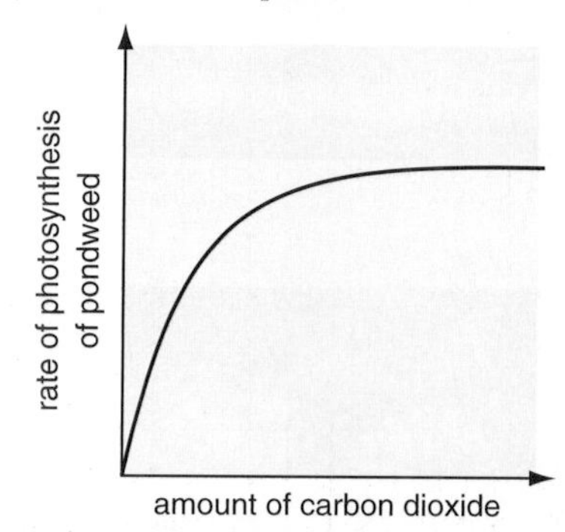

a) What other conditions must be kept constant if this is to be a fair test?
b) How do you think the amount of carbon dioxide was increased?
c) Why did the graph increase to begin with?
d) Why do you think the graph levels off?

3. Three geranium plants were kept in the dark for 24 hours.
Each was then covered with a bell-jar A, B and C.
The apparatus was left in the light for 5 hours as shown here :

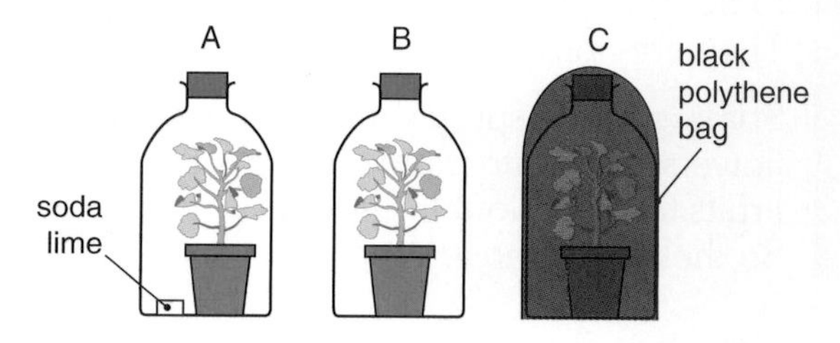

a) Why were the three plants left in the dark before the start of the experiment?
b) What was the soda lime for in bell-jar A?
c) Why was black polythene put over bell-jar C?
d) After 5 hours a leaf from each plant was tested for starch.
What colour would each leaf go with iodine? Try to explain each of the results.

4. Lettuces can be grown in tunnels made with clear polythene.
a) Give two reasons why clear polythene increases the yield of lettuces.
b) Why do the tunnels not need to be moved to water the plants?
c) Why is carbon dioxide added to the air in the tunnels?

5. The apparatus was used to collect the gas released by water plant :

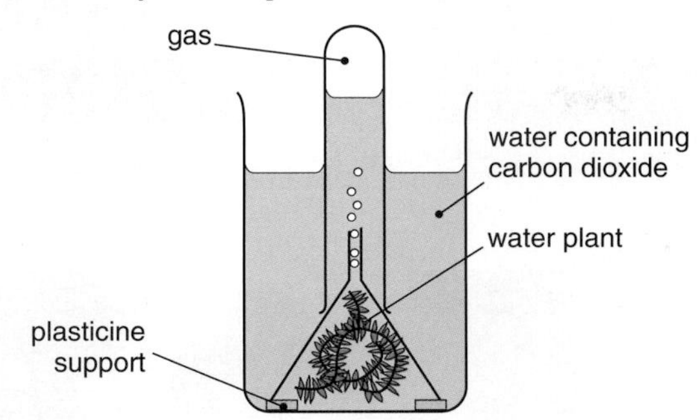

a) How could you test the gas for oxygen ?
b) Why is the gas collected in the test-tube not pure oxygen ?
c) Why was the water enriched with carbon dioxide ?

A lamp was placed at different distances from the water plant.
The number of bubbles released per minute was recorded :

Distance from lamp (cm)	Number of bubbles per minute
100	6
60	10
40	18
30	24
20	25

d) Plot these results as a line-graph.
e) Try to explain any pattern that you find in the results.
f) Why was a piece of thick glass placed between the lamp and the plant ?

6. To find out if photosynthesis has taken place in a leaf we can carry out a test.
Copy out the stages listed on the left in the correct order. Match each one with the correct reason on the right.

Stage in test	*Reason*
wash the leaf in cold water	to test for starch
boil the leaf in ethanol	to soften it
cover the leaf with iodine	to remove the ethanol
dip the leaf in boiling water	to extract the chlorophyll

7. a) Name the parts of the leaf labelled A to G :

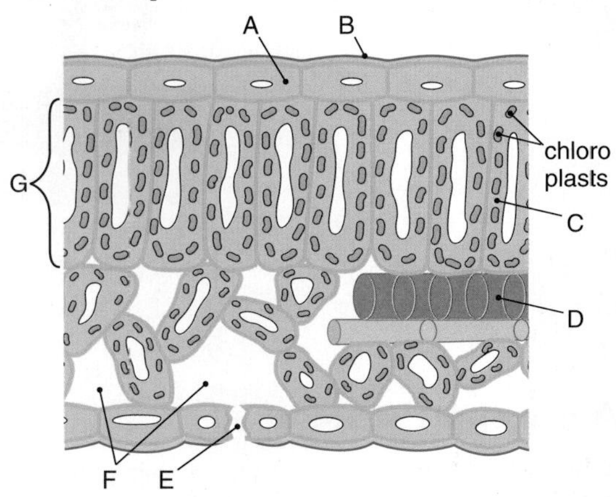

b) Match each label with one of these functions :
i) Carries water and mineral salts to the leaf.
ii) Prevents too much water loss from the upper surface.
iii) Opens to allow gases to pass into and out of the leaf.
iv) Most photosynthesis takes place here.
v) Gases from here pass into the spongy cells.
vi) Light is able to pass straight through this layer.
vii) These cells contain most chloroplasts.

8. The rate of photosynthesis of a tree was recorded for 36 hours.

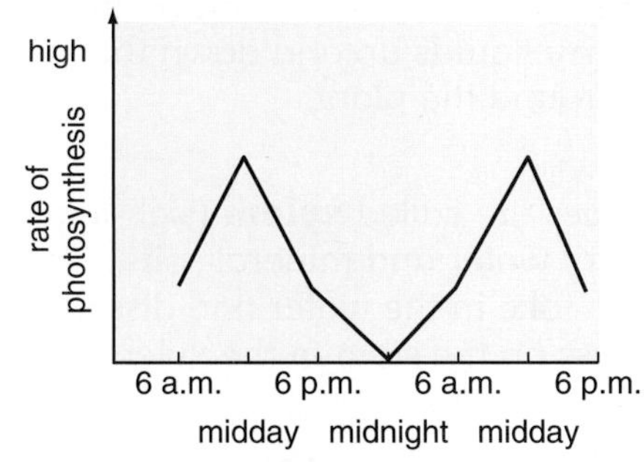

Use the graph to answer these questions.
a) When was the rate of photosynthesis highest ?
b) When would most carbon dioxide be released into the air ?
c) When would most oxygen be released into the air ?

Further questions on page 211.

chapter 13

"General Sherman" redwood tree

A transport system

Most living things need a transport system.
Their bodies are too large for materials to simply diffuse in and out.
Only very small organisms can carry things around their body by diffusion.
They have a large surface area to volume ratio and a short diffusion pathway.
So it is easy for materials to diffuse in and out.

What things do cells need to stay alive?
What do they need to get rid of?

Our transport system is the blood.
It brings food and oxygen to our cells.
It removes carbon dioxide and waste chemicals.

Plants have a transport system too.
They have lots of thin tubes inside them.
These carry liquids up and down the stem and all around the plant.

Some tubes are called **xylem** (sigh-lem).
They carry water and mineral salts.
The roots take in the water and dissolved salts.
These pass up the stem in the xylem to the leaves.

Some tubes are called **phloem** (flow-em).
They carry dissolved food like sugars and amino acids which are made in the leaves by photosynthesis.
The phloem carries the food to every part of the plant.

The phloem also carries **hormones** around the plant.
These hormones control cell division for growth of the stem, roots and leaves.
Hormones also control the growth of flowers and fruits.

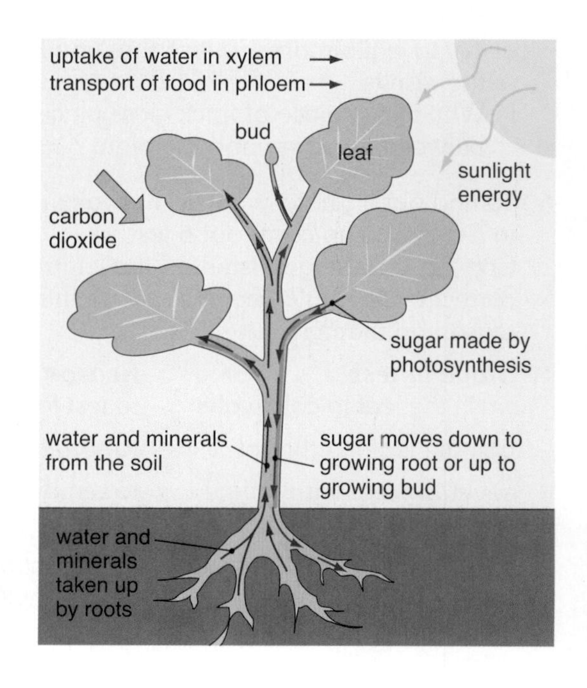

Inside the root

To find the transport tissue of a root we need to slice it open and look inside.
The diagram shows what a root tip looks like under the microscope :

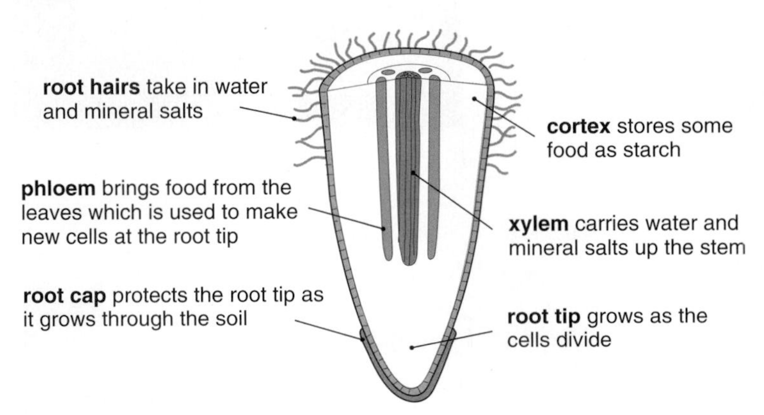

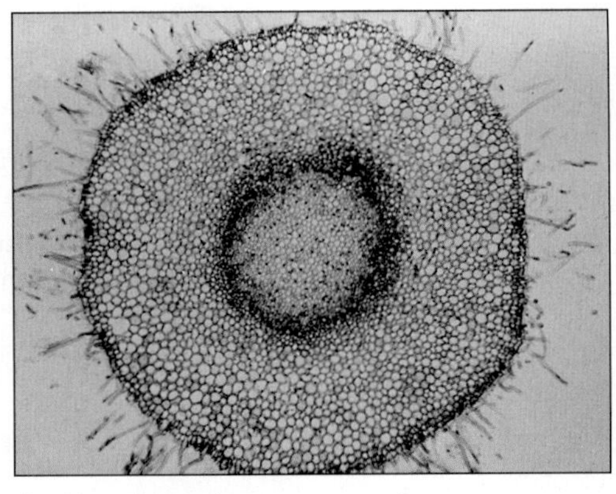

Section through a young root. Notice the many root hairs.

Inside the stem

We can find out what is inside a stem by cutting a thin slice and looking at it under a microscope :

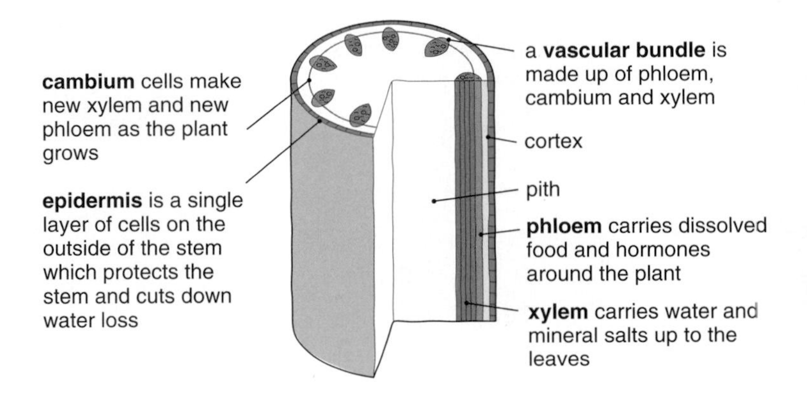

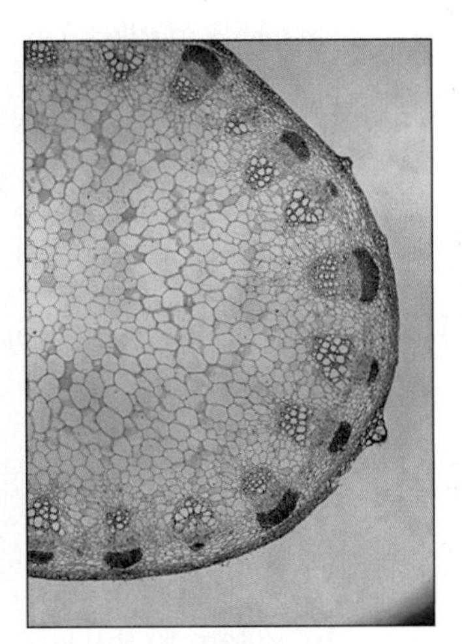

Section through a young stem

Experiment 13.1 Water transport in the xylem

⚠ sharp scalpel

Stand some celery in water containing a blue dye for a few hours.
Carefully cut off a length of about 2 cm.
Look at the cut end. Can you see where the dye is?
The dye has been carried up the xylem tubes.

Carefully cut out a 2 cm length of xylem.
Put it onto a slide with a cover-slip.
Look at it under the microscope.

▶ Into the roots

The roots anchor the plant in the soil.
Another important role of the roots is to take up water and mineral salts.

Just behind the root tip are microscopic hairs.
These are called **root hairs**.
Water passes into the root hairs by **osmosis**.
Do you remember what happens in osmosis ?

The water in the soil has a weak solution of salts.
The cell sap in the root hair cell has a stronger solution.
Water passes from the soil into the root hair cell by osmosis.

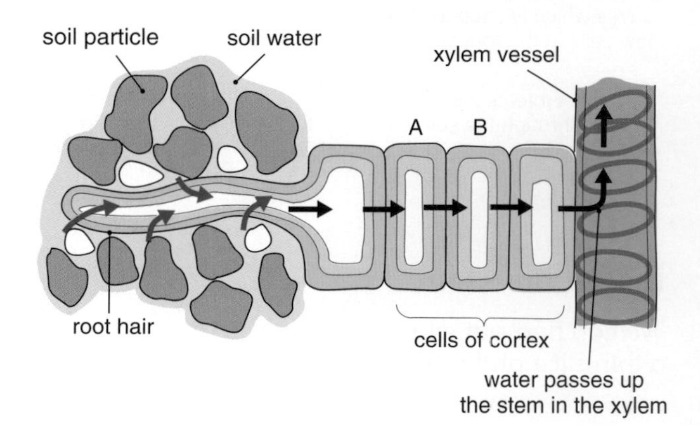

The pathway of water across a root

The water has diluted the cell sap in the root hair cell.
The root hair cell now has a weaker cell sap than cell A.
Water passes from the root hair cell into cell A by osmosis.

The water has diluted the cell sap in cell A.
Cell A now has a weaker cell sap than cell B.
So water passes from cell A into cell B by osmosis.

This continues across the whole of the root cortex.

Water eventually reaches the xylem.

Water is carried up the xylem to the leaves.

Experiment 13.2 Looking at root hairs

Look closely at a section of a young root under the microscope.

Look at the root hairs.

- What is their shape like ?
- How does their shape help them to take in water ?

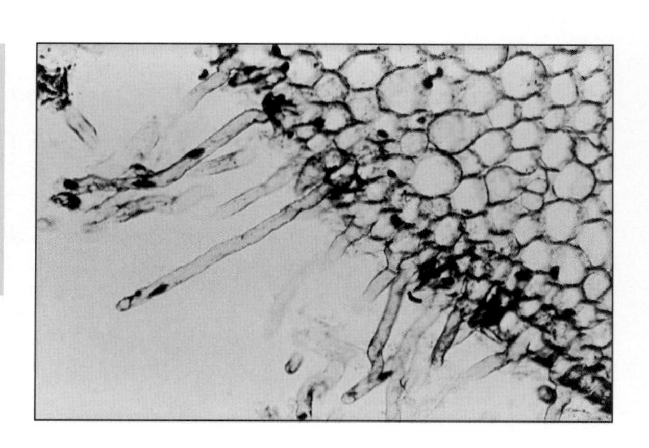

Root hairs are long and thin.
They have a large surface area through which water and mineral salts can enter.

▶ Transpiration

Water is pulled up the xylem in the stem from the roots to the leaves.

The water is used for photosynthesis and to stop the plant from wilting.
Water evaporates from the leaves into the air.
This is called **transpiration**.

As water is used up or lost from the leaves, more is sucked up from the xylem vessels.
It's a bit like sucking water up a straw.
So there is a continuous flow of water from the roots to the leaves.
This movement of water up the xylem is called the **transpiration stream**.

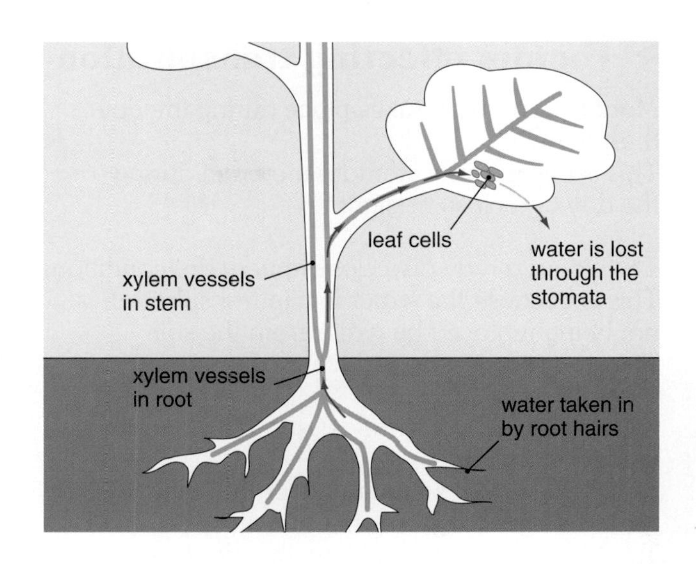

Experiment 13.3 To demonstrate transpiration

You can prove transpiration takes place by setting up the apparatus shown here:

Mark clearly the level of the water in each flask.
Weigh each flask.
Now leave the apparatus for 24 hours.

- Has the level dropped in flask A? Why has it?
- Is flask A now lighter? Why is this?

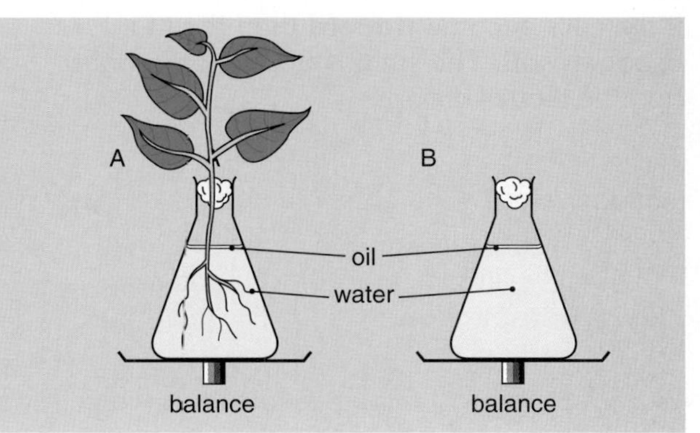

More about transpiration

- Water first evaporates from the spongy cells into the air spaces.
- The air spaces become full of water vapour.
- Water vapour diffuses through the stomata into the air.
- The water lost from the spongy cells is replaced by more water from the xylem.

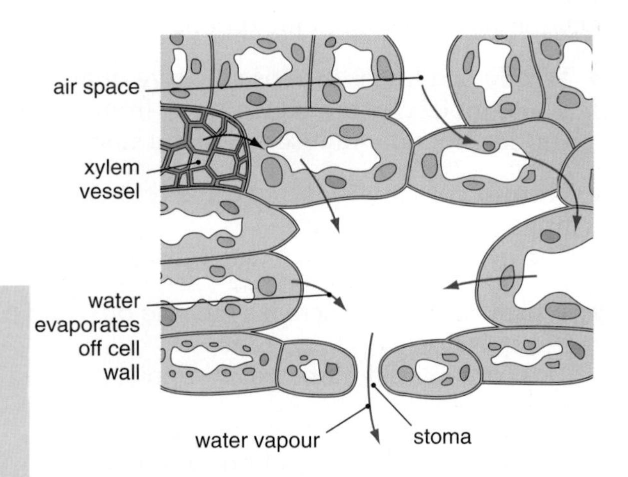

Experiment 13.4 Comparing water loss from each side of a leaf

Cobalt chloride paper is blue when dry and goes pink when it comes into contact with water.
Put a piece of cobalt chloride paper on each side of a leaf. Keep the paper in place with two slides and elastic bands.
See on which side the paper turns pink first.

- Will it be the side with most stomata?

Transpiration is the loss of water vapour from the surface of leaves.

▶ Factors affecting transpiration

Scanning electron micrograph of open stoma

More transpiration takes place during the day than at night.
This is because the stomata are open during the day and close at night.

The stomata may also close in very dry conditions.
This is because the water lost in transpiration is not being replaced by water from the soil.
The stomata close to reduce transpiration.

If the plant still does not get enough water it will start to **wilt**.
Its cells have lost so much water that they are no longer **turgid** or full of water.
Turgid cells are firm and give the plant support.
If the cells become **flaccid** then the plant becomes soft. The stem is no longer upright and the leaves droop.

Experiment 13.5 Stomata and water loss

Set up four leaves as shown here:
Vaseline will block the stomata and slow down transpiration.

Look at the leaves after a few days.

- Which do you think has lost most water ?

four identical privet leaves

vaseline on upper and lower surface

vaseline on lower surface only

vaseline on upper surface only

no vaseline

Other factors affecting transpiration are environmental. Look at the graphs :

- **Windy** conditions increase the rate of transpiration. Water molecules are blown away from the leaf surface, so more diffuse out of the stomata.
- **Humid** conditions decrease the rate of transpiration. The air contains a lot of water already.
- **Warm** conditions increase the rate of transpiration. The air can hold more water vapour.
- **Light** causes the stomata to open. This increases the rate of transpiration.

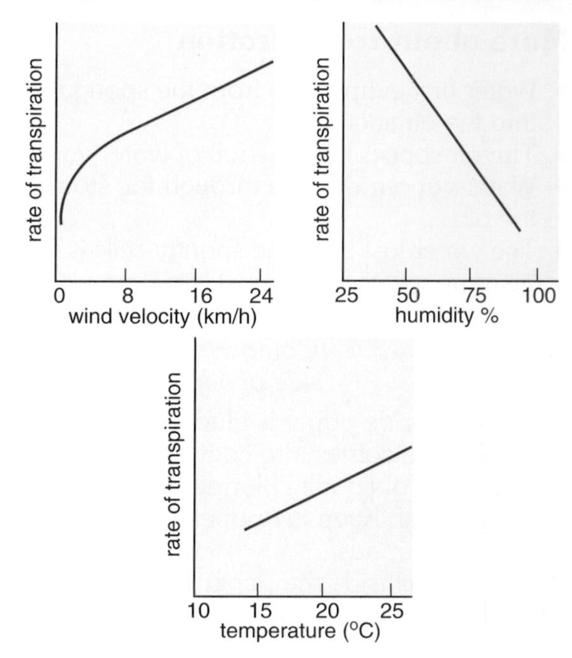

It's a bit like washing on a line.
What conditions dry the clothes quickest ?
What conditions dry the clothes more slowly ?

▶ Measuring transpiration

It is not easy to measure the rate of transpiration.
But you can use a **potometer** to measure the rate of water **uptake**.
The amount of water lost is actually less than the amount of water taken in by the roots.
This is because some of the water is used up in photosynthesis.

Experiment 13.6 Measuring the rate of water uptake

Fill a capillary tube by submerging it in water.
Cut the end of a shoot under the water.
Attach it to the capillary tube with a piece of rubber tubing.
Take the capillary tube out of the water.
Clamp the apparatus in the position shown.
See how far the bubble travels along the tube in 5 minutes.

Now try it with a fan near the potometer.

- Does the rate increase? Why is this?

Now try putting a polythene bag over the shoot.
This makes conditions humid.

- Does the rate decrease? Why is this?
- Would a black plastic bag make the rate decrease even more?
  Why do you think this is?

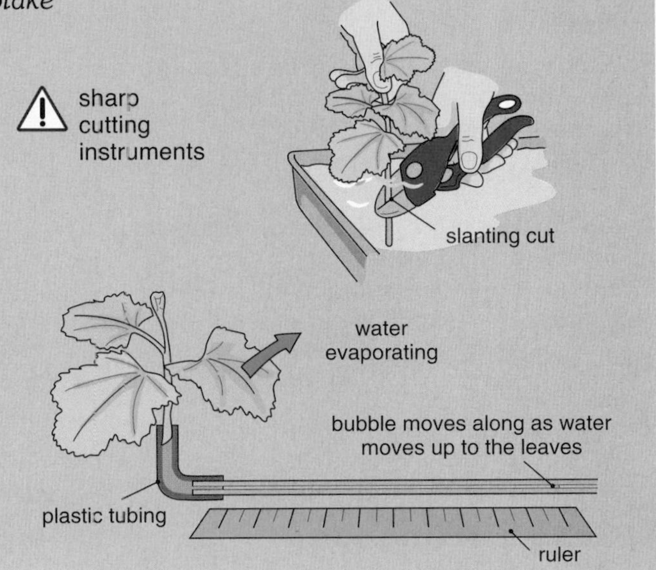

Here is a more accurate potometer.
It works in the same way.
Vaseline is put on the rubber bung.
What do you think the reservoir is for?
How could you get the air bubble back to the beginning of the scale?

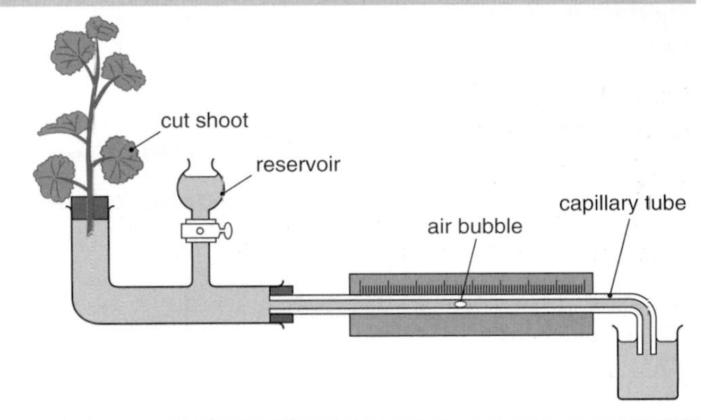

Investigation 13.7 Plan an investigation on the rate of transpiration

You could use weight loss and water intake as a measure of the rate.
You could look at the effects of different variables on different plants.
You could investigate how different numbers of stomata affect the rate.

Check your plan with your teacher before you start.

▶ Mineral salts

Plants need mineral salts or nutrients.
For instance, nitrates are needed to make proteins.

There is only a weak solution of these salts in the water in the soil.
Often salts are taken up even though there are less in the soil than there are in the root.

These salts cannot enter the root by diffusion.
Why not?

The salts are taken up by **active transport**.
Active transport can collect salts against a concentration gradient.
This needs energy from respiration.

Again the root hairs give a large surface area for taking up mineral salts.
There are many air spaces in the soil.
Oxygen passes from this air into the root hair too.

Mineral salts are carried up to the leaves with water in the xylem vessels.

Scanning electron micrograph of xylem vessels. Note the thick bands that support the vessels.

Active transport is the uptake of molecules or ions, against a concentration gradient, using energy from respiration.

▶ Transporting food

Food is made in the leaves by photosynthesis.
The soluble products are sugars, amino acids and fatty acids.
These are carried to all parts of the plant in solution in the phloem. This is often called **translocation**.

Xylem are dead tubes but phloem is ***living tissue***.
Movement of substances in the phloem is thought to involve active transport.
The plant cells have to use energy to move the dissolved substances along.

Where does the food end up?

- Sugars are changed to starch and stored in the root cortex and in seeds.

  Sugars also form cellulose for new cell walls at the growing root tip and shoot tip.

  Sugars are also transported to the fruits.
- Amino acids make proteins needed to make new cells.
- Fatty acids form fats that are stored in many seeds.

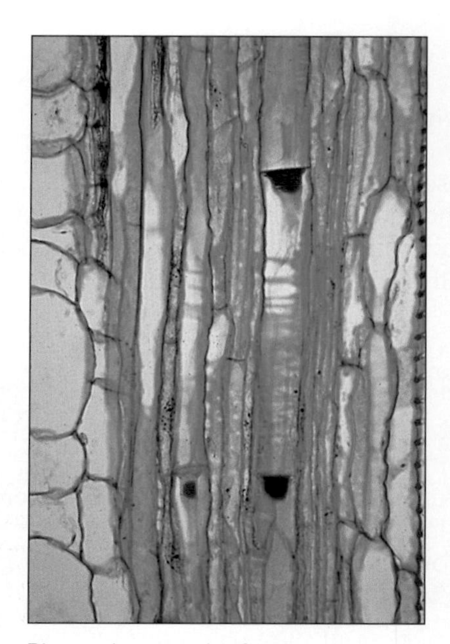

Photomicrograph of phloem vessels

▷ Biology at work: Monocultures and crop rotations

Monocultures

A **monoculture** is growing the same crop on the same land, year after year.
The main benefit of monocultures is an economic one :

- Increased use of machinery and decreased labour costs means that continuous cropping of one crop brings greater economic returns per unit area of land.
- However, monocultures require the use of lots more fertilisers and pesticides to maintain high yields.
- The use of chemical fertilisers does not improve the structure of the soil, unlike organic fertilisers which rot down and provide the soil with humus as well as nutrients.
- The pH of the soil may need to be carefully regulated to meet the needs of the crop. First the soil pH is tested, and then lime is added if the soil is too acid or peat if it is too alkaline.
- Monocultures also provide large areas that can become infested with pests and diseases, which have to be controlled. **Aphids** can spread diseases such as **tobacco mosaic virus**. Aphids feed on the sap in the phloem tubes in crop stems. They use special mouthparts called **stylets** to penetrate the phloem. The viruses enter the phloem in the saliva of the insect and multiply. Aphids are the main **vectors** (transmitters) of viruses between plants.

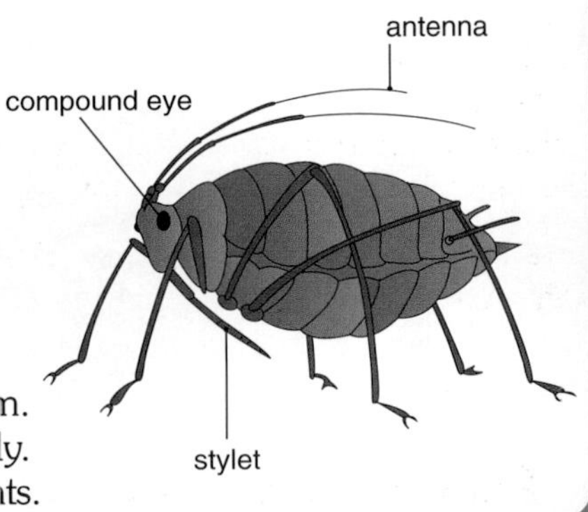

Crop rotations

The use of inorganic fertilisers and monocultures has led to the loss of the traditional crop rotations.

Crop rotation influences the amounts of nutrients that need to be added to grow different crops.
For example, winter wheat grown after another cereal needs far more nutrients than if it is grown after a root crop. This is because a root crop, like potato, takes up far less nutrients than a cereal crop.

Growing a planned sequence of crops has been practised for many years.The Norfolk four-year rotation uses a **ley**. This is a grass/ legume mix that can be grazed by livestock. **Legumes** (the pea family) increase the amount of nitrogen in the soil and so increase its fertility (see page 314).

Different crops need different methods of cultivation, which leads to an improvement in soil texture.
Also, growing different crops breaks the cycle of crop pests. So there is less chance of a crop pest or disease getting a grip than in the case of growing monocultures.

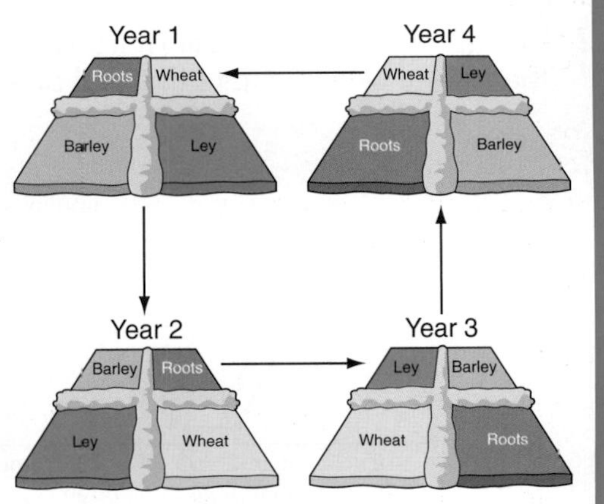

The Norfolk four-year rotation

Summary

- Plants have a transport system made up of tubes called xylem and phloem.
  Xylem carries water and mineral salts from the roots up the stem to the leaves.
  Phloem carries dissolved food from the leaves to all parts of the plant.
  The phloem also transports hormones around the plant.
- Water passes into the root hairs from the soil water by osmosis.
- Mineral salts are taken up by active transport.
- Leaves lose water to the air by transpiration.
  Transpiration stream allows water to travel from the roots up the stem to the leaves.
  Transpiration is controlled by the opening and closing of stomata.
  Environmental factors like wind, humidity and temperature can affect transpiration.
- The soft parts of a plant are supported by turgid cells.

▶ Questions

1. Look at the diagram of the root hair in the soil:

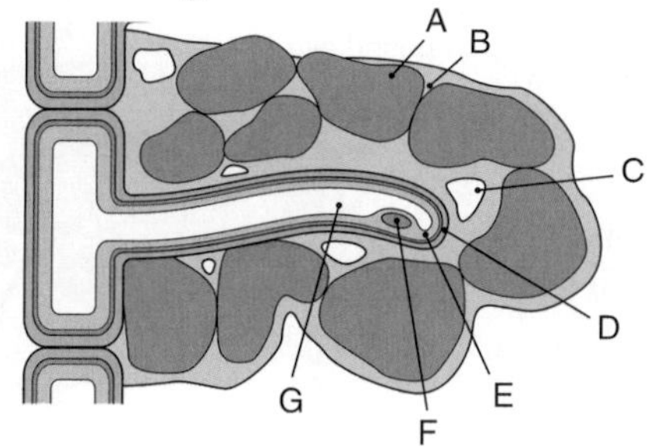

a) Name the parts labelled A to G.
b) Explain how water gets into the root hair from the soil.
c) Give two other functions of a root hair.

2. The graph shows the rate of transpiration and the rate of water uptake in small pine tree:

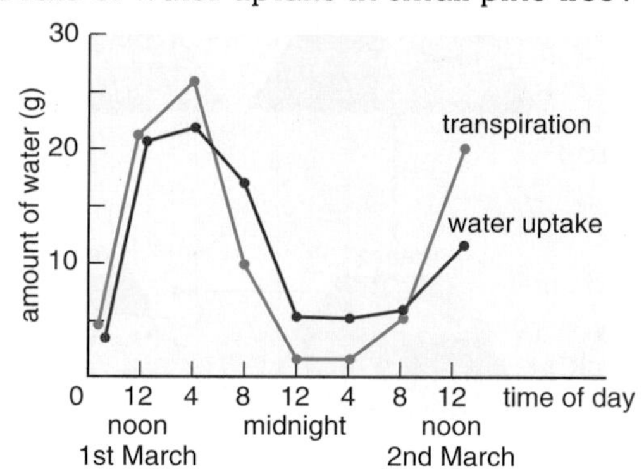

a) Compare the rate of transpiration with the rate of water uptake
i) during the day ii) during the night
b) State the date and the time when the rate of transpiration was highest.

3. Copy and complete:
Water passes into a root . . . . by . . . . . Mineral . . . . are taken up by . . . . transport. A root hair has a . . . . surface . . . . for taking up water and mineral salts.
Water is lost from the leaves by . . . . . This is controlled by the opening and closing of the . . . . . Dissolved . . . . and hormones are carried to all parts of the plant in the . . . . .

4. A potometer was used to measure water uptake by a leafy shoot.

Conditions	Time taken for the water to move 100 mm (minutes)
cool, moving air, in daylight	2
cool, still air, in daylight	6
warm, moving air, in daylight	1
warm, still air, in daylight	3
warm, still air, at night	60

a) From the table, state three conditions which affect the rate of water movement through the plant.
b) In cool, moving air, in daylight, work out the rate of water movement in mm per minute.
c) Give two ways in which the air around the shoot would be affected if it was covered with a transparent plastic bag.
d) Give two reasons why loss of water from the leaves is important to a plant.

Further questions on page 211.

▶ Feeding in plants

1. Leaves are organs of photosynthesis. They come in all shapes and sizes but all of them are adapted to absorb as much light as possible.

a) Give **one** way in which leaves are adapted to absorb light. *[1]*

b) The diagram shows a cross-section through a leaf.

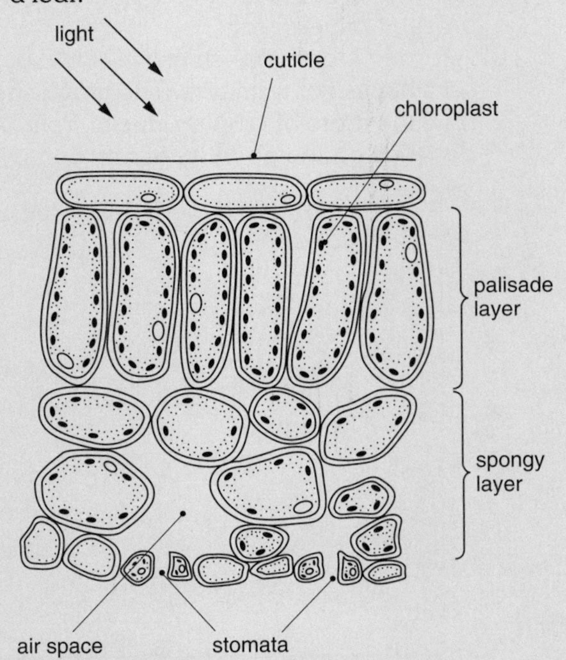

Explain the following observations:

i) The cuticle is transparent. *[1]*

ii) Most chloroplasts are found in the palisade layer. *[1]*

iii) Air spaces are found mostly in the spongy layer. *[1]*

c) What is the substance in chloroplasts which absorbs light? *[1]*

d) Explain how each of the following affects the rate of photosynthesis in a potted plant.

i) Moving it nearer to the window. *[1]*

ii) Moving it to a colder room. *[1]*

(OCR)

2. A student was asked to find if plants need light to make starch.
She was given a potted plant which had been kept in a dark cupboard for 48 hours. She covered part of the leaf with aluminium foil as shown in the diagram which follows.

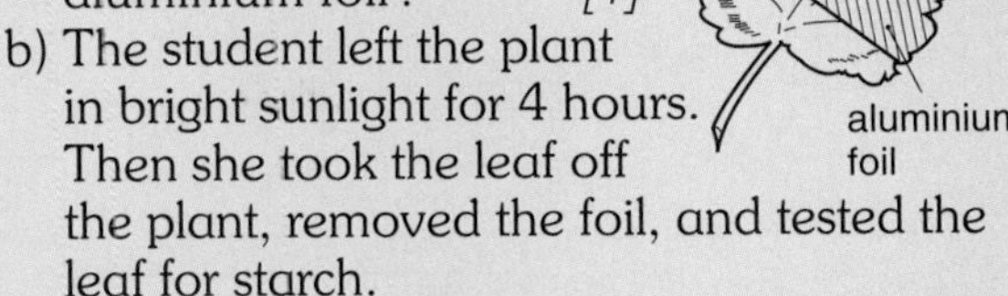

a) Why did she cover part of the leaf with aluminium foil? *[1]*

b) The student left the plant in bright sunlight for 4 hours. Then she took the leaf off the plant, removed the foil, and tested the leaf for starch.

i) Name the solution which is used to test for starch. *[1]*

ii) The diagram shows the leaf after the starch test.
What colour would parts **X** and **Z** go after the test? *[2]*

c) Write a conclusion for the student's experiment. *[1]* (AQA)

3. The graph shows the amount of sugar contained in the leaves of a group of plants in a glasshouse over a period of a week.

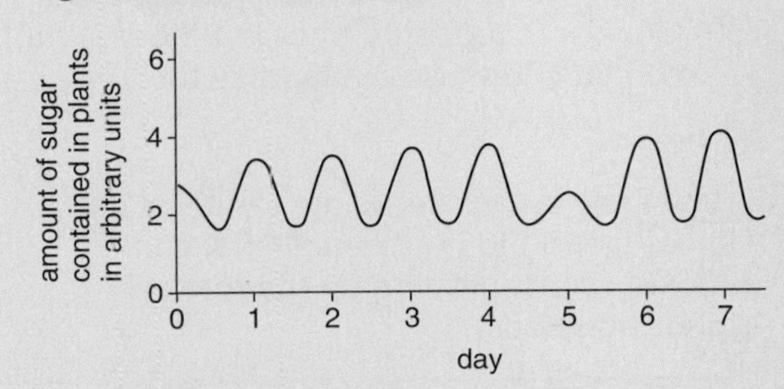

a) i) Copy and complete the word equation to show how sugar is produced: *[2]*

$$\ldots + \ldots \xrightarrow[\text{chlorophyll}]{\text{sunlight}} \text{sugar} + \text{oxygen}$$

ii) Name the process shown by the equation. *[1]*

b) i) Explain the rise and fall in the sugar level each day. *[2]*

ii) Suggest a reason for the overall increase in the amount of sugar present each day. *[1]*

iii) Suggest a reason for the lower peak on day **5**. *[1]*

c) Suggest **two** reasons why putting a gas fire in the glasshouse might increase the amount of sugar produced. *[2]* (EDEX)

4. Plants convert light energy into chemical energy during photosynthesis. The graph shows the effect of light intensity on the rate of photosynthesis.

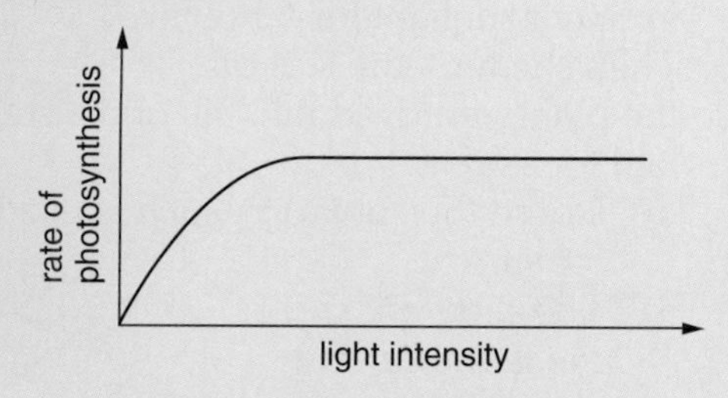

a) i) Explain the relationship between light intensity and the rate of photosynthesis. [2]

ii) Suggest one other variable that affects the rate of photosynthesis. [1]

iii) Sketch a curve to show how this variable would affect the rate of photosynthesis (put the variable on the horizontal axis and the rate of photosynthesis on the vertical axis). [1]

b) Glucose is made by photosynthesis. What can the plant use the glucose for? [1]

(EDEX)

5. The table below shows the results of an investigation to find the effect of carbon dioxide concentration on the rate of photosynthesis.

Concentration of carbon dioxide in air (%)	Rate of photosynthesis (arbitrary units)
0	0
0.2	35
0.4	70
0.6	105
0.8	115
1.0	120
1.2	120
1.4	120

a) Draw a line graph of these results on a sheet of graph paper. [2]

b) Use the graph to describe the effect of carbon dioxide concentration on the rate of photosynthesis. [2]

c) The rate of photosynthesis may be affected by factors other than carbon dioxide concentration. Give **two** of these factors. [2]

d) Some crops are grown in glasshouses. Give **two** advantages of growing crops in glasshouses. [2] (AQA)

6. a) Plants need mineral salts for healthy growth. Give the chemical names of two types of mineral salts. [2]

b) A farmer wants to increase his yield by sensible use of fertilisers. The graph shows how the mass of crop produced from a field depends on the quantity of nitrogen used.

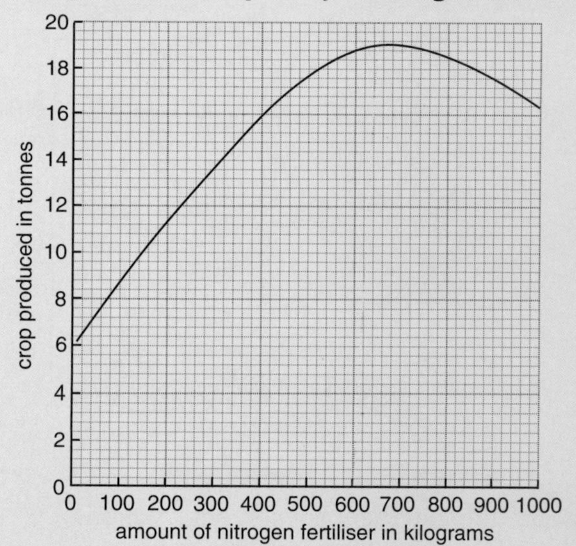

What is the maximum mass of crop that could be produced by using nitrogen fertilisers on the field? [1]

c) Many of the chemicals in fertilisers dissolve in water. When it rains, some of the fertiliser is washed out of the soil into rivers and streams.

What effect does the fertiliser in the river water have on the river plants:

i) Immediately or in the short term; [1]

ii) In the long-term? [1]

d) Some people prefer to eat 'organically grown' food. This is food which has been grown without the use of synthetic fertilisers, pesticides or weed-killers. Excluding cost, describe **two** advantages and **two** disadvantages of eating 'organically grown' food. [4] (AQA)

7. The diagram shows a plant leaf during photosynthesis.

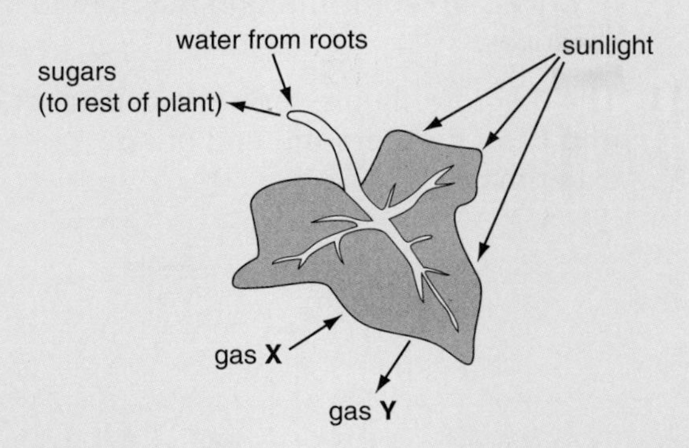

a) Name:
   i) gas **X**
   ii) gas **Y** *[2]*

b) Name the tissue which transports:
   i) water into the leaves
   ii) sugars out of the leaves *[2]*

c) Why is sunlight necessary for photosynthesis ? *[1]*

d) Some of the sugars produced by photosynthesis are stored as starch in the roots. Explain, as fully as you can, why it is an advantage to the plant to store carbohydrate as starch rather than as sugar. *[3]* (AQA)

8. The diagram shows a section through a green leaf.

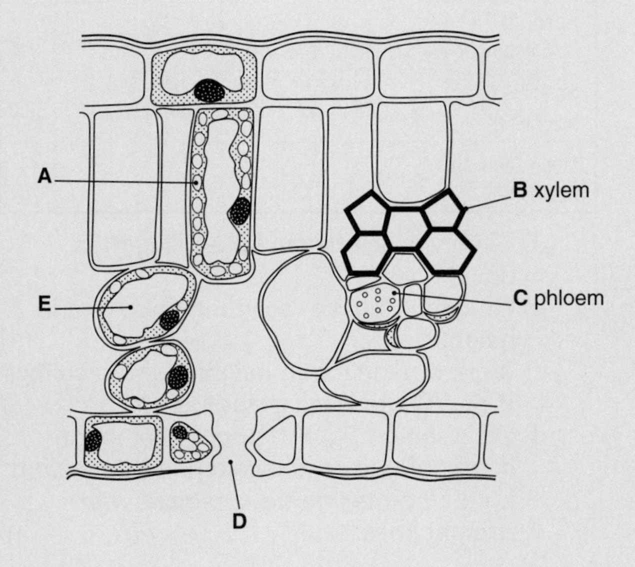

a) Copy the table and match **each letter** to the description of its function. *[5]*

Letter	Description of its function
	transports sugar
	absorbs light
	produces pressure inside cells
	carries water from the stem to the leaf
	allows water to leave by evaporation

b) The amount of carbon dioxide in the air around a crop of wheat was measured during two different days, **X** and **Y**. The results were plotted as the following graph.

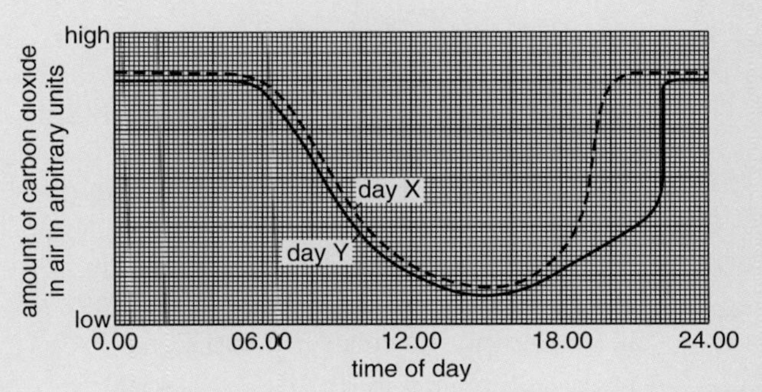

   i) What process was responsible for the drop in carbon dioxide ? *[1]*
   ii) Suggest why there is a difference between the graphs for **X** and **Y**. *[1]*

c) At what time did the wheat plants give out most oxygen ? *[1]*

d) Name **two** substances found in the soil which could help the growth of the wheat. *[2]* (WJEC)

▶ Plant transport

9. a) Plants lose water through their leaves.
   i) What name is given to the loss of water from the leaves ? *[1]*
   ii) What name is given to the pores through which this water is lost ? *[1]*
   iii) Explain why the movement of water through plants is important to them. *[3]*

b) The loss of water from a leafy shoot can be shown using a potometer. A potometer is shown in the diagram. As water is lost from the leaf the bubble slowly moves along the scale from left to right.

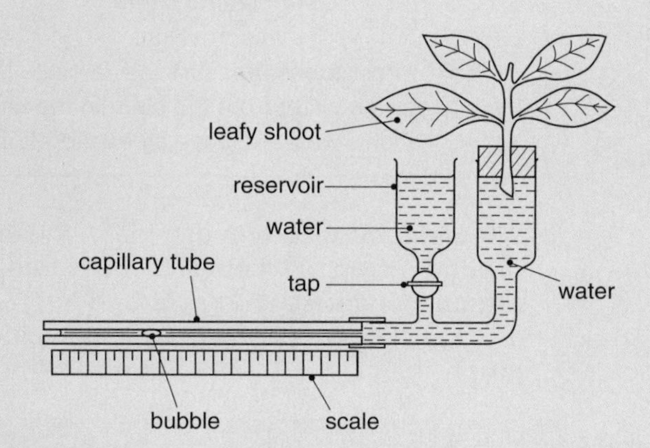

What will be the effect on the movement of the bubble of:

i) increasing the temperature of the air around the leafy shoot; [1]

ii) increasing the humidity of the air around the leafy shoot; [1]

iii) opening the reservoir tap? [1]

c) Plants which live in dry, desert-like areas often have leaves which are modified to form sharp spines or prickles. State two ways that these modified leaves help the plant to survive in the desert. [2] (AQA)

10. The roots of a green plant act as a link between the plant and the water in the soil.

a) For which life process does the green plant need water as a raw material? [1]

b) The drawing shows a sectional view of a root hair on a root in some soil.

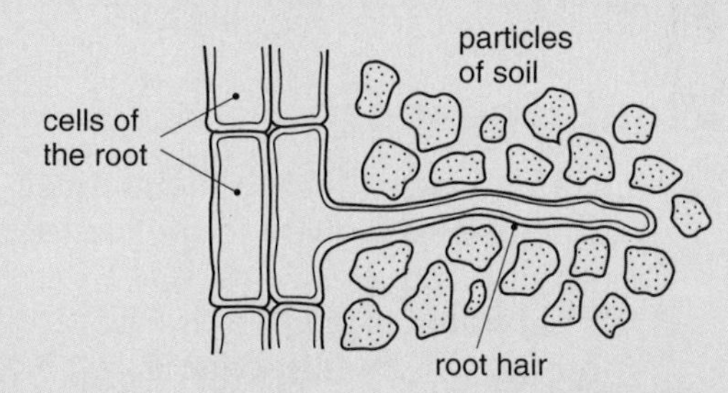

Describe, in detail, how the water passes from the soil into the root hair. [4]

c) Much of the water going into the root has to get to the leaves. Explain how water travels upwards through the stem to the leaves. [3] (AQA)

11. The diagram shows three plant stems, **A**, **B** and **C**, at the start and end of an experiment.

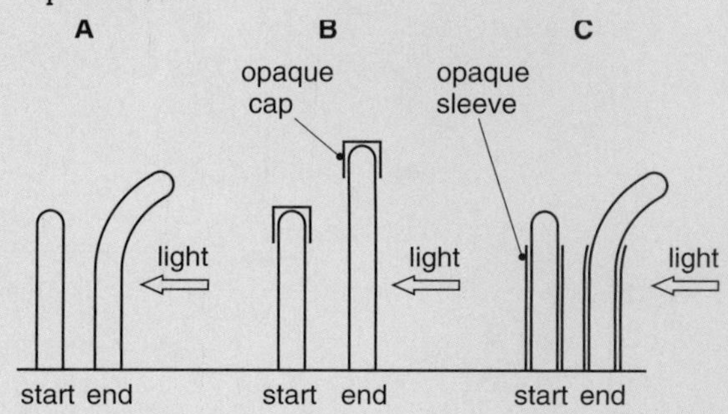

a) What does this experiment suggest about which region of a plant stem is sensitive to the stimulus of light? Give reasons for your answer. [3]

b) Explain what causes the plant stem to bend towards the light. [3]

c) Suggest how this response is beneficial to plants. [2] (OCR)

12. The table shows the height in mm, of two pea seedlings during the first 8 days after germination.

Days after germination	1	2	3	4	5	6	7	8
Seedling **P** height/mm	0	2.5	6.0	14.0	24.0	32.0	44.0	62.0
Seedling **Q** height/mm	0	1.5	4.0	10.0	16.0	20.0	36.0	58.0
Mean seedling height/mm	0	2.0	5.0	12.0				

a) What was the height of seedling **P** on day 3? [1]

b) On what day was seedling **Q** 20 mm in height? [1]

c) Work out the mean height of the seedlings **P** and **Q**, for each of the last four days. [4]

d) On a sheet of graph paper, plot mean height of pea seedlings against time. Join up the points you have plotted with straight lines. [4] (OCR)

Reproduction

chapter 14

Reproduction means producing new living things.
Animals and plants reproduce to make new individuals of the same species.
What would happen if living things didn't reproduce?

There are two main ways of reproducing:
- **asexual reproduction**, and
- **sexual reproduction**.

▷ Asexual reproduction

In asexual reproduction there is only ***one*** parent.
All the offspring are ***identical*** to the parent.
They have exactly the same genes.
They are called **clones**.

This saxifrage makes lots of little plantlets. They become detached to make new plants.

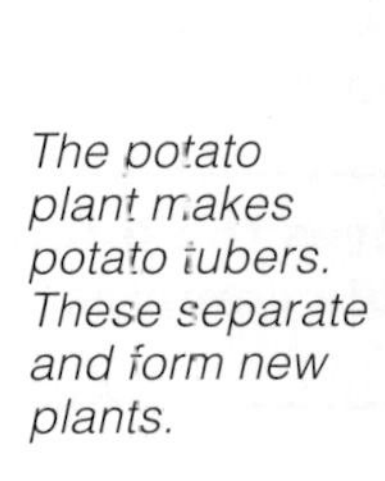

The potato plant makes potato tubers. These separate and form new plants.

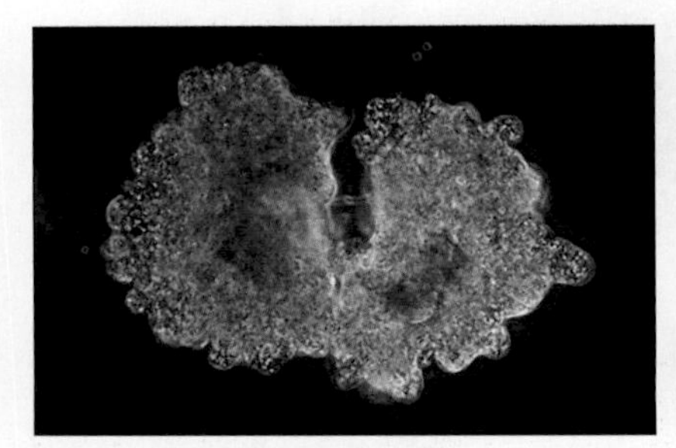

Microscopic organisms like Amoeba are made of one cell. They reproduce asexually by the cell dividing into two.

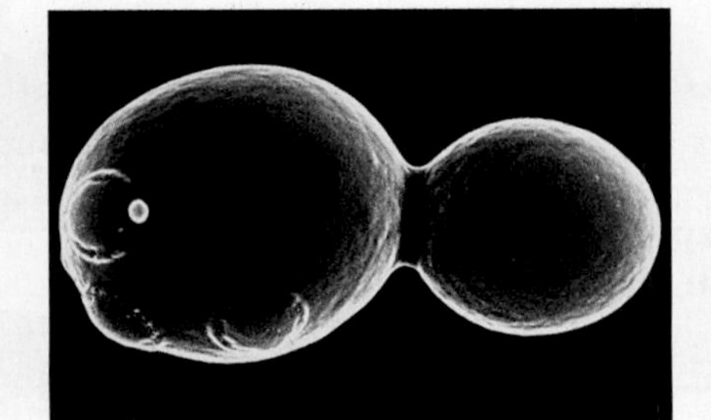

Yeast also divides to make new cells. Each cell separates to form a new individual.

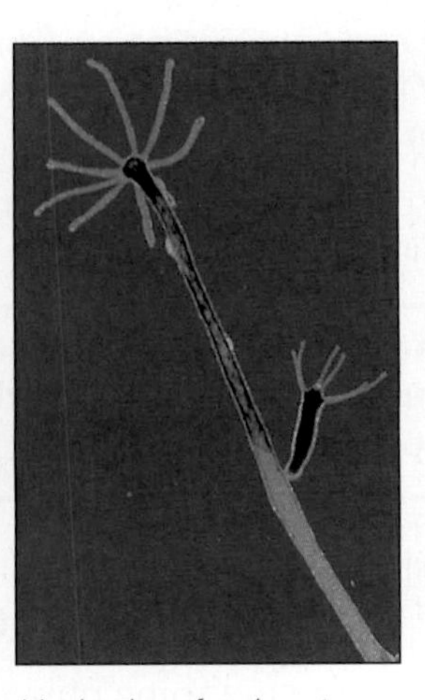

Hydra is a freshwater animal made up of many cells. It grows little buds on the parent's body. They separate and each one grows into a new animal.

In all these plants and animals all the offspring produced have come from ***one*** parent.

Asexual reproduction produces individuals with identical genetic information to the parent.

▷ Sexual reproduction

In sexual reproduction there are ***two*** parents.
The parents have **sex organs**.
The sex organs make **sex cells** or **gametes**.

In male animals the sex cells are called **sperm**.
The sperm are made in sex organs called **testes**
(testis is the singular of testes).

In female animals the sex cells are called **eggs**.
The eggs are made in sex organs called **ovaries**.

During sexual reproduction the sperm and the egg join together.
This is called **fertilisation**.
A fertilised egg or **zygote** is produced.
The fertilised egg divides many times to form a ball of cells.
Soon it will grow into an **embryo**.
Eventually it develops into a separate individual.

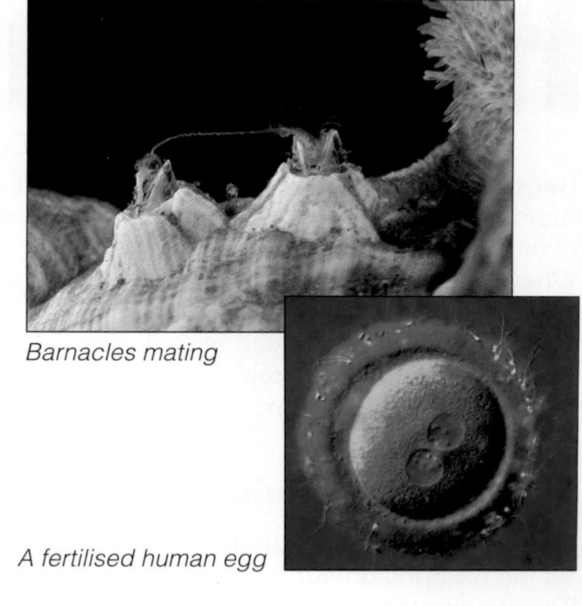

Barnacles mating

A fertilised human egg

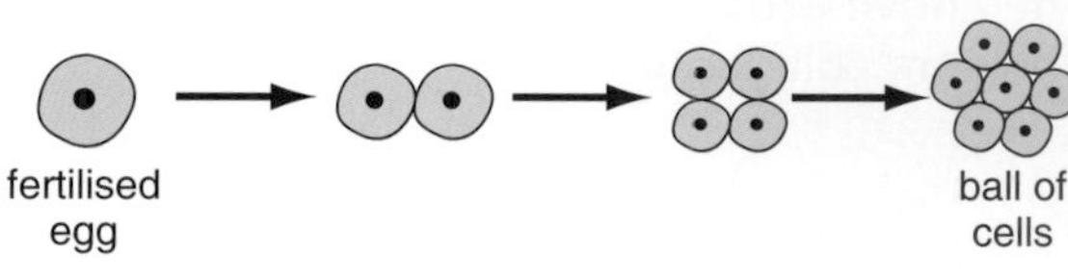

Sexual reproduction involves the joining together of male and female gametes (sex cells).

Getting it together

The sperm contains genes from the father.
The egg contains genes from the mother.
The fertilised egg has a mixture of genes from both parents.

So sexual reproduction brings about greater **variation** in the offspring.

The offspring of sexual reproduction show much more variation than those of asexual reproduction.

Fertilisation can take place ***outside*** the body – in water.
This is called **external fertilisation**.

Can you name some animals that reproduce like this?

In mammals, birds and reptiles the sperm and the egg join ***inside*** the body of the female.
This is called **internal fertilisation**.

Can you name some animals that reproduce like this?

Sex cells

A sperm is a special cell that can swim.
It is designed to carry genetic information from the male parent to the egg of the female parent.
The genes from the father are carried in the nucleus of the sperm.

An egg is much bigger than a sperm.
It contains yolk as a food store.
It also has a nucleus.
The genes from the mother are carried in the nucleus of the egg.

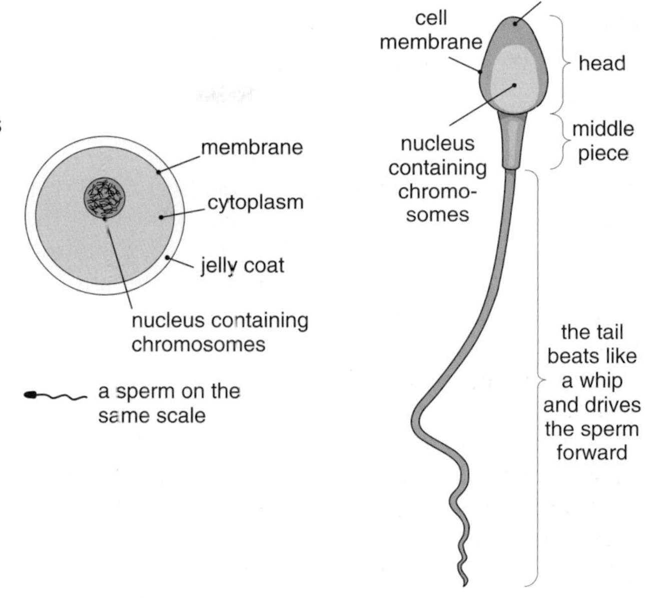

Fertilisation happens when the nucleus of the sperm joins up with the nucleus of the egg.

How many differences can you think of between eggs and sperm?

Sperm	Eggs
small	large
swim using a tail	can not move much
no food store	have a food store
millions produced	much fewer made

Also the sperm cell has many mitochondria to provide energy. What is the energy needed for?
The **acrosome** is part of the sperm's head.
It releases enzymes to digest a way through the egg membrane.

In what ways are eggs and sperm similar?

Many eggs

Animals like this fish have external fertilisation.
The sperm and the eggs join together in the water.
These fish produce millions of eggs and billions of sperm.

Why do you think this is?

What might eat the eggs?

What might wash the eggs and sperm away?

Inside a woman only one egg is usually produced at a time.
The egg is protected inside the woman's body.

▷ Cloning plants

Plant tissue culture is a method of cloning plants. Cloning results in the production of large numbers of genetically identical plants.
These are grown under sterile conditions in a suitable growth medium (usually agar jelly).

- Firstly a parent plant with the desired characteristics is selected.
- Small pieces of tissue are then cut off the plant.
- These are then sterilised (usually in bleach) without harming the cells.
- The tissue is then transferred to sterile agar jelly in a culture bottle.
- The tissue starts to divide and grows and if the agar contains the right nutrients and hormones, shoots, leaves and roots will develop forming an **explant**.
- Eventually the explants will be big enough to be grown on in compost.

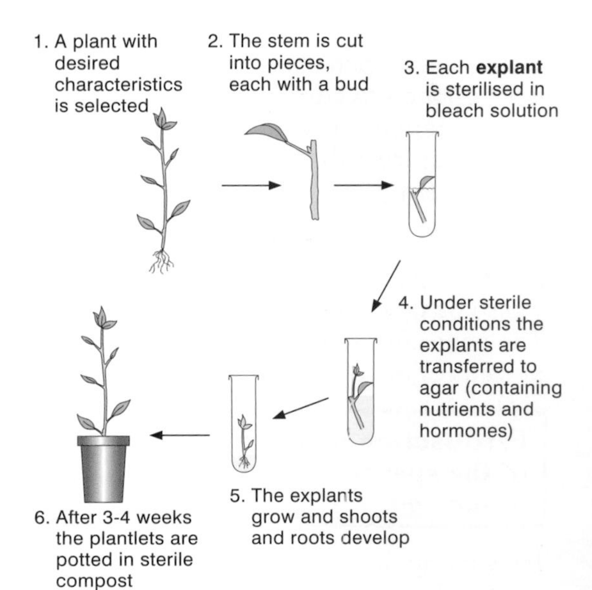

Tissue culture has a number of commercial advantages :

- It enables large quantities of new plants to be produced from a single parent.
- It is relatively cheap to carry out.
- It is time-effective, since it does not rely upon pollination and seed production.
- Consequently it can be used all the year round.
- Large numbers of plants can be transported or stored.
- It ensures that the good, healthy qualities of the parent plant are retained, for example, high fruit yield and resistance to frost.
- It has conservation use in the recovery of endangered plants.
- It is possible to mass produce commercially important plants that are difficult to grow from seed, for example oil palms and bananas.

Explants growing in nutrient agar

There are, however, some disadvantages to the technique :

- If plants become susceptible to disease or to changes in environmental conditions, then all the plants will be affected.
- Since the plants are clones, they will lack genetic variation.

But cloning plants is far easier than cloning animals, since many plant cells retain the ability to differentiate, unlike animal cells, which usually lose this ability at an early age.

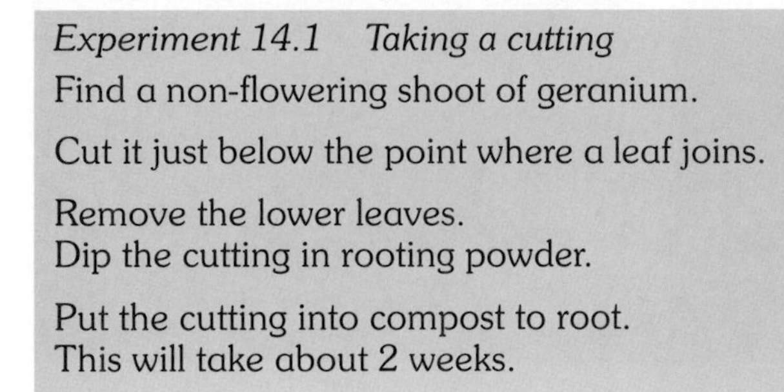

Experiment 14.1 Taking a cutting

Find a non-flowering shoot of geranium.

Cut it just below the point where a leaf joins.

Remove the lower leaves.
Dip the cutting in rooting powder.

Put the cutting into compost to root.
This will take about 2 weeks.

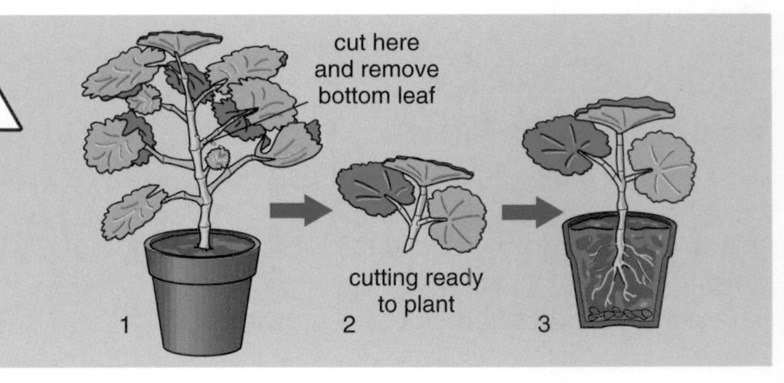

▷ Cloning farm animals

Although the first cloned animal was a tadpole, created in 1952, the most famous example was Dolly the sheep. Dolly, the first cloned farm animal, was created in 1996. What made Dolly special was that she was produced from a single parent.

So just how was this Finn Dorset sheep created?

- A nucleus was removed from an udder cell of Dolly's Finn Dorset mother.
- An unfertilised egg was taken from a Scottish Blackface ewe and its nucleus was removed.
- The udder cell nucleus was put into the unfertilised egg.
- The cell started to divide producing a ball of cells after about 6 days.
- The ball of cells was then implanted into the uterus of another Scottish Blackface ewe.
- After 148 days Dolly was born.
- She was genetically identical to her Finn Dorset mother.

But there are risks of imperfect embryo development associated with this technique.

Also, sadly, Dolly died in 2003, with lung cancer and crippling arthritis, aged six – half the life expectancy for this breed of sheep.

So there are ethical arguments about cloning and animal welfare. These have to be weighed up against issues like using cloned animals to produce suitable organs for transplant into humans.

Finn Dorset ewe
Scottish Blackface ewe
nucleus from a cell
egg without a nucleus
nucleus and egg joined together
cell starts to divide
ball of cells put inside the uterus of a Blackface sheep
after 148 days Dolly was born

▷ Embryo transplants

Artificial insemination means taking sperm from the best bulls and putting it into the best cows.
Why do you think that this is an advantage to the farmer?

You should know about **in vitro fertilisation**.

Eggs are taken from the best cows and fertilised with sperm from a selected bull in a Petri dish.
The fertilised egg divides to make a ball of cells.
These cells can be separated and each one grown into a new embryo.
This is called **tissue culture**.

Each embryo will grow into an individual that will be genetically identical – they will be clones.

The embryos are then transplanted into other cows called **surrogates**.
This technique is called **embryo transplanting**.
It ensures that a large number of offspring develop with the good characteristics that the breeder wants.

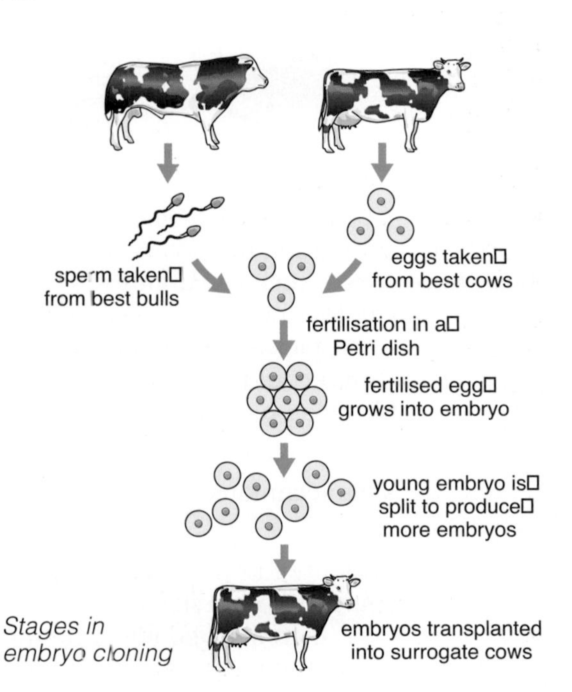

Stages in embryo cloning

▷ Human embryo cloning

In spring 2005, scientists created the first cloned human embryo in Britain.
The team from Newcastle University managed to produce an early stage embryo, using the same techniques that were used to create Dolly the sheep.

At the same time, South Korean researchers announced that they had created cloned **stem cells** that were an identical match to patients with diabetes and spinal injuries. Stem cells are cells that have not yet differentiated and can form any tissue in the body, such as nervous tissue.

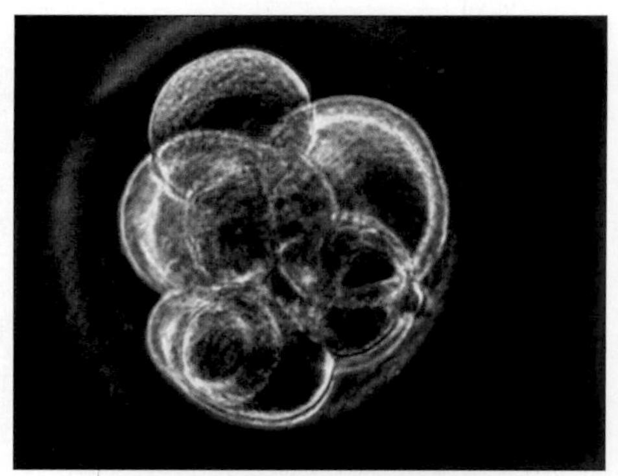
Britain's first cloned human embryo

So stem cells could eventually be taken from cloned embryos that are genetically identical to patients and grown into replacements for damaged tissue. These cells would contain the patient's own genes and could be transplanted without the risk of rejection by the patient's immune system. Unfortunately, it emerged that the South Koreans faked their entire research.

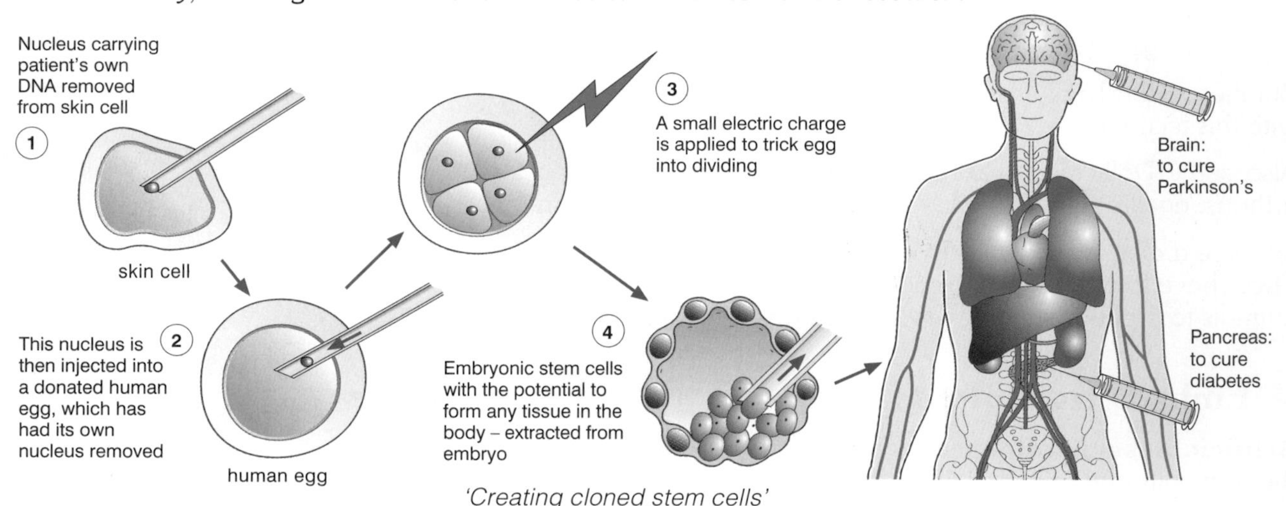

'Creating cloned stem cells'

Scientists still believe these techniques represent a giant step forward in the potential treatment of incurable diseases such as Parkinson's, Alzheimer's, motor neurone disease and diabetes. Whilst these therapies are a number of years away, cloned cells could also be used for testing drugs, possibly as an alternative to experiments on animals.

So how does the technique to create cloned stem cells work?

- First, the nucleus, carrying the patient's own DNA, is removed from a skin cell.
- The nucleus is then injected into a human egg which has had its own nucleus removed.
- An electrical pulse is used to trigger cell division.
- The cloned embryo grows for about five days before stem cells are removed and it is destroyed.

But could the technique ever be used to clone a new person?
In the UK, reproductive cloning which would make a human using this technique is banned. Also there are moral and ethical arguments.
A spokesperson for the Pro-Life Alliance said: 'Cloning for research purposes, which involves the manufacture of human embryos destined for experimentation and subsequent destruction, is profoundly unethical'.

Summary

- Asexual reproduction involves a single parent and results in offspring that are genetically identical to the parent.
- Sexual reproduction involves two parents and the production of gametes (sex cells).
- Fertilisation involves the joining together of gametes (e.g. sperm and egg).
- Sexual reproduction results in greater genetic variation than asexual reproduction.
- Tissue culture involves growing small groups of plant cells in sterile conditions. Plants can be produced cheaply, in large numbers and with all the good characteristics of the parent plant.
- New plants can be produced quickly and cheaply by taking cuttings from older plants.
- Nuclei from body cells can be transferred to unfertilised eggs (with their nuclei removed) to produce a cloned animal like Dolly the sheep.
- A similar technique can be used to produce human embryo clones which provide stem cells to possibly treat incurable diseases like Parkinson's and diabetes.
- Developing animal embryos can be split apart, before they become specialised, and transplanted into surrogate mothers.

▷ Questions

1. Copy and complete : Asexual reproduction involves ... parent and produces .... identical offspring called ......Sexual reproduction involves ... parents and the production of ....., which join together at ....There is far more genetic .... in ....reproduction than there is in .... reproduction. Genetically......... plants can be grown in .... conditions by the technique called .... culture. Human ...... clones can provide ... cells which may be used in the future to treat .... diseases.

2. a) How many sperm are needed to fertilise an egg?
b) Why does a membrane form around the egg after fertilisation?
c) Give three differences between a sperm and an egg.
d) Why is it important that the sperm and the egg each have half the normal number of chromosomes?

3. In the last century, European vineyards were almost destroyed by an insect which kills vines by eating their roots. The American vine is resistant to the insect. All European vines are now grown from stem cuttings grafted onto the rooted stocks of the American vine.

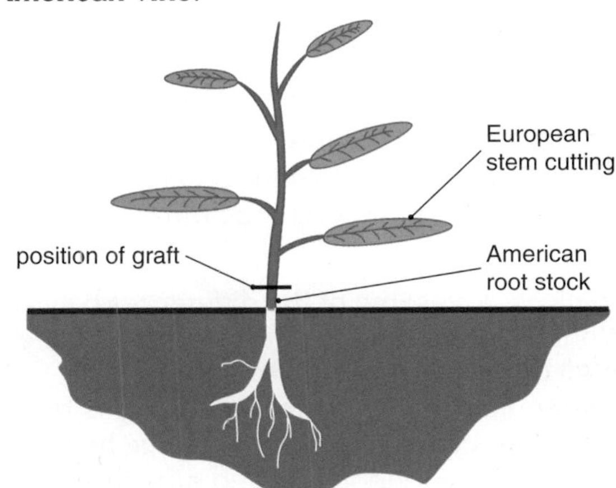

a) Explain why the grapes produced on this type of vine are considered to be European rather than American.
b) Recently, a European vine resistant to the insect has been developed by biotechnologists. Explain how large numbers of disease-resistant vines could be produced quickly from the one vine resistant to the disease.

Further questions on page 276.

chapter 15

Look around at the other people in your class.
We are all similar.
We all have two arms, two legs, two eyes, a nose, and so on.
We all belong to the same **species**.

If you take another look you'll see that there are also many differences.
None of us are identical.
Some people are taller or heavier, others have different colour hair, skin or eyes.
This is called **variation**.
Individuals of the same species still vary quite a lot.

Look at these rose bushes :

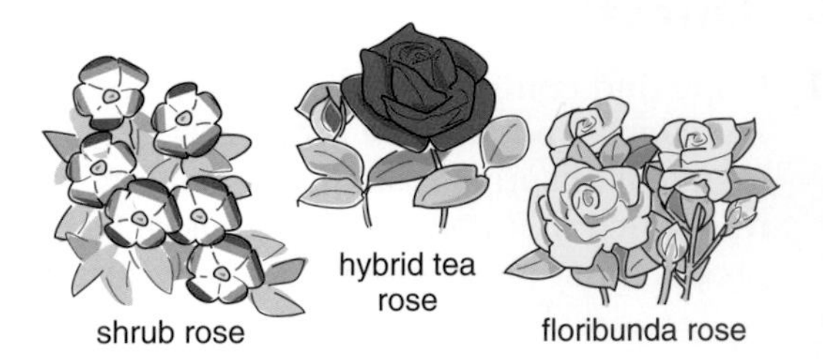

They show variation too.
They have different colours, different heights and some have more flowers than others.

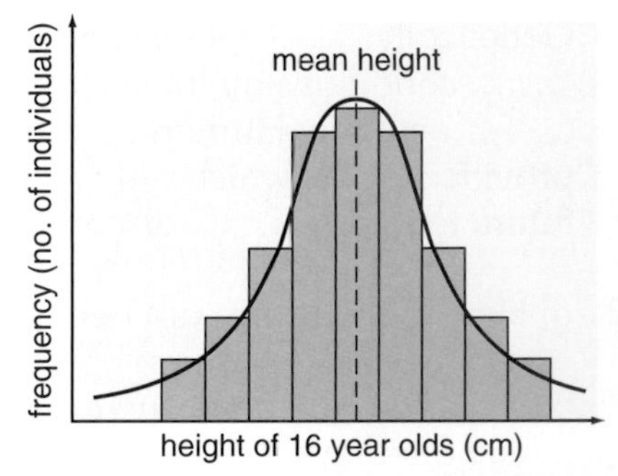

Think back to some of the differences between people.
What would happen if you measured the heights of all the pupils in your year group ?
You would get a whole range of heights from small to tall.
Most pupils would be about average height.
This type of variation is called **continuous variation** because there is a continuous range of heights from small to tall.
Can you think of any other examples of continuous variation ?

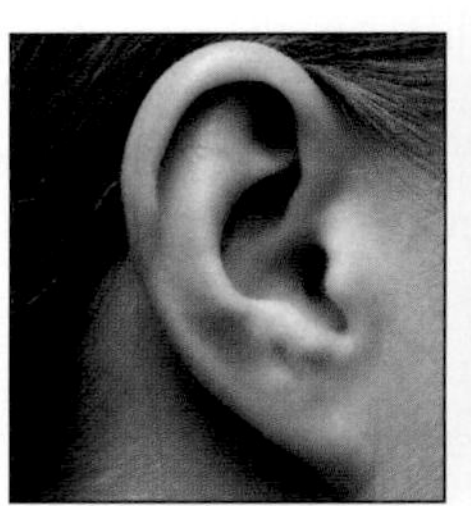
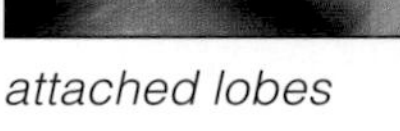
attached lobes

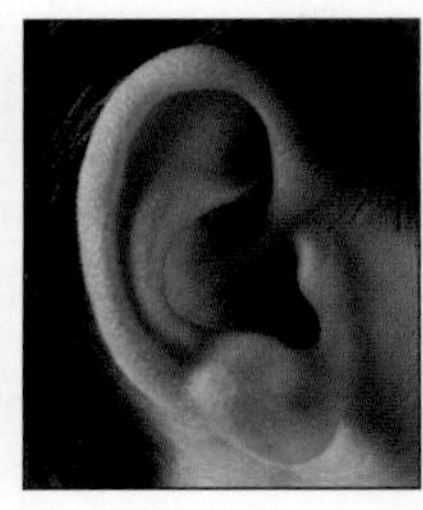
free lobes

Some people have attached ear lobes.
Other people's ear lobes are free and not attached.
Some people can roll their tongues, other people can't.
These are both examples of **discontinuous variation**.
Here there is no range or inbetweens.
You can either do something or you can't.
You either have something or you haven't.

▷ Inheritance versus environment

Imagine if some clones were taken from a carrot plant.
They would all be genetically the same.
Will they all be identical when they grow into adult carrot plants?

It depends upon whether they have the same things from the environment.
What happens if some do not get enough light, water or nutrients?
They will not grow so well.

So individuals will show variation because of two causes: **genetic** and **environmental**.

Why do you look like you do?

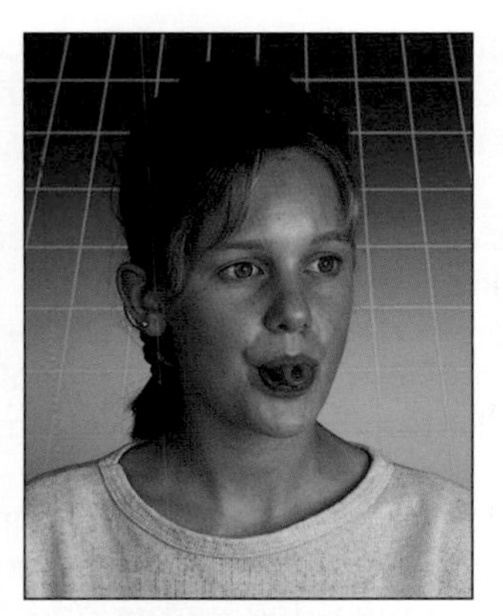

You get some characteristics from your parents.
You **inherit** them.

But other characteristics do not come from your parents.
They are caused by the way you lead your life.
These are due to the effects of your **environment**.

Can you roll your tongue like the girl in the photograph?
It is not something that you can learn to do.
You have either inherited it or you haven't.

Look at this Olympic athlete:

She needs speed, agility and strength.
These are not just inherited.
They are improved by training, diet and the right lifestyle.
These are environmental causes of variation.

Can you think of any other human characteristics that are affected by the environment?

Which of these characteristics are inherited and which are environmental?

blood group	neat writing	hair length	freckles
eye colour	an accent	shape of nose	scars
hair colour	body weight	skill at languages	

▷ The variety of life

There are millions of different plants and animals in the world.
They may differ in their appearance, their behaviour or where they live.

If we look carefully we can see similarities and differences.
Sparrows, wasps, robins and bees are all animals that fly.
But sparrows and robins belong together and so do wasps and bees.

We can divide living things up into groups.
The members of these groups have similar features.

For instance, cats and dogs are mammals because they both have fur.
But there are also many differences between them.
So we divide mammals up into smaller groups like the cat family and the dog family.

Snakes and lizards are reptiles because they both have scaly skin.
But there are many differences between them.
So we divide reptiles up into smaller groups like the snake family and the lizard family.

Organisms are given scientific names using the **binomial system** (binomial means 'two names').
The first name is the **genus** and the second name is the **species**.
A genus is a group of species that are closely related but do not interbreed.
A species is a group of individuals that can breed together to produce fertile offspring.
The scientific name for a lion is *Panthera leo* and a tiger is *Panthera tigris*.
So these members of the cat family are of the same genus but are separate species.
Notice that the genus always has a capital letter but the species is lower case, so your scientific name is *Homo sapiens*.
The binomial system is used by scientists all over the world as it is an international language for naming organisms.

All domestic dogs belong to the same species. They may all look different, but they can mate and give birth to cross-breeds that are perfectly healthy.

There are two types of variation between living things.
There is:

- variation between ***different species***
  and
- variation between ***members of the same species***.

▷ Sorting things out

How could you find out the name of a plant or animal?

You could look through the pictures in a book until you found the right one.
But that would take a lot of time and effort.

Scientists use **keys** to identify living things.
A key has a number of questions.
You start at the beginning and answer 'yes' or 'no' to each question.
It soon takes you to the plant or animal you want.

Use this branching key to identify the animals below.

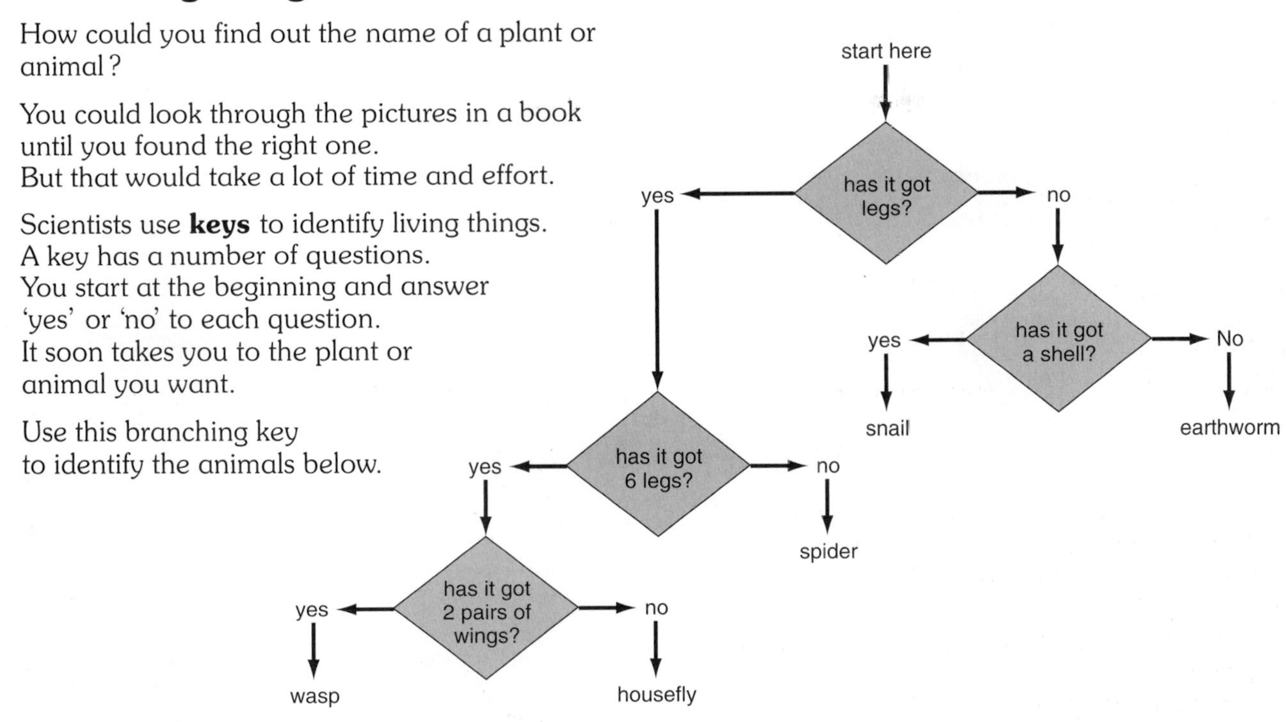

Use the numbered key below to identify the same animals.
It is set out differently from the first key, but it works in the same way.
Start at the beginning and answer the question at each stage.

1	Has legs	Go to 2
	Has no legs	Go to 4
2	Has six legs	Go to 3
	Has eight legs	Spider
3	Has one pair of wings	Housefly
	Has two pairs of wings	Wasp
4	Has a shell	Snail
	Has no shell	Earthworm

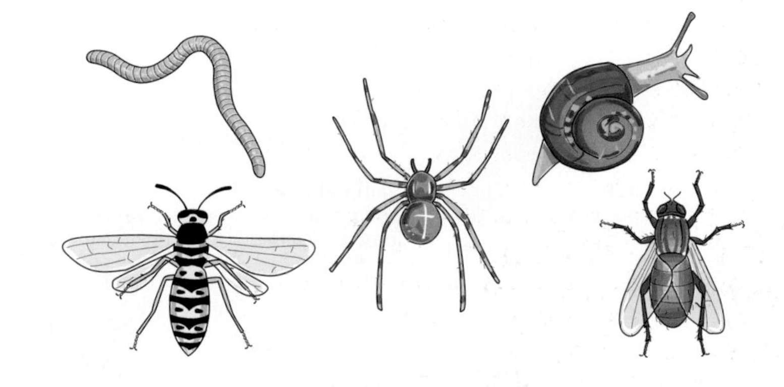

Scientists have tried to give every species a name of its own.
Similar living things have been put in the same group.
This is called **classification**.
The largest groups are called **kingdoms**.
There are five of these kingdoms.

▷ The animal kingdom

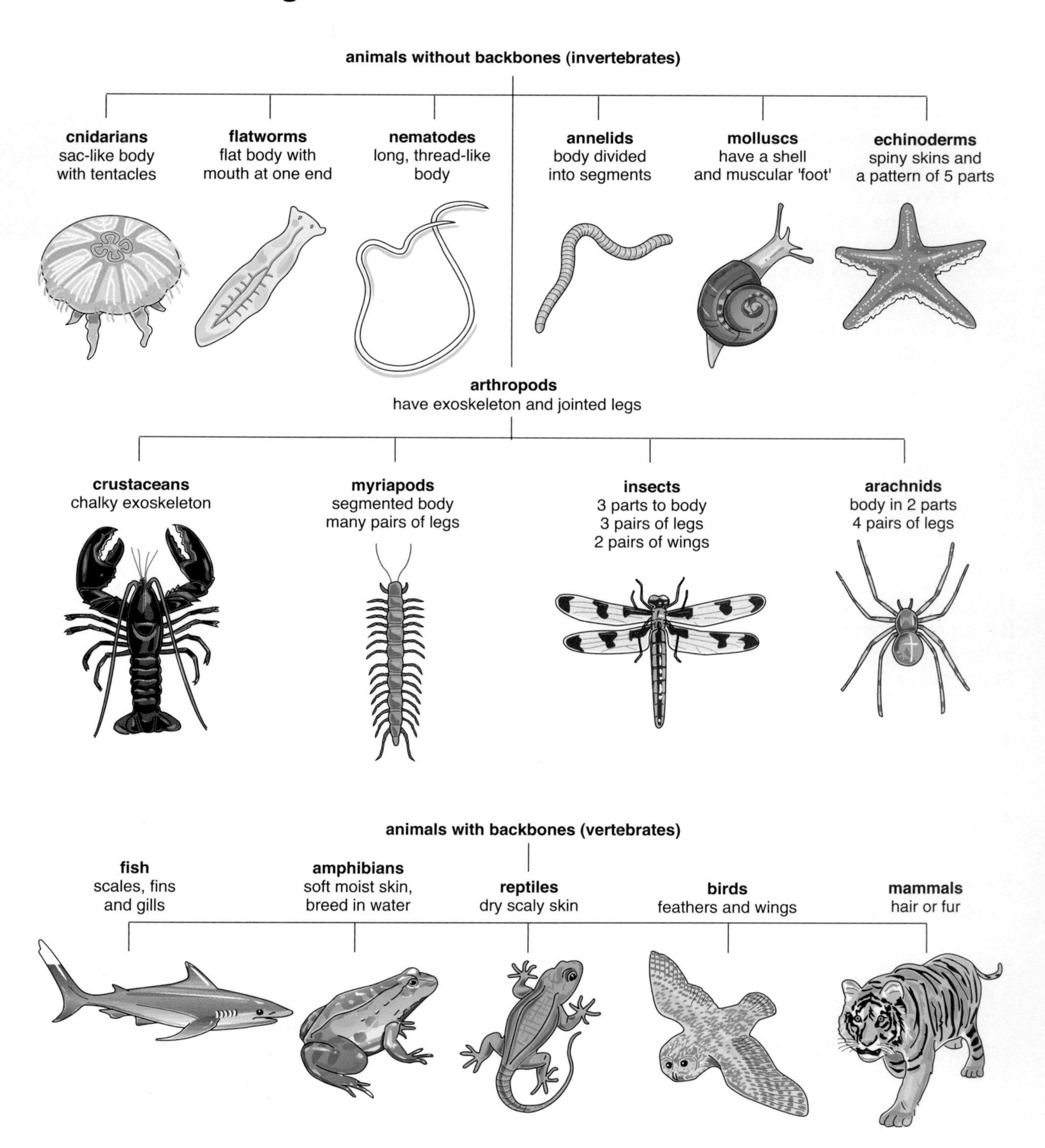

▷ The plant kingdom

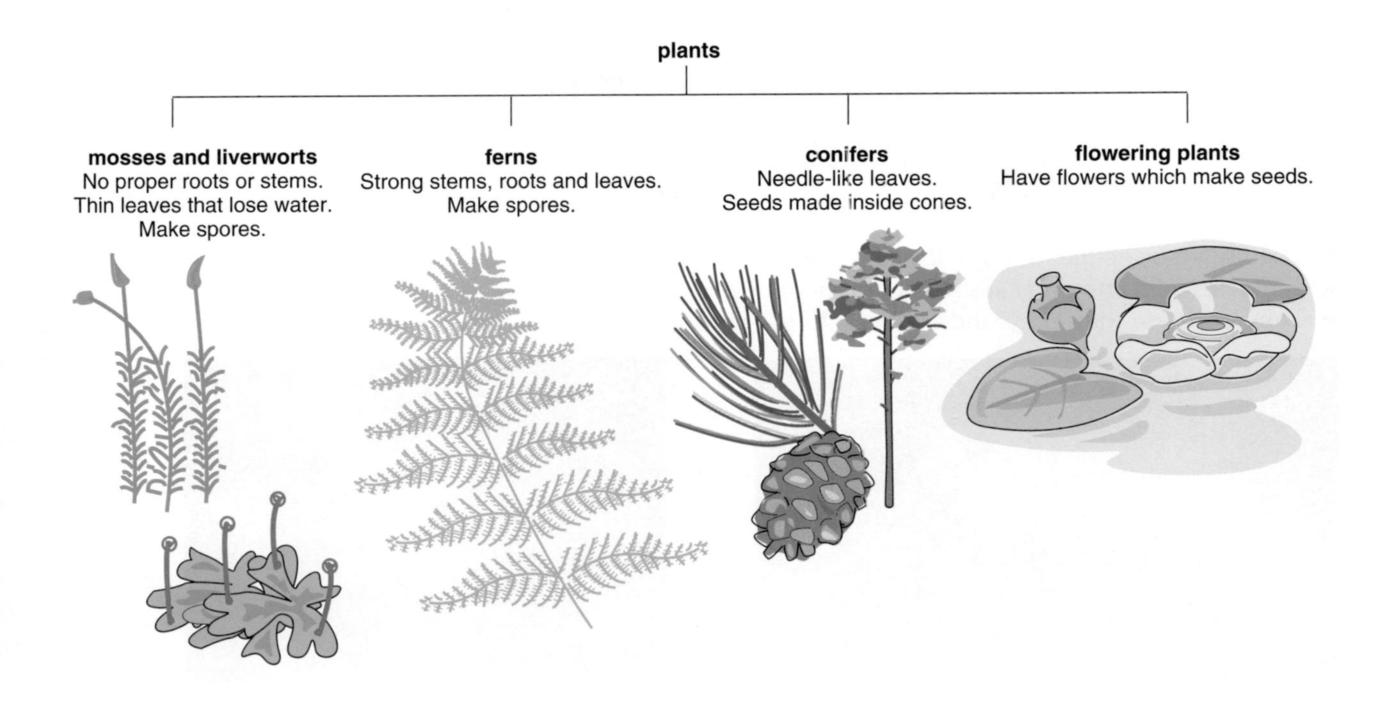

▷ The other three kingdoms

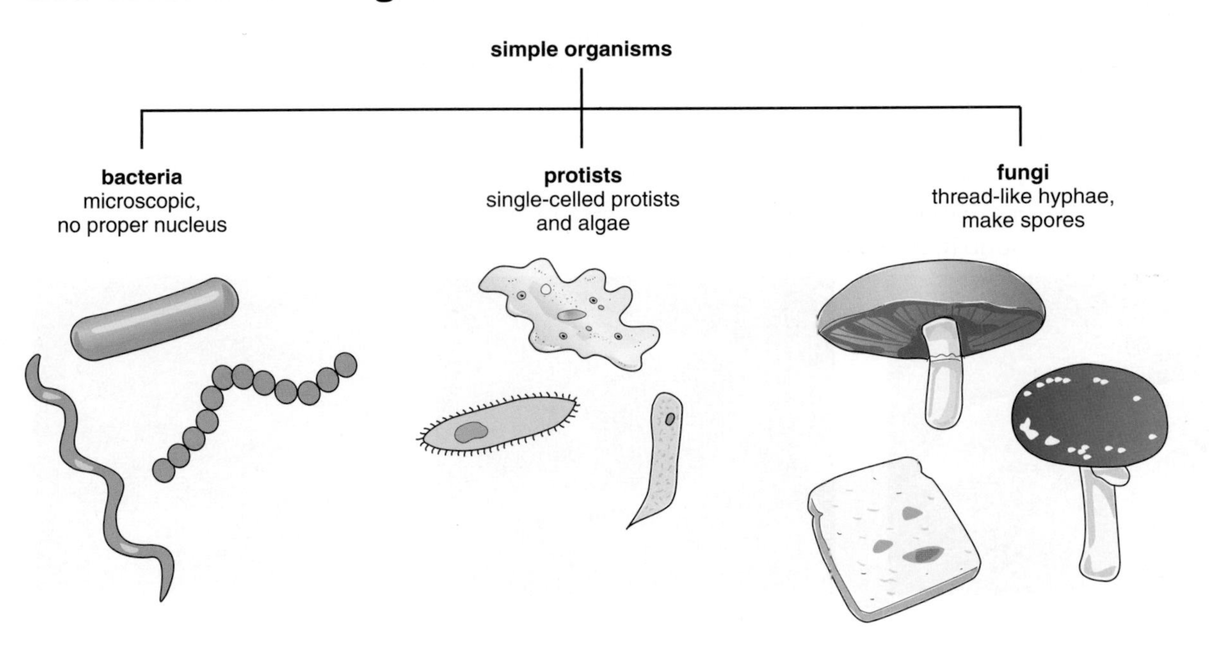

▷ Animals

Animals without backbones

We call animals that do not have a backbone **invertebrates**.
We can divide invertebrates into smaller groups :

1. Cnidarians ('nid-arians')

- Most of these live in the sea.
- They have a sac-like body with one opening.
- Tentacles with stinging cells surround the mouth.
- They paralyse their prey and push it into the mouth.

The sea anemone attaches to a rock using a sucker

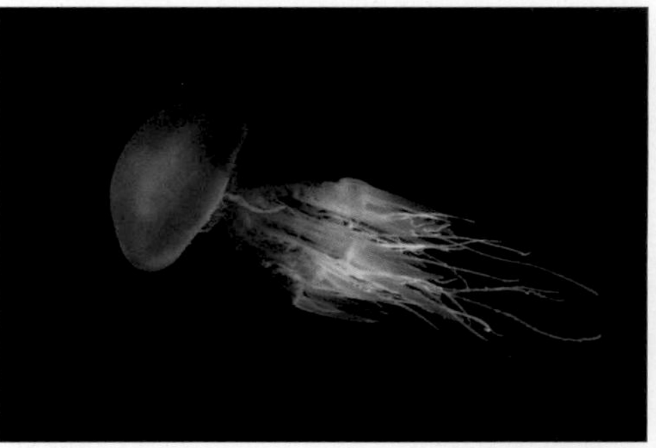

Jellyfish swim by opening and closing like an umbrella

2. Worms

There are three major groups of worms :

Flatworms have a flattened body with a mouth at one end.
Some live in freshwater, but most are parasites of animals, such as the human tapeworm.

Nematodes or roundworms have long, thread-like bodies.
Some live in the soil, but many are parasites inside plants and animals.

Annelids are worms with long, tube-shaped bodies made up of segments.
The earthworm is found in the soil, but most segmented worms live in the sea.

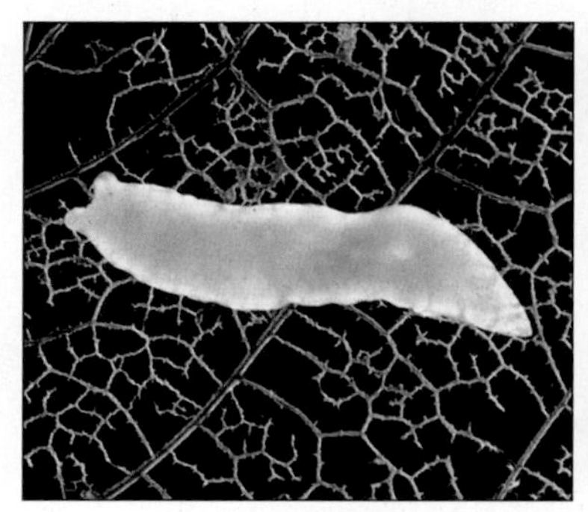

This flatworm glides through the water using tiny hairs or cilia

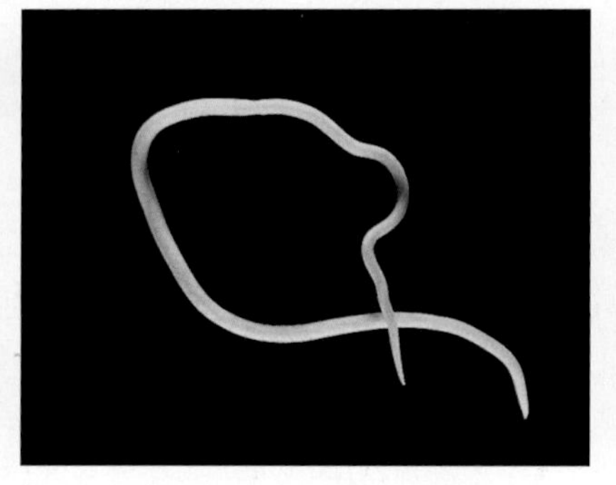

Nematodes do not have segments

Fertile soil contains large numbers of earthworms

3. Molluscs

This group includes snails, slugs and squids.

- Their bodies are soft but not segmented.
- Many of them have one or two shells to protect them.
- They have a muscular 'foot' to burrow or move around with.

Snails use their foot to move along on a trail of slime. They have rough tongues for shredding up plants.

Cockles and other 'bivalves' have 2 shells. They filter tiny plants and animals from the water.

4. Echinoderms

- These animals all live in the sea.
- They have tough, spiny skins.
- The body has a pattern of five parts.
- They move around on tube-feet.

The starfish has five arms. It can use them to pull the two shells of a mussel apart to feed on the soft insides.

Sea urchins have a pattern of five parts on their shells. They are protected by sharp spines and cling to rocks with their tube-feet.

5. Arthropods

These are the largest group of invertebrates.

- The word 'arthropod' means 'jointed leg'.
  All the animals in this group have jointed legs.
- Their bodies are also divided into segments.
- They are supported by a hard skeleton on the outside of the body called an **exoskeleton**. When they grow too big for their exoskeleton, they **moult** and grow a new one.
- On their heads are feelers or **antennae**.

The arthropods are made up of four smaller groups:

Crustaceans ('cru-stations')

- Nearly all of these live in water (woodlice are an exception).
- They breathe oxygen using their **gills**.
- They have more than four pairs of legs but less than 20 pairs.
- Many have a chalky exoskeleton. This protects them like a suit of armour.
- Crustaceans always have two pairs of antennae.

Shrimps do not have such a thick exoskeleton. They have long sensitive antennae.

Crabs have five pairs of legs. They are protected by their thick exoskeleton.

Myriapods

- These are the centipedes and the millipedes.
- They have long bodies made up of lots of segments.
  Do you think that centipedes really do have 100 legs?
  Do millipedes have a million legs?

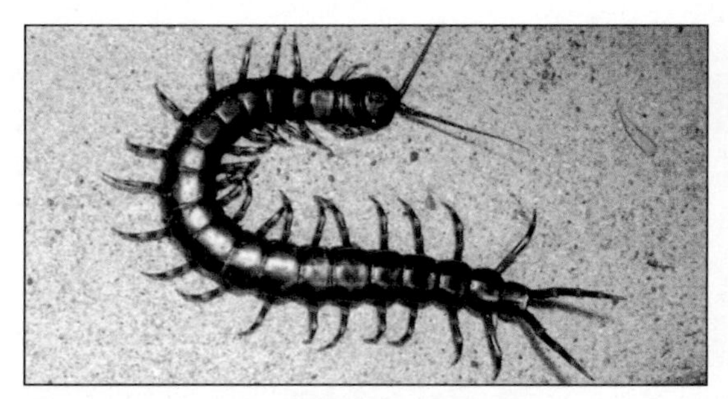

Centipedes have one pair of legs on each segment. So the total number of legs depends upon how many segments they have.
Centipedes are fast-moving carnivores.
They have powerful jaws and can paralyse their prey.

Millipedes have two pairs of legs on each body segment.
They are slow-moving herbivores.
You can often find them feeding in a leaf litter.

Insects

This is the largest group ***within*** the arthropods.
There are hundreds of thousands of different species.
They have been able to colonise most habitats in the world.

One reason why they are able to live on land so successfully is that their skin or **cuticle** is waterproof and stops them losing much water.
Their bodies are divided into three parts : the head, the thorax and the abdomen.
On the thorax there are three pairs of legs and usually two pairs of wings.
They have one pair of antennae on the head and **compound eyes**.
They breathe through holes in the sides of the body called **spiracles**.
Insects often pass through different **larval** stages in their life as they grow.

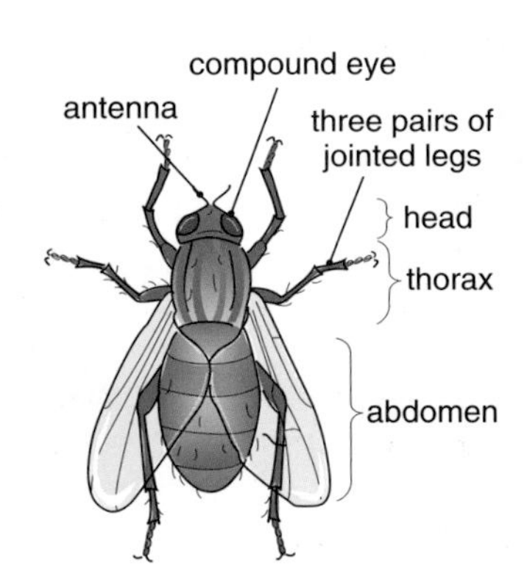

What makes an insect ?

Butterflies are useful because they pollinate flowers

Can you see the three parts of the body on this wasp ?

Arachnids

This is the spider group.

- They have bodies divided into two parts.
- They have four pairs of legs and no wings.
- They have no antennae but paralyse their prey with poison fangs.

Many spiders spin silken webs to catch their prey

Scorpions use a sting in the tail to paralyse their prey

Animals with backbones

We call animals that have a backbone **vertebrates**.
All vertebrates have an internal skeleton made of either bone or cartilage.

There are five main groups of vertebrates :

1. Fish

- These live all the time in water.
- They are streamlined and have fins for swimming.
- They breathe oxygen from the water with their **gills**.
- Their skin is covered with scales.

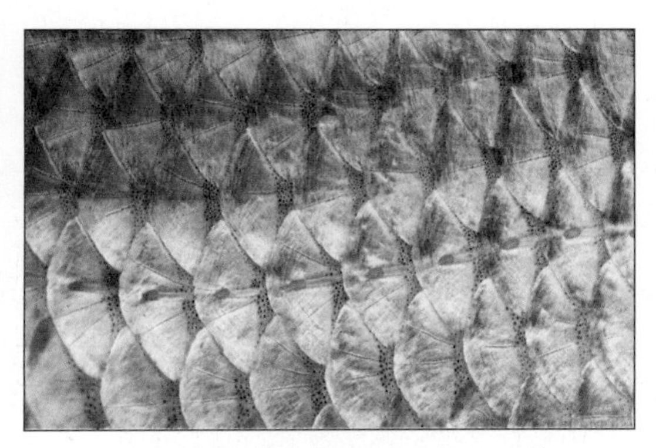

The scales of this fish point backwards for streamlining

Fish use fins to steer through the water

2. Amphibians

- These have smooth, moist skin.
- They breed in water.
  Sperm and eggs are released into the water so fertilisation is external.
- Fertilised eggs hatch into swimming tadpoles.
- On land, the adults breathe by using lungs.
  In water, they can breathe through their skin.

Amphibians have soft, moist skin

Tadpoles are larval stages. They breathe using gills.

More vertebrates

3. Reptiles

- These have dry, scaly skin to cut down water loss.
- They can live in dry regions, away from water.
- They have lungs to breathe air.
- Fertilisation takes place inside the female's body.
- They lay eggs with leathery shells.

Reptiles have dry, scaly skin

Does this fearsome predator remind you of a dinosaur? Dinosaurs were reptiles too.

4. Birds

- They have feathers and wings.
- Most of them are able to fly.
- They have no teeth but their beaks are adapted to deal with different types of food.
- They lay eggs which are protected by hard shells.

The beak and claws of the eagle are adapted for catching and tearing its prey

Sedge warblers feeding young in the nest

5. Mammals

- They have hair or fur.
- All mammals, even aquatic ones, use lungs for breathing.
- Fertilisation is internal and the young are born already well developed.
- Female mammals suckle their young on milk from **mammary glands**.
- Both birds and mammals are **warm blooded**. This means that they are able to regulate their body temperature. They can keep it constant even though the outside temperature changes.

Mammals look after their young

Aquatic mammals still use lungs to breathe air

▷ Plants

There are two kinds of plants :

plants which make spores like mosses, liverworts and ferns. They make **spores** that grow into new plants.

plants which make seeds like conifers and flowering plants. They make **seeds** that grow into new plants.

1. Plants which make spores

Mosses and liverworts

- They live in damp places.
- They have thin leaves that lose water easily.
- They do not have proper stems or roots.
- They make tiny spores instead of seeds. The spores are carried away by the wind.

Liverworts grow flat on the ground

In the summer mosses make spore capsules. The ripe capsules open and the spores are shaken out.

Ferns

- They have strong stems, roots and leaves.
- Their leaves have a waxy layer to cut down water loss.
- They have tubes called **xylem** inside the plant. These transport water and support the plant.
- The spores are made on the underside of the leaves.

Each patch on the underside of the leaf contains lots of spores

Fern leaves grow out in a clump from a thick underground stem or rhizome

2. Plants which make seeds

Conifers

- Many are evergreen and keep their leaves all through the year.
- The leaves are like needles to cut down water loss.
- They have xylem for water transport and support.
- They do not have flowers. Instead they make male and female **cones**.

After fertilisation the seeds are made inside the female cones

Coniferous plantations now cover many hill slopes

Flowering plants

- These have flowers containing reproductive organs.
- Pollen is carried from one plant to another by insects or by the wind.
- The flowers make seeds after fertilisation. These grow into new plants.
- Flowering plants are very successful at colonising the land. They are able to live in dry, hot places where there is little water.

Many flowering plants are pollinated by insects

Plants like the hazel have their flowers pollinated by the wind

When the flowers of the horse chestnut have finished, the seeds are made inside fruits

▷ The other three kingdoms

1. Bacteria

- These are made up of one cell with no proper nucleus.
- They can only be seen by using a microscope.
- There are different cell shapes – rods, spheres and spirals.
- Bacteria are found everywhere – in the air, in the water and in the soil. They can also live in and on plants and animals.

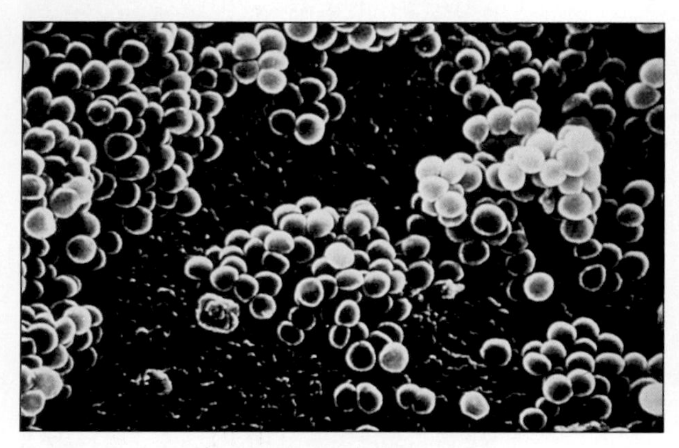

These sphere-shaped bacteria can cause a sore throat

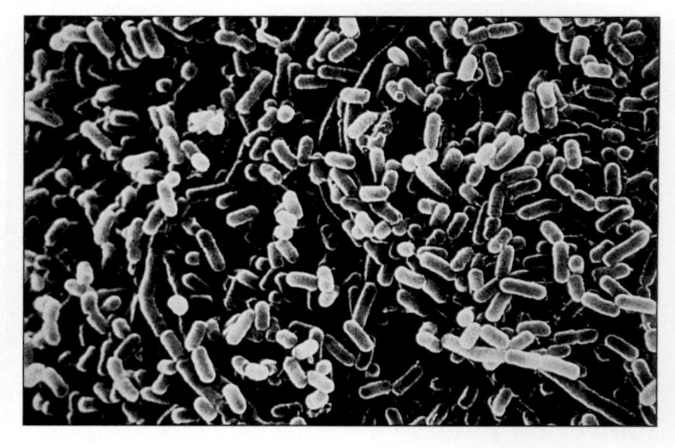

These rod-shaped bacteria are found inside the human intestine

2. Protists

- Some protists are made up of a single cell. (Others have many cells and are called **algae**.)
- They have a proper nucleus in the cell.
- They live in water or inside other organisms.
- They are not plants, animals, bacteria or fungi.
- Some have chlorophyll and can feed like plants.
- Others have to take food into their cells.

Single-celled protists

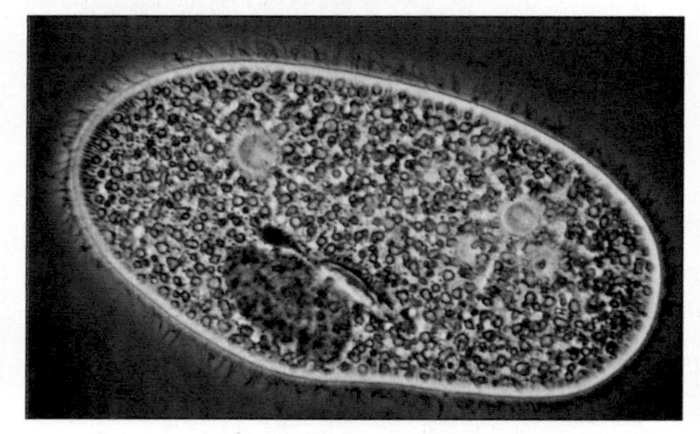

Paramecium is covered in tiny hairs called cilia. They enable it to swim through the water.

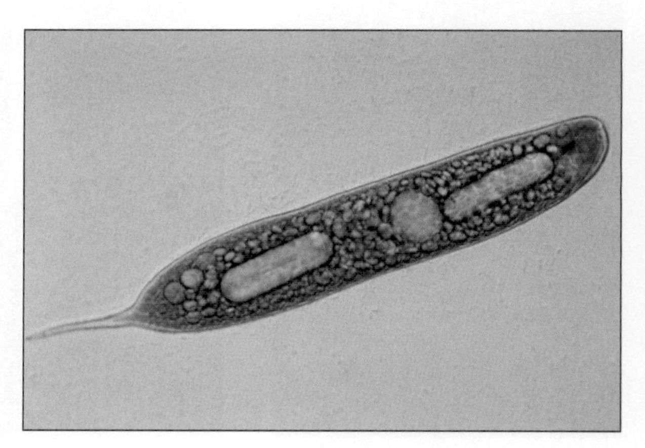

Euglena also moves around in water. But it has chlorophyll and feeds like a plant.

Algae

- These larger protists are often found in ponds or in the sea.
- They are like plants because they have chlorophyll and make their own food.
- Unlike plants they do not have leaves, stems or roots.

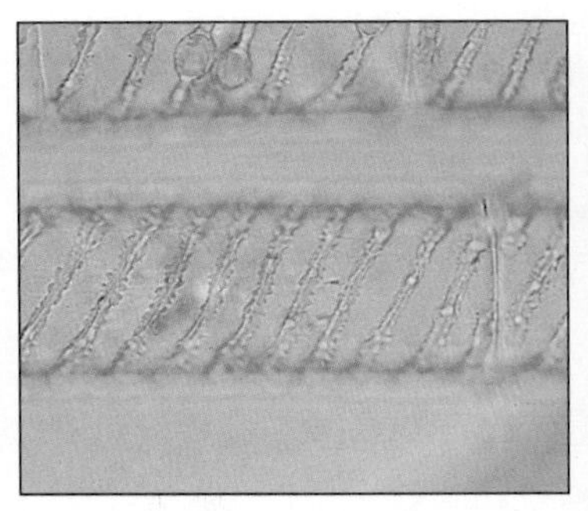

These beautiful filaments of Spirogyra form the green slime that you sometimes see floating on the surface of ponds

The bladder wrack is a brown seaweed common on the mid-shore. It contains a brown pigment as well as chlorophyll.

This red seaweed is called Palmaria. It is found on the lower shore. A red pigment hides the chlorophyll.

3. Fungi

- These are the mushrooms, toadstools, moulds and yeasts.
- They are often made up of thin threads called **hyphae**.
- Some of them look like plants. They do not contain chlorophyll and so can not make their own food.
- They produce spores which grow into new fungi.
- Many fungi are **saprophytes**. They feed on dead and decaying material.
- Others live on or inside other organisms and are called **parasites**.

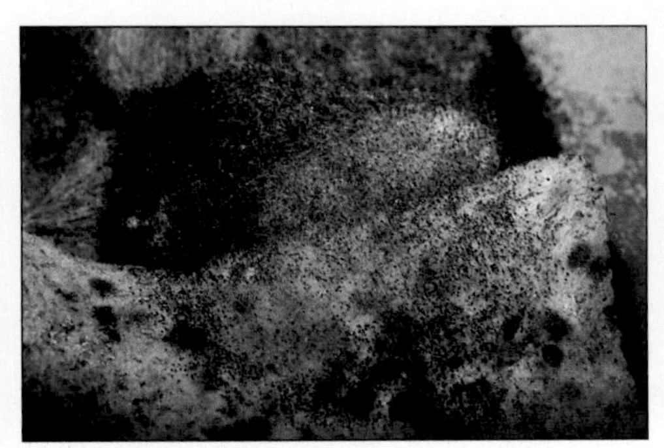

Bread mould spreads its hyphae over uncovered food and so spoils it

Toadstools and mushrooms are the parts of the fungus that make the spores. These Fly Agaric fungi are poisonous.

Summary

- A species is a group of individuals that can breed together to produce fertile offspring.
- Variation occurs between different species and between members of the same species.
- Keys have a number of questions that enable you to identify living things.
- Living things can be classified into five kingdoms : bacteria, protists, fungi, plants and animals.
- Animals can be classified as vertebrates (have a backbone) or invertebrates (have no backbone).
- Plants can be classified as those that make spores and those that make seeds.
- Living things that are neither animals nor plants are classified as either bacteria, protists or fungi.

▷ Questions

1. Copy and complete :
Animals with backbones are called . . . . . They can be divided into five groups : fish, ... , reptiles, ... , and mammals. Animals without backbones are called . . . . . One of the largest groups of invertebrates is the . . . . or jointed-legged animals. This group can be divided up into four smaller groups : crustaceans, ... , insects and . . . . . The plant kingdom can be divided up into four smaller groups : mosses and liverworts, ... , flowering plants and . . . . . The other three kingdoms are the . . . . , protists and . . . . .

2. The animal in the diagram lives inside the bladder of a frog :
It is flat, has no segments, has only one opening to its gut and lacks a skeleton.

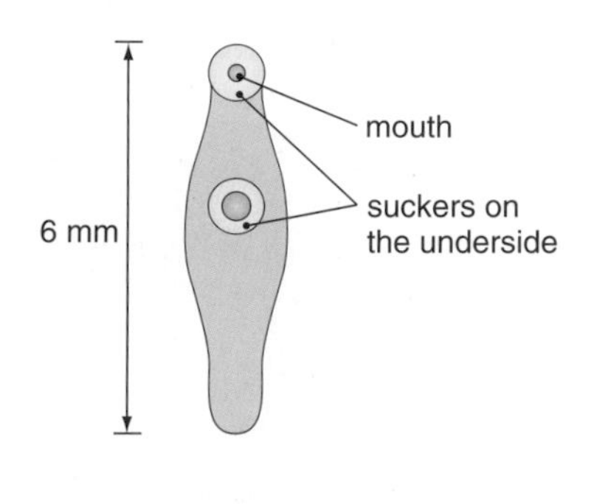

Use your observations of the diagram to answer the following :

a) Give two reasons why the animal is not a segmented worm.
b) Give two reasons why the animal is not a mollusc.
c) Suggest the group that the animal belongs to.
d) What do you think the suckers are for ?

3. Look at the three animals :

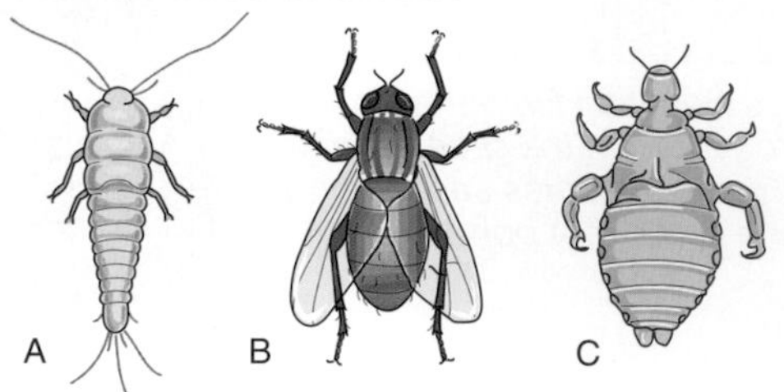

a) Give three features which all three animals have and which you can see in the diagrams.
b) To which group of animals do they belong ?
c) C lives on the skin of a mammal and feeds on its blood.
   i) Suggest one feature in diagram C which helps it to live on the skin.
   ii) How would this feature help ?

4. When a scientist visited a desert island, she discovered some insects. She made some drawings and brought them back to the laboratory.
Here are the sketches :

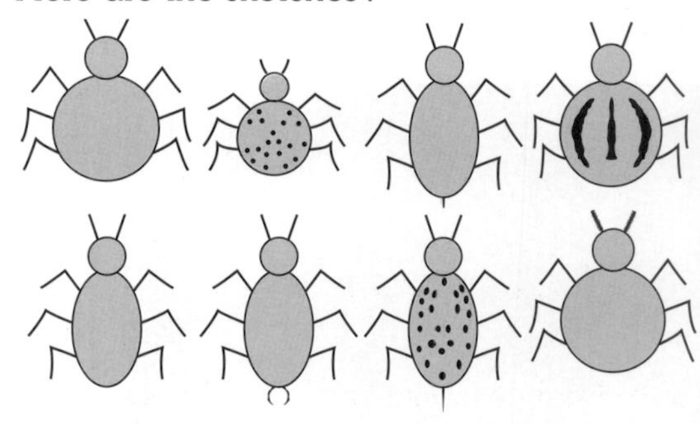

a) Make up a name for each insect.
b) Try making up a key to identify them.

5. Read the descriptions and decide which group each one refers to :
   a) Lay eggs with a shell on land. Have wings and feathers but no teeth.
   b) Body divided into three parts. Have six legs and usually two pairs of wings.
   c) Have thin leaves and live in damp places. Reproduce using spores.
   d) Have no segments. Have a muscular foot and some have a shell.
   e) Do not have chlorophyll. Have a body made of thin threads called hyphae.
   f) Are warm-blooded. Have hair and females make milk to feed their young.

6. Use the key to identify the seashore animals A, B, C, D, E and F.

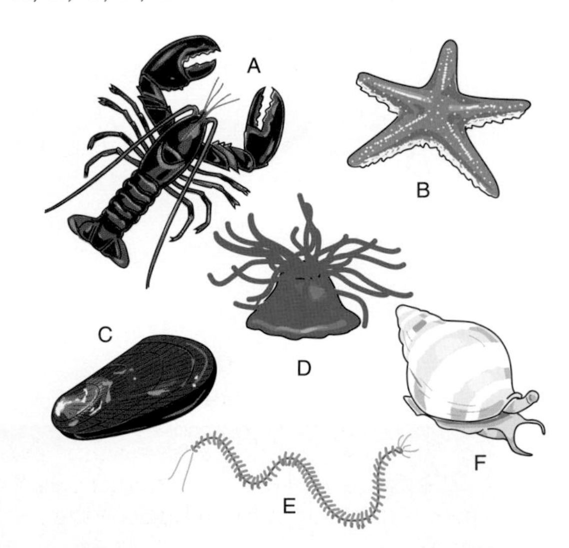

1	Divided into segments	Go to 2
	Not divided into segments	Go to 3
2	Has large claws	Lobster
	No large claws	Ragworm
3	Has a shell	Go to 4
	No shell	Go to 5
4	Shell has two pieces	Mussel
	Shell has one piece	Dog-whelk
5	Animal has five arms	Starfish
	Does not have five arms	Sea anemone

7. Decide, on the basis of their structure, which is the odd one out of the following :
   a) Daffodil, jellyfish, bluebell, grass.
   b) Camel, snake, eagle, tapeworm.
   c) Snail, locust, spider, centipede.
   d) Mould, toadstool, seaweed, mushrooom.
   e) Frog, newt, toad, lizard.
   f) Pine, sycamore, daisy, dandelion.
   g) Carp, dolphin, stickleback, shark.

8. Use the key below to identify the leaves of these common trees :

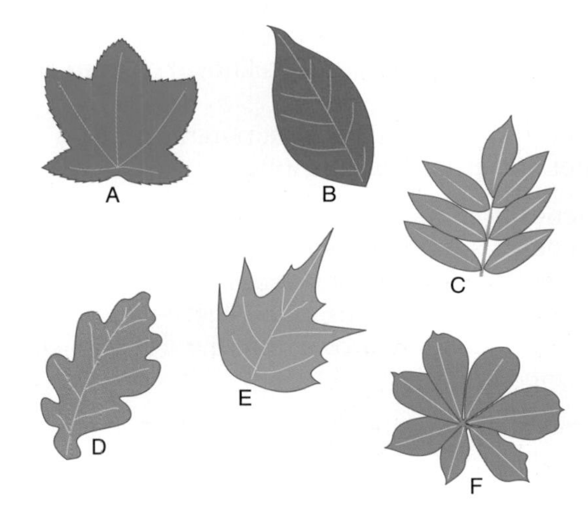

1	Leaves simple (not divided into leaflets)	Go to 2
	Leaves compound (divided into leaflets)	Go to 5
2	Leaves divided into five lobes	Sycamore
	Leaves not divided into five lobes	Go to 3
3	Edge of leaf smooth	Privet
	Edge of leaf not smooth	Go to 4
4	Edge of leaf toothed	Silver birch
	Edge of leaf with rounded lobes	Oak
5	Leaflets arranged like fingers of a hand	Horse chestnut
	Leaflets in pairs on leaf axis	Mountain ash

Further questions on page 276.

chapter 16

Why do we look like our parents?
Why do we have some of our mother's features and some of our father's features?

Inheritance is the way in which parents pass on their characteristics to their offspring.
The study of inheritance is known as **genetics**.

You should remember that parents pass on their genes to their offspring.

Genes from the father are inside the sperm nucleus.
Genes from the mother are inside the egg nucleus.
At **fertilisation** the nucleus of the sperm joins with the nucleus of the egg.
A new individual grows from the fertilised egg or zygote.

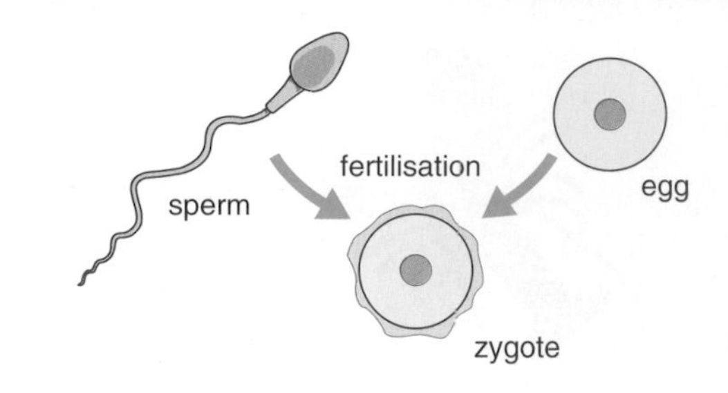

So half of the genes come from the father and half come from the mother.

▷ The material of inheritance

Inside nearly all cells there is a nucleus.
The nucleus contains thread-like **chromosomes**.
These chromosomes carry the **genes** that control all your characteristics.

Look at the picture of human chromosomes:

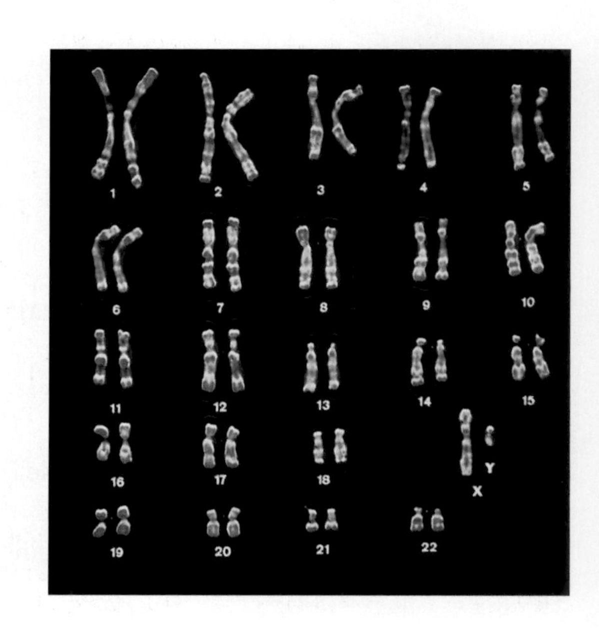

If you were to count them, you would find 46.
This full number of chromosomes is called the **diploid** number.
They are different shapes and sizes.
You can separate them into identical pairs.
Can you see how many pairs there are?

Chromosomes occur in pairs.
But there are different numbers of chromosomes for different species of animals and plants.
Humans have 23 pairs, cats have 19 pairs.
Fruit flies have only four pairs.

▷ What's a gene?

Each chromosome is made up of thousands of **genes** arranged like beads on a necklace.
It is the genes that carry the genetic information that affects how we grow and what we look like.
For instance there is a gene for eye colour, and others for hair colour and for height.

If we could unravel a chromosome, it would form an extremely long thread.
That thread is made up of a chemical called **DNA.**
DNA stands for **deoxyribonucleic acid.**
No wonder we call it DNA!

A single gene is made of a short length of DNA.
So the long thread that makes up a chromosome contains hundreds of genes.

A DNA molecule is made up of thousands of units, each called a **nucleotide**.
A single nucleotide is made up of three molecules :

- a phosphate
- a sugar
- a base

The sugar and phosphate molecules join up and form the backbone of the DNA strand.
The bases are attached to the sugar molecules.

In fact if you look at the diagram, you will see that DNA is made up of ***two*** strands of nucleotides.
It is rather like a ladder.
The sugars and phosphates make up the uprights of the ladder and the bases make up the rungs.
And then the whole molecule is twisted into a **double helix** – a bit like a spiral staircase.

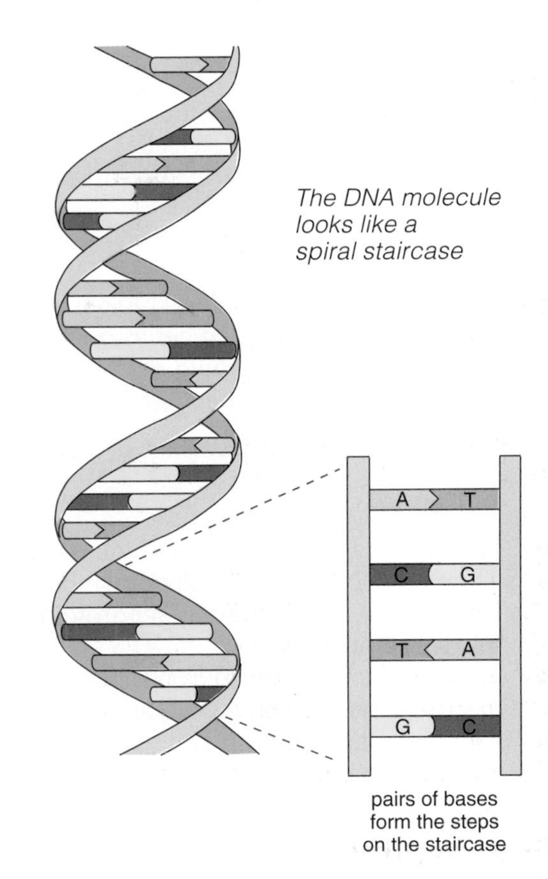

The DNA molecule looks like a spiral staircase

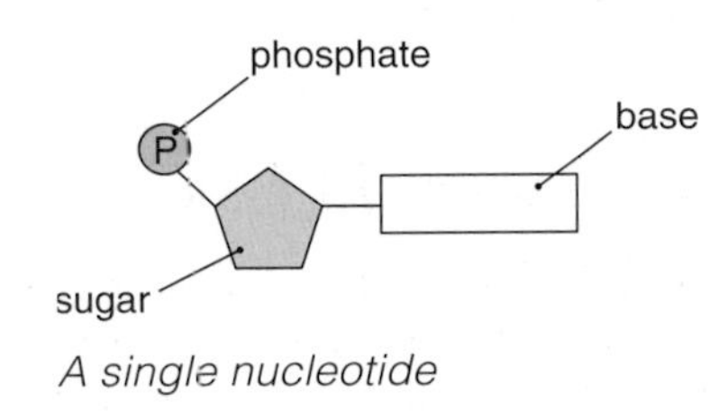

A single nucleotide

Base pairing

So how is the DNA molecule kept together?
If you look at the diagram you can see that the bases join together.
Each pair of bases is held together by hydrogen bonds.

There are four different bases in DNA : **thymine (T), adenine (A)**, **cytosine (C)** and **guanine (G).**

The bases always pair up in the same way :

> **Adenine (A) pairs with thymine (T).**
> **Cytosine (C) pairs with guanine (G).**

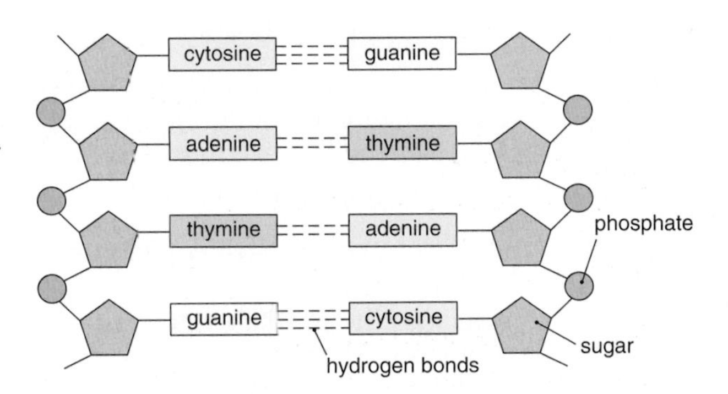

Although the hydrogen bonds holding the two chains of nucleotides together are weak, there are many of them.
So altogether they keep the 'double helix' in shape.

▷ Making new DNA

When a cell divides the chromosomes split length ways and each half enters the new cell.
Why do you think that this is important?

Each new cell must have the same chromosome number as the parent cell.

If the chromosomes are able to make exact copies of themselves then so must the genes and so must DNA. Otherwise the new cells would not have all the correct genetic information that they need.

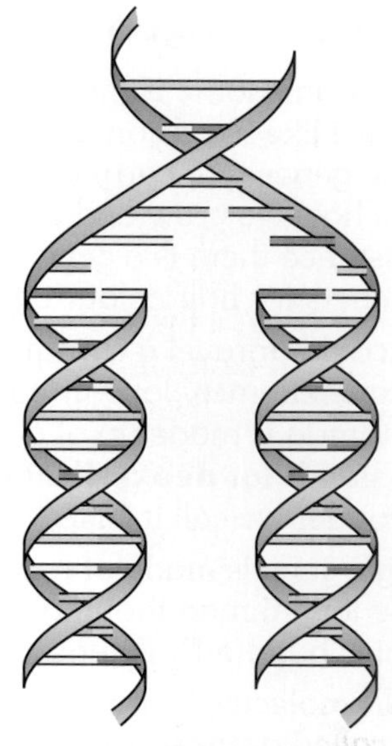
A DNA molecule making two identical copies

Before a cell divides, the amount of DNA contained inside its nucleus, doubles.
But how does this happen?

- Firstly the hydrogen bonds holding the bases together break.
- Then the DNA double helix unwinds to give two single strands.
- Each single strand attracts separate nucleotides present inside the nucleus.
- These nucleotides line up along each single DNA strand following the 'rule of base pairing'. So C lines up alongside G and A alongside T.
- The nucleotides join up and so two new DNA molecules are formed and each one is an identical copy of the parent cell's DNA.

Making proteins

To make a protein, lots of amino acids have to join together.
The type and sequence of the amino acids determines what the protein will be like.
For instance, it could be an enzyme, a hormone or a protein in muscle.

DNA is only found inside the nucleus.
Proteins are known to be made in structures called **ribosomes**, which are found in the cytoplasm of a cell.

So if DNA controls the making of a protein, how does the information get from the nucleus to the ribosomes?

The answer is another molecule called **ribonucleic acid (RNA)**.
This is formed in a similar way to the making of new DNA.
The **m-RNA** copies the base sequence on DNA and carries it out of the nucleus, through a nuclear pore to the ribosomes.

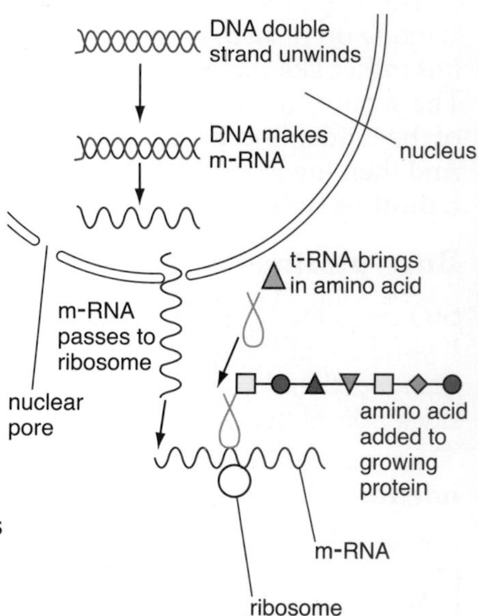

How DNA controls protein synthesis

Another type of RNA called **t-RNA** picks up amino acids and carries them to the ribosomes.
The t-RNA slots into the m-RNA and gives up its amino acid.
The amino acids bond together forming a long chain – the protein.
Each amino acid is coded for by a sequence of ***three*** bases.
The sequence of bases on DNA that codes for a protein is called the **genetic code.**

▷ Biology at work: The DNA detectives

Computer graphic representation of a DNA molecule

In the 1950s, a great deal of work was being carried out by scientists eager to discover the nature of DNA.

The American biochemist **Erwin Chargaff** analysed samples of DNA from different organisms.
He found that the amounts of adenine (A) were always equal to the amounts of thymine (T), and that the amounts of cytosine (C) were always equal to the amounts of guanine (G).

What conclusions can you draw from this evidence?

It suggests that adenine (A) pairs up with thymine (T) and that cytosine (C) pairs up with guanine (G).

Rosalind Franklin

About the same time **Rosalind Franklin** and **Maurice Wilkins** were working at King's College, London.
They used a technique called **X-ray diffraction** to work out how the atoms inside the DNA molecule were arranged.
It involves firing a beam of X-rays into crystals of DNA.
The X-rays hit the atoms and are scattered on to a photographic plate.
When the photographic plate is developed, it can help to build up a picture of what the 3-D structure of DNA is like.

The double helix

The molecular structure of DNA was finally worked out by **James Watson** and **Francis Crick**, working in Cambridge in 1953.
Watson was an American biochemist working in Britain and Crick was an English physicist, turned biochemist.
They used Chargaff's results and the X-ray diffraction pictures produced by Franklin and Wilkins.

They pieced together cut-out models of the molecules involved.
It took hours of discussion and painstaking manipulation of the model.
Eventually they were able to build a 3-D model of the structure of DNA.
It turned out to be a beautiful 'double helix' structure.
Furthermore, each half of the molecule could separate from the other and make an exact copy of itself.
This meant that chromosomes and genes could also make exact copies of themselves when cells divide.

Watson and Crick were so excited at their discovery that they dashed out of the Cavendish Laboratory and ran down the street looking for people to tell!

In 1958, Rosalind Franklin died of cancer.
In 1962, Francis Crick, James Watson and Maurice Wilkins were awarded the Nobel Prize for their work on DNA structure.
No doubt Rosalind Franklin would also have shared the prize if she had lived longer.

Watson and Crick with their DNA model

▷ Mitosis

You should remember that new cells are made by cell division.
Mitosis is a kind of cell division.
All cells are made by mitosis ***except*** the sex cells.
When a cell divides by mitosis it splits into two new **daughter cells**.
These daughter cells are identical to the cell that they came from and to each other.
Each has a diploid number of chromosomes.

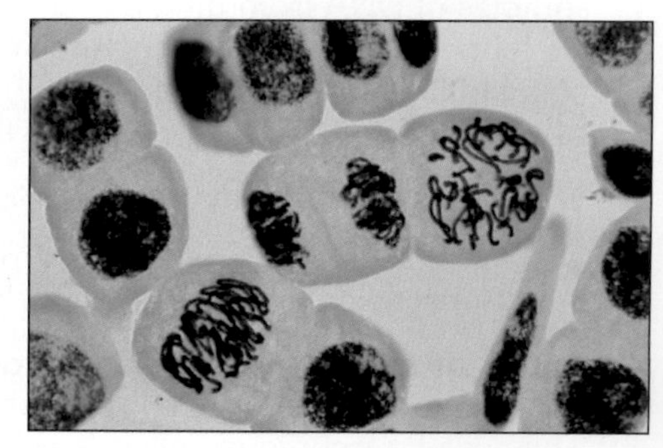
Cells dividing by mitosis

When does mitosis happen?

- Mitosis occurs in ***growth***.
  When living things grow they make new cells.
  Mitosis makes these new cells whether it is in the growth of a baby, the healing of a wound, the germination of a seedling, or replacing red blood cells.
- Mitosis also occurs in ***asexual reproduction***.
  The cells in the parent plant or animal divide to make new cells which form the new individual.

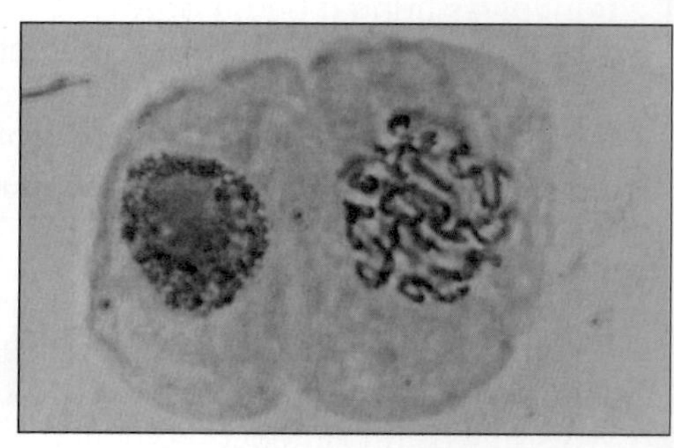
Chromosomes are visible in the cell on the right

Stages in mitosis

Before a cell can divide by mitosis it must make a second set of chromosomes.
What would happen if the cell split into two before it made a second set?
How many chromosomes would each daughter cell have?

In between cell divisions the chromosomes look like a tangle of threads.
When a cell is about to divide the chromosomes become clearly visible.

Let's look at what happens to ***one*** pair of chromosomes during mitosis:

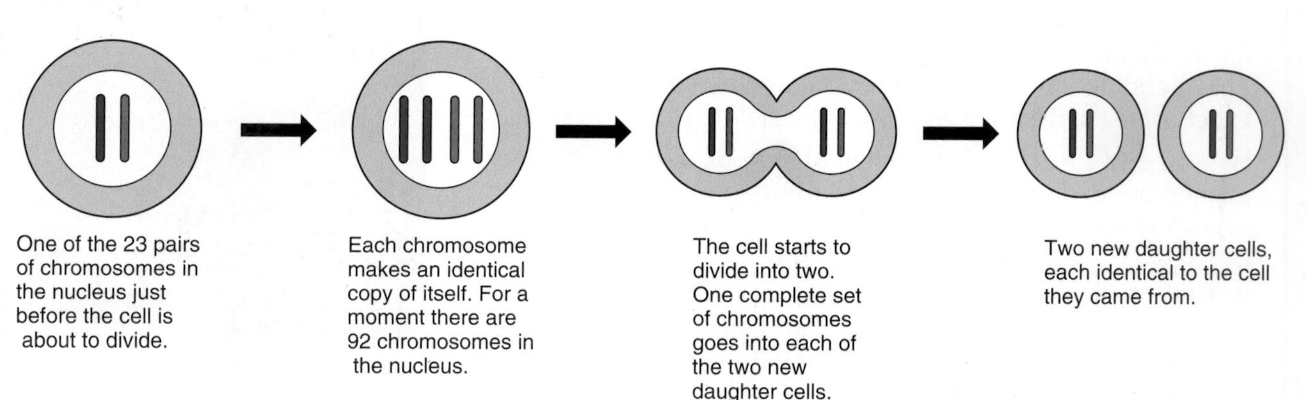

▷ Meiosis

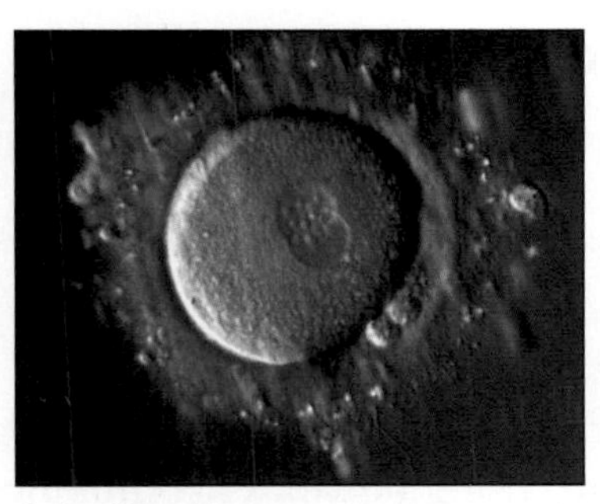
A fertilised human egg or zygote

If a sperm cell and an egg cell both had
46 chromosomes like other body cells,
what would happen at fertilisation?
The fertilised egg would have 92 chromosomes –
twice as many as it should have!

Fortunately sex cells, like sperm and eggs, are
made by a different kind of cell division.
This cell division is called **meiosis**.

Meiosis halves the number of chromosomes.
So egg cells and sperm cells only have 23 chromosomes each.
The fertilised egg will have 46 chromosomes, 23 from the
mother, in the egg, and 23 from the father, in the sperm.
Half the diploid number of chromosomes is called
the **haploid** number.

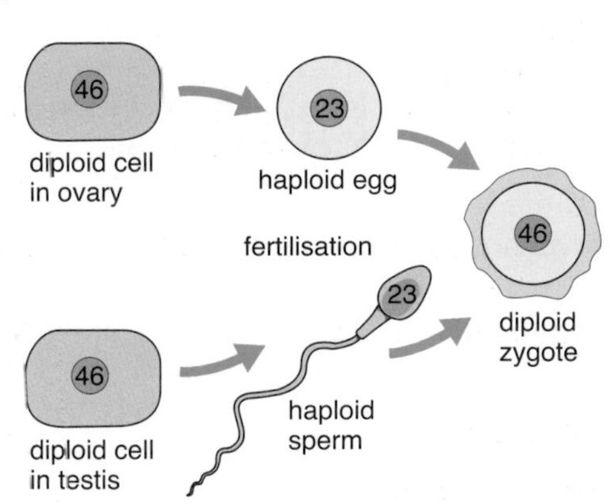

Where do you think meiosis occurs in a woman?
Where do you think meiosis occurs in a man?

Meiosis occurs in the sex organs.
The ovaries make eggs by meiosis.
The testes make sperm by meiosis.

Where do you think meiosis occurs in plants?

The anthers make pollen by meiosis.
The ovaries make egg cells by meiosis.

Let's look at what happens to ***one*** pair of chromosomes during
meiosis:

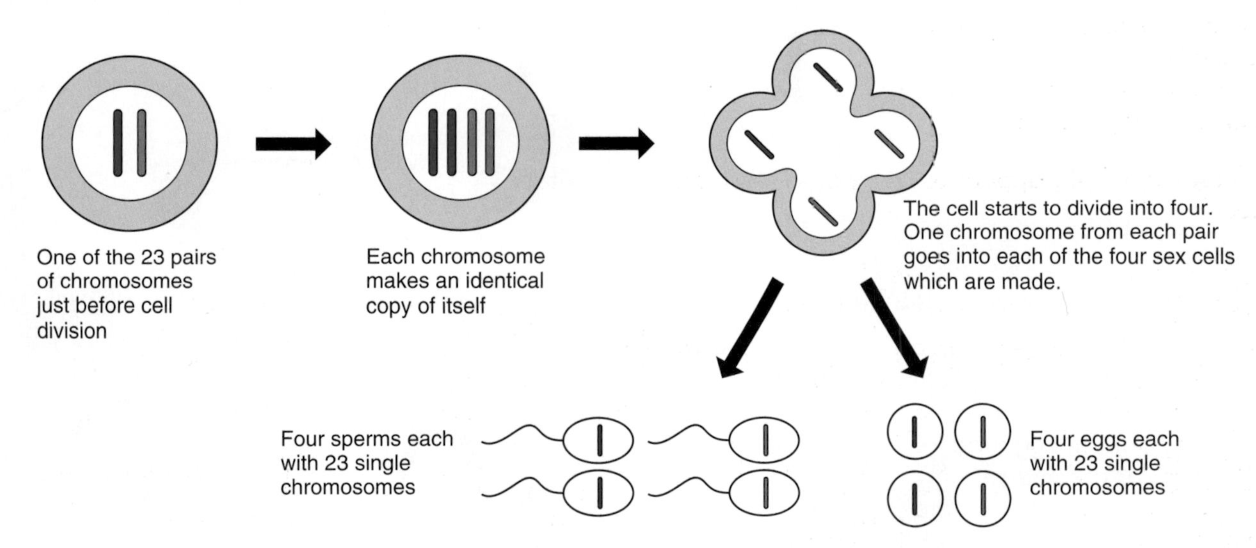

In meiosis the daughter cells are not identical.
They are genetically different and this contributes to variation.

▷ A boy or a girl ?

Your chromosomes also determine which sex you are.

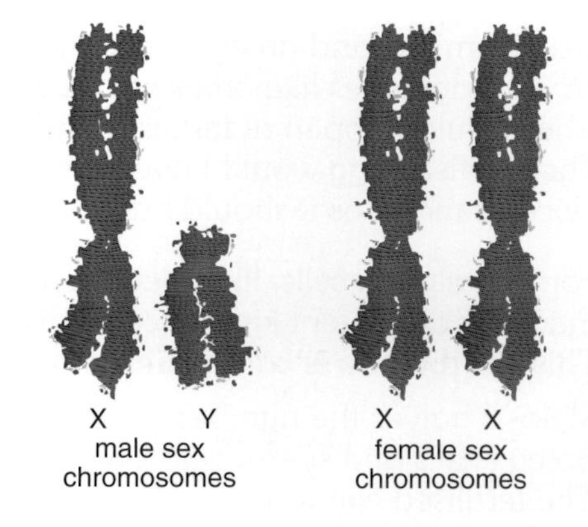

Can you remember how many chromosomes humans have?

46 – these occur in 23 pairs.
22 are matching pairs.
But the last pair sometimes do not match.

Pair 23 are called the **sex chromosomes**.
It is these that determine whether you are a boy or a girl.

If you are male, one of the sex chromosomes is longer than the other.
You will have one long **X chromosome** and one much shorter **Y chromosome**.

If you are female, your sex chromosomes look alike.
You will have two identical **X chromosomes**.

What happens to the chromosomes when eggs and sperm are made?

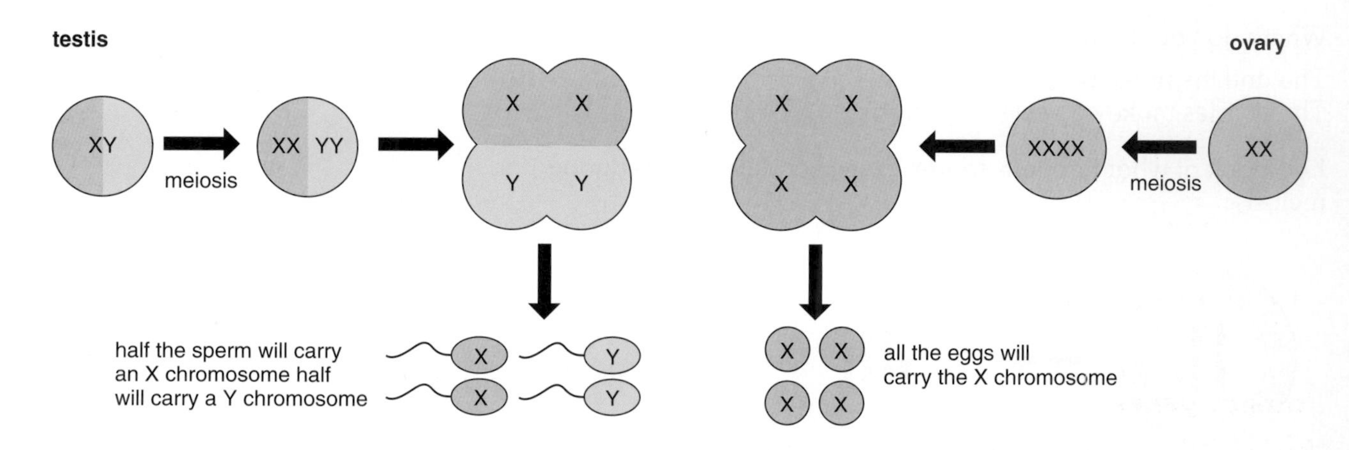

The diagram shows how sex is inherited:

All the eggs contain an X chromosome.
Half the sperm contain an X chromosome and half a Y chromosome.
At fertilisation, the egg may join with either an X sperm or a Y sperm.
Since there are equal numbers of X and Y sperm, the child has an equal chance of being a boy or a girl.

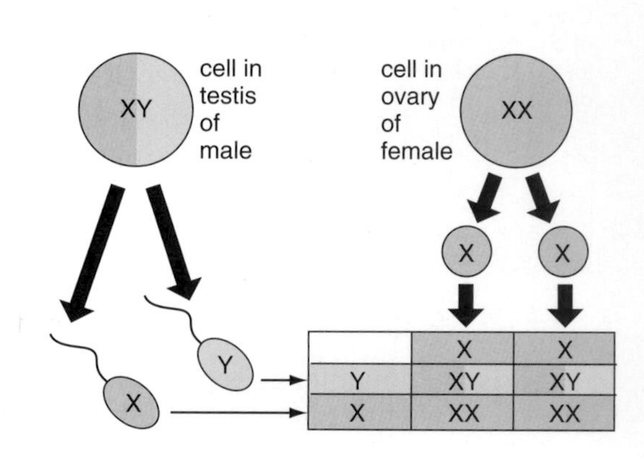

	X	X
Y	XY	XY
X	XX	XX

▷ Gregor Mendel

Gregor Mendel was an Austrian monk and teacher.
He was born in 1822, the son of a farmer.
At the monastery, Mendel kept a small garden plot where he experimented growing pea plants.
He studied the way their characteristics were passed on from one generation to the next, looking for patterns.

Mendel chose to study features that were easy to observe such as plant height, flower colour and seed shape.
Pea plants were also easy to grow and Mendel was able to either self-pollinate or cross-pollinate the flowers.

Mendel was painstaking in his methods : planning his work, and meticulously collecting and recording his results.
He was also able to analyse the huge amount of data that he built up and so come to sound scientific conclusions.

The amazing thing about Mendel's work is that he worked out the underlying rules of inheritance before anything had been discovered about DNA, genes or chromosomes.

Once scientists knew about chromosomes and genes, they could explain how Mendel's 'inherited factors' could be passed on from one generation to the next.
The importance of Mendel's work was not recognised until after his death.

Look at the diagram to see some of the characteristics that Mendel studied :

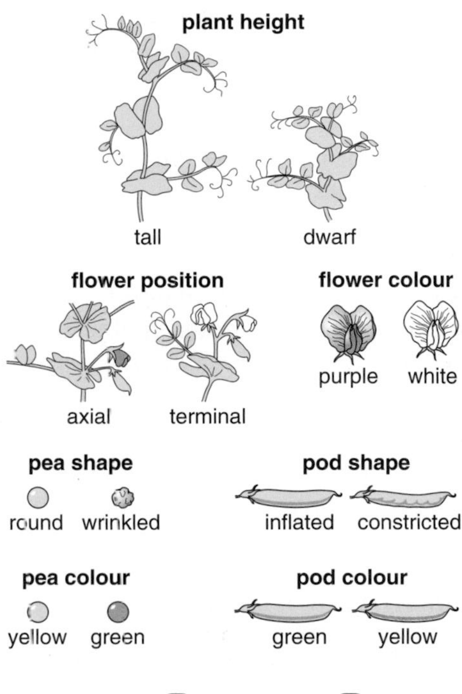

What do you notice ?

The characteristics that he studied were either one thing or another.
This suggests that they are controlled by a single gene.

Pairs of genes

You know that chromosomes occur in identical pairs.
So each chromosome in a pair must carry the same genes along its length.

Let's take a characteristic like hair colour.
The gene that controls hair colour lies on a particular chromosome.
But since chromosomes are in identical pairs – a partner chromosome must also carry a gene for hair colour.

So for a particular characteristic there must be ***two*** genes.
One on each chromosome in a pair.
So you have two genes for hair colour, two genes for eye colour, and so on.

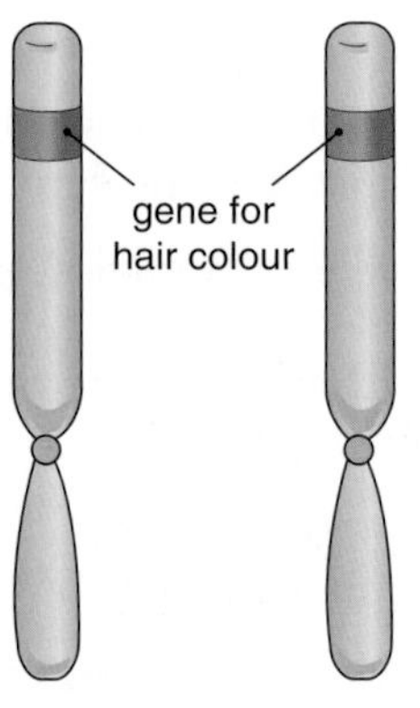

A pair of chromosomes

▷ More about genes

Do you remember how many genes there are for each characteristic?

You have ***two*** genes for each characteristic.
The two genes are found opposite each other on neighbouring chromosomes.

Let's look at the genes for eye colour.

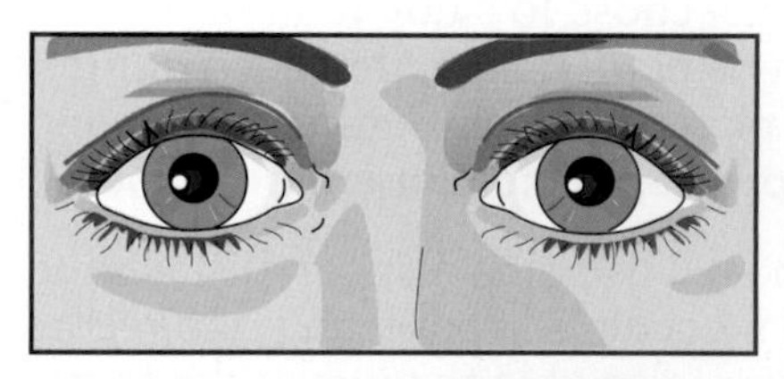

There are different forms of eye colour gene.
There is an eye colour gene that will give you blue eyes, one that will give you brown eyes, one that will give you green eyes, and so on.

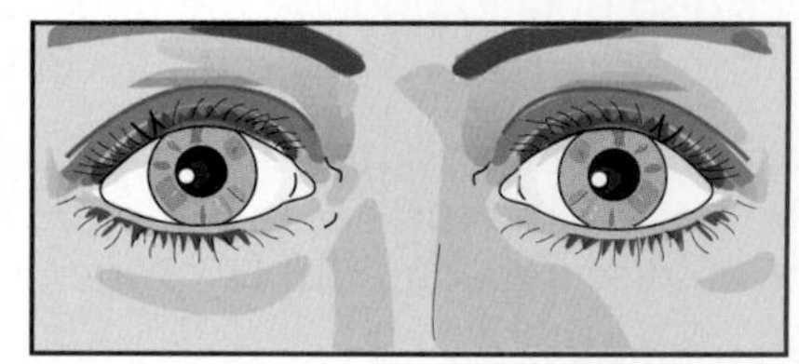

Different forms of the same gene are called **alleles**.

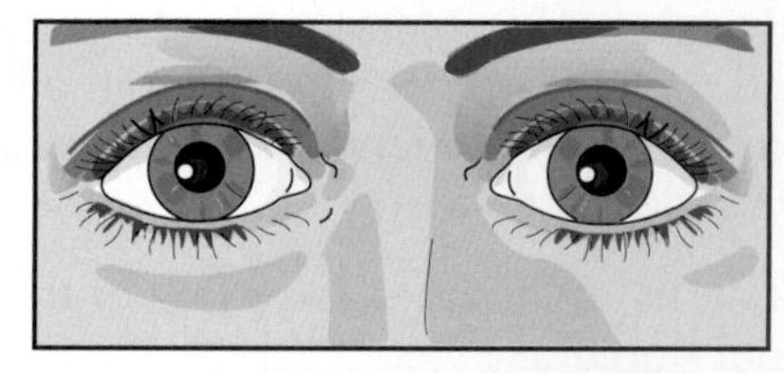

So instead of saying that you have two genes for eye colour you should really say that you have two alleles for eye colour.

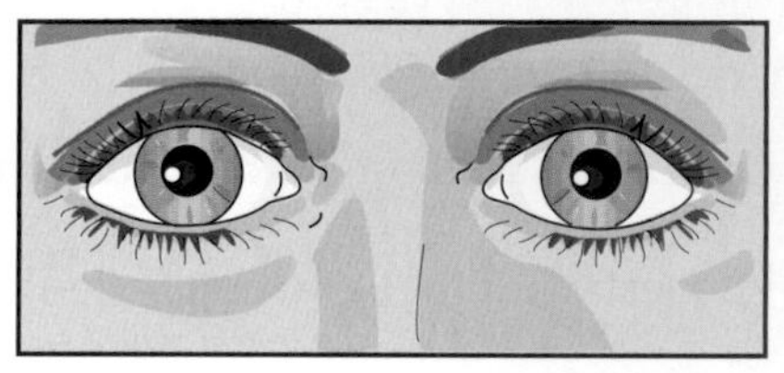

In actual fact, the inheritance of eye colour is controlled by a number of alleles.
But in the following examples, we will just use two alleles to simplify things.
So don't worry if you have brown eyes and both your parents have blue eyes!

Let's say that **B** is the symbol for brown allele.
Let's say that **b** is the symbol for blue allele.

If you have two **B** alleles, you will have brown eyes.

Your **genotype** refers to the alleles that you have.
Your **phenotype** refers to your appearance.

So your genotype is **BB**
and your phenotype is brown.

We say that you are **homozygous** for eye colour because ***both*** of your alleles are the same.

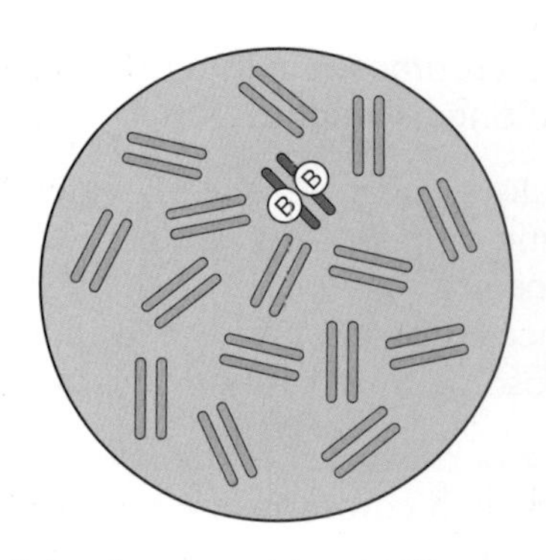

Both alleles for eye colour are the same : brown

▷ Dominant and recessive

If you have two **b** alleles, you will have blue eyes.

Your genotype is **bb**.
Your phenotype is blue.

You are **homozygous** for eye colour because both of your alleles are the same.

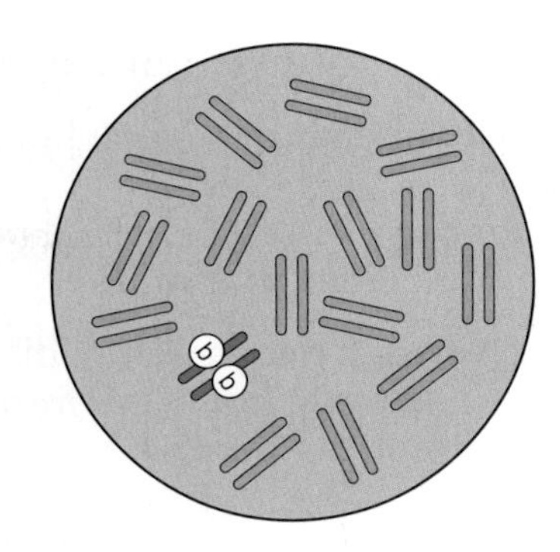

Both alleles for eye colour are the same : blue

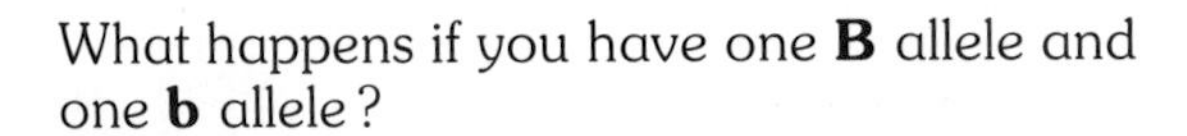

What happens if you have one **B** allele and one **b** allele ?

Your genotype is **Bb**.

We say that you are **heterozygous** for eye colour because your two alleles are different.

But what is your phenotype ?
Will you have one brown eye and one blue eye ?

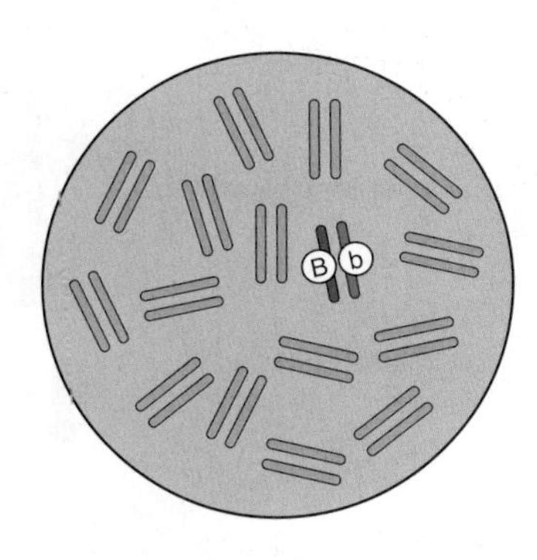

These alleles for eye colour are different : one brown and one blue

When there are two ***different*** alleles, one is stronger than the other.
The stronger allele masks the weaker one.
The brown allele is stronger than the blue allele and masks it.
So the person will have brown eyes.

We say that the brown allele is **dominant**.

We say that the blue allele is **recessive**.

Here are some examples of dominant and recessive characteristics :

Dominant	Recessive
freckles	no freckles
dark hair	light hair
tongue rollers	non-tongue rollers
free ear lobe	ear lobe joined
normal skin colour	albino

How do you inherit your eye colour?

You should remember that you have ***pairs*** of chromosomes.
One chromosome in each pair came from your ***father*** and one came from your ***mother***.

This means that for each pair of alleles that you have, one came from your ***father*** and one came from your ***mother***.

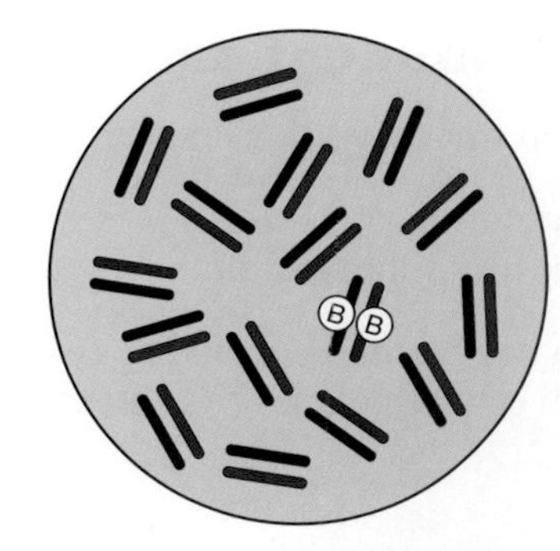

The black chromosomes come from the father and the red chromosomes come from the mother

What happens if a mother and a father are both heterozygous for brown eyes?
What colour eyes will their children have?

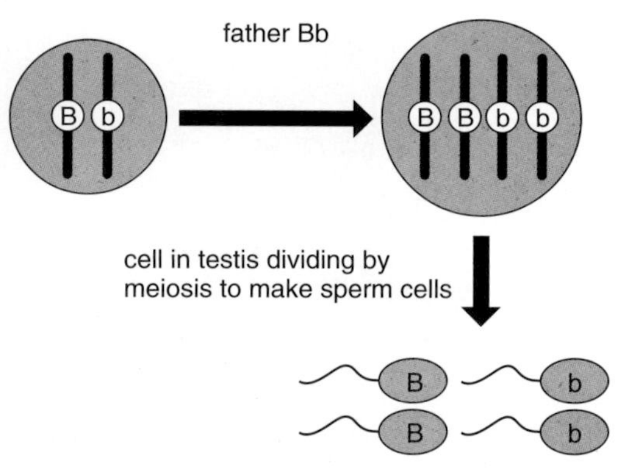

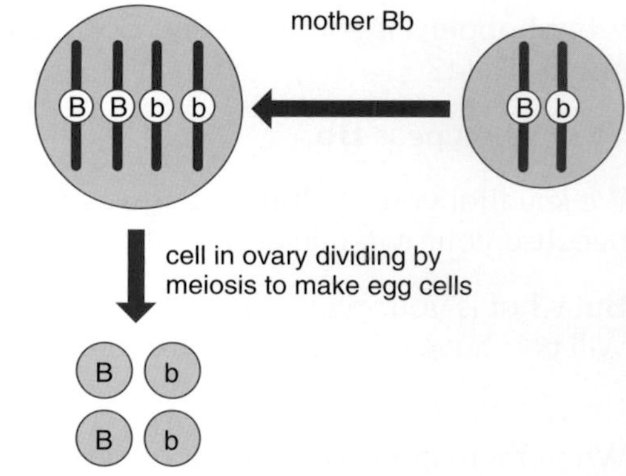

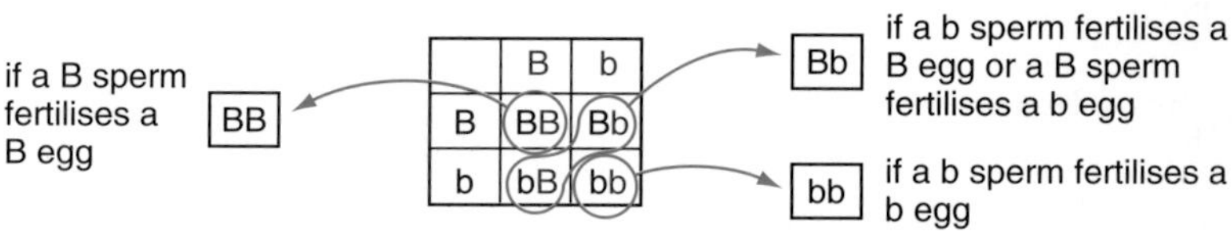

	B	b
B	BB	Bb
b	bB	bb

So two heterozygous brown-eyed parents could have brown-eyed or blue-eyed children.
Which are they more likely to have?

What would happen if the mother was homozygous blue-eyed and the father was homozygous brown-eyed?

What would happen if the mother was homozygous blue-eyed and the father was heterozygous brown-eyed?

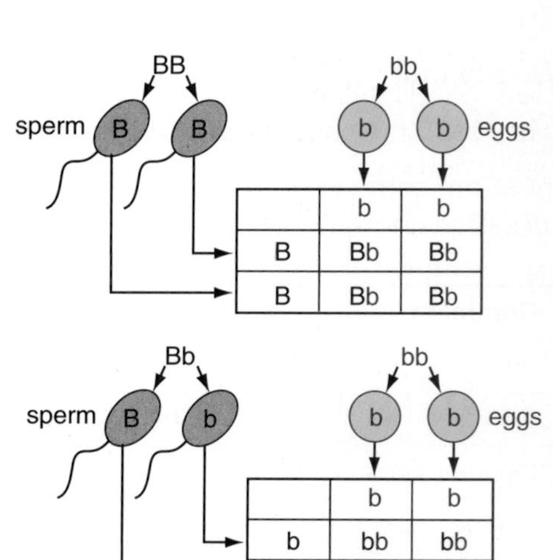

	b	b
B	Bb	Bb
B	Bb	Bb

	b	b
b	bb	bb
B	Bb	Bb

▷ Genes in action

Suppose that you went in for plant breeding.
You want to breed a plant with red flowers with a plant with white flowers.
What do you do?

You take some pollen from the red flower and put it onto the stigma of the white flower.
This is called carrying out a **cross**.
After the seeds develop you grow them into new plants.
They all turn out to be red.
How can you explain this?

Sweet pea flowers show variation

The picture gives an explanation:

There are two alleles for flower colour.
R codes for red and **r** codes for white.
The red flowers were homozygous red (**RR**).
The white flowers were homozygous white (**rr**).

The pollen grains contained only ***one*** allele **R**.
The eggs also contained just ***one*** allele **r**.
So after fertilisation all the offspring were **Rr**.
They are heterozygous red, because the red allele was dominant.

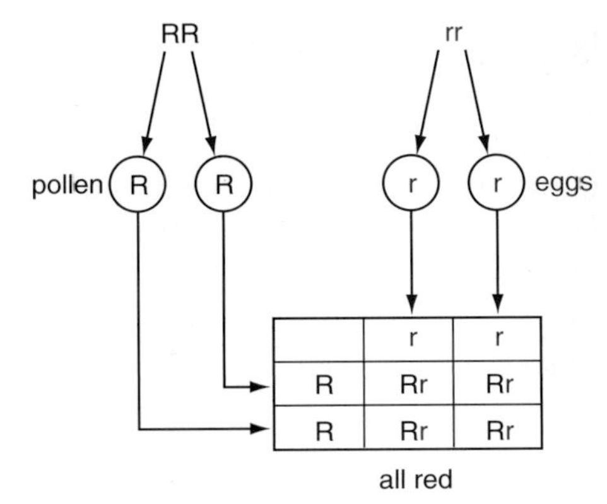

Taking it further

Suppose you breed the offspring of this first cross.
This time you cross a plant with red flowers (**Rr**) with another with red flowers (**Rr**).
Both plants will be heterozygous.
The result is a mixture of red flowers and white flowers.
How can you explain this?

This time each plant made pollen or eggs half of which contained the red allele **R** and half the white allele **r**.
The alleles can now pair up in four different ways at fertilisation:

1 × **RR** – gives red
2 × **Rr** – gives red
1 × **rr** – gives white.

So there will be three red flowers to one white flower.

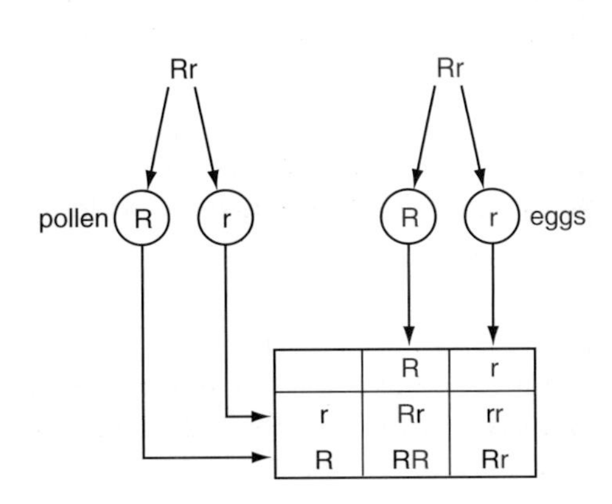

▷ More crosses

Does the same thing happen in animals?

Let's look at the inheritance of coat colour in mice.

There are grey mice and white mice.
We can show the grey allele as **G**.
We can show the white allele as **g**.

What happens if you cross a homozygous grey mouse with a homozygous white mouse?
The picture shows you:

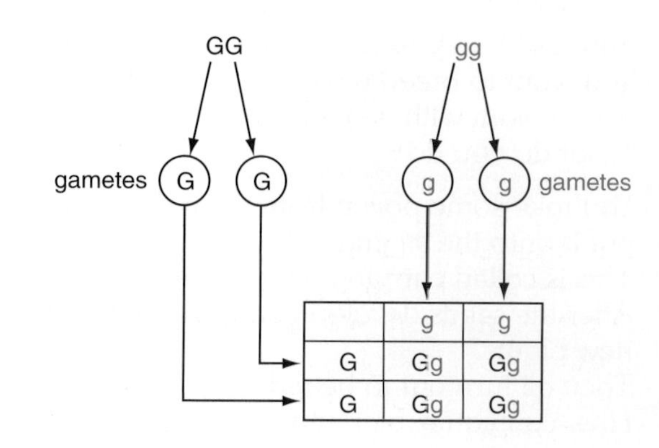

All the offspring are grey.
So the grey allele **G** is dominant to the white allele **g**.

Now cross two heterozygous grey mice (**Gg**):

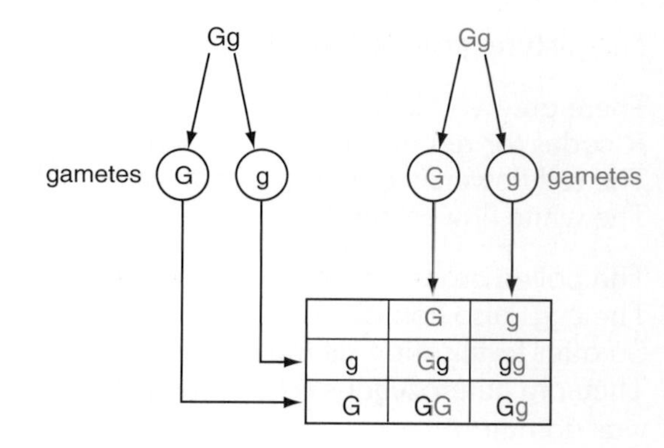

There are three grey offspring to one white offspring.
The white offspring must have two recessive alleles – it must be homozygous white (**gg**).
But the grey can be either homozygous grey (**GG**) or heterozygous grey (**Gg**).

The ratio of the phenotypes is three grey : one white.
The ratio of the genotypes is 1**GG** : 2**Gg** : 1**gg**.

Test cross

But how can we tell if a grey mouse is homozygous (**GG**) or heterozygous (**Gg**)?
Not just by looking at it.

How do we know if our red flowers are homozygous (**RR**) or heterozygous (**Rr**)?

We have to carry out a **test cross**.
This means that we cross the unknown parent with a homozygous recessive parent. That is with a white mouse or a white flowered plant.

Again let's use the picture to explain:

If our red flower is homozygous (**RR**), crossing it with a white flower (**rr**) gives all red flowers (**Rr**).
If our red flower is heterozygous (**Rr**), crossing it with a white flower (**rr**) gives half red and half white.

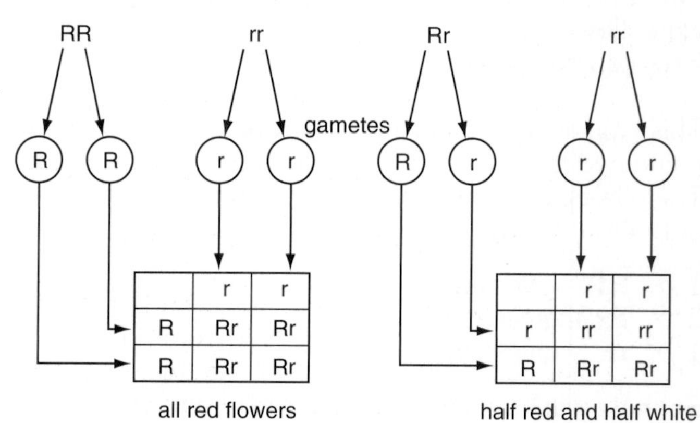

▷ Mutations

A **mutation** is a change in a gene or a chromosome.
It can cause a change in a characteristic.
Sometimes this change can be harmful, but sometimes mutations can be neutral or even beneficial.

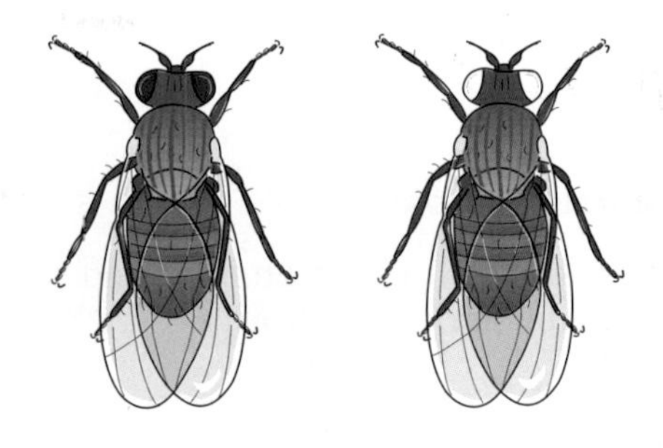

One of the first mutations studied was in the fruit-fly.
The normal eye colour is red.
But a **mutant** white eye form was discovered.
A gene controlling eye colour had suddenly changed.
This was due to a change in the DNA base sequence.
The gene no longer coded for the production of red eye colour. It now coded for white eyes.

A similar example occurs in **albinos**.
A gene controls production of the skin pigment **melanin**.
This protects the skin from ultra-violet light.
It also gives you a suntan and freckles!

In albinos, the structure of a gene changes or **mutates**.
So it no longer codes for the production of melanin.
Albinos occur in other animals too.
Can you think how this hedgehog could be at a disadvantage?

Imagine what would happen if a pathogen, like a bacterium, developed a mutation that gave it resistance to an antibiotic.
The mutant gene codes for an enzyme (protein) that breaks down the antibiotic.
So the bacterium increases in numbers out-competing non-resistant forms.
Good for the bacterium, but not for us!

Gene mutations are usually recessive.
They can be hidden by a dominant allele.
As you will see on the next page, **cystic fibrosis** is a disease caused by a gene mutation.

Mutations can occur naturally at random.
But it is now known that radiation and some chemicals can cause mutations.
Ultra-violet radiation and X-rays and gamma rays are the most damaging.
The greater the dose of radiation, the greater the chance of mutation.
Atom bombs were dropped on Japan at the end of the Second World War.
This exposed people to massive doses of radiation.
The result was an increase in the rate of mutations.
Many babies were born with defects and over a number of years people developed various cancers..

Hiroshima in March, 1946

▷ Inherited diseases

Genes pass on characteristics from one generation to the next.
Some people inherit 'faulty' genes that can cause disease.

Cystic fibrosis

This is an example of an inherited disease caused by gene mutation.

About one child in every 2000 is affected by cystic fibrosis.
They produce thick, sticky mucus.
This can block the air passages and the tubes that carry digestive juices to the gut.
So the child sometimes has difficulty breathing and absorbing food.

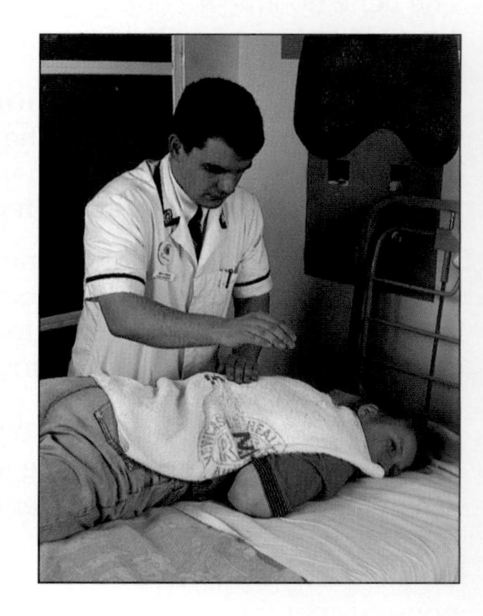

Patients are treated by chest physiotherapy.
The mucus is a good breeding ground for germs.
Sufferers often get infections and have to be treated with strong antibiotics.
Each infection leaves the lungs more damaged and the child becomes more ill.

Scientists are experimenting with ways to replace the faulty gene with a normal one.
Inhalers are used to spray millions of copies of the correct gene into cells lining the lungs.
This technique, called **gene therapy**, can relieve the condition (see page 257).

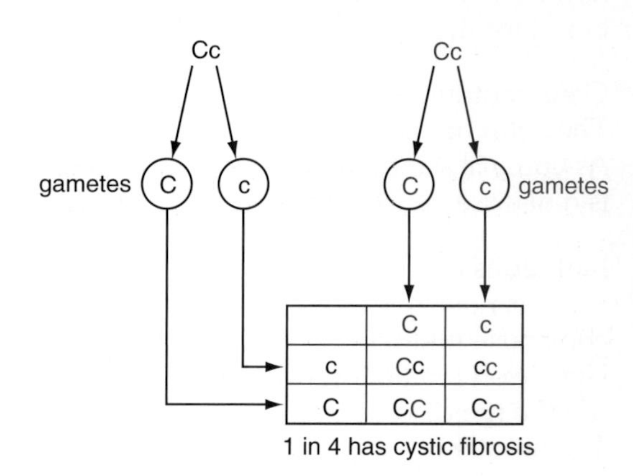

1 in 4 has cystic fibrosis

Cystic fibrosis is caused by a recessive allele.
Let's call it **c**.
So to have the disease a person must have ***two*** recessive alleles (**cc**).
Heterozygous people (**Cc**) do not get the disease.
But they can act as **carriers** and pass it on to their children.

For instance, if a father is a carrier (**Cc**) and a mother is a carrier (**Cc**), what would be the chances of their child having cystic fibrosis?

You can see from the diagram that there would be a 1 in 4 chance of their child inheriting the disease.

▷ More inherited diseases

Huntington's disease

This is a rare inherited disease.
It affects about 1 in 20 000.
It shows up when the patient is about 30 to 40 years old.
The cells of the brain degenerate and the patient makes clumsy and jerky movements.
Sufferers become moody and depressed.
Their memory is affected and they eventually become totally disabled.

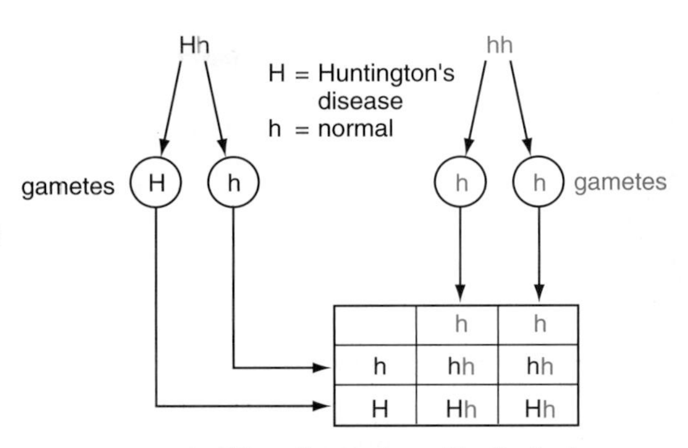

half the offspring have Huntington's

Huntington's disease is caused by a dominant gene.
So only ***one*** allele is necessary to give the disease.
So all heterozygous people are sufferers.
Because the onset of the disease occurs so late, many people may have produced a family before finding that they have the condition.

Sickle cell anaemia

Sickle cell anaemia is an inherited disease of the blood.

Look at these two photographs of red blood cells :

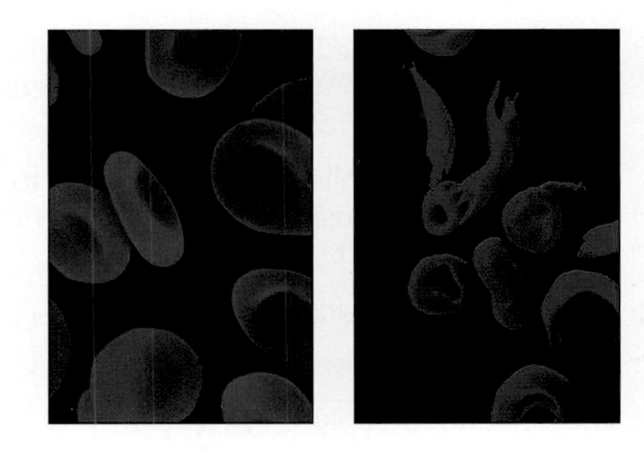

What differences can you see ?

The blood on the right is from a person suffering from sickle cell anaemia.
Can you see that the red cells are an odd shape ?
They have formed an S-shape like a sickle.

These red cells have abnormal haemoglobin.
This makes it difficult for the red cells to carry oxygen.
This inherited disease is common in West Africa.

Sickle cell anaemia is caused by a recessive allele.
The child inherits the allele from each parent and is homozygous recessive.

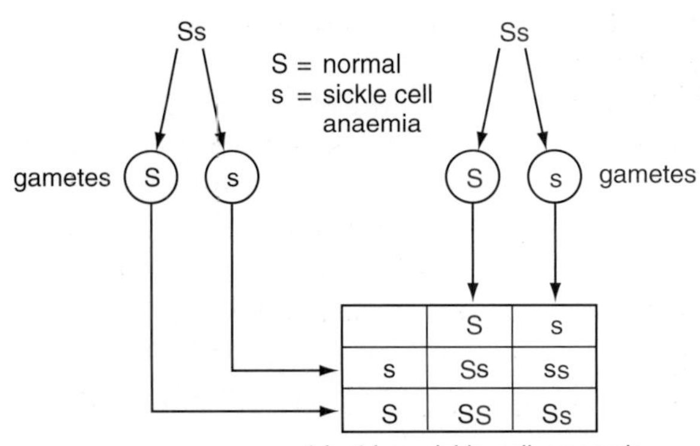

1 in 4 has sickle cell anaemia

The interesting thing is that the heterozygous individual becomes resistant to **malaria**.
Malaria is a fatal disease caused when a microbe gets into red cells (see page 153).
The microbes don't affect sickle shaped blood cells in the same way.
So being heterozygous or a **carrier** can be an advantage in malarial regions.

▷ Genetic engineering

Many inherited diseases are caused when the body can not make a particular protein.

For instance, people with haemophilia can not make the protein Factor 8.
Diabetics can not make the protein insulin.

Genetic engineering can be used to make large amounts of these proteins.

Genetic engineering means removing a gene from one living organism and putting it into another.
This is how it has been used to help diabetics :

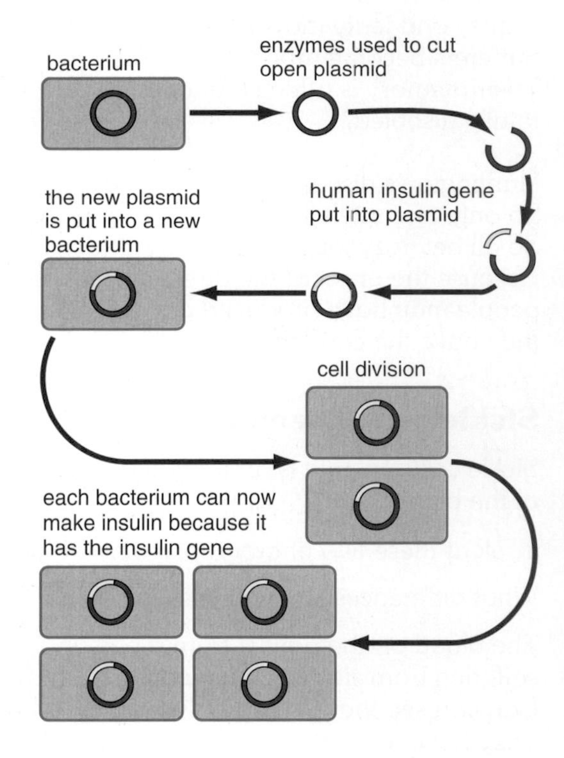

- The human gene that codes for the production of insulin is identified.
- **Restriction enzymes** act as 'chemical scissors' to cut the insulin-making gene from the rest of the DNA.
- A circular piece of DNA called a **plasmid** is removed from a bacterium.
- The same restriction enzymes are used to cut open the plasmid.
- The two ends of the DNA of the insulin-making gene are an exact match with the two DNA ends of the plasmid. These are called '**sticky ends**'.
- Another enzyme called a **ligase** is used to attach the sticky ends of the insulin-making gene to the sticky ends of the plasmid.
- The plasmid is put into a bacterium.
- The bacterium makes insulin.
- The bacteria multiply very rapidly.
  All the bacteria produced will have the insulin gene.
  Lots of insulin will be made.

Genetic engineering makes it possible to make insulin quickly and cheaply on a large scale. The bacteria are grown inside huge industrial fermenters called **bioreactors**.
The microbes grow quickly under ideal conditions.
Each bacterium is an identical **genetic clone** with a copy of the insulin-making gene.
The insulin is extracted and purified.

Before genetic engineering, diabetics had to use insulin that had been extracted from sheep or pigs.
This often produced reactions since it was different from human insulin.
Genetic engineering has made it possible to produce large amounts of safer drugs much more quickly.

Transgenic animals

Transgenic sheep

Transgenic organisms have had genes from another organism transferred into them.
Tracey is a transgenic sheep. She looks healthy and normal, except that she has had a human gene inserted into her DNA. The gene codes for the production of a very special protein. Scientists transferred the gene for the protein into a fertilised sheep's egg and the egg divided to form an embryo. Each time the cells divided, the gene was copied. Eventually Tracey was born with each of her cells containing the gene.
The protein is contained in Tracey's milk, from which it can be extracted and purified. The protein is valuable since it could be used to treat the human lung disease cystic fibrosis.

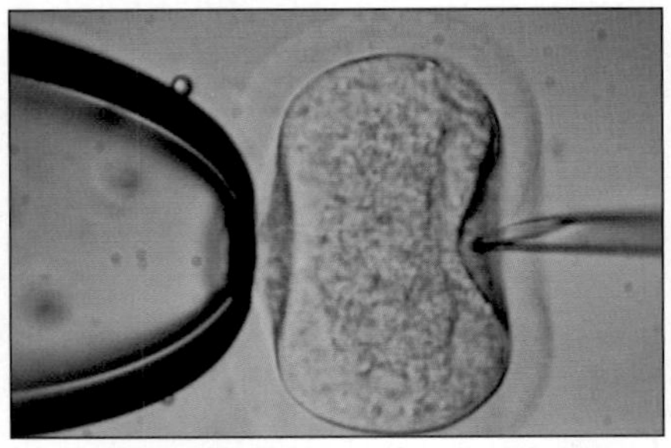
Injecting genes into a fertilised egg

Haemophiliacs lack the protein Factor 8 that helps the blood to clot. Transgenic sheep have been used to make this factor in their milk, from which it can be purified. So called 'designer milk' has been produced containing human antibodies and low cholesterol.

Transgenic plants

'Foreign' genes can also be introduced into plant cells. The soil bacterium, *Agrobacterium tumefaciens*, has been used as a **vector**, to transfer useful genes, like those for herbicide resistance and disease resistance into crop plants (as shown in the diagram).

1. Plasmid extracted from bacterium

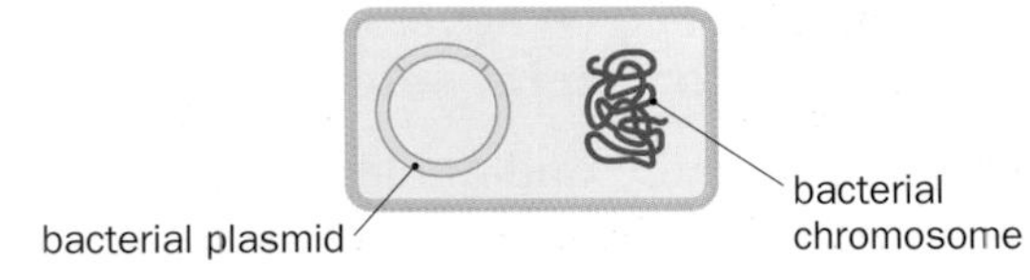

2. Useful gene inserted into plasmid

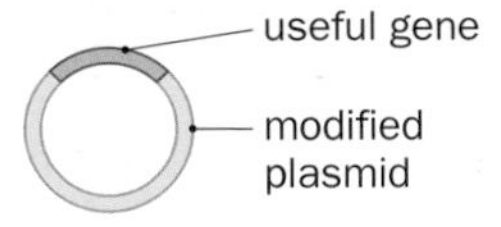

3. The modified plasmid is put back into the bacterium

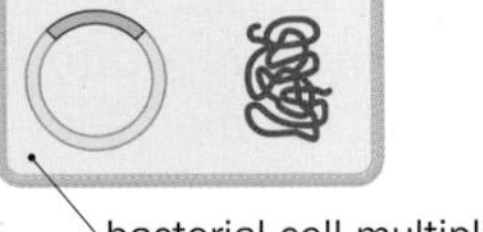

4. Bacterium infects the plant and the useful gene is inserted to one of the plant's chromosomes

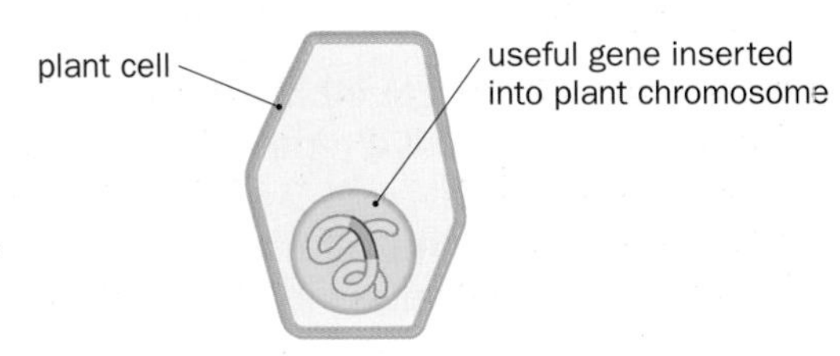

Genes from resistant plants have also been introduced into soya bean plants and so increase their resistance to herbicides. The crop is sprayed to kill the weeds, leaving the soya plants unaffected. This leads to an increase in yield due to reduced competition for nutrients and space, but has the potential to affect the environment (see page 261).

Legume plants, such as peas, beans and clover, have nitrogen-fixing bacteria in their roots. These can convert atmospheric nitrogen into nitrates (see page 314).
Soon it may be possible to transfer the nitrogen-fixing gene into plants such as wheat and rice. Such plants would no longer need artificial fertilisers, since they would be able to fix their own nitrogen. This could limit the use of fertilisers, which can harm the environment.

Genes controlling vitamin A production have been taken from carrots and put into rice. This has helped to solve the problem in countries that rely on rice, but are lacking in vitamin A.

Resistance to insect pests has been bred into some plants by inserting the toxin-producing genes from a bacterium into them. They then produce the toxin which kills off the insect pests.

▷ Selective breeding

People have grown crops and kept animals for thousands of years.
Only fairly recently has genetics been used to 'improve' particular plants and animals.
What is meant by 'improving' animals and plants?

Imagine that you have one plant with huge strawberries that catches diseases easily and one plant that is disease-resistant but only makes small strawberries.
How could you improve your strawberry crop?
First select plants with the desired characteristics. Then cross breed them and select suitable offspring over many generations.
Eventually large, disease-resistant strawberries are produced.

It has been possible through plant breeding to grow crops that have a greater yield, grow faster and are resistant to disease.

In genetic terms, humans rather than the environment determine which genes are passed on to future generations and which are lost.

For example, cattle have been selectively bred (also called **artificial selection**) for two reasons:

- For quantity and quality of their meat. These breeds would include the Hereford and Aberdeen Angus.
- For their milk yield. These breeds would include Jersey and Guernsey cattle.

Hereford cattle are bred for their meat

Techniques such as artificial insemination and embryo transplantation have increased the success of selective breeding of animals (see page 219).

In a similar way, Merino sheep have been selectively bred for their wool.They have been particularly successful since being introduced to Australia from Southern Europe.
Down sheep, on the other hand, have been selectively bred for their meat.

Cereals such as barley and wheat have been bred from grasses.
Increasing the yields of these crops has provided more food.
Also plant breeding programmes have made these crops more resistant to diseases and frost, and even controlled the height to which they grow to aid mechanical harvesting.

Merino sheep in Australia

The danger of selective breeding is too much inbreeding.
This involves selective reproduction between closely related organisms.
This may result in harmful recessive alleles being passed on to the descendants and a reduction in variation.

▷ Biology at work: The human genome project and embryo screening

The human genome project

The **human genome** is a name for all the sets of genes contained in our chromosomes.

The **Human Genome Project** was set up in 1990 and involved scientists from Britain, France, Germany, Japan, China and the US. They set out to decipher the 3 billion bits of DNA containing our genes. They intend to unravel the structure of each gene and the protein for which it codes.

But why do we need to be able to decode the human genome?

Many diseases are caused by tiny mutations in our genes. Like misprints, they pass on the wrong information to our cells. These mutations may be inherited or due to environmental causes such as radiation or pollution.

Some of the biggest killers like heart disease and cancers are thought to result from environment, life style and a whole series of genes. If we can identify these genes then early treatments can be targeted.

Cancer experts have already started to catalogue the DNA changes in cancer cells in the hope of developing new treatments. Gene therapies for diseases like cystic fibrosis and Alzheimer's disease are being trialed.
(Your teacher can give you some internet links for more details.)

Dr John Sulston, Director of the Sanger Centre in Cambridge, where the British genome work was based

Embryo screening and amniocentesis

Embryo screening is a technique that involves checking embryos created by *in vitro* fertilisation (IVF) for genetic abnormalities.
Usually a single cell is taken from the embryo and analysed for genetic conditions such as cystic fibrosis and Down's syndrome.
In 2004, The Human Fertilisation and Embryology Authority ruled that screening could be used to choose an embryo with a tissue type that matches a seriously ill brother or sister, creating a so-called 'designer baby'. So, for instance a healthy embryo could be selected with a tissue type that matches a child with leukaemia. The embryo would then be implanted into the mother and when it was born, stem cells from its umbilical cord would be used to treat the sick child.
The pro-life charity, *Life*, takes the view that: 'It can never be right to manufacture human beings to repair other human beings'.

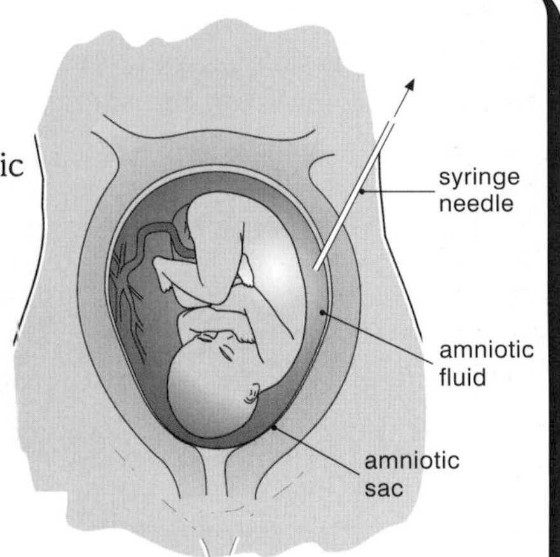

Amniocentesis

Amniocentesis is a longer-established technique.
A long syringe-like needle is inserted into the amniotic sac that surrounds the fetus. A sample of amniotic fluid, which contains fetal cells, is taken. The fluid is centrifuged, to throw down the cells, which are then stained and examined under the microscope.
Chromosome abnormalities, like the one causing Down's syndrome, can be identified.
Down's syndrome is caused by a chromosome mutation.
A woman produces an egg with 24 chromosomes instead of the normal 23.
If the egg is fertilised the baby will have 47 chromosomes – one more than normal.

▷ Biology at work: Genetic fingerprinting

The DNA in your cells is as unique as your fingerprints.
Unless you have an identical twin your 'genetic fingerprint' is different from anyone else's.

Scientists take a sample of blood or hair and extract DNA from it.
Sections of the DNA can be used to produce a pattern rather like a bar-code.
Everyone's bar-code will be different.

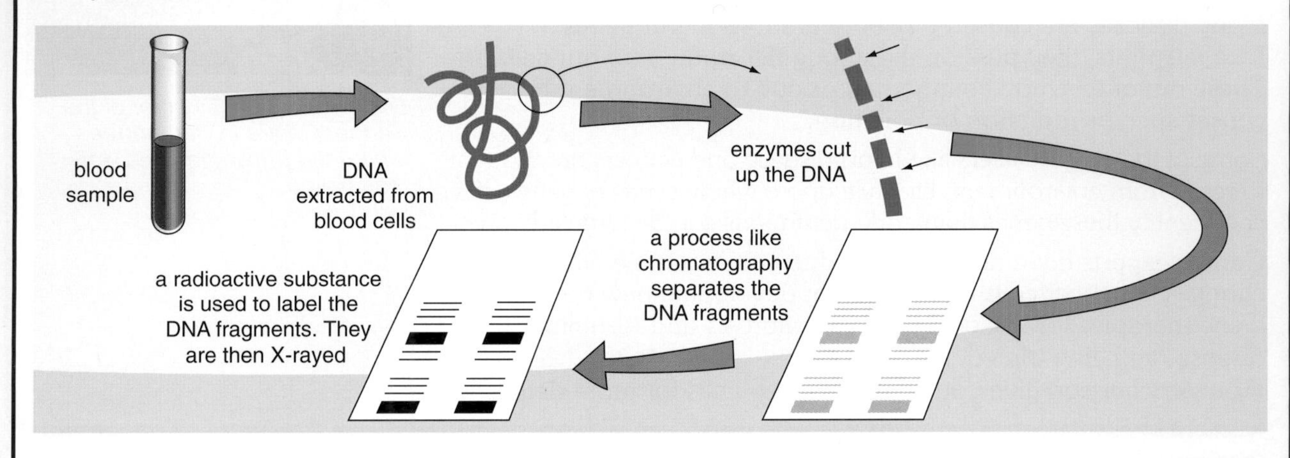

Genetic fingerprinting can be used to solve crimes.
The bar-code of a suspect may match up with a sample taken from the scene of a crime.

Look at the genetic fingerprints in the picture :

Compare them with that of a sample taken from the murder scene.
Are any of the suspects guilty ?

Can you think of any other uses for genetic fingerprinting ?

One of the first times that this technique was used was in the case of a Ghanaian family.
The mother said that her son had been born in Britain and had emigrated to Ghana to be with his father.
When he wanted to return to Britain the authorities claimed that he was not the woman's real son.

How do you think genetic fingerprinting was used to solve this case ?

▷ Biology at work: Genetically modified foods

Genetically modified (GM) foods are the result of the rapid developments that have taken place over recent years in genetic engineering.
Using specialised enzymes, it is now possible to cut out specific DNA sections and transfer them into plant cells.
These beneficial genes can give the plant advantages such as resistance to disease, increased yield or better taste.

Most people have probably already eaten genetically modified food products such as vegetarian cheese, tomato puree and soya. But in 1999 research into GM potatoes prompted debate and public concern about the safety of GM foods.

Greenpeace activists removing GM maize in Norfolk.

GM foods – the benefits

Scientists and the biotechnology companies have been quick to stress the safety of GM foods and their benefits :

- **Solving global hunger** – genetic modification could feed more people if crops are produced that are able to tolerate frost, drought and salty soils. Food production could be increased in marginal areas. Genes are not harmful to eat since we digest all the DNA in our food.
- **Environmentally friendly** – GM crops can be resistant to insects, weeds and diseases so there would be less use of pesticides.
  Also genes that improve nitrogen uptake would mean less need for chemical fertilisers and lessen the environmental threat they cause.
- **Consumer benefits** – GM foods have already been produced with an improved flavour and better keeping qualities.
  They are easier to produce and require fewer additives.

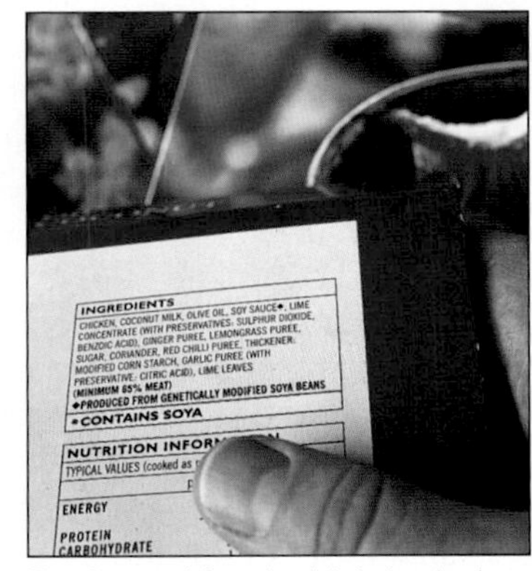

Packaged food which includes soy sauce made from GM soya beans

GM foods – the concerns

- **Environmental safety** – there are worries that new GM plants will become successful weeds. Pollen from GM crops resistant to weed-killers may be transferred to other plants by insects or the wind.
- **Food safety** – how would you like to eat food that contains foreign genes ? These new gene combinations may have effects that are so far unknown. They may result in harmful substances being produced. Has enough research been carried out on the chances of this happening ?
- **Changes in farming structure** – there may be an increase in the trends towards larger farms that are more capital intensive. This would disadvantage smaller, less economical farms.
- **Biodiversity** – increasingly fewer companies will control plant breeding, reducing the number of plant varieties and wild relatives.
- **Animal health** – at present there are no products of animal biotechnology in food shops. Any developments in animal production that affect animal welfare are increasingly likely to be resisted.

Assessing disease resistance in GM rice under glasshouse conditions

Summary

- Genetic information is passed on in the genes which are found on the chromosomes.
- A gene is made up of a short length of DNA.
- Two genes called alleles code for a particular character.
- In a homozygous individual both alleles are the same.
- In a heterozygous individual the alleles are different.
- Cells divide by mitosis so that growth takes place and by meiosis to produce gametes. Meiosis brings about genetic variation, while mitosis produces clones.
- The sex chromosomes determine what sex you are.
- Some alleles are dominant, while others are recessive.
- The phenotype of some offspring will be the same but their genotype may differ.
- Mutations can occur suddenly in genes and chromosomes.
  Some types of radiation and some chemicals can increase the rate of mutations.
- Some 'faulty' genes that can cause disease may be inherited.
- Genetic engineering has made it possible to make large amounts of safer drugs more quickly and cheaply.
- Some species of plants and animals have been 'improved' by selective breeding.

▷ Questions

1. Copy and complete:
Inside the nucleus are thread-like . . . . . Each chromosome is divided up into many . . . . .
Genes are made up of a length of the chemical . . . . . Genes that code for the same character are called . . . . . In a pair of alleles one may be 'stronger' or . . . . to the other 'weaker' allele which is called . . . . . If both alleles are the same, they are said to be . . . . , if they are . . . . , they are heterozygous.

2. Complete these sentences by choosing the correct word from inside the brackets:
a) A pea plant with a tall (genotype/phenotype) could have a (genotype/phenotype) TT or Tt.
b) A tall pea plant with genotype TT is (homozygous/heterozygous) dominant.
c) A tall pea plant with genotype Tt is (homozygous/heterozygous) dominant.
d) A dwarf pea plant with genotype tt is (homozygous/heterozygous) recessive.

3. Chromosomes occur in pairs in all cells except the gametes.
a) What are alleles?
b) Why are there two alleles for each character?
c) Explain what is meant by dominant and recessive alleles.

4. a) Explain the difference between **heterozygous** and **homozygous**.
Use **T** for tongue-roller and **t** for non tongue-roller.
b) i) Draw a Punnett square to show a heterozygous cross.
ii) Write down the ratio of possible genotypes and phenotypes.
c) i) Draw a Punnett square to show the genetic cross between a homozygous dominant and a homozygous recessive.
ii) Write down the ratio of possible genotypes and phenotypes.

5. a) What is meant by a plasmid?
b) What are genetic clones?
c) Explain how genetic engineering has made it possible to produce large amounts of drugs quickly and cheaply?
Why are these chemicals thought to be safer to use than those extracted from animals?

6. a) What is a transgenic organism?
i) How are transgenic sheep created?
ii) How are they able to help in the treatment of some diseases?
b) Give three examples of how transgenic plants have been used to improve crop yield and quality.

7. The diagram shows cell division:

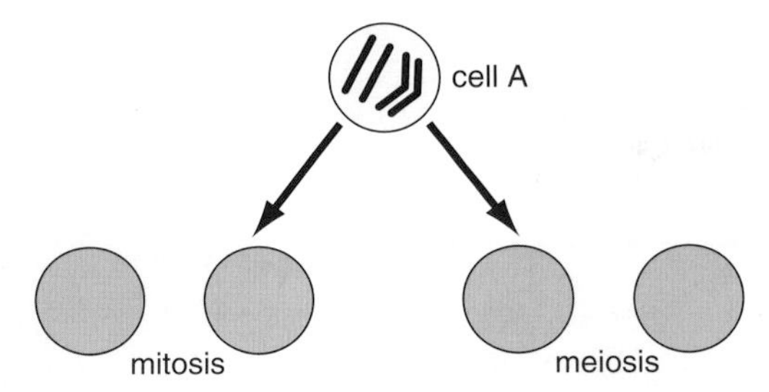

Only two pairs of chromosomes have been shown in cell A.

a) Copy the diagram and in the circles (cells), draw the chromosomes you would expect from the cell division shown.

b) Which types of cell division produces cells which are different from the parent cell? Explain the importance of this.

c) State one place where
i) mitosis occurs ii) meiosis occurs.

8. Using the symbol W = normal wing and w = short wing, write down the following:

a) The genotype of a fly which is heterozygous for this character.

b) The possible genotypes of its gametes.

c) Work out what kind of offspring would be produced if a heterozygous fly mated with one which was homozygous for normal wing.

9. A red-flowered tulip was crossed with a white-flowered tulip.
The seeds were collected and all grew into red tulips.

a) Which colour was dominant?

b) What was the genotype of the offspring?

Some of the offspring were self-fertilised.
The plants produced had three times as many red as white flowers.

c) Use a box diagram to explain this cross.

10. The diagram shows some of the features of the inheritance of sex:

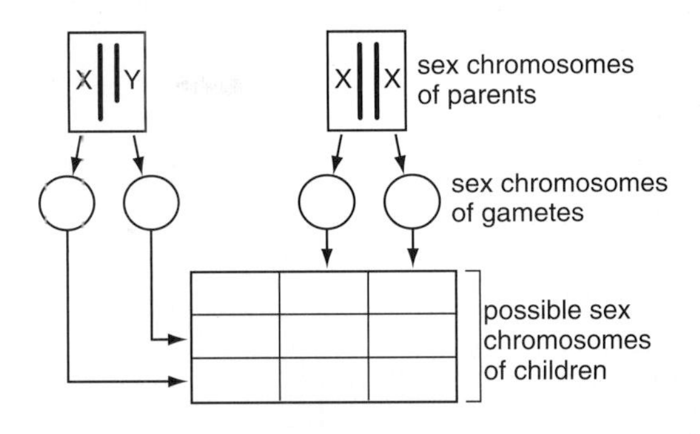

a) Copy the diagram and indicate the sex of each parent.

b) Complete your copy of the diagram by drawing in the spaces the chromosomes present in the gametes and in the children.

The next diagram shows the chromosomes taken from a cell of an adult human:

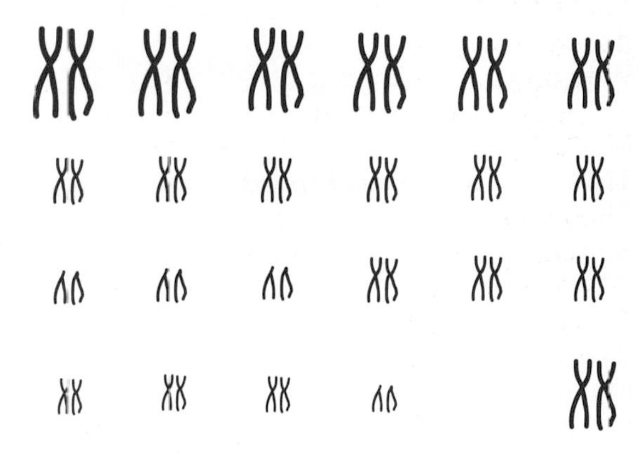

c) State whether the chromosomes are from a male or a female.
Give one reason for your answer.

Further questions on page 276.

chapter 17

Evolution is about change.
Things tend to change with time.
Think about cars, bicycles or aircraft.
How have they changed over time?
They have gradually improved.

Some animals and plants from the past
do not exist today.
Why do you think this is ?

Some of today's animals and plants did
not exist long ago.
Why do you think this is?

Many living things have changed to suit their environment.
They have become **adapted** to suit the conditions.
These **adaptations** help them to survive and to breed.
So the adaptations are passed on to the offspring.

Any plant or animal that occurs in large numbers in
a particular environment must be well adapted to
that environment.

To survive it has to **compete** with other individuals
in its species for things like food and space.
It also has to compete with other species around it.
Not all of the plants and animals will survive.
There is a **'survival of the fittest'**.
But this does not mean the healthiest or stongest.
It means the survival of those individuals that are
best adapted to their environment.

Evolution is the gradual change in the features or
characteristics of a species.
If a living thing has features that help it to survive,
then it will breed and pass on its genes to its offspring.
Living things that don't have useful features are less
likely to survive and to breed.

▷ Survival

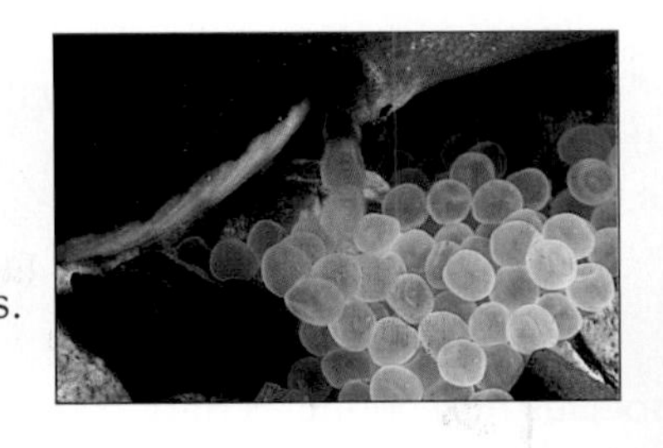

Many plants and animals produce large numbers of offspring.
A cod lays over three million eggs.
Each poppy plant makes over 15 000 seeds.

The scientist Charles Darwin worked out that one pair of elephants could have 19 million descendants after 700 years — if they all survived !

So why is the world not over-run by elephants ?

Why don't poppies completely cover the Earth ?

The reason is that not all of the offspring survive.
Most of the cod's eggs do not grow to adult fish.
Many eggs and young are eaten.

Many poppy seeds may be eaten.
Others may not land in soil where they can grow into new plants.

Can you think of any other factors that prevent offspring surviving in each generation ?

What about :

- competition for food
- predators
- disease
- climate
- drought ?

Predation by hyenas

So which individuals do survive ?

There is some luck involved, but, in general, it is the best adapted individuals that survive to breed.
There is a 'survival of the fittest'.

The best adapted individuals will pass on their characteristics to their offspring.
So the next generation will have a larger proportion of these better adapted individuals.

The sea eagle is a well adapted predator

▷ Charles Darwin

Most scientists used to think that all living things had remained the same since the Earth was created. But as they learned more about the different plants and animals, some scientists started to question this.

Instead they suggested that species had changed and that new species are being formed.
They thought that similar species descended from a common ancestor by a process of gradual change.

This was the **theory of evolution**.
The first person to collect together evidence to support the theory was Charles Darwin.

Darwin was a British naturalist.
In 1831, he set sail on the survey ship HMS *Beagle*.
He travelled around the world.
Darwin visited many different islands studying the wildlife.
He was impressed by the huge variety of plants and animals that he found.
He brought back a large collection of plants, animals and fossils.

HMS *Beagle*

In 1859, Darwin published his famous book, *The Origin of Species.*
In it he presented evidence to support his ideas.
He also described how evolution might have taken place.
He called it the **'Theory of natural selection'**.

About the same time, Alfred Russel Wallace (another British naturalist) also presented his ideas on evolution.
Darwin's and Wallace's theories were based upon the same ideas :

organisms produce large numbers of offspring

in any species there is variation between individuals

there is a struggle for existence

organisms with useful characteristics are more likely to survive and pass them on to the next generation

The Galapagos finches

On his voyage in HMS *Beagle*, Darwin visited a group of islands off the coast of South America.
He was fascinated by the animals and plants of the Galapagos Islands.

Darwin studied 13 different varieties of finches.
He suggested that they must have descended from birds that had flown to the islands, or been blown there, from the mainland.

He noticed differences in the beaks of the finches.
They had different beaks for different diets.
Some had thick beaks to crush seeds.
Others had slender beaks to catch insects.
Could they have all evolved from the same ancestor?

Darwin suggested that seed-eating finches had reached the islands from the mainland,
but that there was not enough food for all the birds.
Finches with slightly different beaks were able to eat other types of food.
These finches survived to breed and passed on their adaptations to their offspring.

Darwin thought that the finches evolved into different varieties by ***natural selection***.

Marine iguana from the Galapagos Islands

How has this woodpecker finch become adapted to feed on insects in bark?

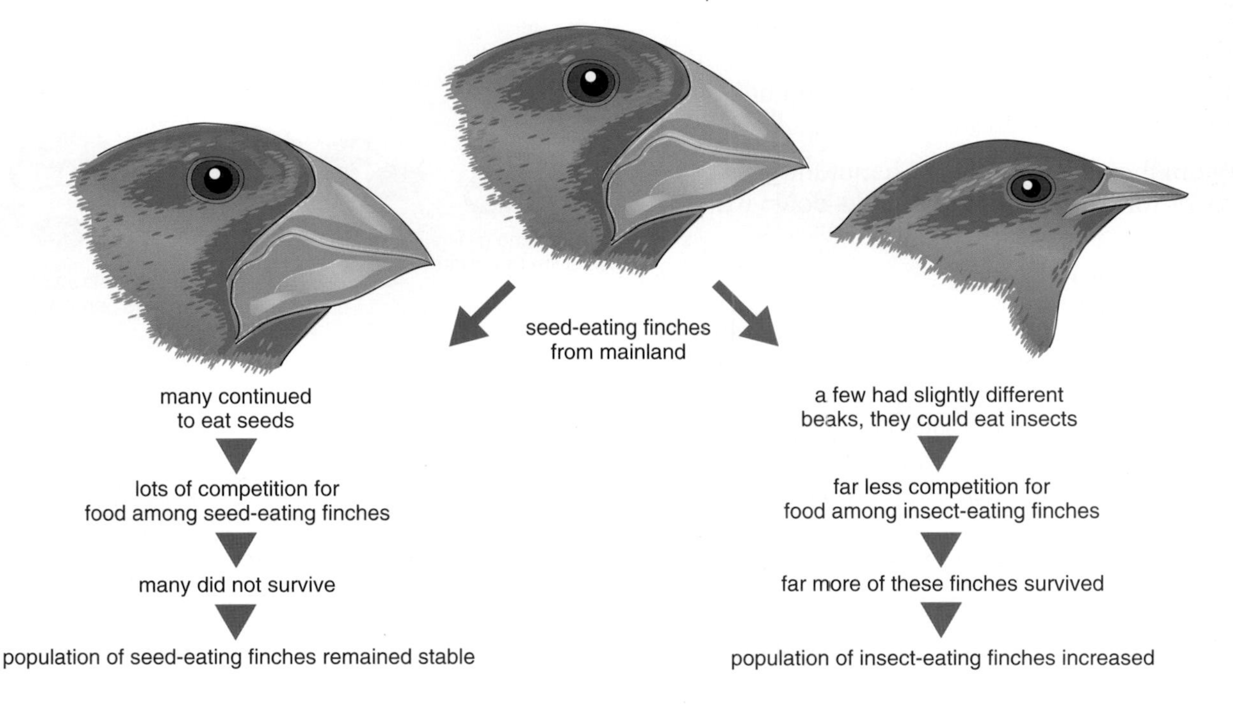

▷ Selection in action

Natural selection results in adaptations to the environment being selected and passed on.
So with time, a population will become better adapted.

Insecticides are used to kill insect pests.
A few individuals do not die. These individuals have a gene mutation.
This enables them to produce an enzyme which is able to break the insecticide down and make it harmless.
We say that they are **resistant**.

These insects will survive to breed.
So the numbers of resistant insects in the population will increase.

Resistance can spread quickly because insects reproduce rapidly.
Larger amounts of insecticide need to be used.
This is very expensive.
Eventually a different insecticide is tried.
But in time, the insects will develop resistance to this too.

insect has gene giving resistance to insecticide

INSECTOZAP

several generations later

INSECTOZAP

Resistant insects survive to breed and so their numbers increase

Super rats

Rats are also pests.
They eat stored food and carry disease.

Warfarin is a rat poison that was first used in the 1950s.
By now many rat populations are resistant to warfarin.
These 'super rats' are not killed even by large doses of warfarin.

Again they have produced a mutant gene that codes for an enzyme that breaks down warfarin.

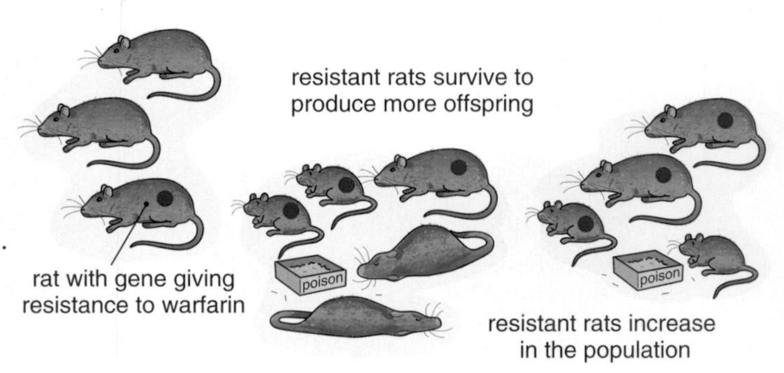

Resistant bacteria

Some bacteria develop resistance to antibiotics.
In a population of bacteria, there will be some individuals that have resistant genes.
These bacteria are not killed by the antibiotic.
Bacteria reproduce very quickly.
Soon most of the bacteria are resistant to the antibiotic.
The MRSA bacterium has developed resistance to penicillin.
The only way to treat this superbug is with a powerful combination of a number of antibiotics.

▷ The peppered moth

Changes in the environment can bring about changes in a population by natural selection.

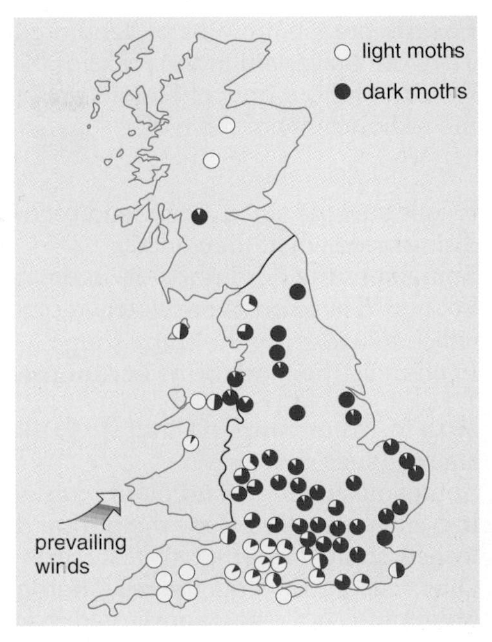

The proportions of dark and light peppered moths found in different areas of Britain today

There are two types of peppered moth :

- a pale, speckled form, and
- a dark form.

The moths feed at night and rest on tree trunks during the day.
Their main predators are birds.

Before 1850 the dark variety of peppered moth was rare. But by 1895 almost the whole population of moths in some cities was dark.
Why do you think the dark moth became so common in industrial areas ?

Pollution from heavy industries killed the lichen that grows on the bark of trees.
Soot from factories also blackened the tree trunks.

Look at the photograph :

Which type of moth is best camouflaged on lichen-covered bark ?

Which type of moth is best camouflaged on dark trees ?

Against a lichen-covered tree, the light variety was difficult for birds to see.
So in clean areas, it survived to breed and its numbers increased.

Against dark trees, the dark form is better camouflaged.
So in industrial areas, it survived to breed and it became the most common form.

Two varieties of peppered moth

Look at the map above showing the proportions of light and dark moths in Britain today.

In which areas are the dark moths more common ?

In which areas are the light moths more common ?

Explain why this is in each case.

▷ The fossil record

Ammonite fossils

Fossils are the remains of dead organisms.
They are preserved in the rocks of the Earth's crust.
We can find out how old fossils are by measuring the radioactivity of the rock.

Fossils are rare since most dead organisms disintegrate when they decay.
Sometimes the hard parts of an animal are covered by mud. These parts are slowly replaced by minerals which take exactly the same shape.
Eventually the mud forms **sedimentary rock**.

Insects preserved in amber

Most fossils are imprints that show the shape of shells, bones or leaves.
Sometimes animals and plants can become trapped in a substance that stops them from decaying.
Insects can get trapped in sticky resin from trees.
Over millions of years the resin hardens to form **amber**.
Mammoths have been preserved in ice, peat bogs and tar pits.

Fossils can give us evidence for evolution.
The Earth's surface consists of layers of rock.
The fossils in each layer act as a record of the life that existed at that time.
The more recent fossils will be in rock layers nearer the surface.

The fossil record shows us that :

- The variety of life on Earth today did not arise all at once.
- The first life was in water — life on land came much later.
- As each 'new' type of animal evolved, the older ones declined — these less well adapted animals often became extinct.
- Some fossils give us clues as to how a particular group evolved. For instance, Archaeopteryx was an early type of bird living 150 million years ago.
  The fossil remains show that it had feathers (like birds) but also it had teeth and other reptile features.
  This fossil provides a link to show that reptiles and birds evolved from a common ancestor.
  However, the fossil record is incomplete, because some body parts, particularly soft tissue, decay and do not fossilise.
  Also many fossils have not yet been discovered.

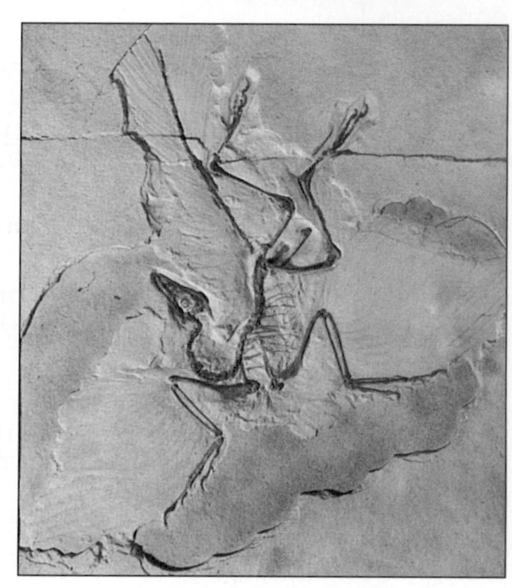
Archaeopteryx fossil

▷ The vertebrate story

The sides of the Grand Canyon, USA, have been eroded by the Colorado River.
The soft, sedimentary rock reveals invertebrates in the lower layers.
These layers are 2000 million years old.
In the layers above, a range of vertebrates are found.

Careful study of the fossils in each layer builds up a story of how each group of animals evolved.
The animals in the upper layers will be the most recent ones to have evolved.

Look at the diagram :

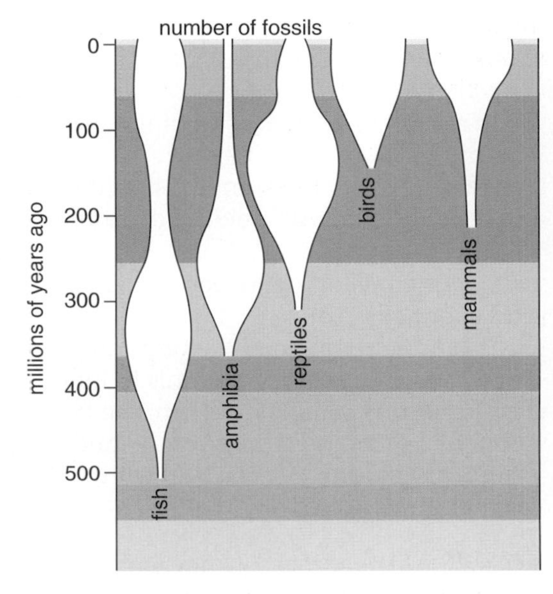

The numbers of vertebrate fossils : the wider the strip, the more fossils found

Can you build up a sequence which shows how the vertebrates evolved ?

- 500 million years ago there were members of all the main invertebrate groups living.
- The first vertebrates to evolve were the fish. These appeared about 400 million years ago.
- About 300 million years ago life moved onto land. Amphibians were thought to be the first land vertebrates.
- Reptiles evolved from an ancient type of amphibian about 200 million years ago.
- About 200 million to 65 million years ago was the age of the **dinosaurs**. The world was dominated by these reptiles before they suddenly became extinct about 60 million years ago.
- Birds and mammals are not represented in the Grand Canyon fossils. But we know that they evolved more recently. The first mammals looked like shrews or mice. They appeared about 65 million years ago.
- The first of our ape-like ancestors lived six million years ago. Fossil evidence from the Rift Valley in Africa shows that they were able to walk upright.

▷ Evolution of the horse

Fossil evidence has been pieced together to suggest how the modern horse has evolved.
The ideas are shown here :

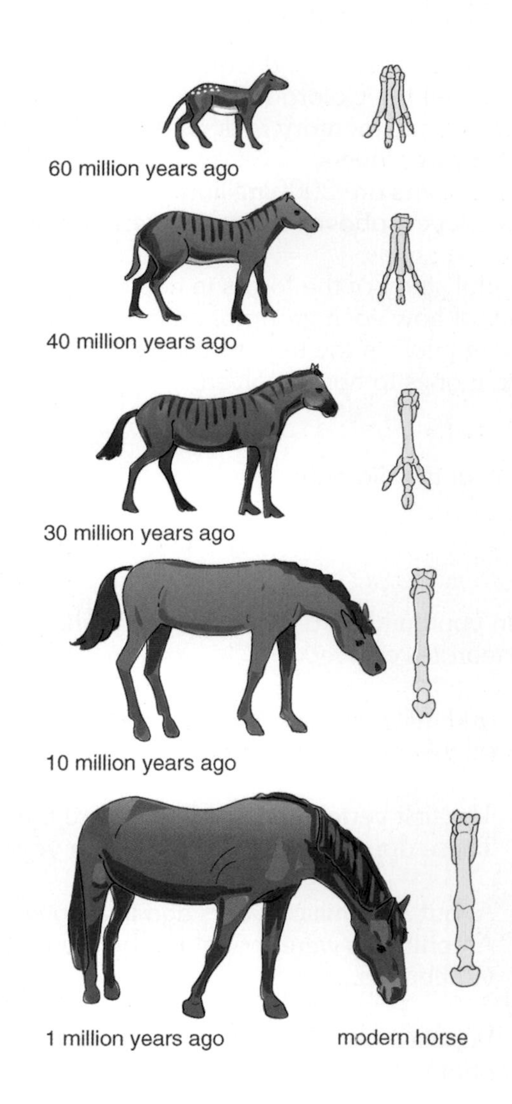

What changes can you see between each of the different stages ?

Why has natural selection operated to produce the modern horse ?
Could there have been a change in its environment ?

Sixty million years ago a lot of the countryside was marshy.
There were small trees and bushes that offered cover so that animals could hide from predators.

But by one million years ago the environment had changed.
Grassland had replaced the trees and bushes.
There was no cover for animals to hide.
The faster an animal could run, the better its chance of escaping a predator — and surviving.
Animals with long necks might get a better view of any predators coming.

Flat feet with splayed-out digits make it less likely that an animal will sink in marshy ground.
But they are no good for fast running.

The modern horse has long legs and runs on one digit.
It can move fast over hard ground.
Would it have done so over marshy ground ?

The ancestors of the modern horse were probably much smaller individuals that hid from predators.
With the change in the environment, natural selection favoured animals that were able to out-run their predators.

There was another reason why natural selection also favoured animals with longer necks.
These were better equipped to graze on the new grasslands.

▷ Extinction

Many species of animals and plants that once inhabited the Earth have died out or become **extinct**.
Nobody really knows why the dinosaurs became extinct, but probably their environment changed.
Natural selection operated against them.
Their dominant position was eventually taken over by the mammals.

The Tasmanian wolf

If natural selection operates then the less well-adapted species will become extinct.
Perhaps they can't compete for food as well as other species can or they don't avoid predators so well.
There may be new diseases introduced to which they have no resistance.

Humans are responsible for the extinction of thousands of species. The giant otter, wood bison, Parma wallaby and Tasmanian wolf have been totally destroyed.
Some species in Britain, such as the red kite, red squirrel and osprey, are endangered and need protection.

An increasing human population needs more food.
This has meant the destruction of natural habitats to give room to grow crops.

Other animals have been hunted to extinction.
Often these animals breed slowly and usually live a long time.
We are all aware of the plight of the whale.
Giant hardwood trees of the rainforests are suffering the same fate.
They are valuable — like the whale meat and oil.
They are being cut down faster than they can reproduce.

The dodo once lived on the island of Mauritius in the Indian Ocean where it had no natural predators. It was a large bird that could not run or fly. Humans hunted it for its meat.
Pigs, cats and monkeys, introduced to the island by humans, ate its eggs and young.
Much of its natural forest habitat was also destroyed by settlers.
By the 1690s it was extinct.
The dodo was unable to survive the rapid changes to its environment caused by humans.

We must help future generations by conserving wildlife and by preserving the environment.

▷ Biology at work: Reclaiming mining tips

Mining produces a lot of waste or spoil.
The spoil contains large amounts of toxic metals like lead, copper and zinc.
What can be done with these spoil tips?

Coal mining produces waste or spoil

Apart from looking ugly, the tips are dangerous.
Some of the poison waste can drain into rivers or get blown onto farmland.
What problems can this cause?

Attempts have been made to grass over the spoil tips.
But plants just would not grow on them.
Apart from the toxic metals, the tips are:

- low in plant nutrients
- very dry, because water quickly drains through
- very acid.

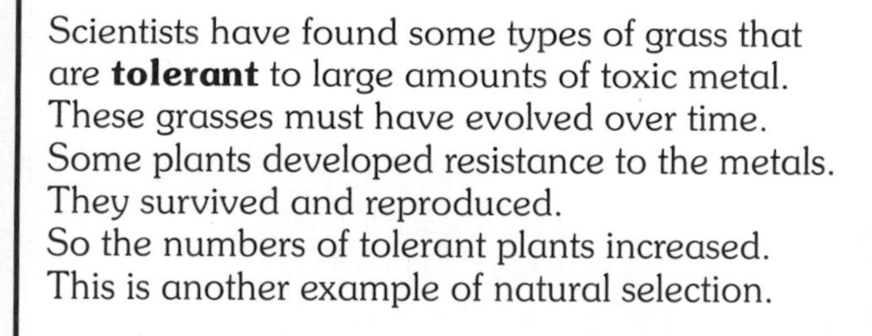

Scientists have found some types of grass that are **tolerant** to large amounts of toxic metal.
These grasses must have evolved over time.
Some plants developed resistance to the metals.
They survived and reproduced.
So the numbers of tolerant plants increased.
This is another example of natural selection.

Grasses tolerant to mine spoil have been used for recolonisation of tips

But just planting tolerant grasses is not enough.
Other work has to be done to reclaim the tips:

- Large amounts of fertilisers are added to correct the shortage of nutrients.
- Lime is added to neutralise the acid.
- With time humus forms and retains the water.
  In some areas sewage sludge was used.
  It was poured over tips to add nutrients and form humus.

Do you think that eventually normal plants will be able to grow on the tips?
Trees planted on reclaimed tips have always died.
Why do you think this is?
Do you think that it would be safe for sheep to graze on the grass of reclaimed tips?
Why not?

Summary

- Evolution is the change in a species that leads to the formation of a new species. It takes place over a long period of time.
- Organisms produce large numbers of offspring but few of them survive.
- Organisms that become well adapted to their environment have a better chance of survival. They survive to breed and pass on their adaptations to their offspring.
- There is a 'struggle for existence' leading to the 'survival of the fittest'.
- Charles Darwin and Alfred Russel Wallace put forward the theory of natural selection.
- Pesticide resistance and camouflage in moths are recent examples of natural selection.
- Fossils provide evidence that organisms have evolved.

▷ Questions

1. Copy and complete :
Organisms are able to produce large numbers of . . . . . Many of these die due to . . . . for food, predators, ... and climate. The best . . . . individuals are more likely to survive and pass on their . . . . to the next generation. Charles . . . . and Alfred . . . . suggested how evolution could take place through natural . . . . . Fossils have provided . . . . to show that organisms have evolved.

2. In the 1940s some strains of bacteria became resistant to the antibiotic, penicillin.
The bacteria were able to survive, reproduce and so cause disease.
a) What was this an example of ?
b) How would you fight the penicillin-resistant strains of bacteria ?

3. Look at these three fossils :

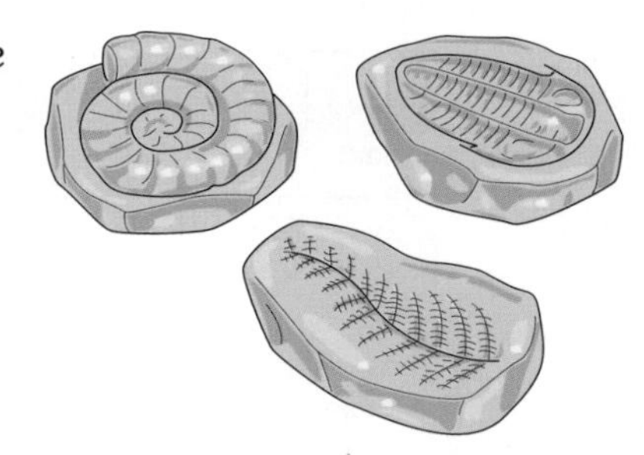

a) Which living things are they most like ? Give the reasons for your choice.
b) Explain briefly how fossils can form.
c) Find out the names of five animals that are extinct.
Try to find out how they became extinct.

4. Snails are eaten by thrushes. Some snails have shells that are very striped, others are unstriped. Each September for several years a scientist counted all the snails he could find in an area of grassland. Here are his results :

Year	% covered by grass	Number of snails with ... very striped shells	unstriped shells
1971	98	58	13
1972	25	24	22
1973	5	2	33
1974	97	34	10
1975	96		
1976		9	43
1977	98	68	13

a) State : i) a probable number of snails that you would have expected to find in 1975
ii) a probable percentage cover of grass in 1976.
b) i) All the snails were of the same species. During the seven years of study a single specimen was found with a completely black shell. What word would you use to describe this unusual form of the species ?
ii) Choose the best answer. The term which best explains the results in the table is :
1 heredity
2 natural selection
3 conservation
4 artificial selection.

Further questions on page 276.

▷ Inheritance

1. The diagram shows a partly completed section of a DNA molecule.

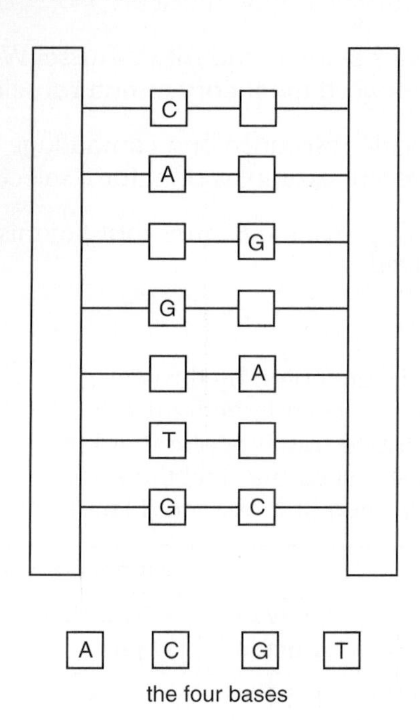

a) Copy and complete the diagram by writing the letters of the missing bases in the boxes. *[2]*

b) Mutations can occur because of changes to DNA.

i) Name **two** possible causes for an increase in the normal rate of mutation. *[2]*

ii) Explain how a change in the DNA structure can cause a cell to form a different protein. *[3]* (EDEX)

2. a) i) Describe in outline the process of mitosis. *[6]*

ii) State **two** ways in which meiosis differs from mitosis and explain the significance of each difference. *[4]*

iii) State where meiosis takes place in males and in females. *[2]*

b) The effect of a mutation occurring during meiosis can have a serious effect on a future child.

i) What is a mutation? *[2]*

ii) Name **one** condition caused by a chromosome mutation occurring during meiosis. Explain how this type of mutation could have occurred and given rise to a child showing the condition. *[6]* (OCR)

3. The gene which controls the formation of haemoglobin exists in two forms. The normal form of gene (H) produces normal haemoglobin. The mutant form of the gene (h) produces 'sickle' haemoglobin. People who are homozygous for the mutant form of the gene suffer from a condition called sickle cell anaemia. When their haemoglobin gives up its oxygen, the red blood cells change to a sickle shape. These sickle shaped cells may stick together and block small blood vessels, often causing death.

People who are heterozygous for the gene produce both normal and 'sickle' types of haemoglobin, but do not usually suffer from sickle cell anaemia.

The family tree below shows the inheritance of haemoglobin type.

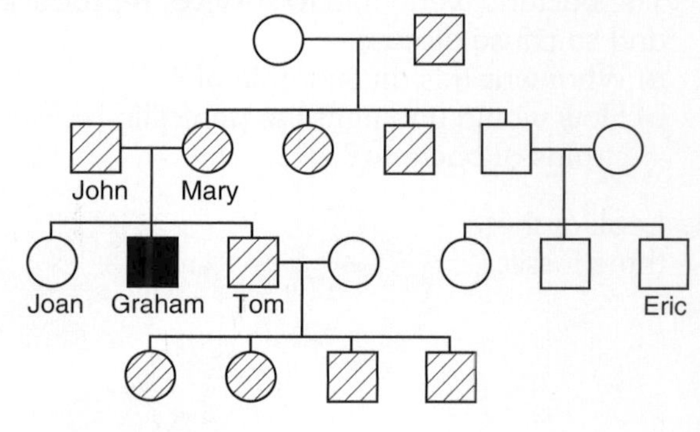

 Note: although a question may be marked (EDEX) etc, it will often be relevant to other examinations as well.

a) Look at the family tree and then copy and complete the genetic diagram below to show how the children of John and Mary inherit haemoglobin type.

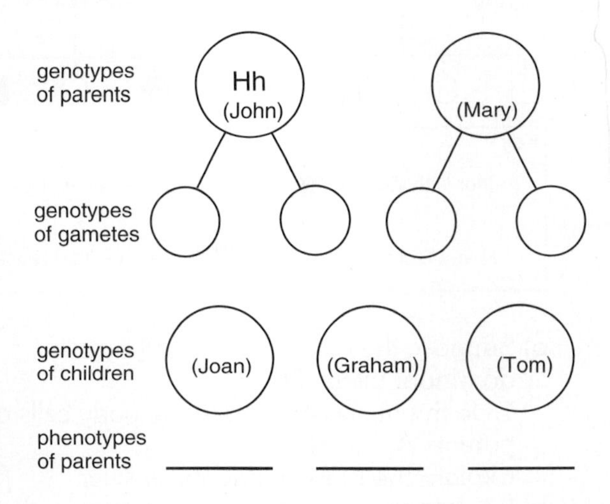

[4]

b) The cousins, Joan and Eric, wish to marry but are worried their children may inherit sickle cell haemoglobin.
What advice would you give to them? Explain the reason for your answer. [2] (AQA)

4. a) The diagram shows the chromosomes from a body cell of a male with Down's syndrome.

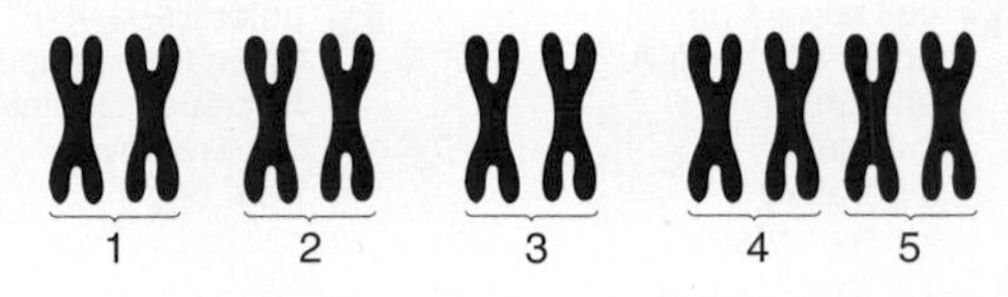

i) How do these chromosomes differ from those of a male who does not have Down's syndrome? [2]

ii) Down's syndrome occurs because of an irregularity that takes place during the development of an egg in the mother's ovary.
What is this irregularity? What must happen at fertilisation to produce a person with Down's syndrome? [2]

b) Huntington's disease is a severe condition which causes mental deterioration and loss of muscular coordination. It is caused by the inheritance of a dominant allele. The effects of this allele do not normally appear until a person is at least over thirty years old.
The diagram shows a family pedigree for the inheritance of Huntington's disease.

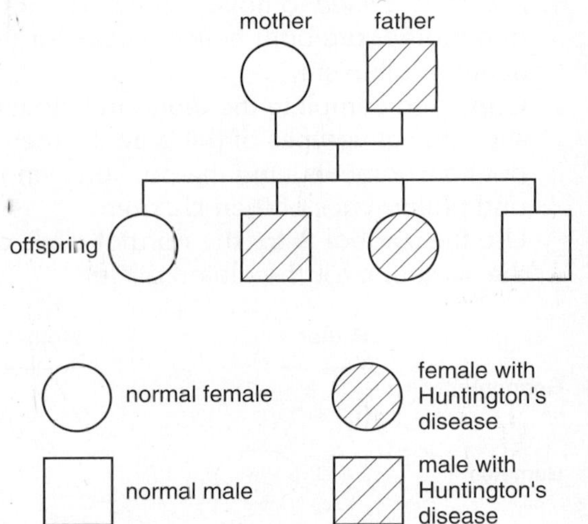

i) Draw a labelled genetic diagram to show the inheritance of the allele for Huntington's disease in this family. Also show how it is possible for "normal" offspring to be born even though one parent was affected.
(Use **H** for the allele for Huntington's disease; use **h** for the recessive allele) [4]

ii) It is possible for an **HH** person to be unaware of the disease and pass it on to their children. Explain how this can happen. [1] (AQA)

5. The features of humans are either inherited or are caused by environmental influences.

accidental loss of an arm blood group
eye colour gender/sex mass

a) From the features listed choose :
  i) one which is controlled by environmental influences only. *[1]*
  ii) one which is controlled by inheritance only. *[1]*
  iii) one which is controlled by both environmental influence and inheritance. *[1]*

b) Which part of the cell nucleus enables features to be passed from one generation to the next? *[1]*

c) What is meant by the term **dominant allele**? *[1]* (OCR)

6. A couple decide to have a child. The father and mother are both heterozygous for the gene for albinism.
Copy and complete the diagram below to show the genotypes of the parents, their possible gametes, and the possible genotypes and phenotypes of their children.
Use the symbol **A** for the normal allele and the symbol **a** for the albino allele.

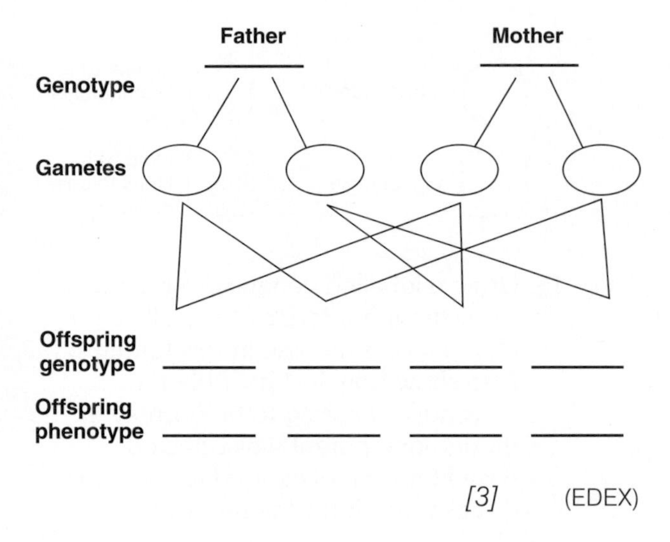

[3] (EDEX)

7. Scientists have traced the way in which a newly discovered disease is inherited through one family. The family tree shows their findings.

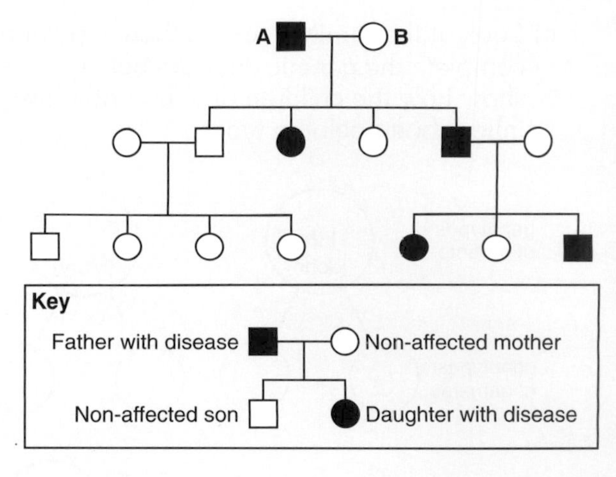

a) Suppose the disease is caused by a dominant allele, D.
Give the alleles present in the body cells of parents **A** and **B**.
Explain the reason for your answer. *[3]*

b) It is impossible to say from the data in the family tree whether the allele that causes the disease is dominant or recessive.
Explain why. *[2]* (AQA)

8. The following diagram shows how scientists produced Dolly the sheep.

a) i) Dolly was produced with the help of an unfertilised egg.
Where did scientists get the DNA to put into this egg? *[1]*

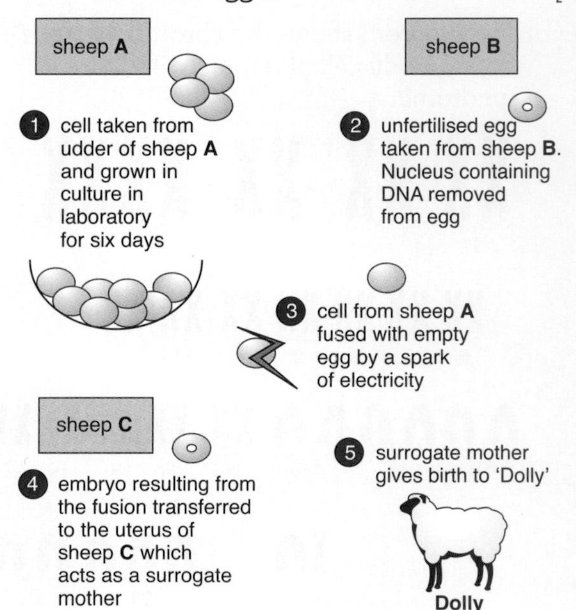

ii) Suggest why it was important to remove the DNA from the unfertilised egg. [2]
iii) Dolly is genetically identical to another sheep in the diagram. Which one ? [1]

b) Give **one** way in which this method is different from the normal method of sheep reproduction. [1]

c) The production of Dolly was a significant advance in scientific work. The work may result in animal clones being produced in large numbers.
Suggest why it is important that people are informed of new scientific advances. [2]

d) Suggest one advantage of producing animal clones. [1] (CCEA)

9. Read the following and answer the questions which follow:
Cystic fibrosis is a genetic disease which affects the pancreas. The ducts of the pancreas become blocked. The disease also affects the mucus-producing glands of the bronchioles and these produce very large amounts of thick sticky mucus. This makes breathing difficult and reduces the ability of the respiratory system to remove microbes.
The disease cannot be cured but some of the symptoms can be eased by the use of antibiotics, physiotherapy and careful control of the diet.

a) What is a genetic disease ? [1]
b) Explain why cystic fibrosis sufferers find breathing difficult. [1]
c) Suggest why antibiotics can help sufferers of cystic fibrosis. [1]
d) Tracy and Peter do not suffer from cystic fibrosis but one of their children, David, does suffer from it. Here is the family tree:

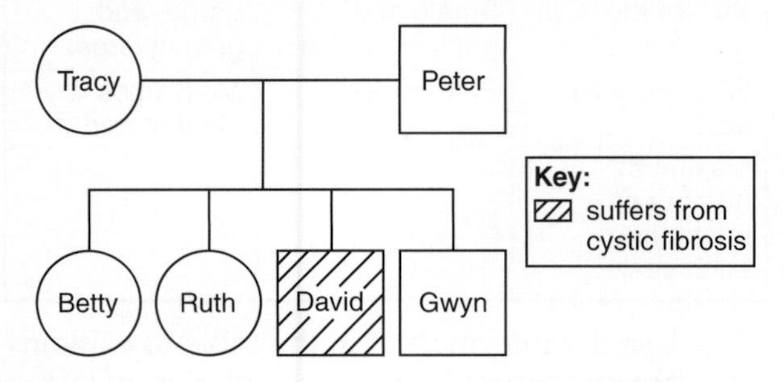

Use the following letters : **N** = normal (dominant) and **n** = cystic fibrosis (recessive)

What are the genotypes of:
i) Tracy [1]
ii) Peter [1]
iii) David [1]
iv) What are the **two** possibilities of Gwyn's genotype ? [2]

e) Name any other genetic disease. [1] (WJEC)

10. Lysenko was an important Russian biologist in the 1930s. This was a time when there were great food shortages in Russia.
He believed that he could develop new varieties of crops by growing them in better environments. Any improvements developed would be passed on to the next generation. He gained the support of the Russian leader, Stalin, and scientists who criticised his ideas were sent to prison camps.

a) Suggest a reason why people accepted Lysenko's ideas at the time, even though many important scientists disagreed with him. [1]
b) Explain why most scientists today do **not** agree with Lysenko. [2]
c) *To gain full marks in this question you should write your ideas in good English. Put them into a sensible order and use the correct scientific words.*
Today, crop plants have been improved by artificial selection.
Explain how a plant breeder would use artificial selection to increase the size of the tomatoes produced on every tomato plant. [4] (AQA)

11. The flounder is a fish that has a gene for making an anti-freeze chemical.
Scientists have transferred this gene to cells from tomato plants. These cells then grow in tissue culture. Hormones are added to encourage the growing cells to develop into small tomato plants. Plants grown in this way are resistant to damage caused by low temperatures.

a) Explain how mitosis ensures that every cell of the tomato plants will contain the anti-freeze gene. [2]

b) The tomato plants grown in this way will be clones.
Suggest reasons why people might object to this method of producing tomato plants. [3] (AQA)

12. Copy the passage below, which describes how genetic engineering is used to make human insulin. Write on the dotted lines the most suitable word or words to complete the passage.
The .... for human insulin is cut out using a .... enzyme. The same enzyme is used to cut open a circle of DNA called a .... from a bacterial cell. The human DNA and the circle of DNA are joined together by an enzyme called .... To produce human insulin, the bacteria containing the recombinant .... are then cultured in a container called a .... Human insulin produced in this way can be used to treat people with the disease .... (EDEX)

13. Read the following newspaper article about genetic engineering.

> **Human gene transplanted into bacterium**
>
> Diabetics who need the hormone insulin used to use insulin obtained from other animals. This was very expensive and sometimes resulted in an allergic response. Scientists have now transplanted the human gene to make insulin into a bacterium. The bacteria produce the insulin quickly and cheaply. There is also no problem with an allergic response.

a) List three advantages of producing human insulin by genetic engineering. [3]

b) The diagrams opposite show how the insulin gene was removed from a human cell and placed and grown in a bacteria. The steps are in the wrong order.

i) Write out the steps in the correct order. [1]

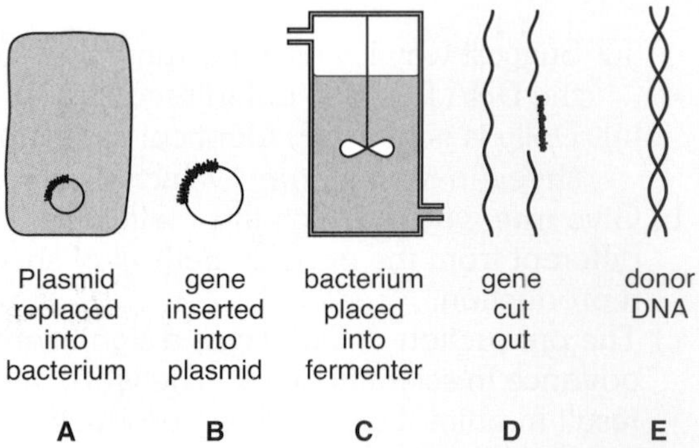

A: Plasmid replaced into bacterium
B: gene inserted into plasmid
C: bacterium placed into fermenter
D: gene cut out
E: donor DNA

i) Explain what will happen to the bacteria in step C. [3]

c) Some people are opposed to genetic engineering.
Give two arguments against genetic engineering. [2] (OCR)

14. In Britain there are two species of squirrels, red ones and grey ones. Adult grey squirrels are usually much heavier than adult red squirrels.

a) i) ***Genes*** can cause this difference in weight. What are ***genes***, and what do they do? [2]

ii) In one group of red squirrels many of the adults were much heavier than expected. Suggest and explain **one** reason for this, other than a genetic one. [2]

b) Below is some more information about red and grey squirrels.

	Red squirrels	**Grey squirrels**
How long have they been in Britain	Thousands of years	Just over 100 years
Where are they found?	In the evergreen forests of northern Britain	In most forests all over Britain
Size of the populations	Small, and getting smaller	Large, and getting larger
What do they eat?	Pine cones	Most kinds of plant material
Maximum number of young born each year	8	12

Use the information in the table to explain **three** reasons why the population of red squirrels is getting less and the population of grey squirrels is increasing. [6] (AQA)

▷ Evolution

15. Galapagos is a group of islands in the Pacific Ocean. The islands are several hundred miles from the mainland of South America. Few animals have reached the islands. On one of the islands there are three types of finch.

- One type feeds on soft seeds and some small insects.
- Another type feeds on large seeds and large insects.
- The third type feeds on small insects which it picks off leaves and twigs.

The drawings show the heads of these three types of finch.

a) Which type of finch :
  i) feeds on soft seeds and some small insects;
  ii) feeds on large seeds and large insects;
  iii) feeds on small insects which it picks off leaves and twigs? *[1]*

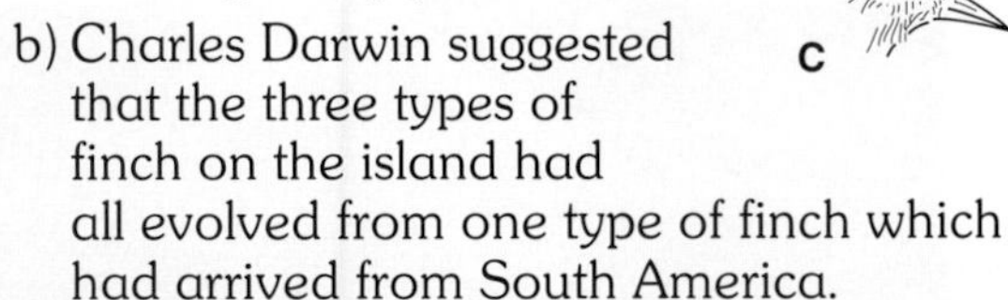

b) Charles Darwin suggested that the three types of finch on the island had all evolved from one type of finch which had arrived from South America.
  i) Name the process by which this evolution may have taken place. *[1]*
  ii) The finch that came from South America probably had a thick beak. Suggest how the thin beak could have evolved. *[3]* (AQA)

16. The diagram shows two types of peppered moth found on the trunks of trees in both city and countryside areas.

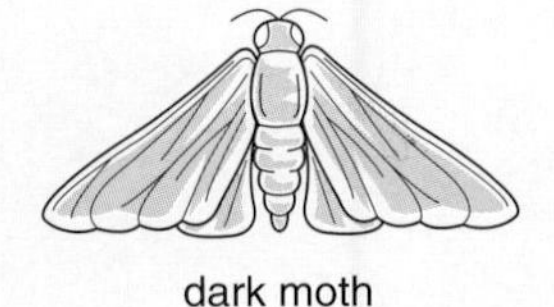

dark moth   light moth

Read the following passage about the peppered moth.

> The peppered moth is often used to provide evidence for evolution. Before the Industrial Revolution the moths found were light in colour. They were harder for birds to see on light coloured tree trunks. Fewer moths are eaten by birds if they are well hidden.
> During the Industrial Revolution, many trees in large cities became black with soot. In the daytime the moths rest on tree trunks. Dark coloured moths were better hidden on the trees than light coloured ones.
> Records showed that few light coloured moths survived in cities and few dark coloured moths survived in countryside areas. In 1956 the Clean Air Act gradually reduced the amount of smoke pollution. After 1956 the number of light coloured moths in city areas gradually increased.

a) Use this information to answer the following questions.
  i) In which area were the greatest number of light coloured moths found after the Industrial Revolution? *[1]*
  ii) Describe and explain the effect of the Clean Air Act on the numbers of the two types of moth in city areas. *[4]*
  iii) Name the process of evolution described in the passage. *[1]*

b) Some students counted the number of moths they found resting on five trees in a city and five trees in a countryside area. The results are shown in the table below. Copy and complete the table by filling in the total number of moths counted and calculating the mean (average) number of moths found. *[4]*

Tree	City trees		Countryside trees	
	Dark moths	Light moths	Dark moths	Light moths
A	10	2	3	8
B	8	3	4	7
C	8	4	3	8
D	7	2	2	6
E	8	2	4	7
Total				
Mean				

c) Which group of trees showed the highest mean (average) number of moths? *[1]* (OCR)

chapter 18

Ecology is about how living things **interact** with each other and with their environment.
Ecology is also sometimes called the study of **ecosystems**.

The environment is made up of lots of different ecosystems, such as a seashore, a wood or a river.
Each ecosystem is made up of two parts :

- a non-living part called the **habitat**, and
- a living part called the **community**.

The habitat is the place where the organisms live.
It has the conditions that they need to survive, such as the right amount of light, oxygen or water and a suitable temperature.

The community is all the plants and animals that live in the habitat.

What is your habitat ?
What conditions does it have to help you survive ?

Look at the ecosystems shown here :
For each one think what the habitat is like.
Some ecosystems, like the ocean depths, are still unexplored, with many undiscovered new species.

Each community is made up of different **populations** of animals and plants.
A population is a group of individuals of the same species.
For instance, a woodland community might have a population of ground beetles, a population of bluebells and a population of beech trees.
Each population in the community is **adapted** to live in that particular habitat.

There is a great variety of different ecosystems.
They are found both on land and in water.
All ecosystems together make up the **biosphere**.

Environmental factors

Each ecosystem has particular conditions or **environmental factors**.
Animals and plants must be adapted to these if they are to survive.

This lizard gets shade under rocks during the hottest part of the day

Water

Water is needed for all life to survive.
All the chemical reactions that take place in animals and plants occur in water.
Organisms that live in dry places have adaptations that cut down water loss.
In rivers and streams the animals and plants have to withstand fast currents.
Seaweeds and seashore animals have to cope with the battering of the waves.

Temperature

Mammals and birds have to maintain a constant body temperature.
This is because the enzymes, that catalyse reactions in their cells, work best at a particular temperature.
Few living organisms can live outside the range of 0–40 °C.
But penguins can withstand temperatures of −80 °C in the Antarctic.
And some bacteria have adapted to live in hot springs at over 100 °C.

Light

Light is needed for photosynthesis which provides energy for the plant and new growth (biomass).
Some plants are adapted to live in shade while others thrive in full sunlight.
On the sea bed or in deep caves there is no light at all.
Light provides the energy input for food chains.

Air

Few organisms can live without ***oxygen.***
They need it for respiration.
Aquatic organisms take oxygen out of the water.
Plants also take in ***carbon dioxide*** for photosynthesis and give out oxygen.
Animals use this oxygen for respiration and give out carbon dioxide that the plants need for photosynthesis.

▶ Biotic factors

These are factors caused by other **living organisms** present in the community.

Competition
Plants compete for light, space, water and soil nutrients.
Animals compete for food, space (territory) and mates.
There can be competition between animals and plants of different species. But there can also be competition between individuals of the same species, as in the case of these terns competing for nesting sites :

Predation
A **predator** is an animal that feeds by hunting and killing its prey. It may have many adaptations to catch the prey such as fast running, swimming or flying and sharp teeth, beak or claws.

The **prey** must be well adapted to escape from the predator if it is to survive.
This killer whale is attacking a sealion.

Disease
Some microbes cause diseases.
A **parasite** is an organism that lives in or on another organism called a **host**.
The parasite benefits by getting food to the host's detriment e.g. fleas and tapeworms.
The fish in the photograph has a fungal disease.

Grazers
Grazers are animals that eat plants.
We sometimes call them herbivores or primary consumers.
Grazers spend a great deal of their time eating plants in order to convert the energy and nutrient content of their food into new growth (biomass).

Decomposers
These are microbes that release enzymes to break down dead and decaying material.
The main decomposers are bacteria and fungi.
They are important in the cycling of nutrients.
Decomposers are found in the soil, but also in rivers, lakes and oceans.

Human activity can disrupt ecosystems

Effect of humans
Human activity affects the survival of other living organisms.
Industry, farming, forestry, transport and housing have all affected the survival of organisms by changing their habitats.

Populations

A population is a group of individuals of the same species living in a particular habitat.

These are all populations :

- a shoal of herring in the sea
- dandelions in a lawn
- greenfly on a rosebush
- owls in a wood.

A population of snappers

Why do you think individuals live in populations ?

There may be many reasons :

- the habitat provides food, shelter, light or other factors needed for survival
- the individuals come together to breed
- individuals may gain more protection in a group.

Can you think of any disadvantages of living in a population ?

A population of wildebeest

As the population grows, there may be overcrowding.
Individuals **compete** for food, space, light and other resources.
Some individuals will be better adapted to compete than others.
Those that are not so well adapted may not survive.

As we will see, competition may influence the distribution and population size of animals or plants.

Scientists study populations to find out how their numbers change :

- Mosquitoes carry malaria.
  Population studies of the mosquito help control the spread of the disease.

- Studying locust populations has led to reducing the damage that they do to crops.

- Monitoring the populations of threatened species, like the tiger, has helped in their conservation.

We try to control locust populations

▶ How populations grow

What happens if rabbits colonise a new area?

First a few individuals enter the new habitat.
There is enough food for them so they start to breed.
There are no predators to keep their numbers down.
At first they start to increase slowly.
But soon each generation doubles the size of the previous one.
Two becomes four then eight, 16, 32, 64, 128, 256, 512, and so on.
This maximum rate of growth is called **exponential growth**.
It can only take place under ideal environmental conditions.

Experiment 18.1 Growth of a yeast population

Put some yeast into sugar solution and keep it in warm conditions.

Every half an hour look at a drop of the yeast under the microscope and count the number of cells in the field of view.

Some model results are shown in the graph:

- Explain what is happening to the yeast population at times X, Y and Z on the graph.
- Why did the yeast population stop growing?

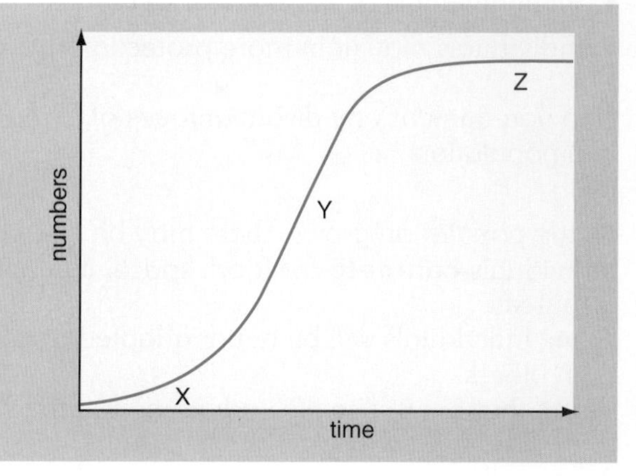

Why doesn't our yeast population go on increasing?

Here are some possible reasons:
- lack of food
- overcrowding
- build-up of poisonous waste made by the yeast.

Populations are able to grow very fast.
Animals can produce lots of eggs, and plants can make lots of seeds.
So why isn't the Earth over-run with animals and plants?

The answer is that not all of them survive.
Some things must be acting to **limit** the growth of the population.

Huge numbers of red crabs on Christmas Island

▶ Checks on population increase

What sort of things could prevent a population increasing?

A number of factors can act as natural checks to stop the population becoming too large:

- **Food and water** are needed by all living things. If they become short then individuals compete for them. Some individuals will not survive so the population decreases.
- **Oxygen** shortage can limit numbers in a population that lives in water. Pollutants like sewage can lower oxygen levels in the water.
- **Toxic wastes** such as ammonia and urea are excreted by living organisms. These poisons can build up and limit population growth.
- **Overcrowding** can lead to unhygienic conditions, the spread of disease and stress.
- **Predators** have to kill their prey to feed. This limits the numbers in the prey population.
- **Disease** can spread quickly through large populations. It acts like predation to reduce numbers in the population.
- **Climate**, such as extreme heat or extreme cold, can reduce populations. Drought, floods and storms all affect population numbers.
- **Lack of shelter** can expose individuals to harsh climate or the risk of being killed by predators.

Human populations can be affected too

Evidence of Dutch elm disease

Sometimes populations do not level off.
Instead they crash dramatically.
The population may have run out of food or been affected by predators or disease.
A crash in population numbers like this can happen very quickly. For instance, a whole swarm of greenfly can soon be eaten by money spiders.

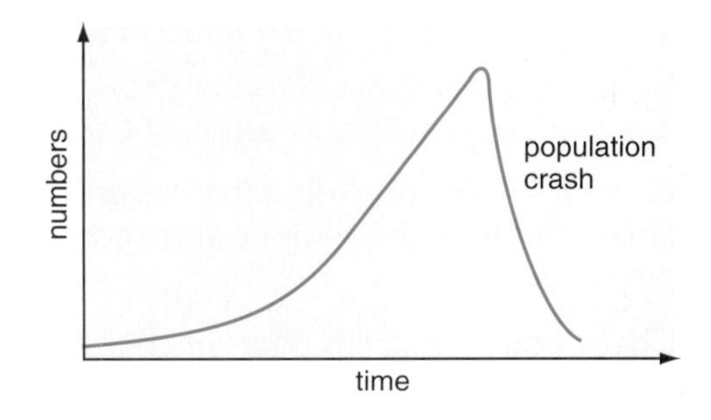

▶ Population size

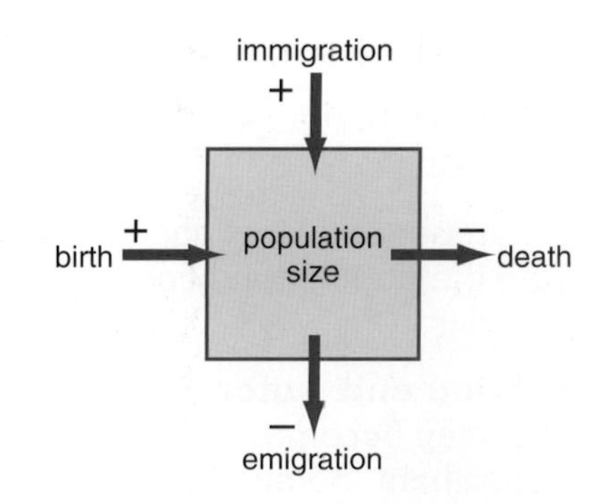

What determines how big a population is?

The number of births adds to the population.
The number of deaths decreases it.

Many individuals can enter and leave a population.
You can probably think of lots of animals that can do this. But plants can use seed dispersal to join another population.

Movement into a population is called **immigration**.
Movement out of a population is **emigration**.

Estimating the size of a plant population

You may need to estimate the size of a population for a scientific investigation.
You won't be able to count ***all*** the individuals in a population so you need to take a **sample**. The more samples you take, the more reliable your data will be.

This is easier to do if you are looking at plants.
You use a metal or a wooden frame called a **quadrat**.
Put the quadrat down on the vegetation.
Now count the number of a particular plant present inside the quadrat.
Estimate how many quadrats you would need to cover the habitat. Multiply this by the number of plants that you found in the quadrat to get the total population.

What is the percentage cover of each of these plants?

To get a quick estimate of a particular plant population you can use **percentage cover**.
This is the amount of ground covered by a particular plant inside the quadrat.
We estimate this as a percentage.

Using a quadrat

Investigation 18.2 What affects the size of a duckweed population?

Duckweed is a small, floating plant found in ponds.
It reproduces quickly to produce a large population.

Investigate what factors affect its growth.
You could try light, temperature, carbon dioxide or nutrients.

Check your plan with your teacher before you start.

Estimating the size of animal populations

Sampling animals is more difficult.
They tend to move about.
Not many animals will stay in a quadrat!
Many animals only come out at night.
To get a sample we have to trap them – humanely.
We then use the **mark, release, recapture** method to estimate the size of the population.

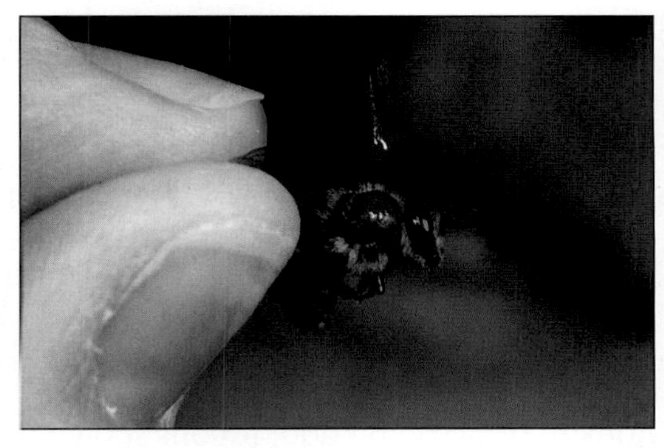

Using a harmless mark on a honey bee

This is how it works:

- collect a sample of animals (M)
- mark the captured animals – this should be a small harmless mark like a small paint dot
- release the marked animals into their habitat
- give them a day or two to mix back into the population
- collect a second sample (S)
- count the number of marked animals (R) in this second sample.

You can now use this equation to get an estimate of the total population (P):

Do not be too ambitious in your choice of animal

$$\text{Total population } (P) = \frac{\text{number in first catch } (M) \times \text{number in second catch } (S)}{\text{number of marked animals in second catch } (R)}$$

$$P = \frac{M \times S}{R}$$

Here's a worked example:

Example

A pitfall trap like the one in the diagram was used to catch 12 ground beetles.
Each was marked with a small dot of paint and released.
After 2 days a second catch gave 16 beetles.
Of these four were marked – they had been recaptured.

Number in first catch (M) = 12

Number in second catch (S) = 16

Number recaptured (R) = 4

$$\text{Total population} = \frac{M \times S}{R} = \frac{12 \times 16}{4}$$

$$= \underline{48 \text{ ground beetles}}$$

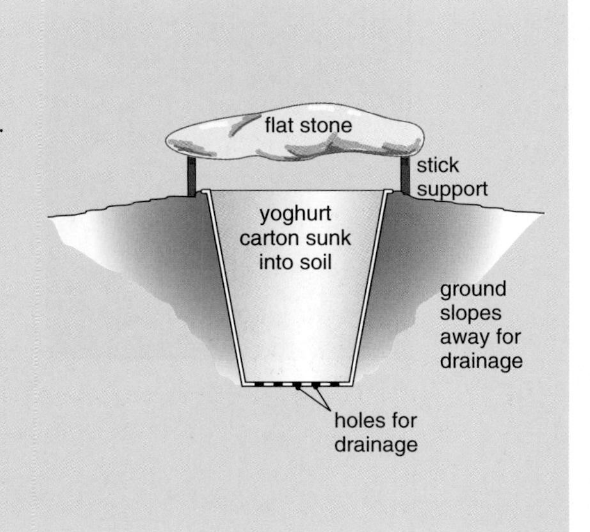

Adaptations

Animals and plants must be adapted to their habitats if they are to survive.

They may have special features that help them survive, for instance, different birds have different beaks that are adapted for a particular diet. The behaviour of some animals is adapted to their habitat, for instance, penguins huddle together to keep warm.

Look at some of the adaptations shown by plants and animals on these two pages. Think how each one aids survival. Say whether the adaptations are physical or behavioural, or both.

The feathery tufts of thistle seeds are blown by the wind

Birds like these swallows fly to South Africa in the winter

This plantain weed grows on paths. It grows very flat and has strong deep roots.

When the tide goes out, this periwinkle shuts its trap door tightly

The mayfly larva lives in fast-flowing streams. It has a flattened, streamlined body and clings to the underside of rocks.

▶ More adaptations

The adaptations on these two pages are inherited.
The better adapted individuals tend to survive.
They produce similar offspring with the same features.
This is how natural selection operates.

Penguins have a compact body shape. They are clumsy on land but fast, agile swimmers. They often huddle together when it is extremely cold.

This flounder can change its colour to fit its background

The arctic fox has to endure extreme cold. Unlike our native red fox, it has a thick, white coat and also has much smaller ears.

This dormouse spends most of the winter asleep

The fennec fox lives in desert conditions. It has a small body but extremely large ears. It lives in a burrow during the day and hunts at night. It has large eyes that help it see well in dim light.

Adaptations to extreme conditions

Desert conditions

Look at the photograph of the camel.
Some adaptations to desert conditions are shown below.
For each adaptation, say how it helps the camel to survive.

- It can drink 40 pints of water at one go.
  This takes 10 minutes.
- The stomach can store 500 pints of water for a short time.
- It loses little water : there is little urine and no sweating.
- No layer of fat under the skin.
- Fat is stored in the hump and can be respired to give 'metabolic water'.

- It has bushy eyelashes and hair-lined nostrils that can close.
- The body has a large surface area to volume ratio.
- It has large feet to spread the load.
- It has long legs (hint : the hottest air is in the 1 metre above the desert sand).
- It can withstand an increase in normal body temperature of 9 °C.

Arctic conditions

Look at the photograph of the polar bear.
Some adaptations to arctic conditions are shown.
For each adaptation say how it helps the polar bear to survive.

- Compact shape.
  Body has a low surface area to volume ratio.
- Polar bears have small ears.
- They have thick layer of fat stored under the skin.
- Their very large feet are covered with thick, rough skin and long, tough hair.

- Their fur is thick and white.
- Greasy fur which sheds water quickly after swimming.
- They are strong swimmers and fast runners over the ice
- The female mates in summer, pregnancy does not occur until autumn.
- Sharp teeth and long claws.

Plants in dry places

Some plants are able to exist in conditions where water is scarce.
Cacti are able to survive in hot, dry (arid) regions.
All plants have to balance water uptake with water loss.
So how are cacti able to reduce water loss?

Cactus plants live in hot, dry places. Their leaves are small spines and they can store water inside their stems.

- They have swollen stems containing water-storage tissue.
- Their leaves have become reduced to spines.
  This reduces the surface area of the leaf over which water can be lost.
- A thick, waxy cuticle covers the plant's surfaces and reduces transpiration.
- They have a shallow, spreading root system to quickly absorb any water from rain and overnight condensation.
- Many cacti have a round, compact shape which reduces their surface area to volume ratio. So there is less surface area over which water can be lost.
- They have shiny surfaces which reflect heat and light.

The leaves of this cactus are reduced to spines

So if the leaves are reduced to spines, how does the cactus carry out photosynthesis?
As you can see, the stems are green and contain the chlorophyll that is needed for photosynthesis.

Conifers are also well adapted to withstanding water loss.
These trees are often found high up on mountain slopes.
Here it can be very windy and normal leaves would easily lose water by transpiration.
The leaves of a conifer are reduced to needles.
Like the cactus, they have a reduced surface area to volume ratio, so there is less surface over which water can be lost.

Sand dune plants like marram have long thin leaves.
The leaves are also rolled up along their length.
The stomata are found inside the groove formed by the rolled up leaf.
Humid air becomes trapped in the groove and so less water vapour passes out of the stomata to be lost to the plant.

Marram grass colonising a sand dune

▶ Competition

What does **competition** mean to you?
In a race, all the competitors try their hardest to win.
In nature, plants and animals compete for **resources** that are in short supply.

What do you think plants compete for?

If resources like light, space, water or nutrients are scarce, plants compete for them.

What do you think animals compete for?

Many animals compete for a **territory** (habitat).
If they are not successful they do not attract a mate and can not breed.

Boobies compete for nesting space

Only those plants and animals that are able to compete successfully will survive.
So competition restricts the size of a population.

There are two types of competition:

- competition between individuals of the ***same*** species
- competition between individuals of ***different*** species.

Competition within a species

What happens if you sow carrot seeds too close together?

The seedlings compete for space, light, water and nutrients.
Colonies of gulls compete for nesting sites.
There is often competition between members of the same species.

Red deer stags fight to mate with the females

Animals and plants tend to produce lots of offspring.
Often there are far more than can ever survive.
There will be competition between individual offspring for scarce resources.
Only the best adapted will survive to breed.

Competition between individuals of the same species means that only the 'best' genes are passed on to the next generation.
As we saw in Chapter 17, there is a 'struggle for existence' leading to the 'survival of the fittest'.

Competition between different species

Have you ever seen a bird table in winter?
What happens when some crumbs are put on it?

Soon there are sparrows, blue tits, starlings and other birds all trying to get at the food.
The different garden birds are competing for a scarce resource – food.

Weeds are excellent competitors.
A weed is a plant growing where it is not wanted e.g. poppies in a field of barley.
Gardeners hate weeds because they are very hard to get rid of.
Weeds compete with other plants for light, water and space.

But how are they so successful?

If you look at the diagram of the dandelion it will give you some clues:

- They are able to reproduce quickly and produce a huge number of seeds.
- Their seeds germinate quickly in poor soil.
- They can grow very quickly and flower and set seed before other plants can.
- They can tolerate poor soil and harsh conditions.

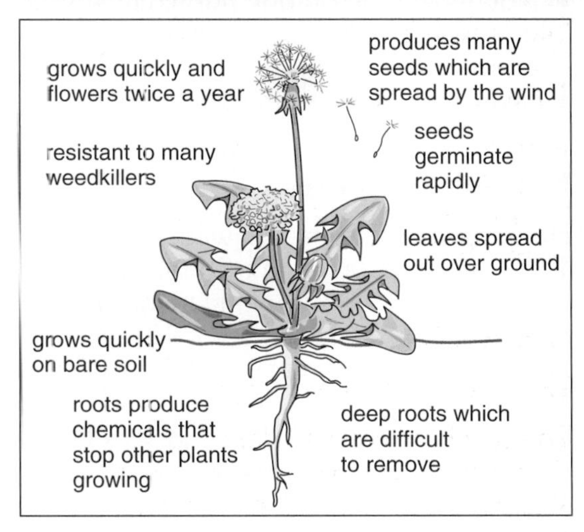

Competing with humans

Can you think of any animals and plants that compete with humans?
Weeds compete with the farmer's crops.
There are many animals that compete with us – we call them **pests**.
Locusts, cockroaches and rats are pests that compete with us for food.
Greenfly and whitefly are pests that do damage to our crops.
Screwworm fly is a serious pest of cattle, and mosquitoes spread malaria.

Cockroaches can spoil our food

Predation

Predators kill other animals (their **prey**) for food.
Predators are usually bigger and fewer in number than their prey. Why do you think this is?

Look at the wolf:

What things make it a good predator?
It has sharp teeth and claws, but also its eyes are at the front of the head to judge size and distance.

What other things make predators successful?

- Some hunt in a pack.
  They work together to catch the prey and share it.
- Attacking prey that is young, old, sick or injured.
  These prey are easier to overpower and kill.
  This also 'weeds out' the weaker individuals in the prey population.
- Catching large prey means that there is more food for the predator per kill.
- Not depending on one particular species of prey.
  If numbers go down, the predator can switch to another prey species.
- Migrating to areas where the prey is more plentiful.

Human predators

Humans still hunt and kill wild animals.
The best example is commercial fishing.
Improved fishing technology means more fish are caught.
We hunt the fish using powerful fishing vessels, sonar to detect shoals, and huge plastic nets.
Fishermen are so well equipped that they could remove all of the fish from the sea.

Many species are now ***overfished***.
Humans have been such successful predators that future fish stocks are threatened.
International agreements have so far failed to control the amount of fishing.

We should agree quotas on how many fish can be caught.
We should avoid fishing during the breeding season and use nets that catch only non-breeding adults, leaving the small fish to survive and breed.

The size of fish stocks is being reduced to such an extent that many are now on the verge of extinction.
(See page 366 for more adaptations to successful predation.)

Avoiding the predator

However well adapted the predator is, some prey escape.

Look at the hare :

How is it adapted to escape predators ?

Well, it has large ears to listen for trouble and eyes on the side of the head for a wide field of view. It also has long, strong back legs.

What other things help prey to escape ?

- Some try to run, swim or fly faster than the predator.
- Staying in large groups, like herds of antelope, helps survival.
  Many pairs of eyes can look out for predators.
- Some animals taste horrible !
  This makes them less attractive as a meal.
  Others like bees and wasps can sting the predator.
- Some prey has warning colours.
  This tells the predator to 'keep clear'.
  Hoverflies look like wasps and bees.
  But they have no sting and could be eaten.
- Camouflage helps to hide the prey.
  Many prey animals try to blend in with their surroundings.
  The trouble is many predators do too !
- Some prey try shock tactics to startle a would-be predator.
  Can you see how this eyed hawkmoth can scare off a hungry bird ?

Predators find monarch butterflies unpleasant to eat

Can you find the katydid insect in the picture ?

An eyed hawkmoth unfolds its wings

Prey that escape are usually the best adapted.
They survive to pass on their genes to their offspring.
Natural selection operates against weaker less well-adapted individuals.
(See page 366 for more adaptations to avoid predation.)

Predator–prey cycles

Predators try to kill their prey.
So obviously they have a big effect on the size of the prey population.
But have you ever thought how the number of prey affects the predator?

What would happen to a predator if the animals it fed upon all died of disease?
Such drastic events do not happen often.
But if the prey becomes scarce, the predator suffers too.

Look at the graph carefully:

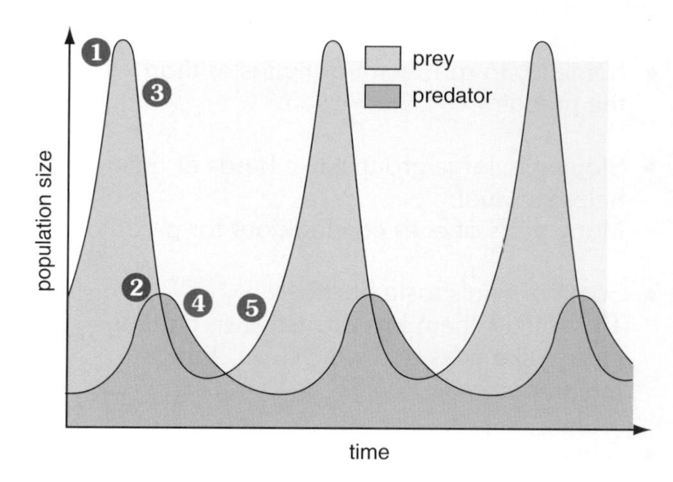

1. The prey has plenty of food.
   It breeds and increases in number.

2. The increase in prey numbers means that there is more food for the predator.
   So the predator breeds and increases in number.

3. There are now lots of predators so more prey will be eaten.
   The number of prey goes down.

4. There are now less prey for the predator to feed on.
   Food will be scarce and many predators starve.

5. With fewer predators, more prey survive to breed.
   The prey numbers increase, and so the cycle continues.

One of the best-known examples of the predator–prey cycle is that of the lynx and the snowshoe hare.
Both these animals were trapped for their fur.
The Hudson Bay Fur Company in Canada kept records of the number of skins that trappers brought in.
The graph shows the numbers between 1845 and 1935:

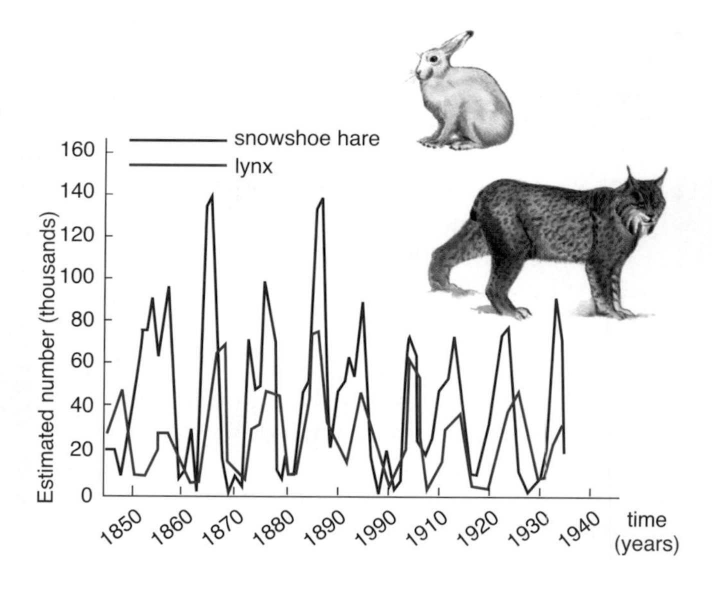

Can you see a pattern in the curves?

▶ Biology at work : The Eden project

Have you ever visited the Eden Project in Cornwall?
It was previously a china clay pit and it took a great deal of work and 85 000 tonnes of soil, made from recycled waste, before 5000 plants could be added.
At the site, a variety of climates are recreated inside huge domes called **biomes**.
Inside these giant conservatories, scientists carefully control temperature, humidity and soil types to grow plants from all over the world.

Humid Tropics Biome

This biome is the largest conservatory in the world at 240 m long, 110 m wide and 50 m high.
Conditions are kept like a tropical rainforest and it contains over 1000 species of plants.
The moist air is maintained at a temperature of between 18 and 35 °C.
Here there are huge trees and, growing on them, high up in the branches are other plants such as orchids and ferns.
Visiting this biome reminds people about the need to conserve the fragile rainforests of the world.

Humid tropics biome

Warm Temperate Biome

Conditions inside this biome are like those in warm Mediterranean regions, with hot, dry summers and cool, wet winters.
These regions include California, South Africa, SW Australia and Chile, as well as the Mediterranean countries.
Natural gardens bloom in spite of the poor, thin soils and the scorching sun.
Many of the plants have thick, waxy cuticles and spines instead of leaves to reduce water loss.
Shrubs are more common than trees in these regions and many flowers grow from bulbs that lie below the sun-scorched soil.
Inside this biome, the air is kept at between 15 and 25 °C in summer and at a minimum of 9 °C in winter.
All the biomes are constructed of special glass that lets ultra-violet light from the sun pass through it.

The Eden Project not only provides a pleasant day out, it lets people experience a variety of natural ecosystems and gives a strong conservation message to visitors.

Mediterranean plants in flower

Summary

- Ecosystems are made up of the habitat (non-living) and the community (plants and animals).
- A community is made up of different plant and animal populations.
- A population is a group of individuals belonging to the same species.
- In any ecosystem there are environmental and biotic factors to which organisms have to adapt.
- Populations are able to grow quickly but natural checks act against this increase. Births and immigration increase a population; deaths and emigration decrease it.
- Structural and behavioural adaptations enable animals and plants to survive.
- Competition exists both within the members of a species and between different species.
- Some animals are well adapted to withstand extreme temperatures, e.g. camels in the desert and polar bears in the Arctic.
- Some plants are adapted to survive in hot, dry regions. They are able to reduce their water loss.
- Some animals are adapted to be successful predators. Other animals are adapted to avoid being caught as prey.
- Predator–prey cycles operate to control the numbers of each population.

▶ Questions

1. Match these words with each of the following definitions:

ecosystems habitat community
population niche biosphere

a) Organisms that interact within the same ecosystem.
b) A group of individuals of the same species.
c) The part of an ecosystem where plants and animals live.
d) All the ecosystems belong to this.

2. Match the animals and plants in Column A below with their correct habitats in Column B:

Column A	Column B
lichen	wood
trout	path
hawthorn	rocky shore
groundsel	pond
squirrel	moorland
heather	river
frog	hedge
crab	wall

3. Duckweed was grown in a beaker of water. The number of plants counted each day is shown in the table:

Day	No. of plants
1	1
4	2
8	4
12	8
16	16
20	32
24	32
28	31
32	31

a) Plot the results on a graph to show how the population size changes with time.
b) Explain the shape of the curve.
c) Suggest two factors that could have caused the population to become stable.

4. a) Name four factors that limit the growth of a population.
b) For each of these factors explain the effect that it has on the population's growth.

5. Ten identical plots of land were cleared of weeds and then sowed with pea seeds.
After sowing, 9 of the plots were kept free of weeds for different lengths of time.
After 9 weeks, all the plants were harvested from each plot and weighed.
The results are shown in the graph :

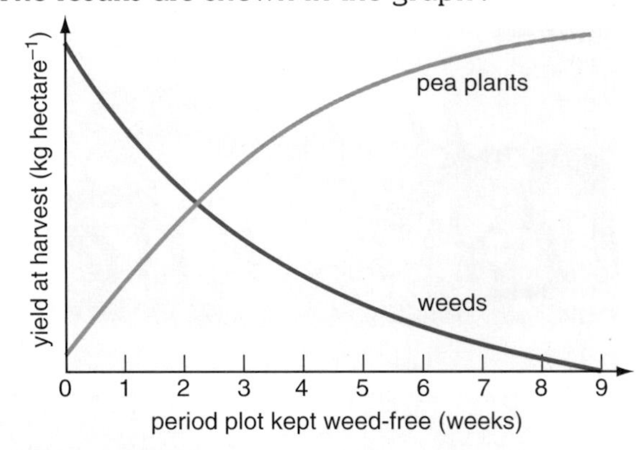

a) What conclusions can you draw about the competition between pea plants and weeds?
b) How could you estimate the total mass of weeds growing in a large field?
c) Design an experiment to test the prediction that pea plants growing at a high density produce fewer peas per plant than those growing at a low density.

6. The number of animals in a habitat were studied using the 'mark, release, recapture' technique. The results are shown in the table :

Animals	No. in 1st catch (*M*)	No. in 2nd catch (*S*)	No. of marked animals in 2nd catch (*R*)
millipedes	40	50	25
centipedes	50	60	20
beetles	16	15	6
woodlice	100	80	40
snails	20	15	10

a) Use the formula

$$P = \frac{M \times S}{R}$$

to work out the population of each animal.
b) Draw a bar-chart for each animal population.
c) Why should the animals not be marked with bright, permanent paint?

7. The graph was drawn from data collected from a lake over a period of 12 months.

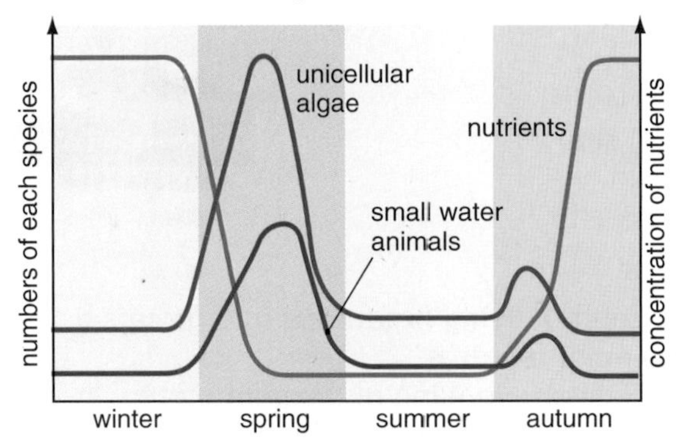

a) Name two environmental factors needed for algae to grow.
b) Explain why the number of algae increased from a winter low to a spring high.
c) Explain why the population of small water animals fell in late spring.
d) Explain why the concentration of nutrients fell in the spring but rose in autumn.

8. A population of rabbits lived on an island. Predators such as weasels fed on the rabbits. Some hunters came to the island and shot all the weasels.
The rabbit population increased. They began to compete for grass. Many rabbits starved. Soon the rabbit population was about the same as it was before the weasels were shot.
a) What were the four populations involved?
b) Why do you think the hunters were wrong to shoot all the weasels?
c) What do you think will happen to the rabbit population in the future?

9. Some students carried out a study in a local cornfield. They took measurements of the height of the corn plants at a number of distances away from a hedge. They also estimated the biomass of the corn plants. Their results showed that the height and biomass of the corn plants increased the further away from the hedge that they were growing.
a) Try to explain the results of the students.
b) The farmer is considering removing the hedge.
Suggest reasons for and against the removal of the hedge.

Further questions on page 340.

chapter 19

We can put living organisms into groups based on similar features.
But if we are looking at a community of living things it is often more useful to group them by looking at the way that they feed.

First of all we can divide up living things into those that make their own food and those that don't.

Producers are able to make their own food from simple substances like carbon dioxide and water.
Do you know of any producers?

Green plants use light as a source of energy to make sugars from carbon dioxide and water.
Many bacteria are also producers.
Some use light as an energy source but most obtain the energy they need from chemical reactions.

Producers ultimately produce the food for all the other members of the community.

Light penetrating the tree canopy

All animals are **consumers**.
They cannot make their own food.
So they have to eat or consume it.

- **Primary consumers** are herbivores.
  They eat the producers – plants or bacteria.
- **Secondary consumers** are carnivores.
  They eat herbivores.
- **Tertiary consumers** are carnivores that eat secondary consumers.
  They are sometimes called top carnivores.
- **Decomposers** are microbes that feed on dead and decaying material.
  Most of these are bacteria and fungi.

Which are the primary consumers and secondary consumers in this photograph?

Each feeding group belongs to a different **trophic level**.
('Trophic' comes from a Greek word and means 'to feed'.)

▶ Food chains

Food chains show us what eats what in a community.
They show the movement of food energy from one organism to the next.
Look at this food chain:

The arrows show the direction in which the food energy is transferred from one organism to the next.
This food chain tells us that the rabbit eats grass and the fox eats the rabbit.

Here is a food chain with four links:

Notice that the food chain always begins with a producer, often a green plant.
This can include parts of a plant, such as seeds, fruits or even dead leaves.
Here is a food chain where the primary consumer feeds on dead leaves:

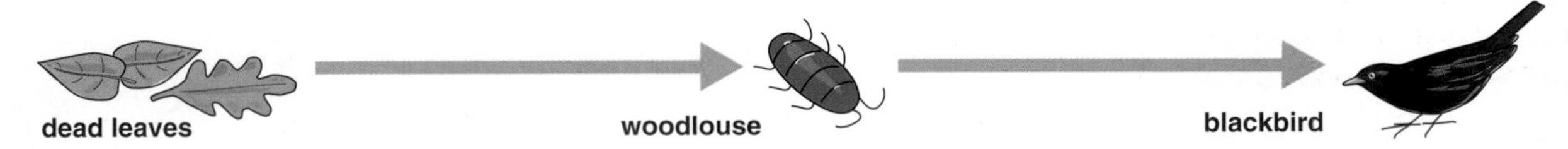

We can draw food chains from any community.
They may live on the land or in water.

Here is a food chain from the sea:

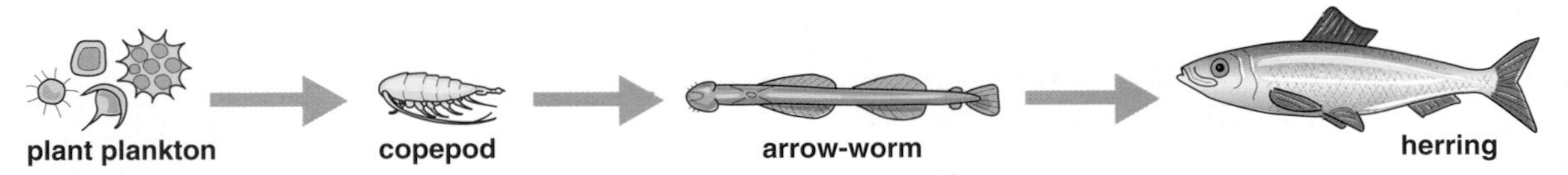

If all the copepods died:
- What would happen to the number of arrow-worms
- What would happen to the numbers of plant plankton?

Here is a food chain from a lake. It has five links:

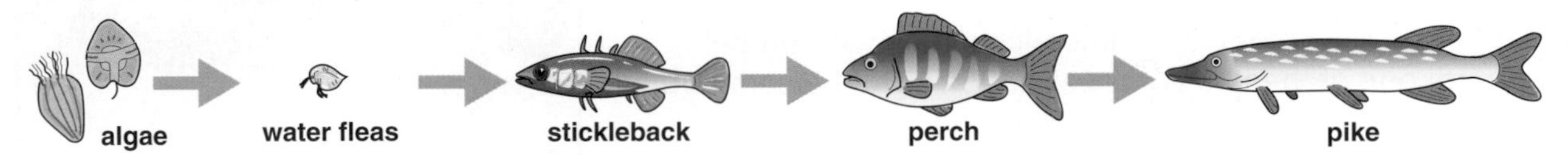

What are the producers in this food chain?
What is the top carnivore?

▶ Food webs

In most communities animals will eat more than one thing.
Hedgehogs would get pretty fed up if they ate just snails!
They also eat beetles, earthworms and slugs.

A **food web** is made up of many food chains.
It gives a more complete picture of how animals feed.

Look at the woodland food web:

Can you find all the food chains?
Try writing them out.
There are six of them.

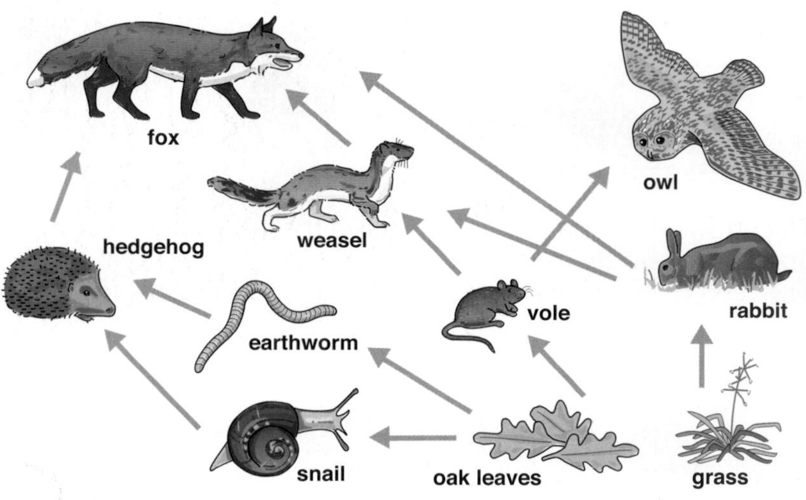

Woodland food web

Look at the seashore food web:

a) How many primary consumers are there?
b) How many secondary consumers are there?
c) Draw a food chain with five links from this food web.
d) Suppose all the starfish died from pollution.
   What would happen to the number of:
   i) mussels   ii) small algae?

sea bird
crab
starfish
dog whelk
limpet
barnacle
mussel
small algae

Seashore food web

The niche

If we look at a food web we can see how a particular organism feeds.
This is part of its role or job in the community.
We call this its **niche**.
For instance, the winter moth caterpillar feeds on the buds of oak trees.
It provides food for many birds and parasites.
This is the ***role*** or ***niche*** of the winter moth caterpillar.

If two organisms occupy the same niche, they will compete, often until one of them becomes excluded from the community.
For instance, in Britain the North American grey squirrel seems to be competing for the same niche as the native red squirrel. They both want the same food and they both want to live in the same nesting sites.

Competing for the same niche

▶ Pyramids of number

Food chains and food webs can show the feeding relationships in a community.
But they do not tell us ***how many*** living organisms are involved.
For instance, it takes many plants to feed one herbivore and many herbivores to feed one carnivore.

Look at the diagram :

Why are there far more leaves than caterpillars ?
Why are there far fewer owls than shrews ?

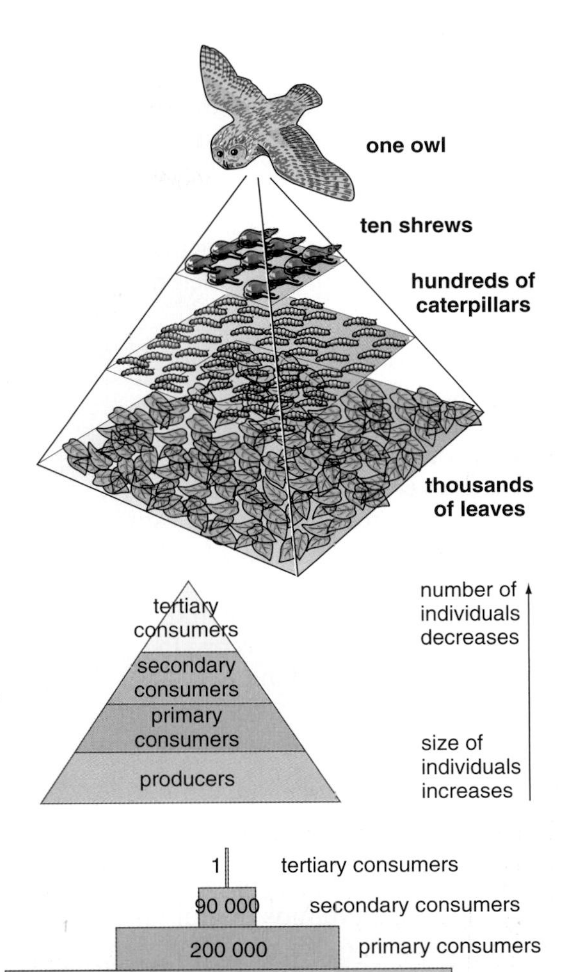

Pyramid of numbers for a grassland community in 0.1 hectare

Look at the numbers in this food chain :

owl	1
shrews	10
caterpillars	100
oak leaves	600

We can show this information in a **pyramid of numbers**.
The area of each box shows us roughly how many living things there are at each trophic level.
You start with the producers on the first level, then the primary consumers on the second level, the secondary consumers on the third, and so on.

- What happens to the ***numbers*** of individuals as you go up this pyramid ?
- What happens to the ***size*** of each organism as you go up this pyramid ?
- Why are the producers (like green plants) always on the first trophic level ?

A problem with pyramids of number is that they do not take into account the ***size*** of organisms at each trophic level.
For instance, an oak tree and a grass plant each count as one organism.
But one oak tree can support many more herbivores than one grass plant can.
As a result some pyramids of number can have unusual shapes.

Look at this pyramid of numbers :

The tertiary consumers are parasites.
Many of them feed on a single ladybird.
So this inverted pyramid looks top heavy.

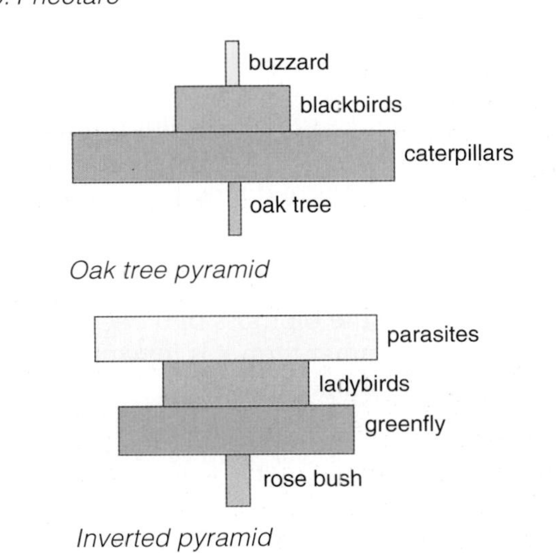

Oak tree pyramid

Inverted pyramid

▶ Pyramids of biomass

One way to overcome the problem of size is to measure **biomass** instead of numbers.

Biomass is the weight of living material

Biomass is the weight of living material.
So a biomass pyramid shows the actual weight or mass of living things at each trophic level.

To draw a biomass pyramid you first need to collect your data.
Take a sample of the organisms from each trophic level and weigh them.
Find the average mass for the sample.
Then multiply the mass by the estimated number present in the community.
Some scientists work out the dry mass because the water content can vary in living things.
But to do this you have to dry the organisms in an oven which would kill them.

Biomass sampling on a rocky shore

Biomass pyramids also have other drawbacks.

- The mass recorded is at one instant in time.
  So biomass pyramids do not take into account ***how fast*** an organism grows.
  For instance, grass grows at a fast rate, but because it is grazed its biomass at a particular time will be low.

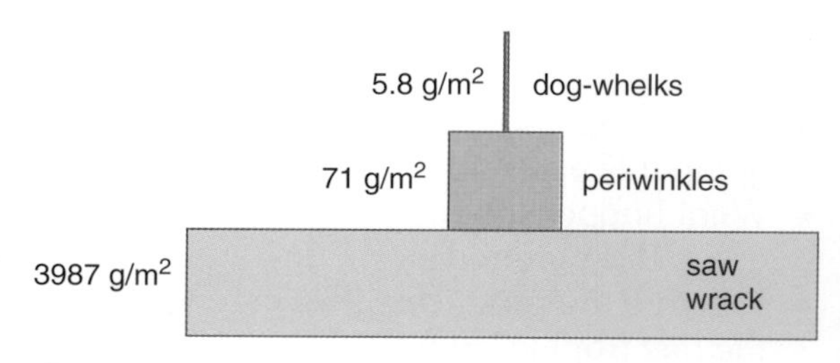

Biomass pyramid for a rocky shore community

  Plant plankton grow quickly in the sea, but they only live for a few days.
  So their biomass at a particular time is small.
  But over say a year, their biomass is huge.
  This biomass pyramid records only a few days' growth and so looks inverted :

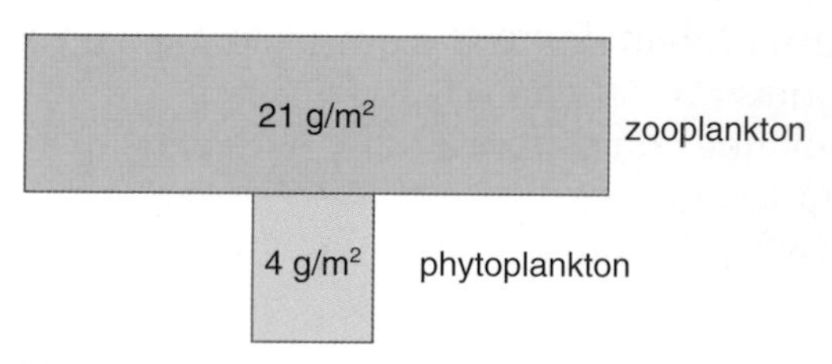

Biomass pyramid for the English Channel

- Biomass can vary with the seasons.
  For instance, the biomass of a beech tree is far greater in summer than it is in winter.
  Why do you think this is ?

  In winter the tree will have lost the leaves, flowers and fruits that grow in the summer.

▶ Pyramids of energy

The best way to show what is happening in the feeding relationships of a community is to use **energy pyramids**.

These show the amount of energy transferred from one trophic level to the next.
This energy pyramid shows that 87 000 kJ/m²/yr is passed to the tadpoles from the water plants.
The tadpoles pass on 14 000 kJ/m²/yr to the small fish, and so on.

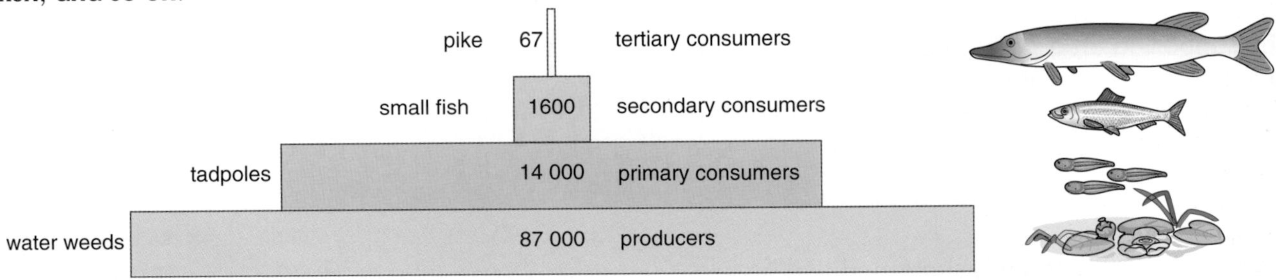

A pyramid of energy for a pond (figures are in kJ/m²/year)

If the tadpoles got 87 000 kJ from the water plants but only passed on 14 000 kJ to the small fish, where did the other 73 000 kJ go to?
What have the tadpoles done with all that energy?
They will have used up a lot of it swimming around and passed out some of it in waste.
In fact the only energy that they do pass on to the small fish is that which they have used in growing.

Energy is always 'lost' in this way as it is passed from one trophic level to the next.
Of the 87 000 kJ of energy we started with only 67 kJ will end up as part of the top carnivore, the pike!

The larva of the great diving beetle also feeds on tadpoles

Since only some of the energy is passed on an energy pyramid is never inverted.
Its shape is not affected by the size of the organisms or how many of them there are since it simply looks at the amount of energy that is passed on.

Unlike pyramids of number or of biomass, energy pyramids make it easy to compare the efficiency of energy transfer from one trophic level to the next in different communities.
If energy transfer is efficient then a lot of energy will be passed on from one level to the next.

Although energy pyramids are better than pyramids of number and pyramids of biomass it is difficult to collect data for the energy at each trophic level.

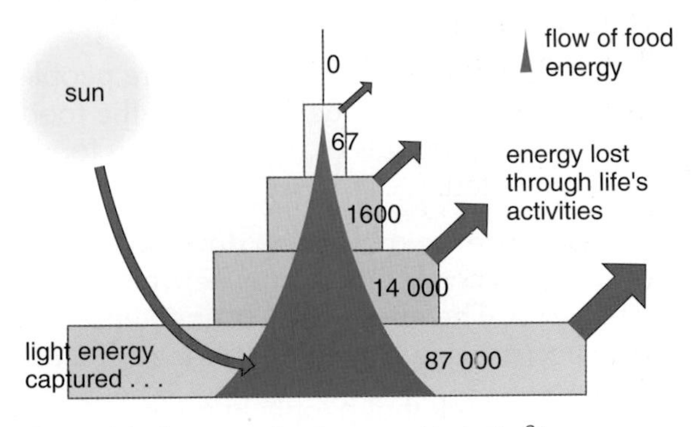

Pyramid of energy for the pond in kJ/m²/year

▶ Shortening the food chain

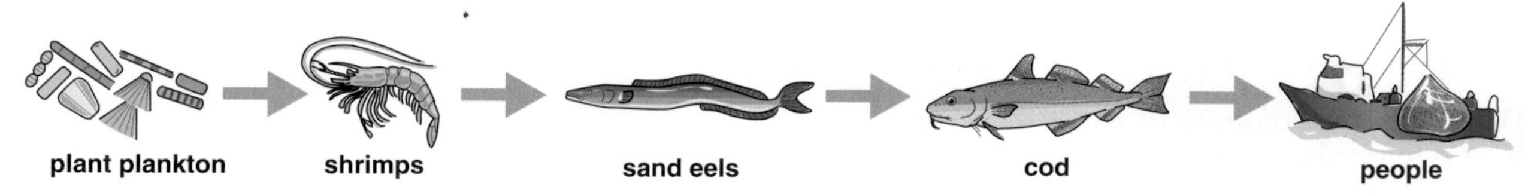

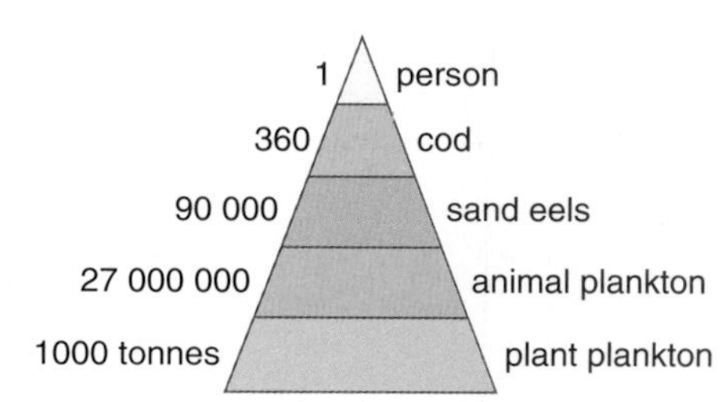

Look at this pyramid of numbers:

It shows the estimated number of individuals that could be supported on a 1000 tonnes of plant plankton in a year. Humans are at the top of this pyramid. How many cod would one human eat in a year? It works out at about one cod a day.

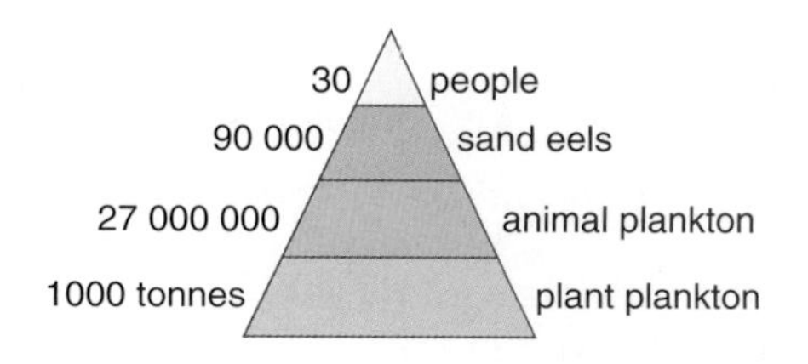

What if the food chain is shortened and people ate sand eels instead of cod? Thirty people could be supported in this way. That's assuming each could get by on about 10 sand eels a day.

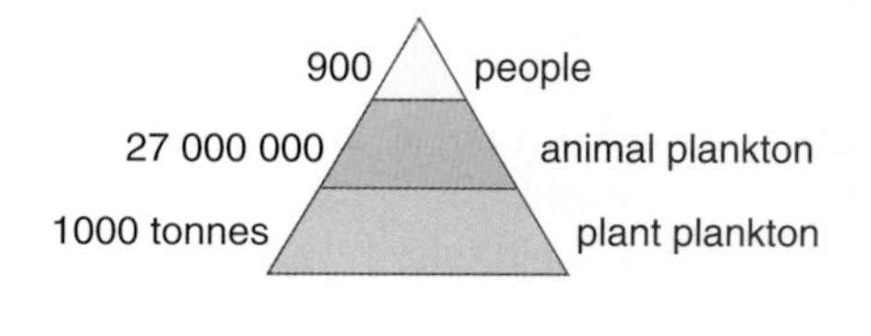

What if the food chain is shortened again? People now feed on animal plankton such as shrimps? Could you get by on 100 shrimps a day? If so this food chain could support 900 people in a year.

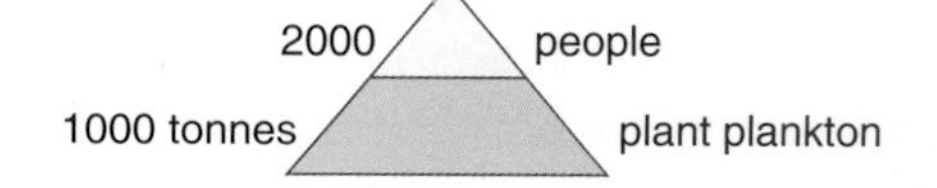

What if we remove the last animal in the food chain and become vegetarian? Feeding on 2 kg of plant plankton a day may not appeal to you. But this could support 2000 people a year.

What is the message from this exercise? A vegetarian diet can support far more people. If we cut down the number of links in the food chain more individuals at the end of the food chain can be fed.

This is because we are cutting down the 90 % 'wastage' of energy that occurs between each trophic level. The energy that is uneaten, undigested or used in respiration at each level.

Why do you think that people in underdeveloped countries tend to have vegetarian diets?

In the Western developed countries people have a varied diet. It includes poultry, fish, lamb, beef and pork. What does this tell you about the economies of these countries?

The human population is increasing at an alarming rate. How do you think this will affect the future price of meat?

The rising price of food is pushing us down the food pyramid towards a vegetarian diet.

▶ Energy flow through producers

The energy in all ecosystems originally came from the Sun.
This energy can be transferred.
In photosynthesis green plants transfer sunlight energy into chemical energy in sugar.

Green plants (and some bacteria) are the only living organisms that are able to do this.
But photosynthesis is far less efficient than we think.

Most of the sunlight that falls on leaves is not absorbed and used.

- Some is reflected from the leaf's surface.
- Some passes straight through the leaf.
- Only part of the light is useful and can be absorbed by chlorophyll.

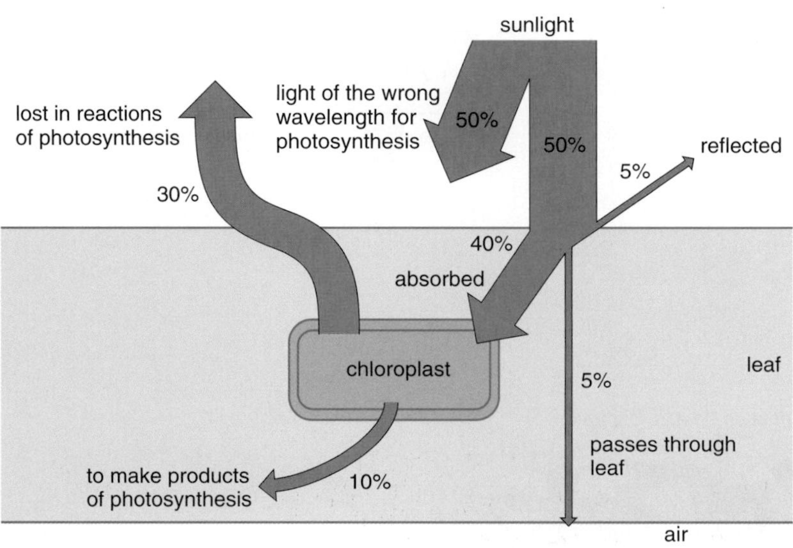

What happens to the light that falls onto a leaf?

The overall efficiency of energy transfer during photosynthesis is less than 10 %.
So only about 8 % of the sunlight energy reaching the plant is transferred into useful chemical energy.

This chemical energy is used by the plant for respiration and growth.

When the plant grows its biomass will increase.
This will provide food energy for herbivores.
It may be transferred between trophic levels from producers to primary consumers.

Some food energy may be transferred to decomposers.
This can happen when leaves are shed, fruits and seeds are dispersed and when the plant itself dies.
Decomposers eat the dead plant tissues to get energy.

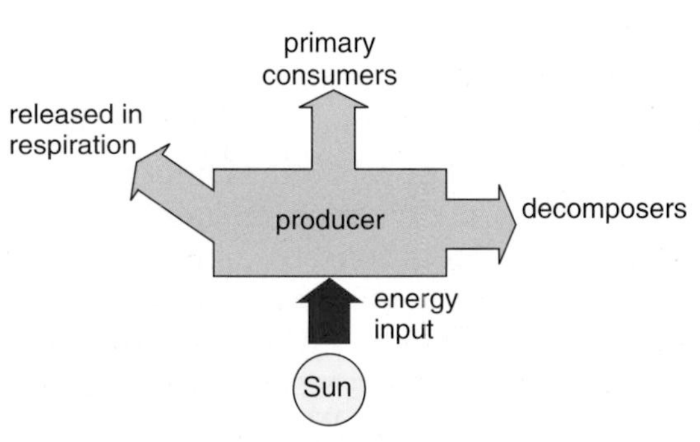

Energy flow through a green plant

▶ Energy flow through consumers

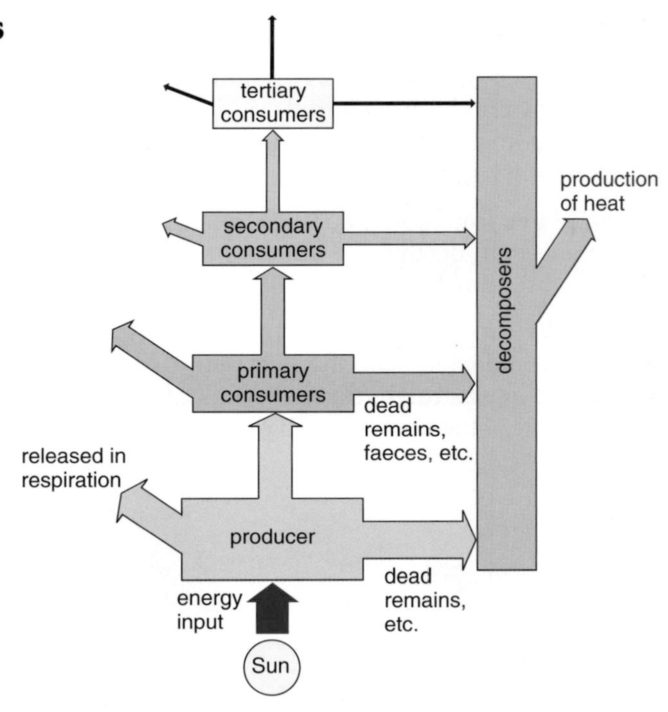

Transfer of food energy from producers to primary consumers also involves 'wastage'.
For every 100 g of plant material available only about 10 g ends up as part of a herbivore's body.

What are the reasons for this 90 % energy 'wastage' between trophic levels ?

- Some food may not be eaten.
- Some food passes through the body of the herbivore without being digested.
- A lot of food is used in respiration.

Similar losses in food energy occur between other trophic levels.
Some carnivores are able to achieve a 20 % conversion efficiency.
So for every 100 g of herbivore that they eat 20 g ends up as part of their body.
This is because proteins are more efficiently digested than are carbohydrates and animals contain a lot more protein than plants.

Look at the diagram showing the energy intake and output of a cow :

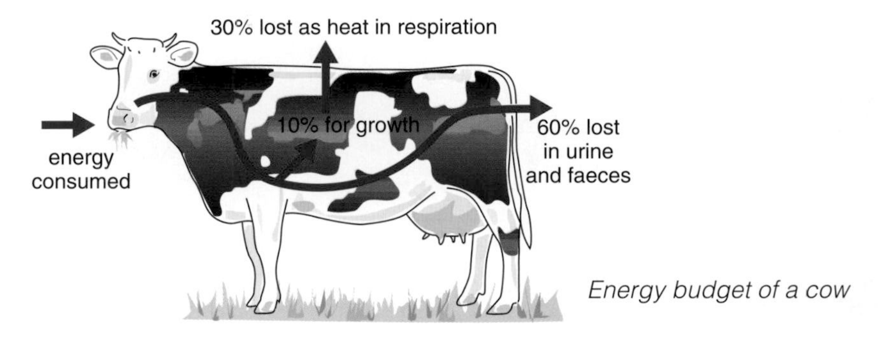

Energy budget of a cow

Of the energy in the grass the cow eats, over half is passed out of the body in faeces.
A lot of energy passes out as heat produced during respiration and in the urine.
What is left goes to increase the cow's biomass.

The cow's energy budget can be summarised as :

Energy intake	=	**Energy transfer in respiration**	+	**Energy transfer into biomass**	+	**Energy in faeces**	+	**Energy in urine**

▶ Nutrient cycling

What happens to dead plants and animals?
They rot away or **decompose**.
Microbes are responsible for decomposition.
The **bacteria** and **fungi** (moulds) that make dead things rot are called **decomposers**.
Decomposers also break down the waste materials made by animals (faeces and urine).

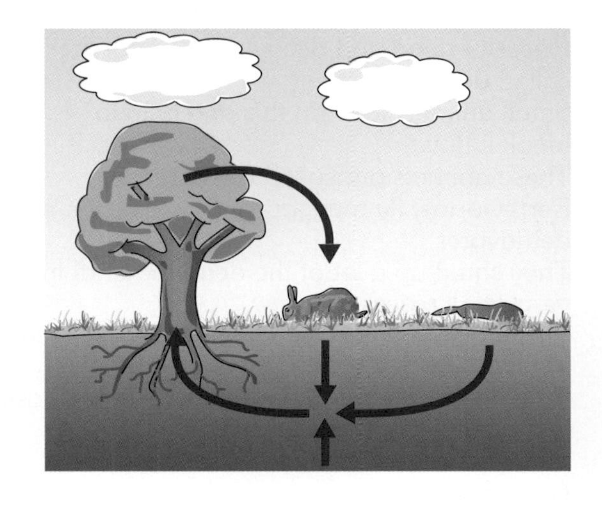

Look at the diagram:

Plants need chemicals called **nutrients** for growth.
These are usually found in the soil.
How do plants take up these nutrients?
How do these nutrients get into animals?
Name two ways in which nutrients get back into the soil.

Decomposers are the vital link in this story.
By decaying dead remains and waste, they free the nutrients that were locked inside.
These nutrients can be used again by other living things.

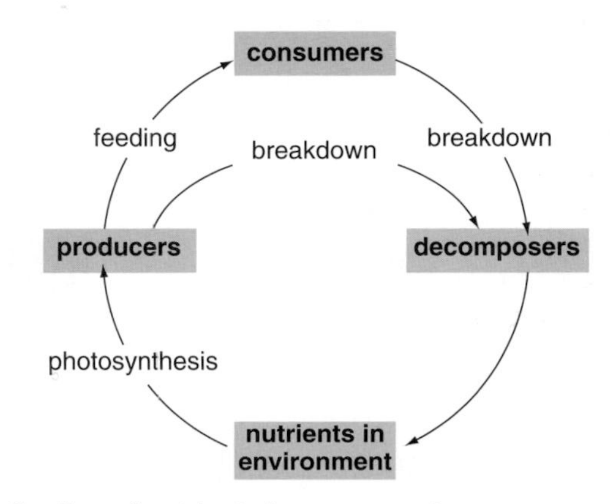

Cycling of nutrients in an ecosystem

The nutrients that make up the bodies of living things can be used again and again.
First they are released into the soil and are taken up by plants.
The nutrients are then passed on to animals when they eat the plants.
We say that nutrients are **cycled**.

Most living matter (95 %) is made up of just six elements:
carbon, hydrogen, oxygen, nitrogen, phosphorus and sulfur.
Living things must have a constant supply of these elements if they are to make proteins, carbohydrates and fats.

These elements are found in the nutrients that living things take in. For instance, carbon is found in carbon dioxide, nitrogen is found in nitrates, and hydrogen is found in water.
If these nutrients were not cycled then living things would not have the elements that they need.

▶ Decomposers and detritivores

Pieces of dead and decaying material are called **detritus**.
Small animals feed on this and help to break it down.
These animals are called **detritivores**.
Earthworms, fly maggots and woodlice are all detritivores.
They shred up a lot of the dead material into very small pieces.
This makes it easier for decomposers to break it down.
Without detritivores the process of decomposition would take much longer.

Some common detritivores

Decomposers are microscopic.
We only really notice them because they make things decay.
These bacteria and fungi are also responsible for rotting food.
So how do they decompose dead things?

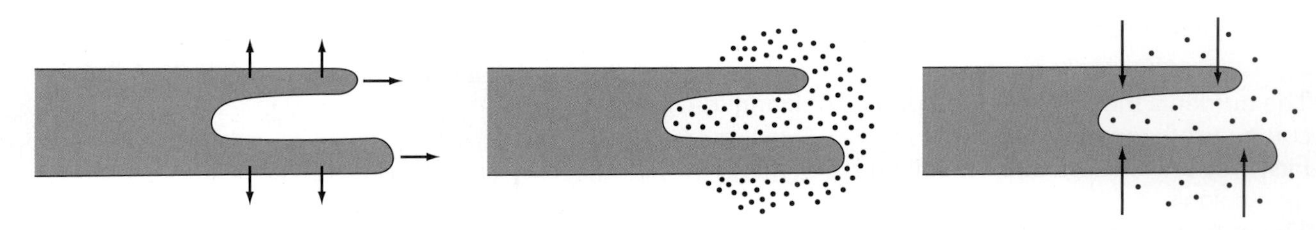
1. A fungus releases enzymes on to the dead remains
2. The enzymes digest the dead matter and make it soluble
3. The soluble products are taken up by the fungus

Fungi and bacteria use enzymes to digest their food.
These work in the same way as the enzymes in your gut.
The soluble products are taken up by the bacteria and fungi.

The decomposers absorb the food and use it for growth and for energy.
These bacteria and fungi may be eaten by other organisms and so the nutrients are passed on.

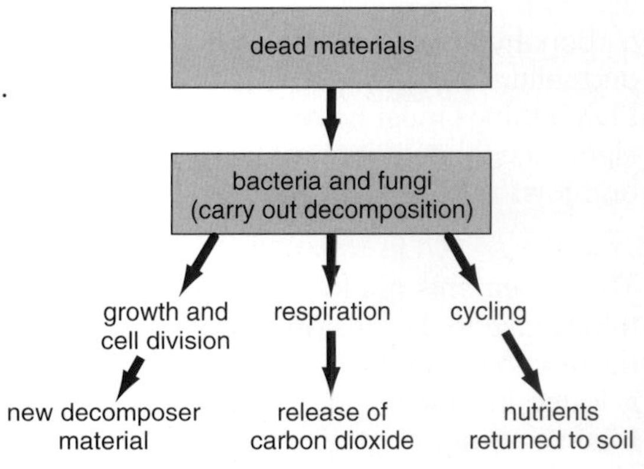

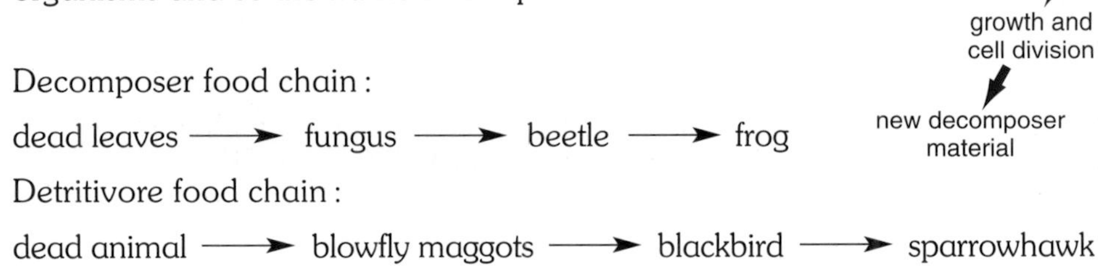
Decomposer food chain:

dead leaves ⟶ fungus ⟶ beetle ⟶ frog

Detritivore food chain:

dead animal ⟶ blowfly maggots ⟶ blackbird ⟶ sparrowhawk

▶ The carbon cycle

All living things need carbon.
It is used to make carbohydrates, proteins, fats, and other important molecules. These molecules make up living organisms.

The carbon comes from carbon dioxide in the air. Plants use it in photosynthesis to make food. Animals get the carbon by eating plants.

How does carbon dioxide get back into the air?

- Plants and animals use some of their food for respiration, releasing energy and carbon dioxide.
- Decomposers use dead plants and animals for food. They use some of the decaying material for respiration, releasing energy and carbon dioxide.
- Fossil fuels like oil, peat, coal, and gas contain carbon. When they are burned, carbon dioxide is released into the air.

These processes put carbon dioxide back into the air as fast as plants remove it by photosynthesis. So the amount of carbon dioxide in the air should stay the same.

carbon dioxide in air
photosynthesis
carbon compounds in animals
respiration and decay
feeding
carbon compounds in plants
burning
formed millions of years ago from dead vegetation
fossil fuels - oil, coal, peat, gas

Can you see that two processes dominate the carbon cycle? These are photosynthesis and respiration.

Photosynthesis takes carbon dioxide out of the air and provides the input for carbon into food chains.

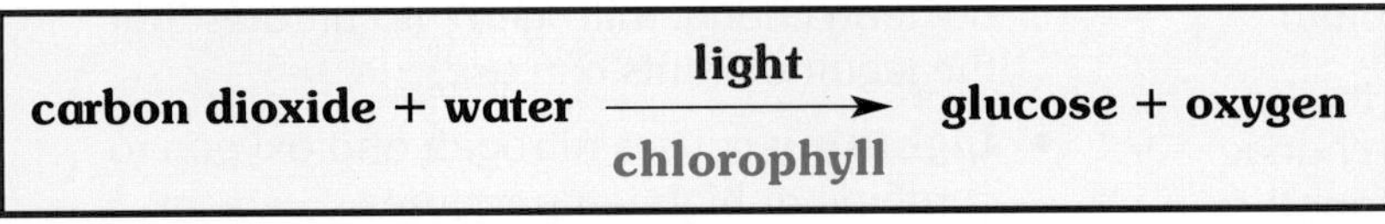

carbon dioxide + water $\xrightarrow[\text{chlorophyll}]{\text{light}}$ glucose + oxygen

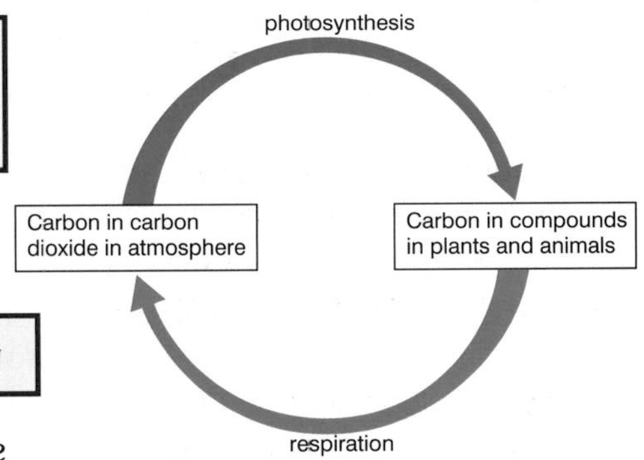

Respiration, by animals, plants and microbes, releases carbon dioxide back into the atmosphere.

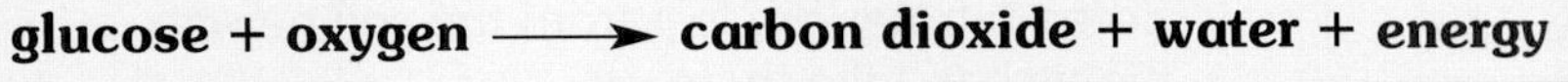

glucose + oxygen ⟶ carbon dioxide + water + energy

The world's oceans, lakes and rivers contain more carbon dioxide (dissolved in water as hydrogencarbonate) than the 0.03% of the carbon dioxide in the air. So, on a global scale, most photosynthesis takes place in the oceans.

▶ The nitrogen cycle

Plants and animals need nitrogen to make proteins.
The air contains nearly 80 % nitrogen.
But nitrogen is no use to living things as a gas.
Plants and animals can not use it in this form.
It has to be changed to **nitrates** before it can be used by plants.
Plants can use the nitrogen in nitrates to make protein.
Animals get their nitrogen from plant protein when they eat plants.
So how is nitrogen gas changed into nitrates ?
You can find out by looking at the diagram :

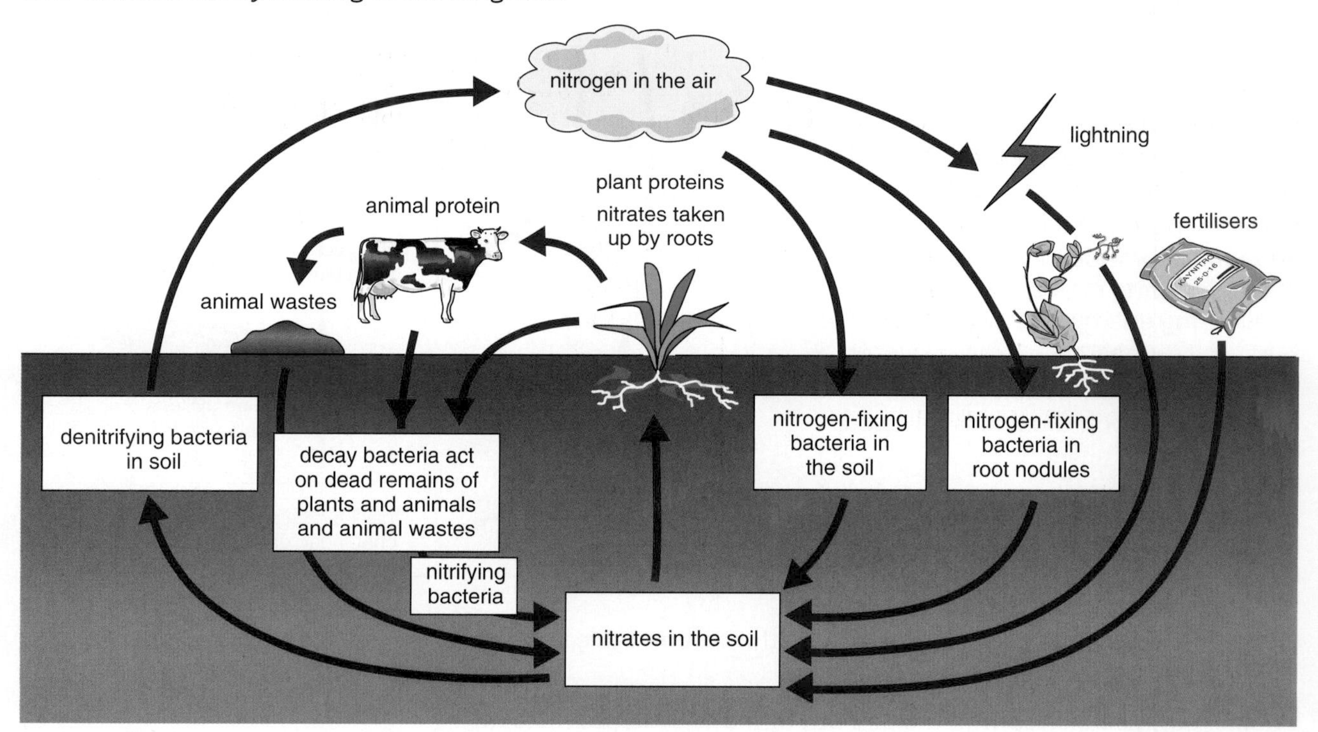

- **Decay bacteria** break down dead remains and animal wastes releasing ammonium compounds into the soil.
- **Nitrifying bacteria** in the soil can change ammonia into nitrates. Ammonia is another chemical that contains nitrogen. It is present in animal waste and dead remains.
- **Nitrogen-fixing bacteria** are found in the soil. These can convert nitrogen from the air into nitrates. Plants are able to take up the nitrates with their roots.
- Nitrogen-fixing bacteria are also found in the roots of legume plants like peas, beans and clover. The bacteria make lumps on the roots called **root nodules**. These bacteria change nitrogen into nitrates that the legume plants can use.
- **Lightning** causes nitrogen and oxygen to combine at high temperatures.
  Nitrogen oxides form.
  These are washed into the soil by rain where they form nitrates.

Some nitrates are lost from the soil before plants can take them up :

- Some nitrates may be washed out of the soil by rainwater. This is called **leaching**.
- **Denitrifying bacteria** live in water-logged soil. They can change nitrates back to nitrogen gas.

▶ Life in the soil

Life below ground is just as diverse as life above ground.
It is essential in maintaining the cycling of nutrients that are vital to plant growth.

Soils are complex mixtures of different-sized rock particles, humus (dead material), air, water and dissolved minerals.
Plants rely upon soils for root anchorage and, in turn, root penetration improves both aeration and drainage.
Plants also rely upon soils for a source of water and nutrients.

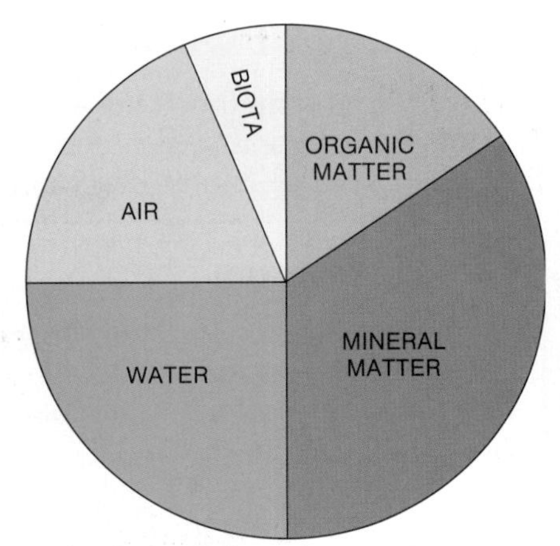

Soil constituents

Bacteria are a vital component of soils, as we have seen when looking at the nitrogen cycle.
Decomposition results in the production of **humus**.
Without the presence of decay bacteria and fungi, this decomposition of dead plant material would not happen.
Also the nitrogen-fixing bacteria such as *Azotobacter* in the soil and *Rhizobium* in the root nodules of legume plants such as peas, beans, clover and gorse, have an important role in converting atmospheric nitrogen into a form that plants can use to make proteins for new growth.

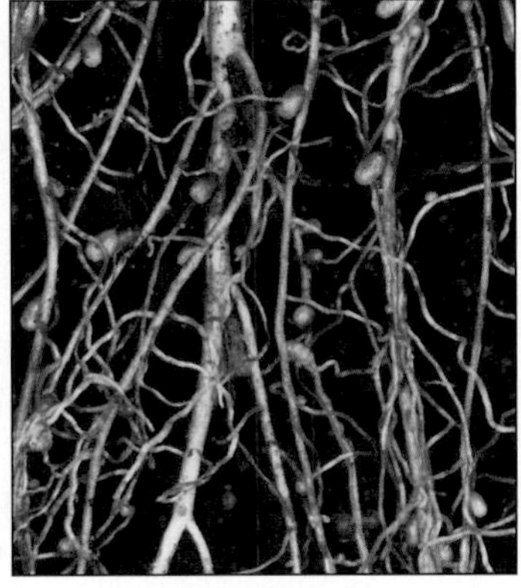
Root nodules of a legume plant

Earthworms are common and extremely important members of the soil community.
They are detritivores, feeding upon the partially decayed leaves that they drag into their burrows.
In this way they help to increase the organic content of the soil.
Any indigestible material is egested at the surface as worm casts, or underground for decomposition by bacteria and fungi.
Not only do earthworms improve soil fertility, their burrowing also serves to aerate and drain the soil.
Some species of earthworm are able to burrow several feet down.
This has the beneficial effect of mixing up the soil layers.
Earthworms eject calcium carbonate in their casts and this helps with neutralising acid soils.

The soil community is just as interactive and complex as many other above-ground communities. It includes herbivores such as slugs, snails and wire worms ; detritivores like earthworms, millipedes and springtails and carnivores such as centipedes, spiders and ground beetles.
This all adds up to a dynamic community, but in the context of this chapter, perhaps the key organisms are the decomposers : bacteria and fungi.

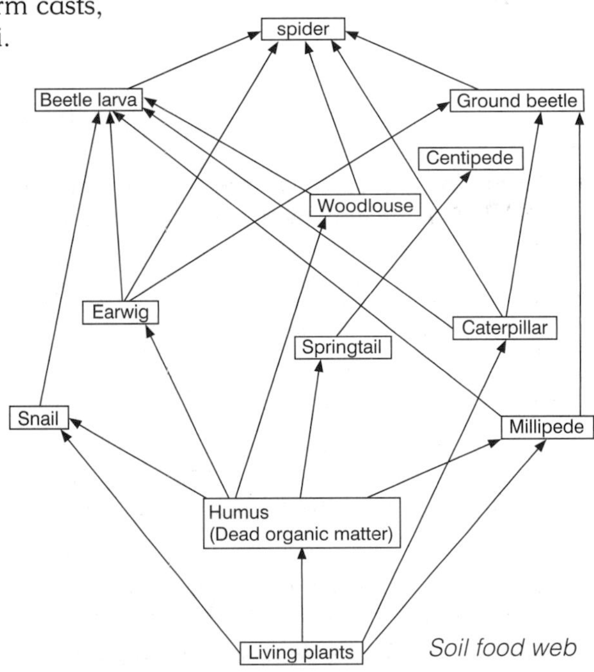

Soil food web

▶ Biology at work : Intensive food production

Modern farming methods have become more **intensive**.
Farmers try to produce as much food as possible by making the best use of the available land, plants and animals.

Factory farming

We have seen that by eating plant foods, far more people can be supported (see page 308).
This is because ***all*** the material and energy in the plant is used directly by your body.
If the same amount of plant food was fed to animal like a cow or sheep, then only about 10 % of the food is converted into animal meat. The other 90 % is either uneaten, not digested or used up in respiration.
So rearing animals is not a very efficient way of producing food.
However, many intensive farming methods have been able to maximise the meat production in some animals.
Animals need the right sort of food and a certain amount of warmth to grow well.
Many animals are reared indoors so that :

- The amount and type of food can be controlled.
  High protein diets and additives make the animals grow as fast as possible.
- The temperature of their surroundings can be kept constant.

This is important because mammals and birds need to maintain a constant body temperature and a lot of the energy in their food can end up being lost to the air as heat.

- The movement of animals can be restricted by keeping them in cages or pens.
  The lack of exercise means that they put on weight quicker.
- Antibiotics can be used to control the spread of disease.

The demand for protein foods can be met by the efficient conversion of food energy into growth (meat). Increased efficiency, better breeding and reduced labour costs make it cheaper than the equivalent free-range products.

But many people do not like to see animals grown in these conditions.
They think that it is more humane for them to be outside.
Keeping animals penned in or in over-crowded conditions can only lead to obesity.
Boredom and frustration can result in bizarre behaviour.
More and more people think that the use of veal crates and other types of animal pens should be banned.
Free-range products are gaining in popularity as people come to understand the suffering that can be caused by factory farming.

Intensive turkey farming

Many people think that veal crates are inhumane

'Wish I could roam the range.'

Crop production

Intensive cereal production

This field of wheat has been grown by intensive methods.
It is a **monoculture**, since only ***one*** type of plant is being grown.

- These crops have been selectively bred to produce a lot of grain.
- Fertilisers have been used to grow larger plants with increased grain yield over a shorter period of time.
- **Insecticides** have been sprayed on the crop to control insect pests and **herbicides** have been applied to kill the weeds.

The farmer has to balance the cost of these chemicals against the increase in the yield of wheat grain.
Most of our bread is made from cereals grown by intensive farming.

We have seen how the yield of some crops can be increased by growing them inside glasshouses (see page 196).
Inside a glasshouse, conditions like light, carbon dioxide and temperature, can be carefully controlled.

Fish farming

Fish like salmon and trout can be kept in large cages.
Here their growing conditions can be carefully controlled by :

- Providing a high protein diet, usually in the form of fish meal, together with a mix of appropriate vitamins and minerals.
- Anti-louse chemicals are added to control the spread of disease in overcrowded conditions.
- Excluding predators and competitors.

In the UK, fish-farmed trout reach a marketable size of between 180 and 280 g in about 11 months depending upon temperature.

The benefits of fish farming include :

- Having a controlled supply of specific fish of the required size.
- Achieving an optimum growth rate and health of fish.
- Controlling genetic selection for useful qualities e.g. disease resistance.
- The efficient conversion of food into fish, because fish are cold-blooded and energy is not wasted in maintaining a constant body temperature.

There are worries that fish farming can cause pollution.
The concentration of fish in one place means that wastes and uneaten food can cause eutrophication problems (see page 336).

Summary

- Producers, including green plants and some bacteria, are able to make their own food.
- Producers provide food energy for primary consumers (herbivores).
- Primary consumers in turn provide food energy for secondary consumers (carnivores).
- Decomposers and detritivores feed upon dead and decaying material.
- These feeding relationships can be shown by food chains and food webs.
- The role that an animal or plant plays in its community is called its niche.
- Pyramids of number, biomass and energy can be used to show feeding relationships.
- A short food chain can support far more people than one with many links in the chain.
- Energy enters ecosystems as sunlight and leaves as heat.
- Only a fraction of the light falling on a leaf will be transferred to new plant biomass.
- There are 'wastages' of energy between different trophic levels.
- Carbon is cycled through ecosystems by processes such as photosynthesis and respiration.
- Different types of bacteria have different roles to play in the nitrogen cycle.
- Fertilisers are added to make up for shortage of nutrients in some soils.

▶ Questions

1. Copy and complete:
Producers are able to make their own ..... . Producers are fed upon by herbivores or .... consumers. These in turn provide food for .... consumers. Dead and .... material provides food for .... and detritivores. Feeding relationships can be shown in food .... and in food ..... . Feeding relationships can also be shown in pyramids of .... , biomass and ..... .

2. Look at the woodland food web:

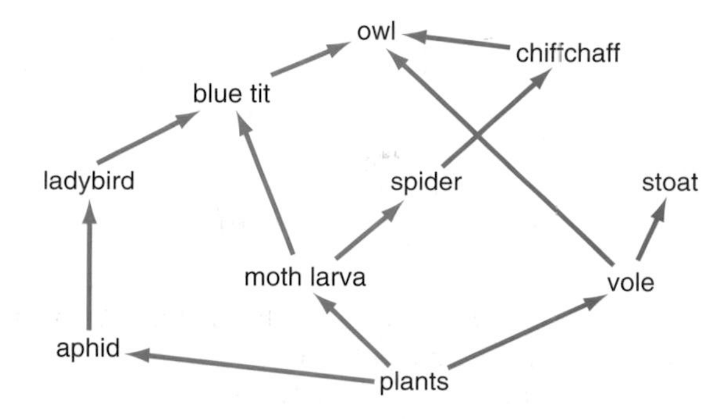

a) Give one example from the food web, of each of these:
i) a producer
ii) a primary consumer
iii) a secondary consumer.

b) How many carnivores are there in the food web?

c) Draw a food chain with five links in it.

d) If all the spiders were killed by disease what would happen to the numbers of:
i) moth larvae ii) plants?

3. Look at this food web:

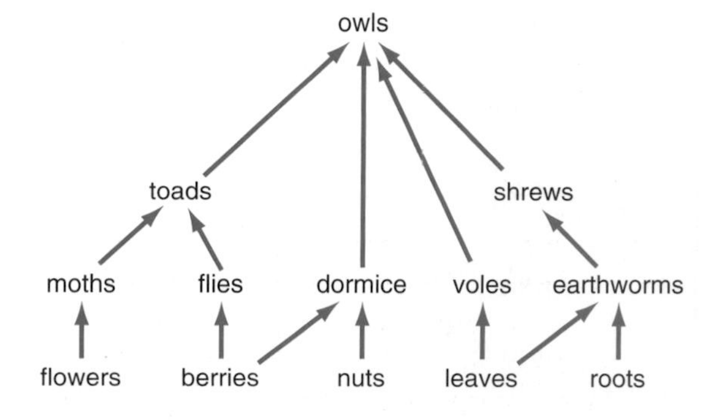

a) From the food web name:
i) two primary consumers
ii) one secondary consumer.

b) Construct, using the food web, two different food chains, each with four links.

c) Why do most food chains begin with green plants?

d) If all the owls were killed what would happen to the numbers of:
i) dormice ii) earthworms?

4. The numbers of plants and animals were counted at three different places in a pond. The results are shown in the table :

Place	Numbers counted			
	Small fish	Water flea	Duck	Small plants (Algae)
1	4	500	1	10 000
2	1	700	0	8000
3	3	680	1	7000
Totals				

a) Copy and complete the table.
b) Use the names in the table to draw a pyramid of numbers.
c) Explain why all the plants in the pond were found near the surface.
d) Plants are food for pond animals. Give two other ways in which these animals depend upon plants.

5. The table shows information about three food chains :

Producer	Primary consumer
200 leaves	100 caterpillars
20 water weeds	200 insect larvae
5 cabbages	100 caterpillars
Secondary consumer	**Tertiary consumer**
5 thrushes	1 kestrel
5 small fish	1 otter
5 thrushes	500 fleas

a) Draw a pyramid of numbers for each food chain.
b) The average masses for the organisms in these food chains are :
leaf (5 g), caterpillar (4 g), thrush (70 g), kestrel (250 g), water weed (250 g), insect larva (10 g), small fish (300 g), otter (1 kg), cabbage (300 g), flea (0.04 g).
 i) Draw a biomass pyramid for each food chain using this data.
 ii) What differences can you see between each pyramid of number and each pyramid of biomass ?

6. For every square metres of grass that it eats, a cow gets 3000 kJ of energy. It uses 100 kJ for growth, 1000 kJ are lost as heat and 1900 kJ are lost in faeces.
a) What percentage of the energy in one square metre of grass i) is used for growth
 ii) passes through the gut and is not absorbed ?
b) If beef has an energy value of 12 kJ per gram, how many square metres of grass are needed to produce 100 g of beef ?

7. Look back at the diagram showing the energy budget of a cow on page 310.
a) How efficient is the cow at converting grass into biomass ? Explain your answer.
b) What percentage of the energy intake is:
 i) present in the faeces and urine
 ii) used up in respiration ?
c) Cows spend a lot of time grazing. In view of your other answers, why do you think this is ?

8. a) Give two ways in which nitrogen can be added to the soil.
b) How can nitrogen be taken out of the soil ?
c) Why do some farmers grow clover and then plough it into the soil before growing wheat ?

9. The diagram shows part of the carbon cycle :

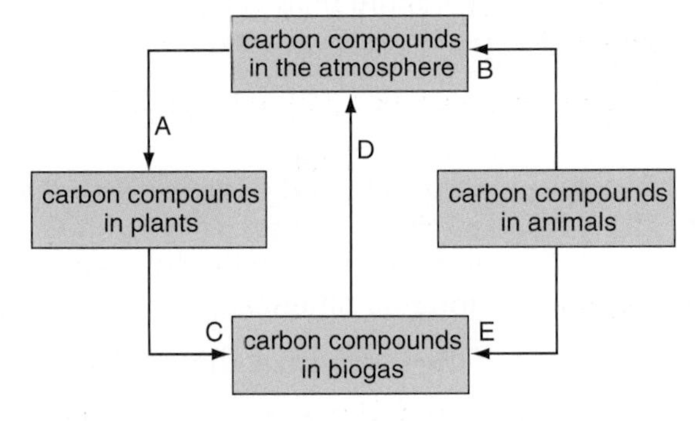

Copy the diagram and replace the letters A to E with the correct label from this list :
respiration   decay by bacteria
photosynthesis   burning

Further questions on page 340

chapter 20

Humans and the environment

At present the number of people on the planet is growing at an alarming rate. In 2011, the Earth's population is estimated to pass 7 billion people.

It has not always been so in the past. For thousands of years there was only a slow increase in the human population. Lack of food, diseases, wars, and lack of shelter meant that people did not live very long.

Six thousand years ago the world's population was about 0.2 billion people. They lived in small communities, so much of the world was unaffected by human activities.

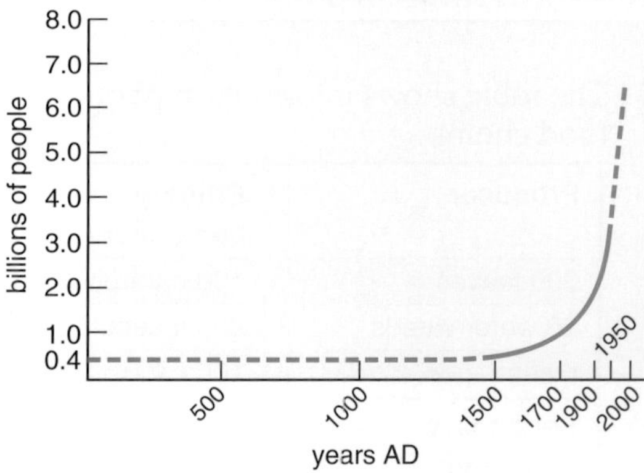

Look at the graph :

What do you think has caused the huge increases over the last 300 years ?

- Improved agriculture means that most people are better fed.
- Public health has improved. There are better water supplies and sanitation.
- Medical care has improved. People can be vaccinated against many diseases.
- Many disease-causing organisms can be controlled inside the body with drugs or outside the body by other chemicals.

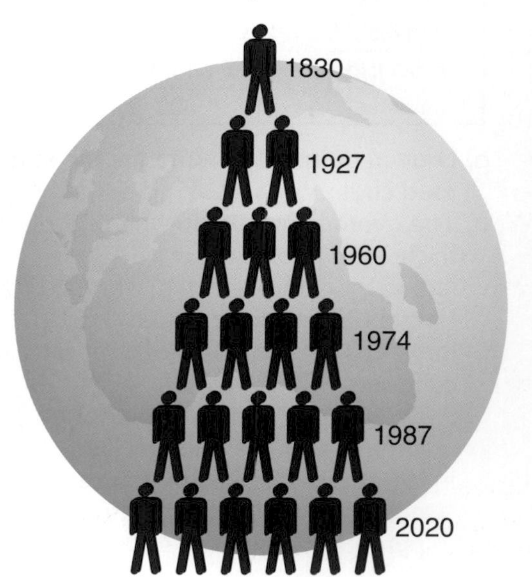

What has been the effect of all these advances ?

- Fewer children are dying from disease and lack of food.
- People are now living much longer. In Europe and North America the average life expectancy has risen to 68 years for men and 73 years for women. In India life expectancy has been much lower. But improved health and living conditions has now lifted the average life expectancy there to 56 years.

▶ Controlling human population growth

There are still controls on population increase. Famines, floods, wars, plagues, earthquakes, and other disasters, all take their toll.

But the overall trend is a rapid increase in the world's population.
It is estimated that it could double in the next 30 years.

There are wide variations between different areas.

Look at the graph:

In Europe and North America the population is virtually stable.
In other places the populations continue to grow.

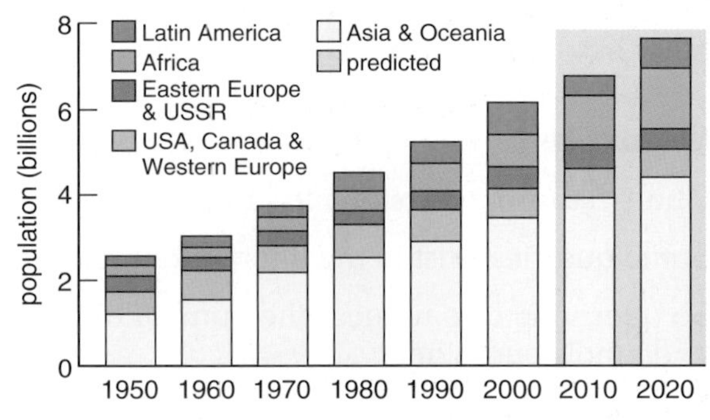

World population by regions, 1950–2020

The Earth has limited resources and limited space.
How can we reverse these trends?
The most obvious way is to reduce the birth rate.
But many groups of people have strongly held religious or moral views on birth control and family size. This means they may often have large families.

The rate of increase is most influenced by the proportion of child-bearing women in the population.

Look at these two population pyramids:

The base of the pyramid shows the percentage of children below the age of 5 years.
The oldest people appear at the top.

Which country has:
- the greatest proportion of young people
- the greatest proportion of old people?

Why do you think this is?

What forecasts can you make about:
- the numbers of child-bearing women in each country in 10 years' time
- the birth rate in 10 years' time?

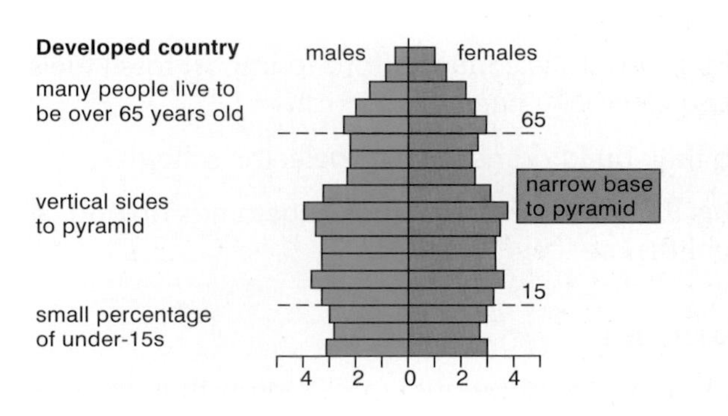

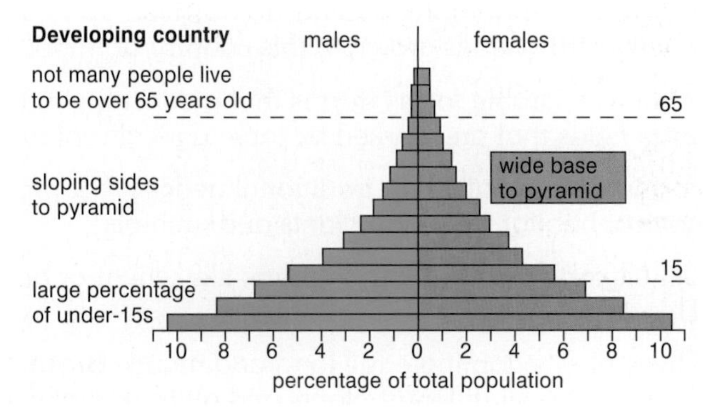

Percentage of the population in each age group

Increasing human population size brings greater demands on resources and problems for the environment.

▶ Taking over the land

Housing

New housing estates eat into the green belt

The picture shows a familiar sight, countryside being taken over for housing :

An increasing population requires housing.

Every year more homes have to be built to house the increasing numbers of people in the world.

Buildings reduce the number of habitats available to plants and animals.

More homes could be built on **brownfield** sites. These are areas, often in towns, which were once occupied by industry.

Quarrying

This quarry has reduced the habitats available for wildlife

Quarries supply the stone to build new houses and roads.

Some quarries exist in the heart of attractive countryside.

So quarrying also reduces the number of habitats available to animals and plants.

Energy needs

All these new houses need to be supplied with electricity.

Many countries cannot afford to import fossil fuels to generate the extra electricity needed.

So they build dams for hydroelectric schemes.

This involves the flooding of huge areas of land, so still more habitats are lost to wildlife.

Farming

Growing one crop reduces plant biodiversity

An increasing population also means that we need more food. This means that more land has to be given up to agriculture, whether the food is grown in this country or imported from abroad.

In the UK, arable farms (farms that grow crops) are often very large fields that are worked by large agricultural machines.

Farmers have pulled up traditional hedges that provided the natural habitat for many plants and animals.

Usually one type of crop is grown, like wheat or barley. This is known as a monoculture.

These plants dominate the land and reduce **biodiversity**, that is the numbers of different plants and animals that can exist within the habitat.

▶ Using up resources

As the population of the world increases, so more raw materials are being used up.
Raw materials fall into two main categories: **renewable resources** and **non-renewable resources**.

Renewable resources can be replaced as fast as plants and animals can reproduce and grow, for instance, harvesting timber from a coniferous forest and fishing for cod in the North Sea.
Non-renewable resources include fossil fuels such as coal, oil and natural gas.

Non-renewable means that once we have used these resources, they cannot be replaced, they are gone forever.
Possible alternative energy sources include solar, hydroelectric and wind power.
Nuclear power is used in a number of industrialised countries like France, using uranium in power stations.
But even supplies of uranium will run out eventually.

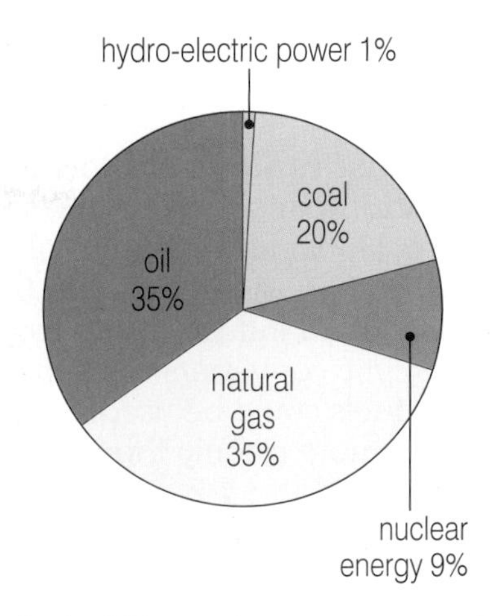

In the UK we rely on non-renewable energy sources

▶ Producing waste

Another consequence of an increasing population is the production of more waste.
Unless this waste is properly handled and disposed of it may cause pollution.
This can cause harm to animals, plants and ourselves.
Dumping waste in landfill sites also deprives plants and animals of their natural habitats.

The solution of conserving useful materials is to recycle them.
Glass, metals, paper and plastics can all be recycled.
This saves raw materials because the recyclable materials do not have to be made in such large quantities and less energy is used to recycle than to make the material 'from scratch'.

Packaging is a major source of waste.
In the USA 35 % of municipal waste is made up of packaging.
In the UK 75 % of glass, 40 % of paper, 30 % of plastics and 15 % of aluminium waste comes just from packaging.
Each person in the UK uses up one tree's worth of paper or cardboard per year.

Much of our waste ends up in landfill sites

Recycling our waste saves raw materials and energy

Polluting the air and land

Humans are filling the air with many harmful gases.

Smog haze caused by air pollution in Los Angeles

- **Exhaust fumes** from cars contain lead, carbon monoxide (a gas poisonous in small amounts), nitrogen oxides and unburnt hydrocarbons. Motor exhaust fumes cause 60–90 % of all air pollution in industrialised countries. Catalytic converters could be fitted to cars and new fuels could be used, for instance ethanol burns more cleanly than petrol.
- **Carbon dioxide** is given off when we burn fossil fuels like coal and oil. Deforestation is also causing a build-up of carbon dioxide in the atmosphere contributing to the **greenhouse effect**. (For details of the greenhouse effect and global warming see page 331.)
- **Sulfur dioxide** is also released when fossil fuels are burnt. Together with the nitrogen oxides from exhaust fumes, they cause **acid rain**. These gases can be carried over large distances by the winds before coming down as dry particles or dissolved in the rain.

  As lakes and rivers become acid, fish and small invertebrates die. The acid rain dissolves nutrients like potassium and calcium out of the soil, leaving the soil infertile. Toxic minerals, such as aluminium, are also washed out into the rivers and lakes killing fish and other wildlife. Acid rain also kills large number of trees – especially conifers – by damaging the roots and causing them to lose their leaves.

  The prevailing winds of Europe come from the south-west. Most of the acid gases are carried to Scandinavia, where they fall as acid rain in Sweden and southern Norway. In a similar way, Canada is paying the price for the acid gases released by industries in the United States.

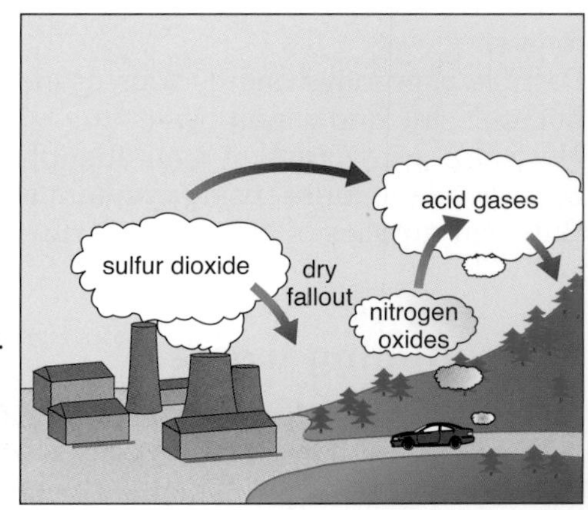

The technology exists to combat acid rain :

- **Low sulfur fuels** could be used. Crushing coal and washing it with a solvent reduces its sulfur content.
- **Chemical plants** can be installed to remove the sulfur from emissions before they are released into the atmosphere.
- **Flue gas desulfurisation** removes the sulfur from power station chimneys by bombarding the waste gases with wet powdered limestone, neutralising the acid gases.
- **Catalytic converters** can be fitted to reduce the nitrogen oxides in the exhaust fumes of cars.

  These solutions are expensive, but are being gradually introduced to counter the expense of damage from acid rain.

Acid rain damage to conifers

CFCs (chlorofluorocarbons)

CFCs are used in spray cans, refrigerators, air-conditioning systems and in making plastic foam. CFCs are also adding to the 'greenhouse effect'. Along with carbon dioxide, methane and water vapour, they are adding to the problems of global warming.

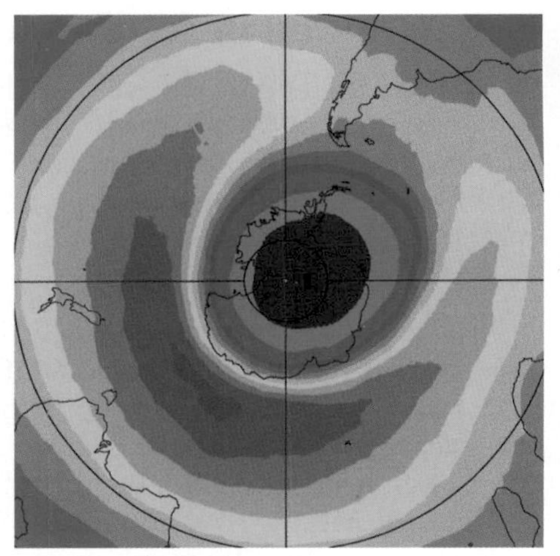

A map showing ozone concentration over the Antarctic. The ozone hole is at the centre.

In addition, CFCs are causing the **ozone layer** to become thin. This layer of ozone in the upper atmosphere protects the Earth from harmful ultraviolet (UV) rays. UV radiation is known to be a contributing factor associated with an increase in skin cancer. The use of blocking creams and wearing a hat reduces the risk of skin cancer.

The first hole in the ozone layer appeared over the Antarctic in 1985. The size of the hole is increasing each year and a similar hole is developing over the Arctic too.

Spray cans now use different propellants and are 'ozone-friendly'. Chemists are working hard to find substitutes to use in refrigerators and air-conditioning systems.

Radiation

Non-natural radiation comes from the testing and use of nuclear weapons and leakages from nuclear reactors.

A nuclear power station

In 1986 there was an accident at the Chernobyl nuclear power station. A huge cloud of radioactive material was released into the atmosphere. The winds blew the cloud across Europe. Countries like Poland and Scandinavia were showered with radioactive chemicals. Some types of radiation are known to cause cancers and deformed births.

Agricultural chemicals

The 'Green Revolution' between 1945 and 1975 brought about a doubling of world food production. Agricultural chemicals had a lot to do with this success.

- **Fertilisers** made it possible to grow crops where the soil was previously too poor. Their use dramatically increases crop yields. But artificial fertilisers can cause pollution if they drain into rivers and streams (see page 336).

- **Pesticides** have been used to kill insects that eat crops, weeds that compete with crops, and fungi that cause disease. Without the use of pesticides, 45% of a crop could be lost. Pesticides have also saved millions of lives by killing the insects that spread malaria, typhus and yellow fever. But pesticides can be dangerous if they get into food chains (see page 326).

▶ Pesticides in food chains

Pesticides are chemicals used to kill pests.
The main farm pests are insects, weeds and moulds.
Why do pests need to be controlled?
Without pesticides there would be a large decrease in crop yield.

DDT is a very effective pesticide.
Only small amounts are needed to kill any insect.
DDT has saved millions of people from disease and starvation.
It has been used to control the mosquitoes that spread **malaria**.
It also helps reduce the numbers of insects that eat food crops.

But DDT is dangerous and does not break down easily.
It stays in the environment for a long time.
It does not break down inside the body of an animal either.
This means that it can pass along food chains.

Clear Lake in California was sprayed with DDT to control midges.
Soon fish-eating birds like grebes began to die.
Their bodies had large amounts of DDT in them.

How do you think the pesticide got into the grebes?
What happens to the level of DDT as you go along this food chain?
How do you explain this increase?

The DDT was first taken up by the plant plankton.
The animal plankton feed on many plant plankton.
So the level of DDT builds up in their bodies.
Each fish feeds on many animal plankton.
For each one it eats, a fish will get a dose of DDT.
Each grebe feeds on many fish.
For each one it eats, the grebe gets a dose of DDT.
So the DDT reaches a lethal level in the grebe first.
The pesticide has built up along the food chain.
This is sometimes called **bioaccumulation**.

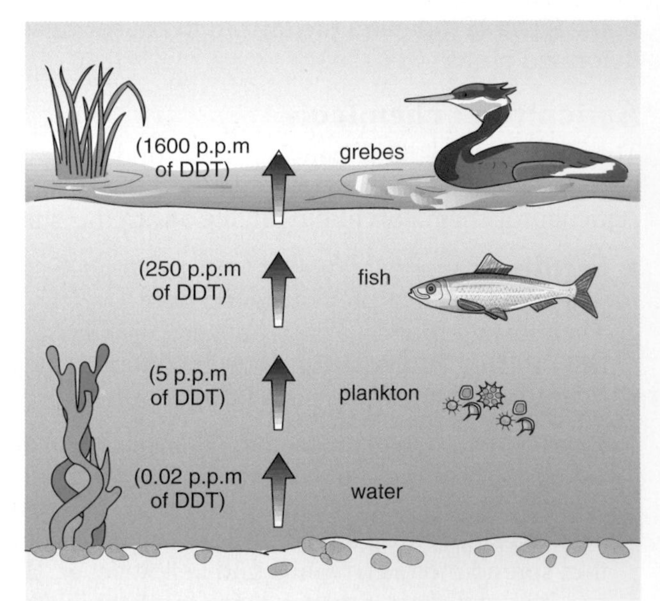

Pesticides in Britain

In the late 1950s pesticides caused deaths to birds in Britain.
In the spring of each year large numbers of different bird species were found dead.
These included a lot of seed-eating birds like woodpigeons, pheasants and partridges.
Also predators like sparrowhawks, peregrine falcons and foxes.

High levels of a pesticide called dieldrin were found in the bodies.
Seeds were often dipped in dieldrin to protect them from pests.

Why do you think so many seed-eating birds died?
How did dieldrin become concentrated in the bodies of predators?

Sparrowhawk with a kill

Birds of prey in particular were affected.
The dieldrin not only built up in their bodies it caused them to lay eggs with thinner shells.
Many eggs were crushed when the birds sat on them to incubate them.

Dieldrin was also used in sheep dips.
How could this have poisoned birds of prey like the golden eagle?

Pesticides like DDT and dieldrin are now banned from most industrialised countries.

Peregrine falcon at its nest

▶ What's the alternative?

In Holland lice are damaging trees.
Ladybirds are being set free into the Dutch countryside to kill the lice.
The ladybirds have been imported from California where they are specially bred.
This is an example of **biological control**.
Biological control is the use of predators, parasites and pathogens to control a pest species.
Many pests are alien species introduced into a country by accident.
The bicontrol agent can often be found in the pest's original country and can be imported to control the pest.
The big advantage of biological control is that it avoids the use of pesticides completely.

▶ Pollution of the rivers and seas

Pollutants, like fertilisers, drain from the land into our rivers.
Domestic and industrial pollutants are often discharged straight into rivers.
Sewage is our biggest single pollutant.
It can encourage the growth of algae and bacteria which use up lots of oxygen.
Fish and small invertebrates die.

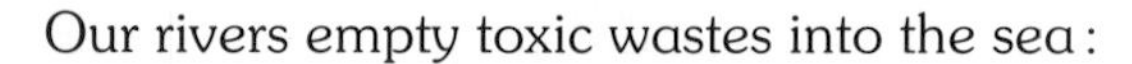

Our rivers empty toxic wastes into the sea:

- fertilisers and sewage encourage the growth of toxic algae
- pesticides are becoming concentrated in the tissues of shellfish
- radioactive chemicals are found in high concentrations around coastal nuclear power stations
- toxic metals, like mercury, copper and lead, are finding their way into the sea's food chains.

Oil spillages often hit the headlines.
The ***Sea Empress*** (1996), the ***Braer*** (1993), ***Exxon Valdez*** (1989) and the ***Amoco Cadiz*** (1989) released thousands of tonnes of crude oil into the sea.
But the worst oil pollution disaster occurred in Kuwait (1990–91).
Iraqi forces destroyed oil wells, oil tankers and installations by the coast. Hundreds of millions of gallons of oil spilled into the Arabian Gulf.
In April 2010, a huge explosion on BP's Deepwater Horizon oil rig resulted in 185 million gallons of oil spewing into the Gulf of Mexico. This was the worst environmental disaster the USA has faced.

Kuwait oil wells set on fire

We have become familiar with pictures of oil-covered beaches.
Sea birds die when their feathers get clogged with oil.
They take in the oil when they try to clean themselves.
They soon die of exposure, drowning or starvation.
Seashore animals and plants become smothered by the oil.
Detergents are sprayed on the oil to try to disperse it.
But these are often toxic to marine life.

We have for too long thought of the sea as a vast dumping ground.
The way we have polluted the seas in the past is storing up problems for the future.

Deforestation

Forests help to keep the correct balance of carbon dioxide and oxygen in our atmosphere.
They do this by taking in carbon dioxide and giving out oxygen during photosynthesis.

Why do you think that this is important?

Forests also act as 'stores' of water, their leaves slow down the rate of evaporation and the rate at which water reaches the soil.

So what are the reasons for deforestation ?
Why is there large-scale clearance of forests ?

- The world demand for timber as building materials.
- The demand for paper for newsprint, photocopiers, printers and office consumption.
- The clearing of land for farms, cattle ranches and plantations
- Clearing for the construction of new roads and towns.
- To provide firewood and charcoal as fuels.

What are the consequences of deforestation?

- Destruction of forests increases the amount of carbon dioxide (a greenhouse gas, see page 330) in the atmosphere and so contributes to **global warming** and the chances of disastrous changes in climate.
- Dense vegetation prevents heavy rains from washing away the soil.
  With no roots to bind the soil together, **soil erosion** occurs, washing away nutrients and causing floods.
- Destruction of the rainforests means the extinction of thousands of species of plants and animals.

So what are the answers to stop the wholesale destruction of forests?

- **Reforestation –** involves the replanting of native trees. It is important that plantations do not replace native forests.
- **Sustainable management** of forests would involve removing trees but allowing natural replacement or planting of native species.
- **Recycling and energy conservation** would result in a reduced need to for 'new' sources of timber.

A paper recycling plant

▶ The greenhouse gases

Our Earth is protected by a warm blanket of gases. These are the so-called **greenhouse gases**. They are mainly naturally occurring gases like carbon dioxide, water vapour and methane. These gases allow solar energy to pass through to the Earth's surface. They absorb some of the heat energy radiating from the Earth's surface and allow some back into space.
Greenhouse gases maintain a balance between the heat that is coming in and the heat that is going out. They keep our atmosphere at the sort of temperatures that allow life to exist.

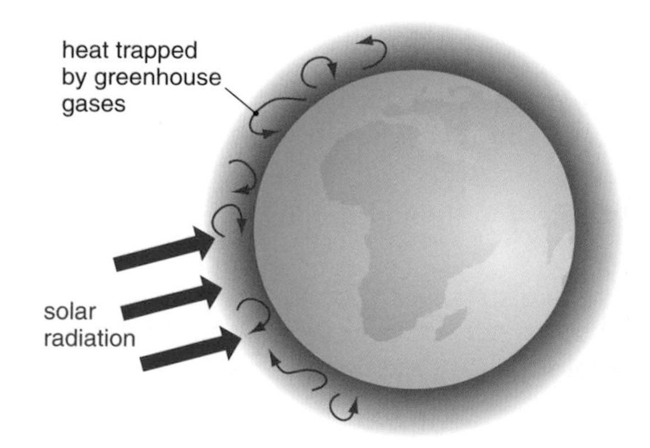

It is important to understand that the **greenhouse effect** is a ***natural*** process and without it the average temperature on the Earth would be about −17 °C.
However, over the last 100 years, there has been a build up of these gases, along with man-made gases like CFCs and nitrogen oxides. Where have these gases come from?

- More fossil fuels are being burnt than has been in the past. Power stations, factories, domestic heating and transport use fuels like coal, oil and natural gas which release huge amounts of carbon dioxide into the atmosphere.
- As we have seen, **deforestation** has resulted in large areas of forest being removed. In South America the trees are cleared for farming. As a result of fewer trees there is less photosynthesis, so less carbon dioxide is being taken out of the air.
- To make matters worse the wood that is not needed is burnt and this gives off even more carbon dioxide. Roots and other remaining tree parts are decomposed by microbes in the soil, producing even more carbon dioxide.
- There has been a significant increase in **methane** due to the expansion of both rice growing and cattle rearing. Methane is belched out of the stomachs of cattle and is released as a result of the anaerobic conditions found in rice fields.
  Rotting material in landfill sites is another source of methane.
- CFCs have been used as aerosol propellants and as coolants in fridges, freezers and air-conditioning systems. Although only present in small amounts, CFCs are many times more active than carbon dioxide as a greenhouse gas.
- Nitrogen oxides are present in vehicle exhaust fumes.

Deforestation on a large scale

Of all the greenhouse gases the largest increase has been in carbon dioxide which has risen by 10 % in the last 30 years.

▶ The greenhouse effect

- Solar radiation passes through the atmosphere and warms the Earth's surface.
- The Earth radiates heat energy back into space. This is mainly infra-red radiation.
- Some of this heat energy is absorbed by the greenhouse gases. This causes the air to warm up.

Without carbon dioxide and water vapour the heat energy would pass straight back out into space.

But you can have too much of a good thing. Human activity is causing an increase in carbon dioxide and other greenhouse gases like methane, nitrogen oxides and CFCs.

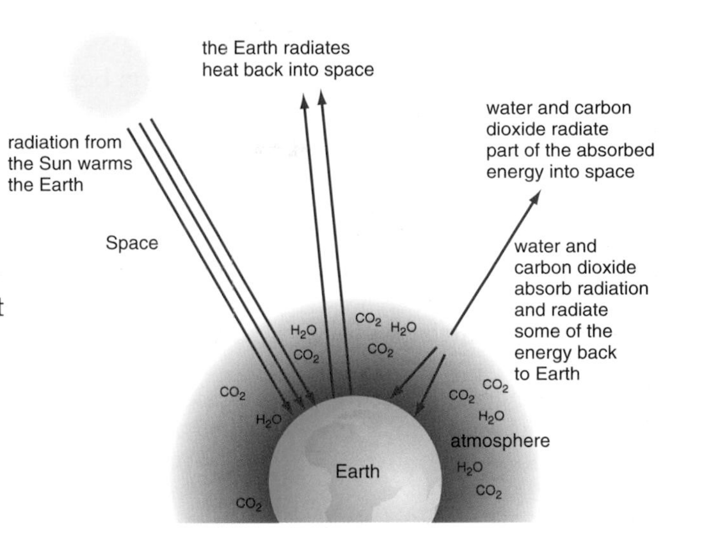

Global warming

Too much heat energy is being absorbed so the atmosphere is getting warmer.
This is increasing the **greenhouse effect**.

The surface of the Earth has warmed by 0.7 °C over the past century.
There are fears that this warming is increasing.
If the temperature of the Arctic and Antarctic were to rise above 0 °C then the polar ice would start to melt.

- This would cause a rise in sea level.
  Many low-lying areas would be flooded.
  These would include some of the capital cities of the world.
- There could also be a change in wind patterns and the distribution of rainfall leading to more extreme weather.
- A warming up of the climate could also affect grain production. This could mean a massive reduction in the grain crops of Central Asia and North America.
- The pattern of the world's food distribution could be affected with economic and political consequences.

What can be done?

No one wants global warming to happen but some of the solutions are proving unattractive to some industrialised countries.
These solutions could include:

- Cutting down on the burning of fossil fuels and especially reducing carbon dioxide emissions.
- **Reforestation –** plant more trees to take in carbon dioxide and help to restore the Earth's natural balance.
- Recycling materials would mean less energy is needed by industry.
- Greater use of public transport would reduce energy consumption.
- Catalytic converters would help to remove nitrogen oxides from vehicle exhaust fumes.

More forests could mean less carbon dioxide in the atmosphere

Sustainable development

Protecting the Earth's natural resources can best be achieved by **sustainable development**.
This means using natural resources wisely, in a way that does not destroy them for future generations.

We have already seen how recycling waste materials such as newspapers, bottles and aluminium cans, can help to conserve natural resources.

Making our homes more energy-efficient would help us to conserve energy resources.
Loft and cavity wall insulation, double-glazing and the possible use of solar panels all help energy conservation. Even turning off a light when you leave a room will help.

Loft insulation conserves energy

Making less use of private motor vehicles would also help. How often do we see cars being driven to work with just one person in them ?
The energy consumption per person is far more efficient if public transport is used. Or why not walk to the shops ?

Who's doing their bit for energy conservation?

Sustainable timber production

The UK is a major importer and user of timber.
Most of this comes from the coniferous forests of Scandinavia and North America.
We could reduce the need to import so much timber by recycling and using wood that has come from sustainably managed forests.
This means replacement planting as soon as trees are felled and establishing new forests on surplus agricultural land.
We should also plant more native trees in order to maintain and enhance biodiversity.
This means providing more woodland habitats for the greater variety of plant and animal species that live there.
A policy of sustainable development should also be applied to our fish stocks. As we have seen on page 296, far too many of our native fish species are being overfished.
We should only be taking fish out of the seas in quantities that can be replaced by natural reproduction and growth.
Failure to bring in legislation and ensure that it is carried out will inevitably result in the extinction of many species like cod and haddock.

▶ Biotic indicators of pollution

Making planning decisions about sustainable development requires data to be collected from field studies.
We can use living organisms as indicators of pollution.

Lichens and air pollution

A **lichen** is a combination of an alga and a fungus.
The algal cells have chlorophyll and photosynthesise, so providing the fungus with sugars. In return the alga gets a supply of water, stored by the fungus. This relationship where ***both*** partners benefit is called **mutualism**.
Lichens are able to grow in exposed areas like walls and garage roofs. But they are very sensitive to the levels of sulfur dioxide in the air. So an area where no lichens are growing is likely to have air of a poor quality.

What do you think the air is like here?

Freshwater invertebrates as biotic indicators

Freshwater animals show differing tolerances to pollution.
The larvae of insects such as mayflies and stoneflies are found in only clean, well-oxygenated water.
On the other hand, midge larvae and sludge worms can withstand badly polluted water with low oxygen.

Stonefly larva

Mayfly larvae

Freshwater shrimp

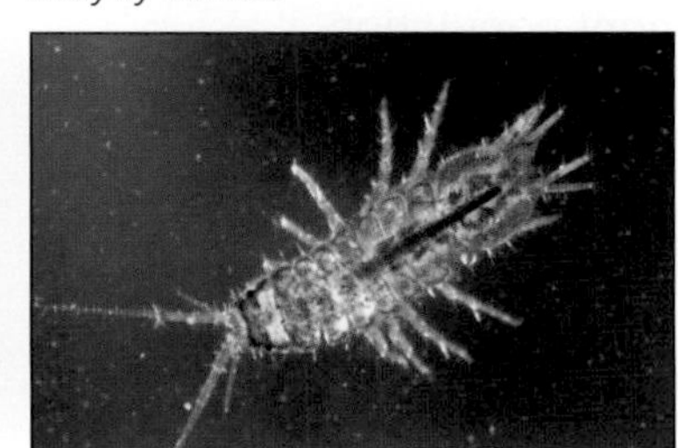
Water louse

Blood worms

Sludge worms

Biological monitoring is used by water authorities to classify water quality and monitor pollution.
The information in this table can be used to classify the water quality of a particular stream or river:

Class	Indicator animals	Description
A	stonefly and mayfly larvae	clean water (**B**,**C** and **D** may also be present)
B	freshwater shrimp caddis fly larva	mildly polluted
C	blood worm (midge larva) water louse	polluted
D	sludge worm rat-tailed maggot	badly polluted
E	no apparent animal life	grossly polluted

▶ Conservation

Conservation aims to keep ecosystems stable as environmental conditions change.
It is important that we conserve the environment for the benefit of future generations.
We have a duty of care to maintain the **biodiversity** (number of different plant and animal species) and protect endangered species.

As we have seen, habitats are being destroyed due to increased land-use for building, quarrying, dumping and agriculture.
Human populations are creating greater demands upon food and energy and producing more waste.

Endangered species

Many plants and animals have become extinct : the rock wallaby, wild ox, spectacled bear and Atlantic walrus are extinct or close to extinction.
Deforestation has meant the extinction of thousands of rainforest plants that could have provided us with new medicines.

American bison

Their fate has been sealed owing to the destruction of their habitats and their over-exploitation for commercial use.
However, the American bison and the Saiga antelope in Russia have been brought back from the brink of extinction.

What are the facts ?

- We have already mentioned the need to conserve fish stocks. Many marine molluscs from the tropics, such as cowries, scallops, cone shells and clams are harvested for food or for their shells.
- Illegal ivory poaching resulted in a loss of half the elephants in Kenya and 90 % in Uganda in the 1970's. As a result CITES, the Convention of International Trade in Endangered Species, imposed a worldwide ban on the ivory trade in 1989. This move led to a significant increase in the elephant population.
- The trade in furs and other animal skins seems senseless. There are plenty of imitation furs available, but the shooting and trapping has taken its toll on wild species. The demand comes mainly from the affluent countries in Europe and the USA.
- The trade in exotic birds takes 10 million birds from the wild each year. About half of these die even before they reach their destination.

The trade in exotic shells

Good news

In 1973, the World Wildlife Fund cooperated with the Indian government to set up 'Operation Tiger'. For many years, tiger numbers had been in decline owing to hunting, trapping and habitat destruction.
The aim of the operation was not only to protect the tiger by legislation but also to conserve its whole environment.
Poaching to satisfy the Chinese market for traditional 'medicines' based upon tiger products still remains a threat to its survival.

Zoos and captive breeding programmes

Breeding animals in captivity, building up their numbers and eventually releasing them back into the wild has been increasingly common in many of the world's zoos.

The Arabian oryx (shown here) has been bred in captivity in Phoenix Zoo, Arizona, and herds released in areas where the species was previously extinct, such as Oman. Other species saved by captive breeding include the European bison and Pere David's deer.

Botanic gardens and seed banks

Botanic gardens are public gardens that keep collections of plants for conservation, research and education. We have seen the threat that deforestation, land development and agricultural expansion can bring to plant diversity.

There are now about 1600 botanic gardens worldwide, between them growing tens of thousands of plant species (see page 356). Many of these are endangered species – by reintroducing them back into the wild we can conserve the natural vegetation.

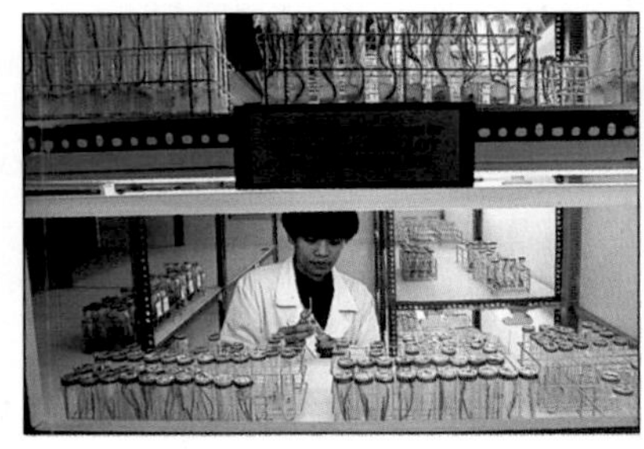

Seed bank at the Agricultural Research Centre, Taiwan

Seed banks are cold stores of seeds that originally concentrated on commercial crops such as cereals and potatoes. They also conserve seed stocks of endangered or valuable species.

In southern England, the 80 million pound Millenium seed bank has been constructed. This building will store seeds from 10 % of the world's estimated 250 000 wild flowering plants. This project stemmed from Britain's signing of the Convention on Biological Diversity in Rio, 1992.

Nearer home

In the UK, legislation protects wildlife in a number of ways :

- National Parks have been set up in England and Wales to protect large areas of outstanding natural scenery for the benefit of the public. For example : Snowdonia, Exmoor, the Broads and the Yorkshire Dales.
- National Nature Reserves (NNRs) are smaller and more numerous than the National Parks. They were set up to protect biodiversity in Britain and are so geared to conserving our native species.
- Sites of Special Scientific Interest (SSSIs) are areas that have been identified to conserve particularly rare and endangered species in Britain.

Other schemes in existence to protect our native wildlife include Heritage Coasts, the Farm Woodland Scheme, Set-aside, Tree Preservation Orders, Nitrate Sensitive Areas and the Royal Society for the Protection of Birds. Your teacher can provide you with websites for these organisations.

The ten National Parks and two equivalent areas (the Broads and New Forest) in England and Wales

▶ Biology at work : Fertilisers

We have seen in Chapter 12 how using fertilisers can increase the yield of crops.
The major elements in fertilisers are nitrogen (N), phosphorus (P), and potassium (K).
Different fertilisers have different amounts of nitrates, phosphates and potassium.
But before knowing which fertilisers to use the farmer needs to know the nutrients already present in the soil.
Tests are carried out by the Agricultural Development Advisory Service (ADAS).

The farmer then knows :

- the best type of fertiliser to use for his or her particular soil and crop
- how much of the fertiliser to add.

Problems can occur if :

- the farmer uses too much fertiliser
- the fertiliser is added before a period of heavy rain.

The result of either of these is that fertiliser can cause water pollution.

- Fertiliser can be washed through the soil into rivers and streams – this is called **leaching**.
- Once in the water it causes weeds and algae to grow.
- These plants eventually die and rot on the river bed.
- Decomposers like bacteria thrive with all the dead vegetation to eat.
- They multiply rapidly and use up a lot of oxygen.
- The river may become so low in oxygen that fish and freshwater invertebrates die.

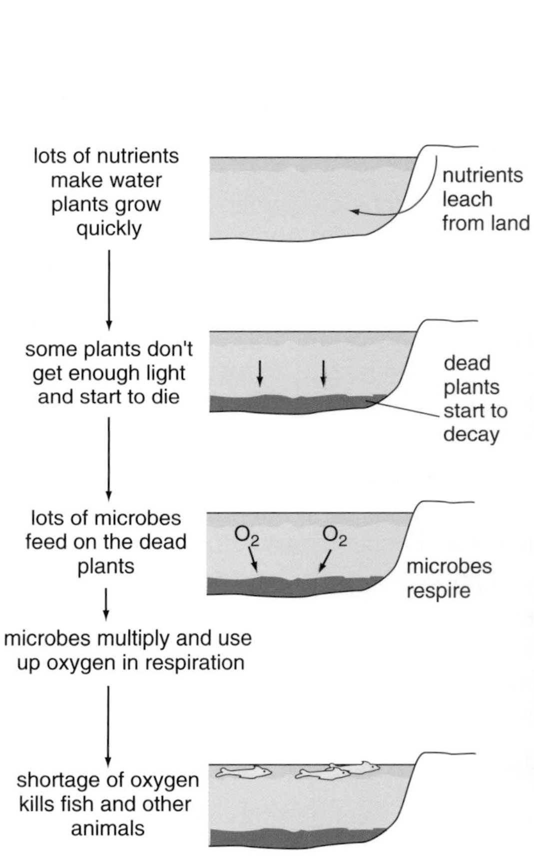

Adding nutrients to the environment is called **eutrophication**.
The same chain of events can happen if sewage gets into waterways. Bacteria multiply quickly, use up oxygen in respiration, which can result in the death of fish.

The nitrate time bomb

Nitrate fertilisers can become leached out of the soil.
They can trickle down into the bed-rock.
Some scientists believe that it is only a matter of time before the nitrates enter our drinking water.
High nitrates in drinking water are known to cause 'blue baby syndrome'.
This stops the haemoglobin carrying enough oxygen.
The result can be respiratory failure.

▶ Biology at work : Biodegradation of oil and plastics

Biodegradation of oil

Oil pollution is usually dealt with in two ways :

- the oil is skimmed or pumped off the sea
- chemicals are used to break the oil down.

Eventually the oil sinks to the sea bed.
Here it can smother and kill marine animals and plants. Chemicals in the oil are thought to enter the food chains.

But oil is biodegradable – there are many micro-organisms that can break it down.
The trouble is it usually takes a long time for this to happen.

Chemical dispersants used to deal with oil pollution are often toxic to marine life

An improved technique has been used in the Gulf.
Oil-polluted areas are 'seeded' with special types of microbes.
The complex hydrocarbons making up the crude oil are split into simple, non-polluting compounds.

Recovery time is about 2–3 years, but growth of the oil-degrading bacteria may be limited by lack of nutrients.
Bags of fertiliser (containing nitrates and phosphates) can speed up bacterial growth and aid recovery.

But there is no quick answer to oil pollution.
The spills should be controlled at source.
The policy should be 'prevention is better than cure'.

Biodegradable plastics

Plastics used in packaging are a major pollutant.

British scientists have developed a type of plastic called Biopol.
This can be broken down by microbes in the soil.
AstraZeneca is a leading UK chemical company.
Scientists there put bacteria into fermenters with glucose and other nutrients.
The microbes make a chemical that can be turned into Biopol.
When Biopol decomposes it produces carbon dioxide.

Biodegradable plastic bottles

Summary

- The natural checks on human populations have been removed resulting in huge increases.
- As a result raw materials are being used up and more waste is produced which can potentially cause pollution.
- Humans reduce the amount of land available for other animals and plants, by building, quarrying, farming and dumping waste.
- Raw materials, including non-renewable energy resources, are being rapidly used up. Recycling can help to conserve useful materials.
- Sulfur dioxide and nitrogen oxides are the causes of acid rain.
- Chlorofluorocarbons (CFCs) are causing a thinning of the ozone layer which protects the Earth from harmful ultra-violet light.
- Pesticides can build up along food chains to reach toxic levels.
- Water can become polluted by sewage, oil, fertilisers and toxic chemicals.
- When excess fertilisers get into rivers and lakes, they can result in eutrophication.
- Deforestation is resulting in a rise in atmospheric carbon dioxide.
- Increased levels of carbon dioxide and methane in the atmosphere are contributing to the greenhouse effect.
- Sustainable development involves the wise use of natural resources such as forests and fishing stocks.
- Lichens and freshwater invertebrates can be used as indicators of pollution.
- Conservation aims to keep ecosystems stable and maintain biodiversity as environmental conditions change.

▶ Questions

1. Copy and complete:
Pollution occurs when .... put harmful ..... or energy into the ..... When fossil fuels are burned, they give off gases like .... These gases dissolve in water to give ....CFCs are causing a thinning of the .... layer and letting in harmful ..... light. Bioaccumulation is the build up of .... or toxic .... along food chains. When excess .... get into rivers they can stimulate the growth of .... The algae ..... for light and start to die and are decomposed by .... The bacteria multiply and use up oxygen in ....The deletion of oxygen can led to the death of .... and freshwater ....This process, occurring in a river is called ..... Increased levels of carbon dioxide and ..... in the atmosphere are contributing to the .... effect, which results in global .... Sustainable ..... involves the wise use of natural ..... such as ..... and fishing stocks.

2. The table shows the amounts of methane given off from various sources:

Source of methane	Percentage (%)
farm animals	19
marshes	27
rice fields	23
landfill sites	11
mining	15
oceans	5

a) Draw a bar chart of these figures.
b) Which source contributes most gas?
c) Which two sources are not influenced by humans?
d) Apart from being a greenhouse gas, how else is methane a problem?

3. a) Explain why normal rainfall is slightly acidic.
b) Which gases dissolve in the clouds to form acid rain?
c) What are the sources of these gases?
d) Explain the effects of acid rain on:
i) conifer trees ii) fish iii) buildings
e) What can be done to reduce the effects of acid rain?

4. a) Which items of household waste can be recycled?
b) If more rubbish was recycled, how would this affect:
i) the supply of raw materials ii) our energy needs iii) the amount of land needed for rubbish tips?
c) In connection with building, what is the difference between a 'greenfield' site and a 'brownfield site? Explain the advantages of building on 'brownfield' sites.

5. a) What are CFCs and where do they come from?
   b) Explain the damage done by CFCs with reference to:
      i) the greenhouse effect ii) the ozone layer.
   c) What can be done to reduce the effects of CFCs on the environment?

6. a) Name the greenhouse gases and in each case give one source.
   b) Explain how the build up of these gases is contributing to the greenhouse effect.
   c) What are some of the consequences of global warming?
   d) What could humans be doing to reduce global warming?

7. The graph shows some of the effects of the release of sewage into a river.

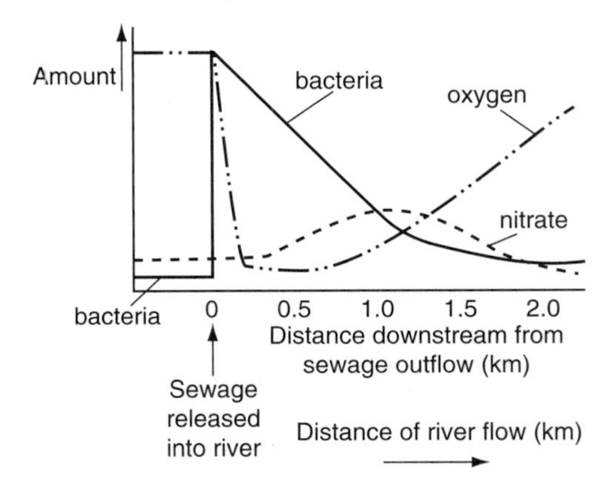

   a) Explain the effect of the release of sewage on the numbers of bacteria in the river.
   b) Explain the effects that the numbers of bacteria have on oxygen concentration.
   c) What would be the likely effects of this on fish and freshwater invertebrates?
   d) i) Explain the rise in nitrate concentration downstream from the sewage outfall.
      ii) What effects would this have on the growth of algae in the river?
   e) Why do you think that the oxygen concentration increases between 1 km and 2 km downstream from the sewage outflow?

8. In 1963, it was decided to kill mosquitoes by spraying a lake where they lived with a pesticide. The pesticide used is not poisonous to vertebrates unless it is in a concentration of 950 parts per million (p.p.m.). In 1964, large numbers of fish-eating birds were found dead in the lake. Study the table and the pyramid of numbers for the lake, then answer the questions:

Organism	Concentration of pesticide (p.p.m.)
plant plankton	1
animal plankton	10
fish	100
fish-eating birds	1000

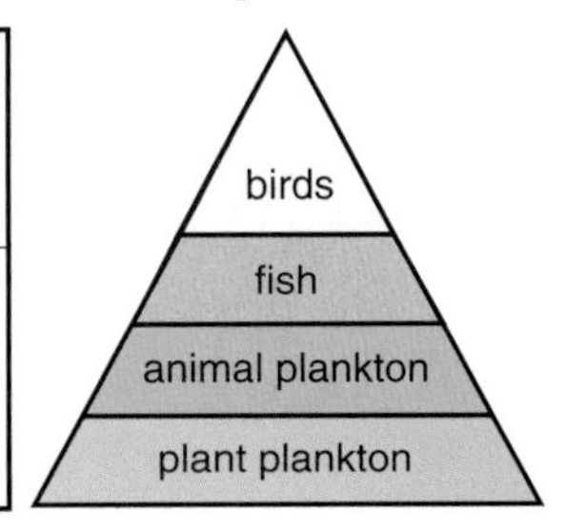

   a) Name i) the producers
      ii) the primary consumers
   b) Explain why fish survived in the lake in 1964 but not fish-eating birds.
   c) Explain what you would expect to happen to the population of fish in the lake during 1965 if spraying continued.
   d) Explain what you would expect to happen to the population of animal plankton as a result of c).
   e) Name a heavy metal that can act as a poison.

9. Lichens are easily damaged by sulfur dioxide gas in the air. The table below shows the number of lichen species found at various distances from a city centre.

Distance from city centre in km	Number of lichen species
0	1
2	4
4	8
6	14
8	20
10	12
12	20
14	29

   a) Plot a graph of the data in the table on graph paper.
   b) Describe the pattern shown by the results.
   c) A motorway passes the city. From your graph suggest the distance of the motorway from the city centre.
      Give a reason for your answer.
   d) Write down one other harmful effect that sulfur dioxide has on our environment.

Further questions on page 340.

▶ Adaptation and competition

1.

Tree on its own *Trees inside a wood*

The drawing above shows the shapes of trees grown on their own and inside a wood.

a) Write down **two** differences you can see between the tree grown on its own and those growing inside a wood. [2]

b) Trees inside the wood have to compete with each other for the things which they need to grow. List **three** things for which the trees compete. [3] (AQA)

2. Read the following information.

> Many animals and plants find it difficult to survive in hot deserts.
> - These deserts are very hot during the day, but very cold at night.
> - The ground is often sandy.
> - There is not much water.

> Camels can survive in these conditions. They have the following features.
> - They have humps in which body fat is stored.
> - They do not sweat very much.
> - They have large feet.
> - Their bodies are covered in fur.

Copy and complete the following table by explaining how each feature can help camels to survive in a desert.

Feature	How it helps survival
Has a fat store	
Does not sweat very much	
Has large feet	
Has fur	

[8] (AQA)

3. The graph shows how a population of bacteria in a muddy puddle changed over a period of four days.

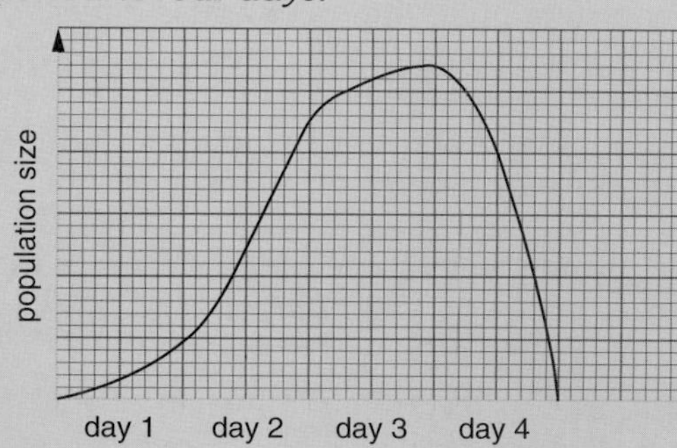

a) During which day, 1, 2, 3 or 4, is
   i) the population of the bacteria increasing most rapidly? [1]
   ii) the death rate becoming greater than the rate of reproduction? [1]
   iii) the rate of population growth beginning to be affected by limiting factors? [1]

b) State **three** factors which may limit the size of the population. [3]

c) i) What has happened to the bacteria by the end of day 4? [1]
   ii) Suggest a reason for this. [1] (OCR)

4. This question is about cacti.

Cacti are adapted to live in deserts.

 Note: although a question may be marked (AQA) etc, it will often be relevant to other examinations as well.

a) In which two of the following ways are the cacti adapted? [2]
Flat leaves fleshy stem
many stomata thick waxy cuticle

b) i) Name the process by which water is lost from plants. [1]
ii) Stomata are small holes in the leaves and stems of cacti.
The stomata can open or close.
The stomata of cacti open only at night.
Suggest why. [1]

c) Cacti have green stems.
The stems contain chlorophyll.
Why must cacti stems be green? [1]

d) Many cactus flowers are closed at midday.
Suggest why. [1] (OCR)

5. A lynx is a type of wild cat which eats hares. The table shows the changes in the populations of these animals in an area of Canada between 1985 and 1995.
Use the information in the table to answer the following questions :

a) i) How many years did it take for the hare population to reach the size it was in 1985 ? [1]
ii) In which year was the largest population of lynx ? [1]

Year	Number of lynxes (in thousands)	Number of hares (in thousands)
1985	72	130
1986	80	15
1987	40	85
1988	15	30
1989	7	20
1990	7	45
1991	11	55
1992	16	65
1993	25	60
1994	42	80
1995	55	130

b) When the hare population reached its peak in 1995 :
i) What happened to the lynx population ? [1]
ii) Suggest how this happened. [1]

c) Suggest **three** reasons for the large decrease in the number of hares from 1985 to 1986. [3]

d) In 1996 would you expect the lynx population to decrease, increase, or stay the same ? [1]

e) Since 1996 there has been a large increase in foxes which also feed on hares. Suggest :
i) How this may affect the lynx population. [1]
ii) Why it is affected in this way. [1] (WJEC)

▶ Energy and nutrient transfer

6. The diagram shows part of a food web in a pond.

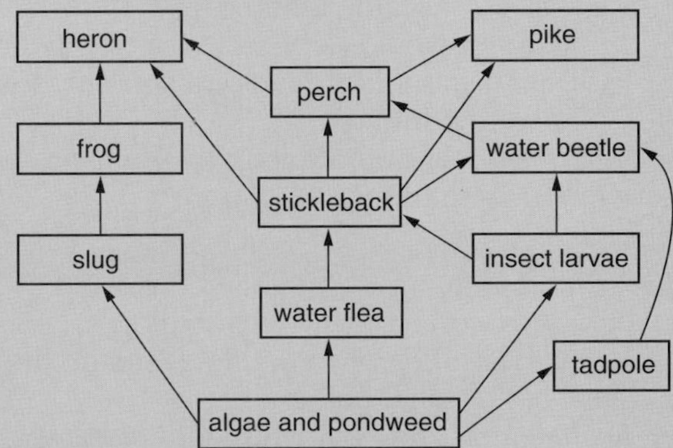

a) i) Name a carnivore shown in this food web. [1]
ii) How many primary consumers are shown in this web? [1]

b) A local fishing club removes all of the pike from the pond. Explain what will happen to :
i) the number of sticklebacks [1]
ii) the number of frogs. [2]

c) The fishing club now stocks the pond with many carp. These are fish that eat a lot of plants. Explain the effect this is likely to have on the food web. [4] (EDEX)

7. Read the following account and answer the questions which follow.

THE SCOTTISH MOORS
The Scottish moors cover thousands of hectares of land. The main type of vegetation is heather and grass. These may grow to a height of 0.5 metre. The heather and grass provide food for grouse. The moors are also home to small mammals, called voles. These also feed on the heather and grass. The main predators on the moors are foxes which feed on both the grouse and the voles. During certain times of the year, the grouse are shot for food by grouse hunters. During the shoot, loud noises are made to frighten the grouse and make them fly. The hunters use guns to shoot them down.

a) Draw a food web for the organisms mentioned above, including humans. Your food web should make clear the direction of energy flow. *[5]*

b) Suggest what the heather and grass provide for the grouse, other than food. *[1]*

c) Gamekeepers try to reduce the number of foxes by shooting them.

  i) What would happen to the population of grouse if hunting and shooting foxes were banned? *[1]*

  ii) How would this change affect the vegetation on the moor? *[1]* (AQA)

8. A community in a woodland consists of oak trees, caterpillars, voles and owls.
Many thousands of caterpillars feed on the leaves of a single oak tree.
A single vole may eat a hundred caterpillars each day.
An owl may eat three voles in one day.

a) The diagram shows four pyramids of numbers.

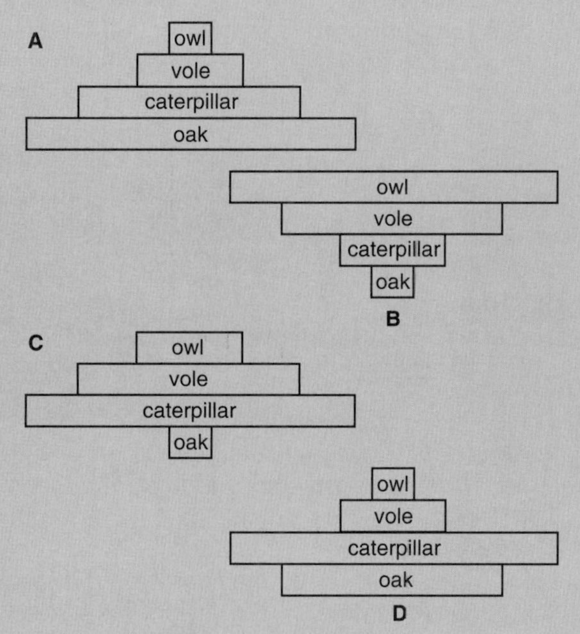

  i) Which **pyramid of numbers** is correct for this wooded community? *[1]*

  ii) What is meant by the term **biomass**? *[1]*

  iii) Draw a **pyramid of biomass** for the woodland community. *[2]*

  iv) Explain how energy is lost to the surroundings between each level of your pyramid of biomass. *[1]*

b) In a town near to the woodland many additional houses and factories are built. Suggest and explain **one** effect this might have on the woodland community. *[2]*

(OCR)

9. The diagram below shows the flow of energy through a food chain.

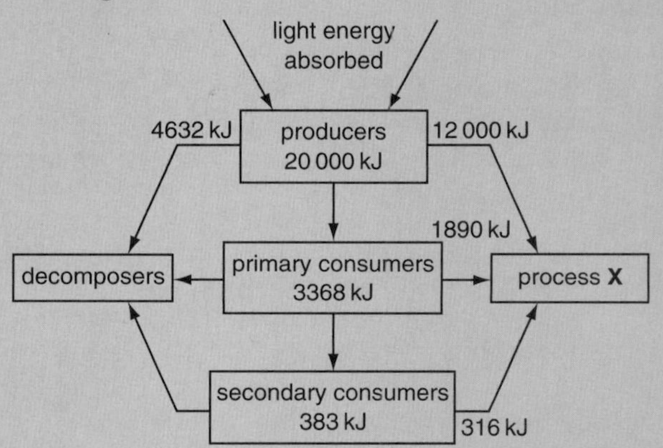

a) i) Name the process that occurs when energy is absorbed by the producers. *[1]*

  ii) What energy change occurs in this process? *[1]*

b) i) Name the process marked **X** in the diagram. *[1]*

  ii) In what form is the energy released at **X**? *[1]*

  iii) What percentage of energy absorbed by the producers is then released by them in process **X**? *[1]* (WJEC)

10. Some farmers use intensive farming, others farm organically.

a) For each of the following methods, explain whether it is an example of intensive or organic farming.

- using artificial fertilisers *[1]*
- not using herbicides *[1]*
- having a compost heap *[1]*
- crop rotation *[1]*
- having very large fields *[1]*
- keeping hedgerows *[1]*
- weeding by hand

b) Farmers use intensive farming because they say it increases productivity.

i) Explain what increasing productivity means. *[2]*

ii) Give one example of intensive farming.

Describe how it increases production. *[2]*

iii) Suggest and explain why organic food costs more in shops than intensively farmed food. *[2]*

c) The diagram shows how energy is lost in the food chain.

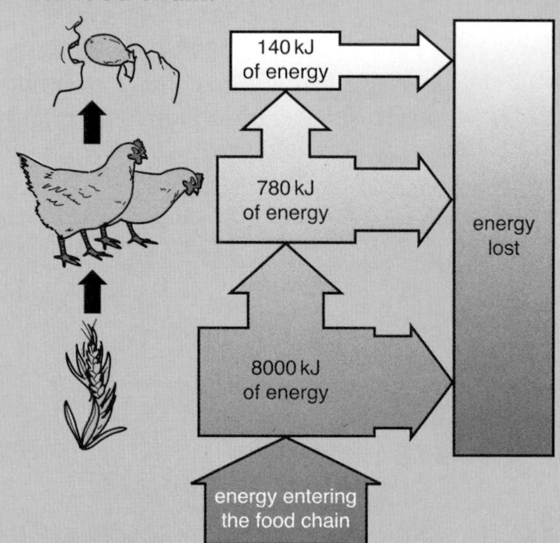

i) Suggest why less energy is usually lost from the food chain in intensive farming than organic farming. *[1]*

ii) Some parts of the world are short of food.

Suggest why it would help to have a vegetarian diet. *[1]*

11. The diagram shows the flow of energy through 1 m^2 of an ecosystem.

unit in each case is kJ per m^2 per year

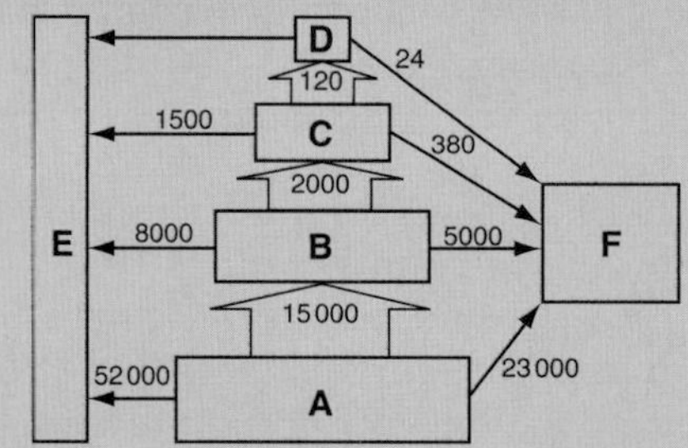

Key

A producers
B primary consumers
C secondary consumers
D tertiary consumers
E heat transfer to environment
F detritus feeders and decomposers

a) i) Name the process in which green plants transfer solar energy into chemical compounds.

ii) Name the process in living organisms which results in the transfer of heat to the environment. *[1]*

b) Tertiary consumers receive energy from secondary consumers.

i) Calculate the amount of heat energy which tertiary consumers transfer to the environment as a percentage of the energy received from secondary consumers. Show your working. *[2]*

ii) Primary consumers transfer a low percentage of their energy intake to the environment as heat. Tertiary consumers transfer a much higher percentage of their energy intake to the environment as heat. The tertiary consumers are mainly mammals and birds. The primary consumers are mainly insects and molluscs. Explain why mammals and birds lose a greater percentage of their energy intake to the environment as heat than do insects and molluscs. *[2]* (AQA)

12. The table shows the food intake and egg production for the same number of hens living in different environments. Battery hens are kept in small cages inside a barn whereas free-range hens spend much of the time outside.

	Battery hens	Free-range hens
Food intake in kg per week	80	100
Egg production in kg per week	12	9

a) Calculate the percentage of good biomass which is converted to egg biomass in battery hens. Show your working.

Answer ....% *[2]*

b) Give **two** reasons why some of the food biomass is not converted into egg biomass. *[2]*

c) Explain why the battery hens are more efficient at converting food into egg biomass. *[3]* (AQA)

13. This is a diagram of the carbon cycle.

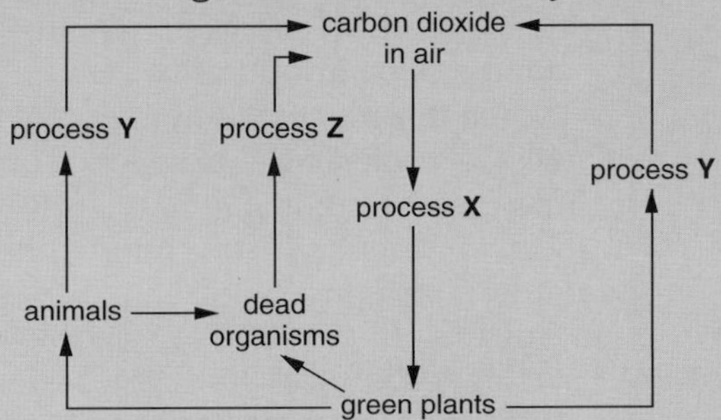

a) Name the processes **X** and **Y**. *[2]*

b) How does the carbon transferred from green plants become part of the body of an animal? *[1]*

c) Under the right conditions green plants can be changed to peat or coal.

i) How does the carbon in coal become part of the carbon dioxide in the air? *[1]*

ii) What environmental problem does this carbon dioxide cause? *[1]*

iii) What is process **Z**? *[1]* (OCR)

▶ Humans and the environment

14. Between 1880 and 1980 it has been estimated that about 40 % of all tropical rainforest was destroyed; much of it was destroyed by burning.

a) Give **three** reasons why this large-scale deforestation has happened. *[3]*

b) Large-scale deforestation is affecting the levels of carbon dioxide in the air.

i) What is happening to carbon dioxide levels? *[1]*

ii) How does deforestation cause a change in the carbon dioxide levels? *[2]*

iii) Explain some long-term effects that deforestation is likely to have on climate and soil fertility. *[5]*

c) Many types of habitat are being destroyed, with serious effects on the wildlife living there. What methods can scientists and governments use to protect this wildlife? *[2]* (EDEX)

15. In some countries farmers clear areas of forest by burning. The ash helps crops to grow well at first, but after a few years good crops cannot be grown. On mountain slopes the soil is easily washed away by heavy rain because there are no tree roots to hold it together.

a) How does the ash help the crops to grow well at first? *[2]*

b) Many farmers keep large numbers of cattle. Apart from producing carbon dioxide, explain how cattle make a particularly large contribution to the greenhouse effect? *[2]*

c) An area of forest was cut down. The concentration of nitrate in a stream in this area was measured before and after the forest was cut. The table shows the results.

Time	Concentration of nitrate in stream (mg per litre)
6 months before cutting	0.3
2 months before cutting	0.3
2 months after cutting	2.2
6 months after cutting	63.0

Suggest an explanation for the change in nitrate concentration. *[2]* (AQA)

16. Read this newspaper report about whales.

a)

A whale of a problem

In 1989 an international agreement was signed to ban the hunting of whales.
In 2003 Icelanders resumed the hunting of Minke whales. They said that the whales were eating too many fish.
It is thought that they have killed about 250 whales each year.
The whale meat is sold and eaten to people living in Iceland. The fat is used to make cosmetics.

i) Explain why Iceland resumed the hunting of Minke whales. *[1]*

ii) Explain what happens to the whales that are killed. *[2]*

iii) Explain whether you think whales should be hunted.
You should explain both sides of the argument in your answer. *[3]*

b) Fish stocks in the North Sea are falling. The few fish that are caught are getting smaller.
Scientists think that the fish population needs to be treated a 'sustainable resource'.
   i) Explain what is meant by a sustainable resource. [1]
   ii) Suggest how the fish stocks in the North Sea could be protected. [1] (OCR)

17. Copy and complete the table to show the contribution of carbon dioxide and water vapour to the greenhouse effect.

Gas	Greenhouse effect factor	Percentage by volume gas in the atmosphere	Contribution to the greenhouse effect
Chlorofluorocarbons	6560.0	0.00000008	0.00052
Carbon dioxide	1.0	0.037	....
Water vapour	0.1	1.0	....

What conclusions can be drawn from the information in the table? [2]

The greenhouse gases form a layer in the atmosphere. The diagram shows what happens when radiation from the Sun reaches the Earth's atmosphere.

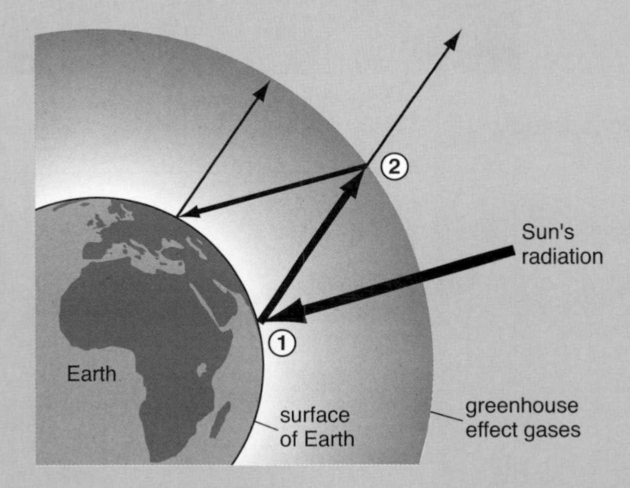

The arrows represent radiation from the Sun. The width of each arrow represents the amount of radiation.

Use the diagram and your knowledge to answer the following questions.

b) Explain what takes place at stage **1** and stage **2**. [2]

c) Suggest possible consequences of the greenhouse effect. [2]

d) The greenhouse effect is often confused with the reduction of the ozone layer around the Earth.
Explain one effect of the hole in the ozone layer. [2] (EDEX)

18. a) Why do farmers use fertiliser containing nitrate on their fields? [2]

b) Read the information in the box.

> **Fish die in Mill Pond**
> The fishing club has blamed local farmers for the death of fish in Mill Pond. A fisherman said that after the heavy rain of the last few months the pond had turned green. A week later there were dead fish floating in the pond. He thought that the cause of the problem was the fertiliser used on the wheat field next to the pond.

Explain how the fertiliser that was spread on the field could have caused the death of the fish in the pond. [6]

c) Most of the nitrogen from the fertiliser ends up in the protein of the decaying material on the bottom of the pond.
Explain how microbes can convert this nitrogen into nitrate.
To gain full marks in this question you should write your ideas in good English. Put them into a sensible order and use the correct scientific words. [4] (AQA)

chapter 21

Did you have yoghurt or toast for breakfast today ?
Is there a cheese roll in your sandwich box ?
How about smothering those chips in vinegar ?

If the answer to any of these questions is 'yes', then you have just used a few of the products of **biotechnology**.

Biotechnology is the way that we use living organisms, in particular microbes, to produce useful substances.

Although it sounds like something 'bang up-to-date', many of the processes involved have been around for centuries.
The use of yeast in brewing and bread-making, for example, goes back thousands of years.

Nowadays fermentation (which is the basic process behind brewing) can be carried out on an industrial scale. This allows scientists to produce vast quantities of useful products.
For example, have you ever eaten **Quorn™** ?
This is a meat substitute produced from a fungus.
When did you last have an antibiotic like penicillin ?
This is also produced by large-scale fermentation.

It is not just the food and drug industries that use biotechnology.
The efficient treatment of sewage uses microbes to convert organic waste into simpler substances.

In countries like Brazil with limited supplies of oil, biotechnology is being used to make petrol substitutes from materials like cane sugar.

Have you ever seen someone testing their blood sugar with a hand-held electronic meter ?
This is yet another example of biotechnology in action using something called a **biosensor**.

So, as you can see, there is hardly a person on the planet whose life is not touched by biotechnology.

Some of the products of traditional biotechnology ...

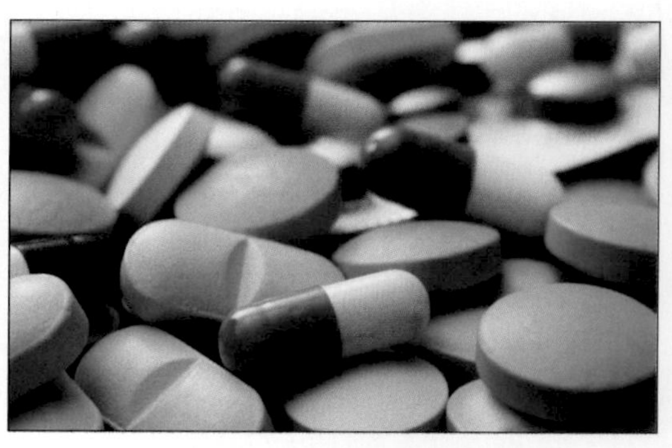

... and a more up-to-date example

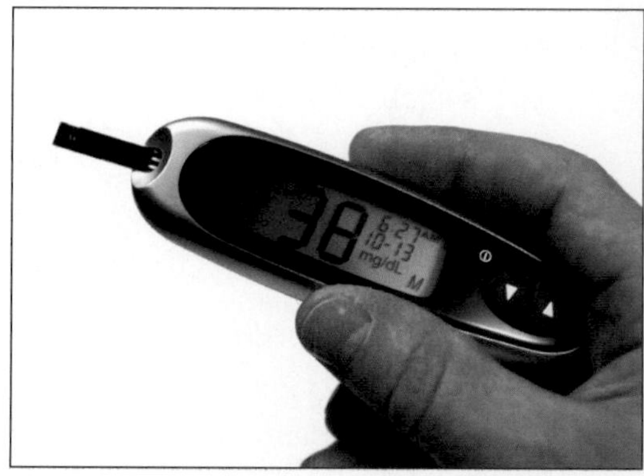

An electronic biosensor for testing blood glucose level

▷ Microbes and biotechnology

Many biotechnological processes use microbes to make their products. This applies equally to traditional processes such as bread-making and to more recent developments like antibiotic production.

So why are microbes so widely used ?
Here are just a few of the reasons :

- Microbes reproduce very quickly.
  This means that in a short space of time, scientists can grow a large quantity of the required organism.
- Unlike animals or plants, microbes can convert raw materials into the finished product very quickly, i.e. in hours rather than months or weeks.
- The use of microbes means that food production can be independent of the climate.
- Microbes grow very easily on a variety of cheap waste materials, possibly produced by other industrial processes.
- With the aid of genetic engineering, scientists can quickly alter microbes and so modify the product. Breeding new varieties of plants and animals can take a long time.

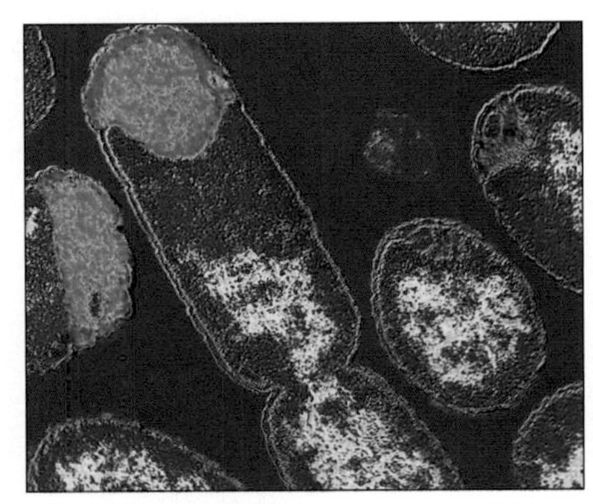

Microbes can reproduce very quickly

Traditional food production is very climate-dependent

Growing microbe cultures

Before scientists can use microbes in industrial-scale fermenters, they must grow cultures that are uncontaminated.
This means cultures that contain ***only*** the microbe they want.

You may have carried out simple experiments with microbes in school.
Hopefully you will have followed safety precautions when doing this work. These rules apply to biotechnologists too.

Some simple but important rules are :

- Any cuts should be covered with a clean, waterproof dressing.
- No eating or drinking during practical work with microbes.
- Washing hands before and after handling microbes.
- Swabbing down your work surface with disinfectant.
- Taping the lids of Petri dishes securely.
- Never opening the lid of a sealed Petri dish.

▷ Aseptic techniques for growing microbes

The word **aseptic** literally means 'excluding microbes'.
Using aseptic technique actually means following certain procedures so that you only grow the microbes you want.

Step 1

- Before you start to work with microbes:
  - –wash your hands and
  - –swab the bench with disinfectant.

Step 2

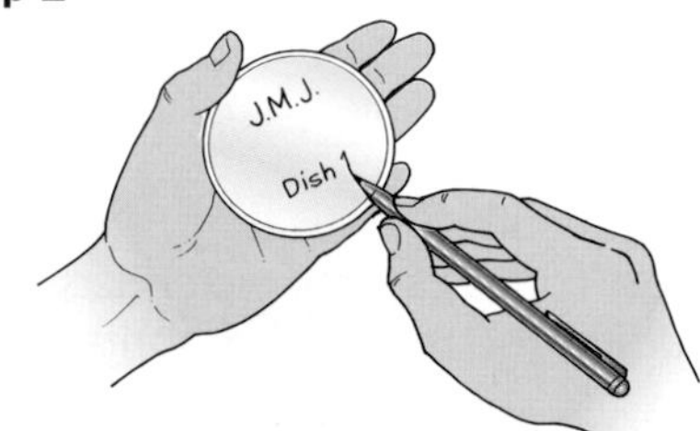

- You will be given a sterile agar plate. Keep the lid on the Petri dish.
- Label the lid with your name.

Step 3

wear eye protection

- Heat an inoculating loop in a Bunsen flame until it is red hot.

Step 4

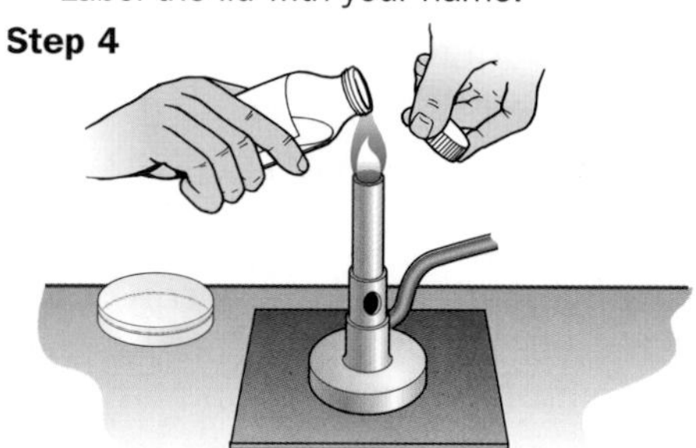

- Unscrew the bottle and hold the opening of it in a flame for ***2 seconds.***

Step 5

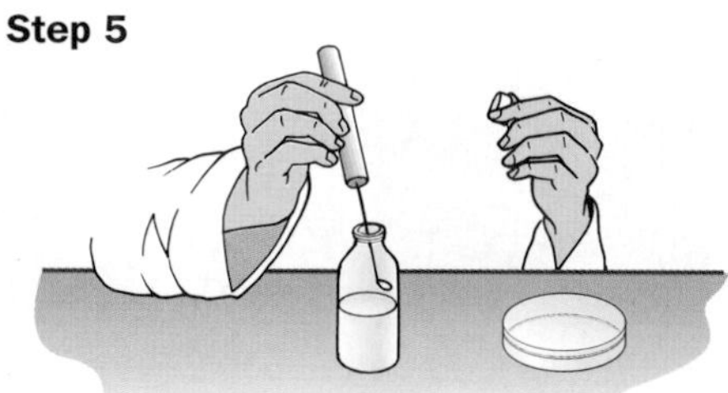

- Dip the sterile loop into the microbe sample and then replace the cap on the bottle.

Step 6

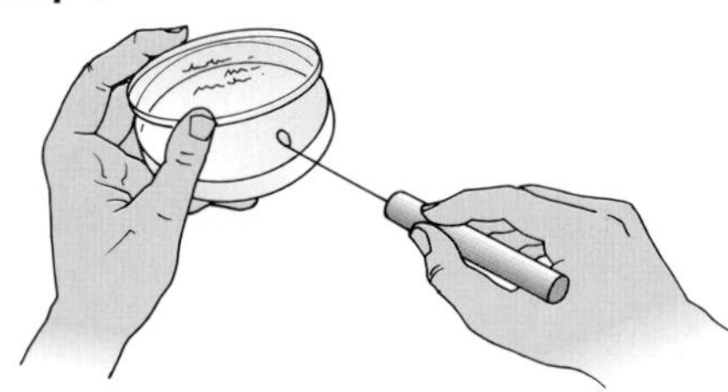

- Slightly lift the lid. Gently streak the loop over the surface of the agar. Replace the lid.

Step 7

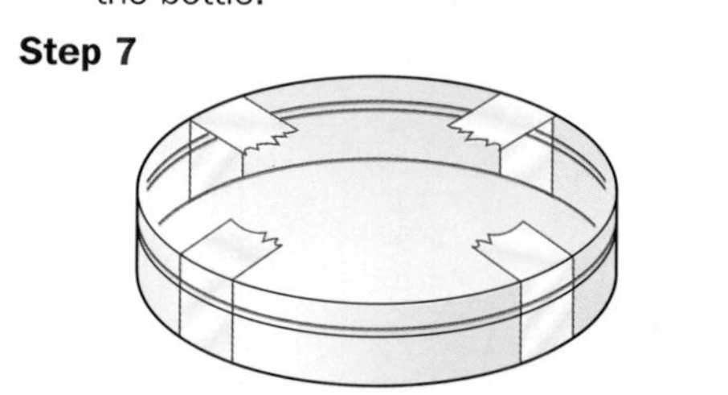

- Seal the Petri dish with Sellotape. Put the dish upside down in an incubator at 25 °C for 2–3 days.

Never open a sealed Petri dish.

Step 8

- Swab the bench with disinfectant.
- Wash your hands.

▷ Biotechnology and food production

As we have already seen, the use of microbes in food production goes back thousands of years. But if we look at processes such as cheese, bread and wine production, we can see how the traditional methods have been improved with the aid of modern technology.

Cheese making is big business nowadays

Cheese-making

Cheese is produced by the action of bacteria on milk.

Nowadays, cheese makers use pasteurised milk.
Why do you think this is necessary?
Pasteurisation kills the bacteria naturally present in milk. This means that the only bacteria present will be the ones that are actually put there. These bacteria are known as **lactic acid** bacteria (***Lactobacillus***).
They turn **lactose** (milk sugar) into lactic acid.

Curds that form the basis of Wensleydale cheese

The low pH now present makes the milk **curdle**. This means that the protein in the milk turns into a semi-solid called **curd**. This process is aided by the addition of an enzyme called **rennin**.

This enzyme was originally extracted from the stomachs of calves. However, it can now be produced in greater quantities by genetic engineering and is called **chymosin** (see page 355).

Salt is now added to the curd.
This not only enhances the flavour, but it also acts as a preservative.

Depending on what type of cheese is being made, other bacteria will now be added. These microbes are known as **ripening bacteria** and they break down the protein and fat in the cheese.

Blue cheeses, like stilton, gain their characteristic appearance through the action of a fungus which is added to the curd.

A fungus gives blue cheese its veiny appearance

In order to speed up cheese production, manufacturers can add bacterial enzymes rather than the bacteria themselves.
Can you see why this would speed things up ?
It is the enzymes themselves that change the lactose into lactic acid. If enzymes are added directly, there is no delay while the bacteria make them.

Yoghurt manufacture

Yoghurts have become very popular over recent years. Yoghurt-making shares some similarities with cheese production.

Pasteurised milk is once again the starting point. Firstly the milk is thickened with skimmed milk powder often used as a thickening agent.

Unlike cheese-making which is best in cool conditions, yoghurt production needs a temperature of about 40 °C. This temperature has three advantages :

- It helps to thicken the milk protein.
- It reduces the oxygen level.
- It is the ideal temperature for growth of the bacteria.

Why do you think a low oxygen level is required ? Most of the bacteria used in cheese and yoghurt production prefer anaerobic conditions.

Once the milk is at the ideal temperature, the bacteria are added. In yoghurt manufacture the bacteria used are different to those used in cheese production. However they still do the same job, namely converting milk sugar into lactic acid. This usually takes place in large, stainless steel fermentation tanks.

As with cheese production curds are made, but in yoghurt they are much less solid.

The yoghurt is then cooled before it undergoes the final stage of production. This often involves mixing the yoghurt with fruit to create the many different flavours of yoghurt now available.

Some yoghurts are treated to remove all bacteria, whilst others contain 'live' cultures. These are known as 'pro-biotic' yoghurts. The bacteria supplement the bacteria naturally found in the gut, and aid digestion.

Cheese and yoghurt manufacture are both examples of batch processes.

This type of process involves producing a set amount of product. The process then stops and all the equipment is cleaned and sterilised before starting all over again.

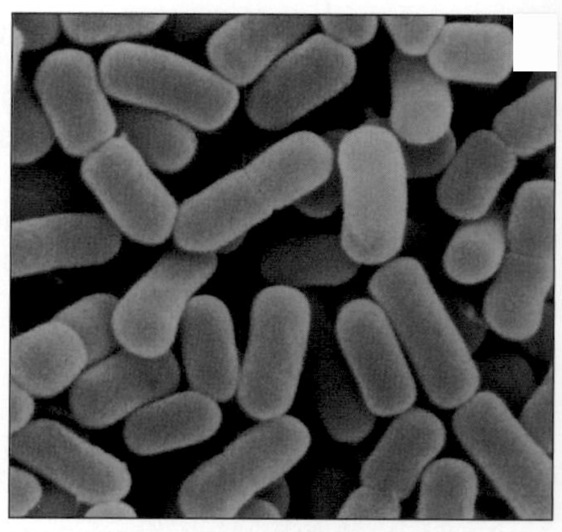

Lactic acid bacteria under the electron microscope

Adding the bacteria to the pasteurised milk

A probiotic yoghurt containing live bacteria

Wine-making and brewing

Wine and beer production is yet another example of centuries-old biotechnology.
As with cheese and yoghurt, microbes are the all-important living organisms.

This time, though, not bacteria but yeast – a microscopic fungus – is used.

Look back at page 73.
Why is yeast used to make alcohol ?
You will remember that when yeast respires without oxygen it is carrying out **fermentation**.
Yeast uses sugars as its energy source and produces alcohol, carbon dioxide and some energy.

One of the main differences between wine and beer production is the ***source*** of the sugars.

To make wine, ripe grapes are crushed to extract their juice. This juice is rich in sugar and this is the energy source for the yeast.

In beer production, barley grains are the source of the sugar.
In a process called **malting**, these grains are allowed to germinate for a few days. During this time, enzymes break down the starch in the grains into a sugar called **maltose**.
This sugar is contained in a brown liquid called **wort**.
Now in a process called **mashing**, yeast is added to the wort and fermentation begins.
To give beer its characteristic bitter flavour, hops are then added.

The mashing process produces some useful by-products.
A foamy layer of carbon dioxide covers the fermenting mixture.
This is often collected for use in other industrial processes.
Also some of the yeast can be removed.
It can then be used as a starter culture for another brew, and also to make yeast spreads.

Brewing can be done at home with 'home-brew kits'.
But most beer is brewed on an industrial scale in huge copper vats. These containers can produce thousands of litres at a time. Brewers also use computer technology to carefully monitor and adjust the conditions in the vats.

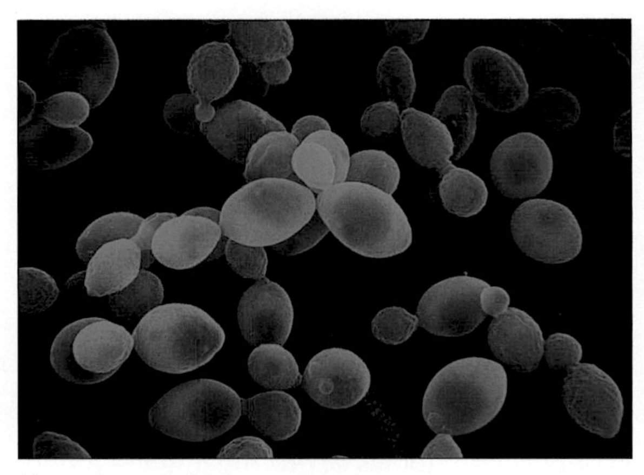

Yeast is a useful fungus

Treading grapes to extract the juice

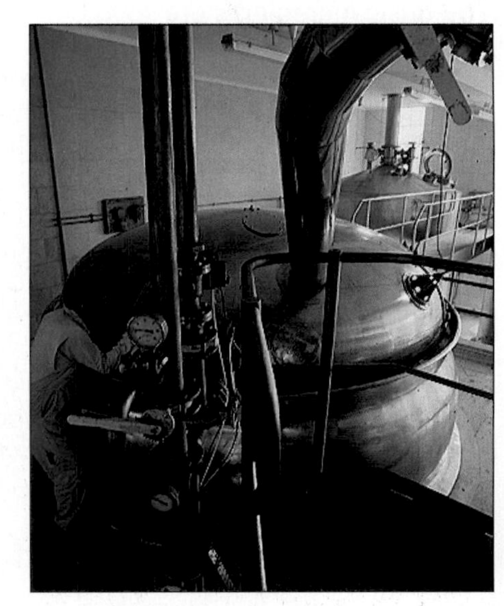

Checking the brewing process in a large copper vat

Baking

Baking is another example of using yeast to help produce a food.

A commercial bakery

Bread is made from **dough**. This contains flour, water, salt, sugar and yeast.
This mixture is kept at a warm temperature.
The yeast starts to ferment the sugar and, as we have already seen, produces alcohol and carbon dioxide gas.
The bubbles of gas cause the dough to rise.
The bread is then baked in a hot oven. This expands the bubbles of gas making the bread 'light' in texture. It also evaporates the alcohol, leaving behind the traditional taste of bread.

Soy sauce

If you have ever eaten a Chinese meal, you will know that soy sauce is an important ingredient.
What you probably don't know is that soy sauce is also produced with the aid of microbes.

The commercial production of this sauce involves not only yeast, but another fungus called ***Aspergillus***.
The third member of the microbe team is the lactic acid bacteria we met in cheese-making.

The basic ingredients are soya beans and wheat grains.
To a mixture of cooked beans and roasted grains is added a culture of *Aspergillus*. This fungus grows on the grains and turns starch into sugar.

The next step is to add yeast which ferments the mixture using the newly formed sugars.
This is followed by a long period of cold fermentation carried out by the lactic acid bacteria.

The mixture is now filtered to remove the raw sauce.
This is then pasteurised to kill any bacteria present.
Finally it is put into bottles which have been sterillised by steam cleaning.

▷ Industrial fermentation

You may have carried out simple experiments on fermentation in school. If so, you probably used basic laboratory apparatus like that shown on page 73.

Clearly, this kind of apparatus is no good for producing large quantities of useful materials such as **penicillin**.
Industrial fermenters can, in fact, hold as much as 500 000 dm^3 of fermenting mixture.
Also the conditions within these huge tanks can be very carefully controlled.

A large industrial fermenter

We can use the example of penicillin production to show how these fermenters work.

A culture of the fungus ***Penicillium*** is added to the fermenter. It then thrives in the ideal conditions maintained inside.
These include :

- **Adding nutrients** such as sugar, ammonia and vitamins.
- **Maintaining a constant temperature** of about 30 °C.
- **Maintaining a constant pH** of about 6.5.

Once fermentation has started, it takes about 30 hours for penicillin production to start.

Why does it take so long?
The fungus has to complete its main growth phase, and use up most of the nutrients **before** it starts to release penicillin into the surrounding liquid.

After about six days, fermentation is complete. The mixture is drained out of the fermenter and then filtered. The penicillin is then extracted as a salt-like material.

This process is known as **batch cultivation**. After the six days, the fermenter is emptied, cleaned and sterilised ready for the next batch. **Continuous cultivation** allows production to take place in a fermenter for several weeks.

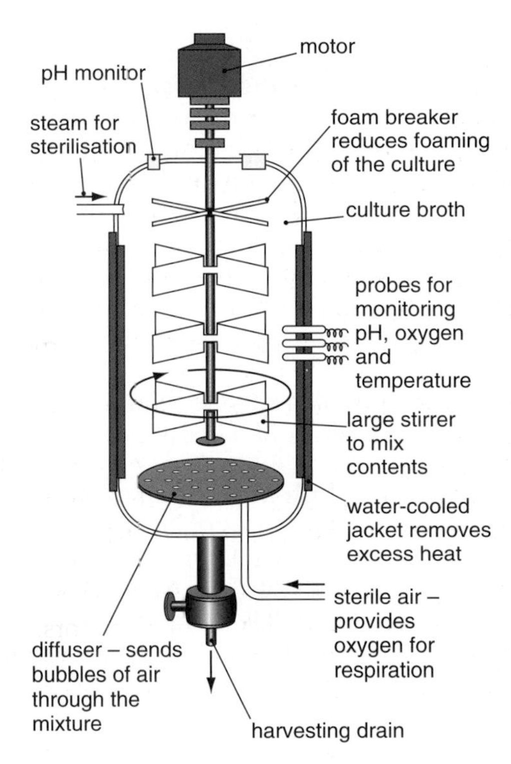

This type of industrial fermenter allows for continuous cultivation

▷ Food supplements

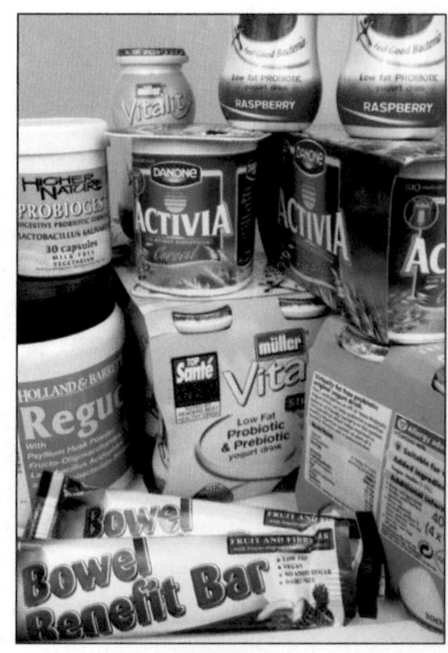

These foods all contain prebiotics

Prebiotics are non-digestible food ingredients that stimulate the growth of 'friendly bacteria' in the colon (large intestine).
To be effective, prebiotics must escape digestion in the upper parts of the gut and encourage the activity of 'friendly bacteria' in the colon, whilst reducing the population of harmful bacteria.
The main group of prebiotics is **oligosaccharides**, these are carbohydrates including fructo-oligosaccharides (FOS), galacto-oligosaccharides (GOS) and inulins. FOS, also called neosugar, is produced on a commercial scale from sucrose using an enzyme from a fungus.
FOS and inulins are found naturally in Jerusalem artichokes, chicory, leeks, onions and asparagus.
Prebiotics improve colon function by preventing constipation, enhancing mineral absorption and may have anti-carcinogenic effects.
Oligosaccharides are common ingredients in food found on supermarket shelves and are thought to lower blood sugar in people with diabetes, as well as reducing high levels of cholesterol and triglycerides.

Some vinegars have herbs added to them.

Acetobacter is a nitrogen-fixing bacterium which uses the enzyme nitrogenase to convert atmospheric nitrogen into a form that can be used by plants. The bacterium forms a beneficial **symbiotic** relationship with a number of grasses, providing them with a source of nitrogen, in exchange for carbohydrates produced by photosynthesis.
In terms of biotechnology, *Acetobacter*, is probably best known in the production of vinegar. Ethanoic acid (also known as acetic acid) is produced by the bacterial oxidation of ethanol (alcohol). There are several types of vinegar, depending upon the type of alcohol that is fermented.
Acetobacter, is also used to oxidise sorbitol to sorbose, which are involved in a series of reactions that ultimately yield vitamin C.

Carrageen or Irish moss, is an edible seaweed, found on the rocky Atlantic shores of Northern Europe.
It is a red seaweed, 5-30 cm long and highly branched.
An extract from it (E407) is used commercially as a gelling agent in ice cream, jellies, soups and confectionary.
It is also sold bleached and dried for home use. It can be used in cough medicines, as an absorbent in surgical dressings and as a feed for cattle.

Invertase is an enzyme extracted from yeast.
It splits sucrose into glucose and fructose (invert syrup) and is commercially used in liquefied cherry centres, creams, mints, truffles and marshmallow. It is used to improve the shelf life of confectionary and can prevent sugar crystallisation in fondants and chocolate-coated candies with soft centres. Invertase is able to do this by again converting sucrose to glucose and fructose.

▷ More food supplements

Citric acid is much used in the food and drink industry as well as in pharmaceuticals.
For many years it was extracted from citrus fruits, such as oranges, lemons and limes. However, as demand for citric acid increased, strains of the fungus *Aspergillus niger* have been used. The citric acid is produced when *A.niger* breaks down glucose during aerobic fermentation.
As a result of genetic engineering high-yielding strains of the fungus have been developed.
Citric acid is used in soluble aspirin and fizzy indigestion products. The indigestion powder or tablets contain sodium hydrogencarbonate which reacts with citric acid producing a 'fizz' of carbon dioxide bubbles.
Citric acid is also extensively used to give the tangy flavour and the 'fizz' to soft drinks.

Citric acid puts the fizz into soft drinks

Chymosin

As we have seen, in cheese production, the enzyme rennet is added to milk to clump the milk protein together and form the curds. Rennet was extracted from the stomachs of calves, but in the 1960's an increased demand for meat meant that more calves were raised to maturity.
Also a growing number of people followed vegetarian diets and rejected cheese made with calf rennet. Today, rennet has largely been replaced by **chymosin**, a similar enzyme produced by genetically modified yeast.
Copies of the genes responsible for rennet production are isolated from calf stomach cells and inserted into the genetic material of yeast cells. These are then grown on an industrial scale and the chymosin isolated.
Vegetarian cheese is increasing in popularity and in the UK, the Vegetarian Society have given cheese made with genetically modified chymosin its seal of approval.

A variety of vegetarian cheeses

Monosodium glutamate (MSG)

In 1907, Professor Ikeda of Tokyo Imperial University, stated that 'There is a taste that is common to asparagus, tomatoes, cheese and meat but which is not one of the four well known tastes of sweet, sour, bitter or salty.'
He carried out experiments on the bacterium, *Corynebacterium glutamicum*, and succeeded in isolating crystals of the amino acid, **glutamic acid** or **glutamate**. Monosodium glutamate (MSG) has since turned out to be an ideal seasoning. Because MSG has no smell or special texture of its own, it can be used in many different dishes where it naturally enhances the original flavour of the food.

▷ Biology at work: The Chelsea Physic Garden

The Chelsea Physic Garden was founded by the Society of Apothecaries in 1673, in order to promote the study of plants in relation to medicine, then known as 'physic' or healing arts.
It still fulfils the traditional functions of scientific research and plant conservation, but also carries out an educational role and provides the amenity of a 'secret' walled garden in the heart of London.
Its site by the Thames was chosen to provide a warmer microclimate and the river also acted as a transport route to other open spaces, giving easy movement to both plants and botanists.
In the early 1700s, Dr Hans Sloane, purchased the Manor of Chelsea and the site of the garden was leased to the Society of Apothecaries for £5 a year in perpetuity.
The Pharmaceutical Garden displays medicinal plants which yield drugs of proven value in current medicine throughout the world today.

The statue of Sir Hans Sloane in the centre of the Garden

Aspirin is made from salicylic acid which was first extracted from the plant Meadowsweet in 1835. It is also found in the bark and leaves of willow plants and is used as an analgesic for pain relief.
Aspirin also acts as an anti-inflammatory agent, providing some relief from the swelling associated with arthritis and minor injuries.

Taxol which is used as an anti-cancer agent, is derived from the bark of the Pacific yew tree, which is a protected species and one of the slowest growing trees in the world. Isolation of the compound from the bark involves killing the tree and it has been estimated that it would take six 100-year old trees to provide enough taxol to treat one patient.
Luckily an alternative source has been discovered in a European species of ornamental yew.

Some of the pharmaceutical beds

Quinine is a drug made from the bark of the Cinchona tree and until the 1930s it was the only real treatment for malaria.
Quinine has also been used as a flavouring, providing the bitter taste in tonic water.
In fact 'gin and tonic' was originally consumed in the past to prevent attacks of malaria!

Artemisinin is an anti-malarial agent extracted from the dried leaves of the Chinese herb *Artemisia annua*. The drug acts rapidly against the malarial parasite, reducing fever and without significant side effects.
In a malaria epidemic in the early 1990s in Vietnam, artemisinin reduced the death rate by 97 %.

A Victorian impression of the 'demonstration' of medicinal plants in the Chelsea Physic Garden

▷ Biology at work: Biofuels

Biofuels are literally fuels made from biological material, such as animal dung, sugar cane and plant waste. This material can be fermented to produce a variety of fuels such as methane gas, alcohol and biodiesel.

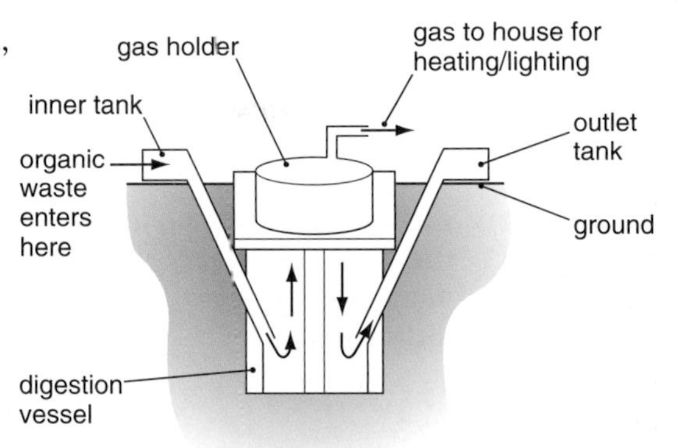

A simple biodigester

Have you ever seen gas flares burning on waste-disposal sites?
These flares are burning off a **biogas** that builds up underground where waste material is decaying.
This biogas is mainly a gas called **methane**.
Methane can be produced when cattle dung is digested by anaerobic bacteria. In parts of the developing world, such as Africa, small fermenters called **biodigesters** (or digesters) are used to make this gas.
It can then be used to provide heat and power – just as in this country we use bottled gas in caravans.

The material left over, after digestion is completed, can make an excellent fertiliser for crops.

Have you ever thought how we would manage without petrol ?
Some countries that have no oil supplies of their own have developed a biofuel substitute.

Brazil, for example, uses fermenters to produce ethanol (alcohol).
The raw material often used is sugar-cane juice which contains a lot of carbohydrate. Glucose from maize starch is another raw material. This is obtained by treating the starch with carbohydrase enzymes.

Alcohol is a good substitute for petrol, because it has a high energy content and when burned creates less pollution.

Have you noticed fields of bright yellow flowers in the countryside ?.
This crop is **oil seed rape**. The oil that is obtained from it can be converted into a fuel called **biodiesel**.
This fuel again has the big advantage over petrol-based fuels of being less polluting when burned.

As fossil fuels become more and more scarce, it is possible that biofuels will play an increasing role in world fuel supplies.

▷ Biology at work: Mycoprotein – a food for the future ?

We have already seen how fermentation of microbes can be used to produce many traditional food products.
Also, how fermentation on an industrial scale allows the production of vast quantities of material.

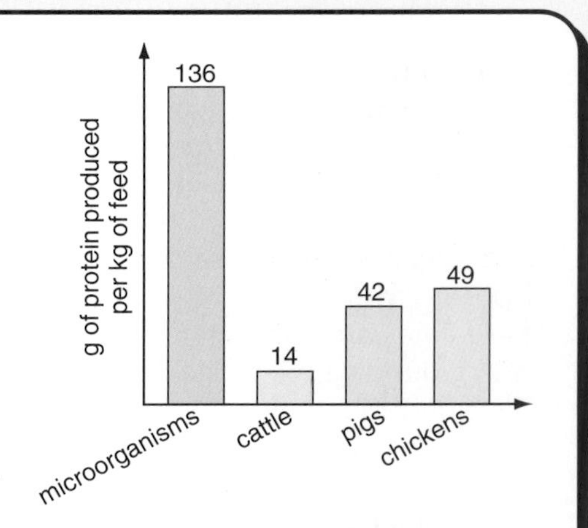

Microbes are very good at producing protein.
In the 1960s, the food producers Rank Hovis McDougall (RHM) began a research programme that led to the production of **mycoprotein**.

'Never heard of it !'
Well, the chances are you have eaten it in the school canteen.

Mycoprotein is a high protein material produced by a fungus called ***Fusarium***.
This fungus was originally discovered in a field in the south of England.
RHM quickly realised how valuable it might be as a food material.
Some of its advantages are :

- It is fibrous and so can take on a meat-like texture.
- It is high in protein.
- It is low in fat.
- It doesn't have an unpleasant taste.

Fusarium *growing on a cereal*

Just like penicillin, mycoprotein is made in huge fermenters.
This time, though, the technique is **continuous culture**.
This means that the nutrients are *continually* added and the product *continually* removed.

Mycoprotein makes an ideal meat substitute.
Since the mid-1980s it has been actively used in this way.
It is marketed under the name **Quorn™**.
You can find it in a variety of meat dishes, such as savoury pies and curries.

Some food products derived from mycoprotein

Is mycoprotein the food of the future ?
Could it help to relieve the threat of famine ?
Well, yes, in theory, if it can be produced cheaply and in sufficient quantities.
But at the moment its big attraction is as a healthy low-fat alternative to meat.

Summary

- Biotechnology involves the use of living organisms to make useful products.
- In most cases the living organisms are microbes – mainly bacteria and fungi.
- Microbes can reproduce and convert raw materials into products very quickly.
- Working with microbes requires careful aseptic techniques. These avoid contamination and danger to health.
- Fermentation is the key reaction in many biotechnological processes.
- Industrial fermenters allow mass production under carefully controlled conditions.
- Many traditional foods, like bread and cheese, are products of biotechnology.
- Biotechnology is also responsible for products with great future potential, such as biofuels and mycoprotein.
- A number of food supplements have become available as a result of biotechnology.
- Plants continue to act as a source of drugs of important medicinal value.

▷ Questions

1. Copy and complete :
Biotechnology uses . . . . organisms to make useful products. The most commonly used organisms are . . . . and . . . . . .
Microbes have a number of advantages, such as their fast rate of . . . . . Many of the products of biotechnology depend upon microbes carrying out . . . . . This reaction plays an important part in making bread and . . . . . As well as traditional foods, biotechnology also produces . . . . .
This material is a very good substitute for meat. Drugs such as . . . . are also produced by microbes in huge . . . . .

2. Explain the need for the following procedures :
a) Petri dishes should be sterilised before use.
b) Inoculating loops should be passed through a flame and then allowed to cool before use.
c) The lid of a Petri dish should be sealed and not opened once microbes have grown.

3. Microbes are commonly used in biotechnology.
Explain the advantage of each of these features
of microbe growth :
a) Microbes can reproduce quickly.
b) Microbes can grow easily on waste material.
c) Microbes are very efficient protein producers.

4. a) Give three examples of traditional foods made with the help of microbes.
b) What are the main differences between the production of cheese and yoghurt ?
c) Describe how fungi are used in the production of both blue cheese and soy sauce.

5. a) Which microbe is involved in brewing, baking and wine-making ?
b) What is the source of the sugars that are fermented in :
i) brewing and
ii) wine-making ?
c) How do bubbles of carbon dioxide gas help to make bread ?

6. This drawing shows a fermenter used to make penicillin.

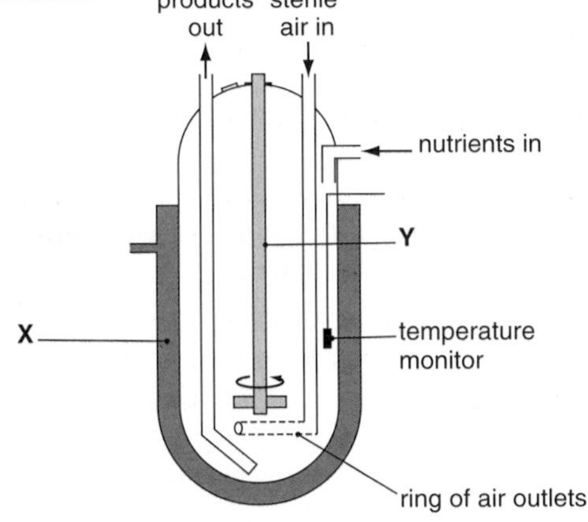

a) Name parts **X** and **Y**.
b) Name two nutrients that would need to be added.
c) Why is air bubbled through the fermenter ?
d) Why must this air be sterile ?

7. This graph shows the concentration of mould, glucose and the antibiotic streptomycin in a fermenter.

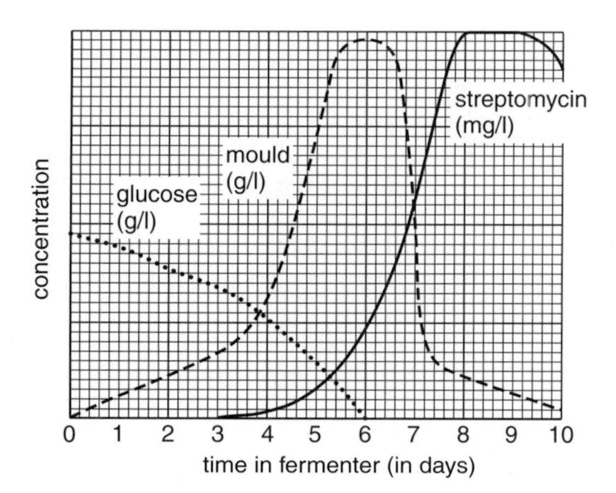

a) What happens to the glucose concentration during the manufacture of streptomycin ?
b) Explain why the glucose concentration changes in this way.
c) Why does the concentration of antibiotic reach a peak *after* the peak in the concentration of the mould ?

8. a) What is the name of the fungus from which mycoprotein is produced ?
b) Give two advantages of this fungus for food production.
c) How is mycoprotein manufacture in a fermenter different to that of penicillin ?

This table shows a comparison between mycoprotein and beef.

Nutrient	Mycoprotein (% dry mass)	Beef (% dry mass)
protein	40	60
fat	10	30
minerals	3	1
fibre	30	0

d) Use this information to explain why mycoprotein is a healthy alternative to meat.

9. An investigation was carried out to investigate how quickly milk curdled in different pHs.
The enzyme rennin had been added to the milk as part of the cheese-making process.
The results are shown in this table.

pH	2	3	4	5	6
Time taken to curdle milk (mins)	4	2	3	6	13

a) Plot a line graph of these results.
b) What is the best pH for the enzyme to curdle the milk ?
c) It was found that milk did not curdle at all at pH 9.
Suggest a reason why the enzyme does not curdle milk at this pH.

10. Yoghurt manufacture requires a temperature of around 40 °C.
a) Explain precisely why this is the best temperature to use.
b) What is meant by the term 'live culture' ?
c) Why is pasteurised milk often used in yoghurt manufacture?

11. Foods such as cheese, yoghurt, wine and bread are all made with the aid of microbes.
a) Explain why during their manufacture temperatures no higher than 40 °C are used.
b) Explain why the final part of bread manufacture is at over 200 °C.

12. a) Name four food supplements and explain their importance to the food and drink industry
b) i) From which medicinal plants are the following drugs extracted : aspirin, taxol, quinine, artemisinin ?
ii) In each case explain their value in treating disease
c) Why are botanic gardens important to our modern society ?

Further questions on page 371.

Behaviour

chapter 22

The responses that animals make to the various stimuli that they receive are termed **behaviour**.
These stimuli may come from other animals or from the environment.
An animal's behaviour has survival value.
Those animals that respond appropriately to changes in their environment are more likely to survive and to reproduce.
Behaviour enables an animal to find food, avoid predators and find a mate with which to reproduce.

We can divide animal behaviour into two categories : **instinctive** or **innate behaviour** that is inherited and **learned behaviour** which is modified by experience.
Instinctive behaviour depends upon the animal's genetic make up, whereas learned behaviour is the result of trained changes in behaviour that take place during an animal's lifetime.
The differences between instinctive and learned behaviour are summarised in the table opposite.

Innate behaviour
inherited
not changed by environment
inflexible
similar in all members of species or breed
Learned behaviour
not inherited
changed by environment
quickly adapts to new circumstances
differs between species

▷ Instinct

Animals inherit certain patterns of behaviour from their parents.
There are many examples where animals display a type of behaviour without any previous experience.
Shortly after it hatches from the egg, a hungry herring-gull chick will peck at the tip of its parent's beak.
This causes the parent to regurgitate semi-digested food which the chick eats.
Closer observation shows that the chick directs its pecks at the red spot on the yellow beak of the parent.
Scientists have used models to study this instinctive behaviour.
When presented with a model with a red spot on the beak, the newly hatched chick pecked at it three times as much as it did at a model with a plain yellow beak :
So what is the benefit to the herring-gull chick of having this innate response to a red spot on a yellow beak ?
Well, it means that it can obtain food immediately from the parent.
It does not have to waste time by learning how to obtain food.

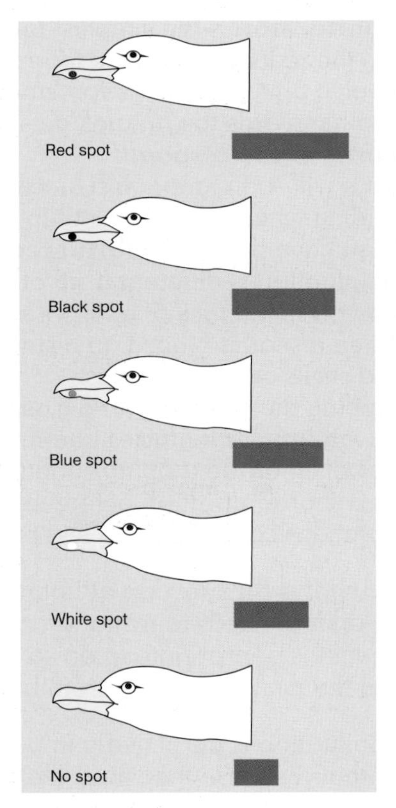

Results show the length of the bar under each model as the number of pecks over 30 seconds.

Many birds such as warblers, like the blackcap, are able to migrate from Germany to winter in the Mediterranean just by instinct.
Geese, on the other hand, migrate to wintering grounds as family groups.
So young birds learn to find the traditional wintering areas by following their parents.

▷ Learned behaviour

Learning is a change in behaviour caused by experience.
Bees will learn to visit those flowers with the most nectar.
A three-day old chick soon learns to peck at food rather than stones on the ground.
In general, the larger an animal's brain, the more it can learn.
Humans have a huge capacity for learning because of their well-developed cerebral hemispheres in the brain (see page 115).

Animals learn in order to:

- avoid predators
- find food
- find a suitable mate
- avoid harmful environments
- recognise individuals within the group
- find their way back home.

Habituation

Habituation is the simplest form of learning.
It is the reduced response to repeated stimuli when it does not involve any form of reinforcement (reward or punishment).
In other words the animal 'gets used' to the stimulus and ***learns not to respond***.
Birds will soon ignore a scarecrow which prevented them from landing when it was first put in a field.
They have become **habituated** to it.
Habituation is different from other forms of learning because it involves the ***loss*** of a response.
When a snail is placed on a smooth surface it emerges from its shell and sticks out its tentacles.
Tapping the surface with a glass rod at regular intervals causes it to withdraw its tentacles and retreat into its shell.
However, as the tapping continues the snail stays inside its shell for a shorter duration before resuming its journey, the repeated vibrations cause less and less response.

So what is the function of habituation?
An animal needs to respond only to changes in the environment when it is appropriate to do so. Habituation prevents sense organs and the nervous system from being saturated by useless information.

Habituation is particularly important in the development of young animals because they must learn not to react to neutral stimuli around them. The movement and noise of the wind must be ignored otherwise the nervous system would be constantly firing off 'false alarms'.

Habituation in the garden snail

▷ Conditioning

Conditioning is another type of learning.
An animal is able to detect a stimulus and predict what will happen, simply because it has happened many times before.
Pets that share our homes quickly find out where the food is kept.
The sound of a tin being opened can bring our cat or dog to the kitchen because it has learned to **associate** the sound of the tin opener with food.

The dog salivates at the sight of food.

Conditioned reflex

Ivan Pavlov (1849-1936), a Russian physiologist, was one of the first people to carry out experiments on conditioning.
He investigated the production of saliva by dogs in response to food.
By fitting a tube to the dog's salivary duct, he was able to collect and measure the amount of saliva it produced.
Pavlov rang a bell before giving the dog its food.
At first the neutral stimulus of the sound of the bell did not make the dog salivate.
However, after a number of such tests, the dog began to salivate after the bell was rung but ***before*** the food appeared.
The dog had learned to associate the sound of the bell with food.
Pavlov called this type of learning in which the usual stimulus (food) had been replaced by a new stimulus (the sound of the bell), a **conditioned reflex**.
This type of learning is known as **classical conditioning**.

The dog does not salivate at the sound of a bell.

The dog undergoes a period of training in which a bell is rung whenever the dog is fed.

The dog now salivates at the sound of the bell alone.

Source : adapted from MacKean, Introduction to Biology, Murray 1979

Operant conditioning

Burrhus Skinner invented the **Skinner box**.
With it he trained rats and pigeons to press a lever in order to receive a reward of a food pellet. At first the animal presses the lever by accident. But it soon associates lever-pressing with the food reward.
This is called **operant conditioning** because the animal is rewarded for the operation (action). The food reward makes it more likely that the lever will be pressed and so acts as **reinforcement** for the behaviour.
Examples of conditioning can be found in many situations.
Working dogs are often trained by building on their innate behaviour.
English springer spaniels and Labradors have an innate ability to chase and retrieve rabbits and birds.
By the use of reward, they can be trained to sniff out drugs like heroin and cocaine that have been sprinkled onto soft toys and hidden.
Similarly, sheepdogs, guide dogs for the blind and rescue dogs can be trained by the use of operant conditioning techniques.
Parents reward their children for good behaviour with treats or pocket money.
Adults can also be conditioned by television adverts that they may associate with positive images, such as an attractive appearance, success and intelligence.

▷ Communication

Communication between animals of the same species is vital if they are to survive and reproduce.
Through communication, animals are able to avoid predators, find their food (by hunting or foraging together), maintain social behaviours and attract mates.
Messages can be passed between animals using a range of stimuli, including sounds, visual signals and chemicals.
Communication between two individuals involves the following:

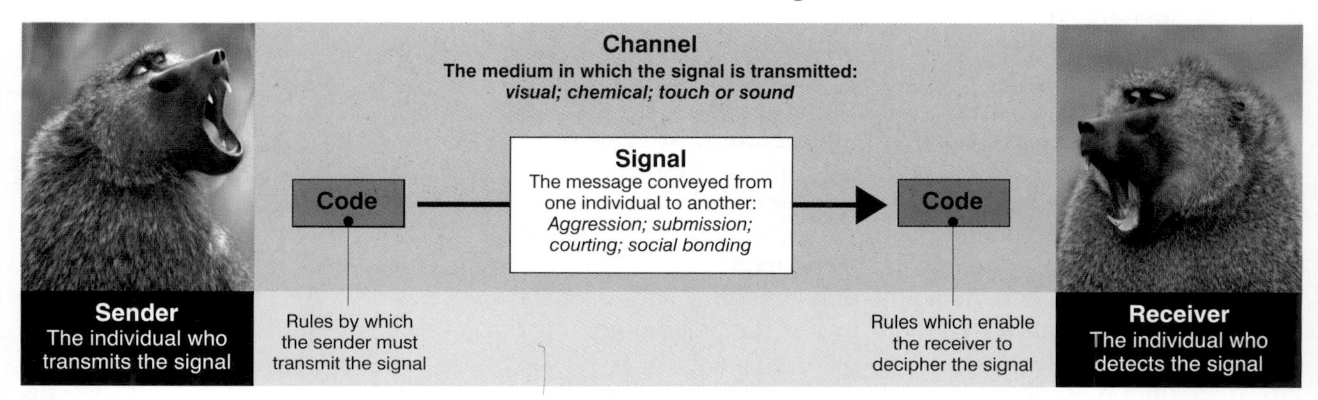

Sounds may be used to communicate over a wide area.
Birds not only use sounds to keep rivals at bay, but also to attract a mate with birdsong.
Fin whales are able to send messages over thousands of kilometres of ocean.
The calls made by mammals can serve to attract a mate, keep in touch with other members of the group or warn away competitors.

Visual signals

Many animals convey information to other members of their species through their appearance, as well as gestures and body language.
Through visual displays, it is possible to deliver threat messages, show submission, attract a mate and even exert control over a social group.

Visual display of male peacock

Chemicals

Pheromones are hormonal substances that are released into the environment in order to communicate with other animals of the same species.
Bees and ants produce alarm pheromones when they are attacked.
They excite other insects of the same species to swarm around the attacker.
Moths (and possibly humans) release chemicals that attract the opposite sex.
Female moths release a sex attractant pheromone into the air in minute quantities.
However, the male has huge antennae which make it extremely sensitive to the pheromone.
This enables the male moth to locate its mate from many kilometres away.
Cosmetic firms may claim that the same properties are found in their products, but they are unlikely to be as potent as this!

Huge antennae of male gypsy moth

▷ More about visual signals

Most mammals are able to communicate their intentions through facial expression and body posture.
Humans, monkeys and apes are able to employ a wide variety of gestures and facial expressions to convey information to other members of the group.
The development of facial muscles allows the expression of an extensive range of emotions, as can be seen in the faces of these chimpanzees:
Facial expressions are species-specific, so a gesture or expression may appear as a threat to one species, but may mean something totally different to another.

The meanings of facial expressions and body posture have to be learned by watching the responses of other animals of the same species.
Threat and appeasement displays often occur at the boundaries between territories. A dominant male wolf will protect his territory by threat behaviour ; the subordinate male will display appeasement behaviour. Both types of behaviour use body posture and facial expressions. These behaviours have the advantage that they avoid physical conflict and possible injury to the two parties.

'This food's gone off'
'That looks good'
'I just don't know what to do now'

Non-verbal communication in humans involves postures, gestures and facial expressions of considerable complexity and subtlety.
We soon learn to move our facial muscles to indicate such emotions as indignation, curiosity, amusement, approval and fear.
Look at the photos and see if you can choose which of the three statements the person might be thinking:

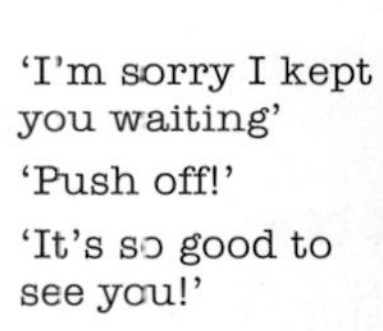

Much of this non-verbal communication may not be conscious. Both men and women will subconsciously register approval of an object that they have seen by enlarging the pupils of their eyes. This is thought to be why people prefer photographs of individuals whose pupils look large.

Humans have developed highly complex ways of communicating. We are able to tell other people about past events, for example, war veterans are able to relate their experiences to young students. Humans obviously communicate their emotions : just compare the responses of joy and disappointment in soccer fans depending on which team has scored a goal.
Since they are conscious of the outcomes of their actions, humans are more self-aware than other animals.

What are the facial expressions and body language saying here ?

▷ Feeding behaviours

Animals display different feeding behaviours depending upon the type of food that they consume.

This chimpanzee has learnt to use a stick to extract insects from a termite mound

Feeding in herbivores

Have you ever chewed on a piece of grass on a fine summer's day? But how about having to live on the stuff?
Afraid not, grass just doesn't contain enough protein for us.
You may have noticed that cattle and sheep spend a great deal of their time feeding on grass.
This is because they have to eat more of this food if they are to obtain the nutrients that they require (particularly amino acids which make up protein, that then forms new biomass).

In the wild, large herbivores such as gazelles and wildebeest feed in large groups or herds. They do this for protection in numbers.
This has proven to be a successful evolutionary strategy, since although some members of the herd will be killed, most survive.
Herds of large herbivores like antelope, have to be continually on the move if they are to find new feeding areas.
They have also evolved effective methods of avoiding predation :

- sharp horns and hooves to ward off attack
- strong legs to out-run the predator
- camouflage to avoid being seen
- eyes on the side of the head for a wide field of view.

(See page 297 for more adaptations to avoid predation.)

The counter-predator alliance

Feeding in carnivores

Unlike herbivores, carnivores spend far less time actually feeding because they have a protein-rich diet.
Some carnivores such as the tiger hunt effectively as individuals.
Successful predators like the tiger are well adapted to catch prey.
They possess :

- Eyes at the front of the head to judge size and distance.
- Sharp teeth and claws for capturing and killing their prey.
- Camouflage to remain undetected until they attack with great speed.

Even with all this, the tiger has to work hard for its meal.
For every wild prey that it kills, the tiger may fail 20–30 times.
Some predators, like hyenas, hunt in a pack.
They cooperate to catch the prey and then share it.
Pack hunting enables the predators to catch and bring down large prey, so there is more food to go around.

(See page 296 for more adaptations to successful predation.)

Hyenas hunt in packs

▷ Reproductive behaviours

Many types of behaviour are aimed at achieving successful reproduction. These include courtship behaviour, designed to attract a suitable mate. Other reproductive behaviours are geared to assessing how receptive the mate is, defending the chosen mate against other suitors and rearing the young.

Courtship

Courtship is behaviour that has the aim of attracting a mate. Courtship enables animals to :

- approach each other closely
- recognise their own species
- choose a strong, healthy mate
- synchronise breeding behaviour.

Courtship enables males and females to enter each other's ***individual space*** without triggering aggression.
Many animals find a new partner each breeding season, but swans, geese and gibbons mate for life.
Other animals may have several different mates during the breeding season, as in the case of pheasants, peacocks, red deer and baboons.

Courtship behaviours are often stereotyped and ritualistic, aimed at reducing any conflict between potential mates. It is common in many bird species for the male to provide a ritual offering, such as food or nesting material, to the female, as is the case of the great-crested grebe.
Females tend to select males with the most impressive displays and this accounts for such features as large body size in male elephant seals, large antlers in red deer and the red belly in the three-spined stickleback.

female fish with a belly swollen by eggs enters the territory of a male

male responds to the stimulus of the female's swollen belly with a zig-zag dance towards the nest– the female follows

pointing by the male makes the female enter the nest

the male makes a trembling movement that induces spawning

the eggs stimulate the male to enter the nest and fertilise the eggs

Source : adapted from Tinbergen, The Study of Instinct, Oxford University Press, 1951

Parental care

The males of many bird species assist their mates in collecting enough food to form the eggs. Nest building, breeding and rearing a skylark brood lasts about 6 weeks, so cooperation between the parent birds is essential.
In contrast, many invertebrates offer no parental care whatsoever. Species that display parental care tend to produce fewer offspring, but offer substantial parental care to the young after birth.
Mammals provide considerable care for their offspring that includes food in the form of nourishing milk.
Young mammals tend to be dependent longer than other animals. Parental care works well as a successful evolutionary strategy.
It may involve the risk of predation to the parents, but it can increase the chances of parental genes being passed on.

▷ Humans make an appearance

Humans (*Homo sapiens*) are one of the great apes and have developed from small family groups, closely related to *bonobos* (pygmy chimpanzees), into complex societies.

About 1.5 million years ago *Homo erectus* (an early type of human) acted as hunter-gatherers, moving from place to place in search of food.
They were opportunistic omnivores, able to dig up underground food items, such as roots and tubers and scavenge meat from predator kills.
They were able to make tools to compensate for their lack of sharp teeth and claws possessed by other predators and scavengers.

H.erectus was also the first hominid to discover fire and with it the ability to cook its food.
Cooking makes food easier to eat and more digestible.
It means that an individual needs less time to extract more nutrients and energy from its food. As a result *H.erectus* would have been better able to cope with the increased energetic costs of a larger brain. Incidently brain sizes of *H.erectus* are approximately two-thirds that of the size of a modern human brain.

An example of cave paintings showing hunters and hunted

One of the features that marks the arrival of *Homo sapiens* is the sudden appearance of cave paintings, engraving, beads and worked bone tools at about 40 000 years ago.

Human societies have much in common with apes and monkeys. Kinship is common to both and certain individuals appear to display greater dominance than others.
However, as we have seen, humans differ in the subtlety and precision of their communication.
We also possess distinctive intelligence and a tremendous capacity for learning from others. These are all a consequence of our huge increase in brain size over other hominids.

Behaviour in the boardroom

Much of our behaviour is socially rather than genetically determined. We learn to act and respond in the ways that we do. As a result we have been able to develop complex societies with the capacity to bring about immense change to our environment in terms of housing, transport, education, politics, farming, commerce, energy provision and communication systems.

▷ Human behaviour in relation to other animals

Arrow-heads made from flint

Hunter-gatherers lived in small, extended family groups.
They cooperated in the hunting of meat and the gathering of vegetable food.
They were nomadic, not staying long in an area, but moving on in search of food.
They used effective hunting weapons such as spears and bows and arrows which they made from sticks and stones like flint.

It is thought that around 10 000 years ago, people in the Middle East started to harvest wild wheat and other grain crops.
They were able to gather a whole years' supply of grain in just a few weeks.
Having this store of grain meant that they did not have to keep moving about in search of food.

Humans started to live in small, permanent communities.
Originally hunters, humans began to domesticate animals, like dogs and birds of prey, to help them hunt.
They started to develop agriculture and exploited herd animals such as sheep and cattle to provide a constant and dependable source of food.

Humans started to exploit animals in other ways as a source of clothing and other domestic materials, as with wool from sheep and leather from cattle.
Humans have also used animals as a source of entertainment, for instance : horse racing, dog racing, hunting and fishing.
Animals have also been exploited in circuses and zoos, although zoos and wildlife parks do have an important conservation element. Animals such as dogs and cats provide companionship for people of all ages.

People have started to debate the ethics of the use of animals in some of these ways, but especially in animal testing of new drugs and treatments.
Some people think that animals should have rights comparable or identical to those of humans, whilst others think that such beliefs are untenable.

It is a mistake to interpret behaviour observed in other animals as having human characteristics.
This is known as **anthropomorphism**.
But equally it is a mistake to assume that human and animal behaviours have nothing in common.

... a man's best friend?

Summary

- The responses that animals make to various stimuli are known as behaviour.
- Behaviour can be innate (instinctive) or learned.
- Innate behaviour is inherited from the parents.
- Learning is a change in behaviour caused by experience.
- Learning can be as simple as ceasing to respond to a stimulus that previously caused a response. This is called habituation.
- Conditioning is a form of learning where animals associate one thing with another. Conditioning needs either reward or punishment to reinforce the behaviour.
- Communication happens in many ways, by sounds, signals and chemicals (pheromones).
- Mammals are able to communicate their intentions through facial expressions and body posture.
- Herbivores eat more food in order to get the nutrients they need and so spend a lot of their time feeding.
- Carnivores eat a protein-rich diet so spend less time actually eating.
- Some mammals and birds defend their territory. This helps them to maintain a reliable food supply, attract a mate and protect a nest or sleeping site.
- Territories are defended by displays, songs, sounds, smells and ultimately fighting.
- Finding a suitable mate can involve courtship behaviour.
- Mammals and birds show a high degree of parental care.
- Humans have developed from small family groups to complex societies.
- Humans have exploited other animals as a source of food, clothing, entertainment and companionship.

▷ Questions

1. Copy and complete : Behaviour is the .... of animals to various . . . . . Innate behaviour is . . . . from the parents. A change in behaviour as a result of experience is called . . . . . Not responding to a stimulus that previously caused a response is called . . . . . Conditioning needs either . . . . or punishment in order to . . . . the behaviour. Mammals are able to communicate by way of facial . . . . and body . . . . . Some mammals defend a . . . . in order to attract a . . . . Mammals and birds show a high degree of . . . . care.

2. a) Give three differences between innate and learned behaviour.
   b) Give two examples of innate behaviour.
   c) Give two examples of learned behaviour.

3. What are the advantages and disadvantages of living in a large social group?

4. a) Explain how animals with little or no parental care can compensate for not caring for their young.
   b) Name two animals that exhibit little or no parental care.
   c) Name two animals that exhibit considerable parental care.

▷ Biotechnology

1. The drawing shows a commercial yoghurt-manufacturing process.

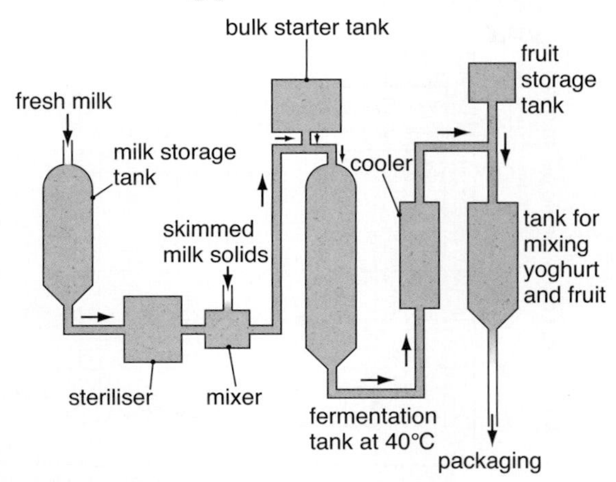

a) i) Suggest how the fresh milk is sterilised. *[1]*

ii) Suggest why it is necessary to sterilise the fresh milk. *[1]*

b) The bulk starter tank contains a culture of bacteria. Describe the effect of these bacteria on the milk. *[2]*

c) Explain why the mixture in the fermentation tank is kept at 40 °C. *[2]*

d) In the cooler, the yoghurt is cooled to 4 °C. Suggest why this is done. *[2]* (AQA)

2. The diagram shows a biodigester used to manufacture penicillin.

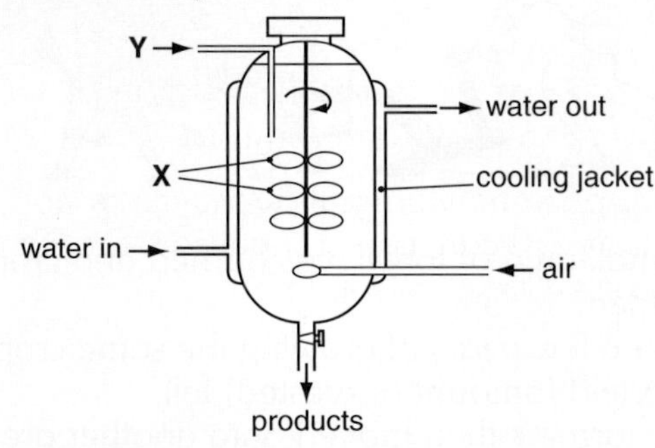

a) What is the function of **X** ? *[1]*

b) What is added to the biodigester through **Y** ? *[1]*

c) Explain why the cooling jacket is necessary ? *[2]*

d) Suggest why air is bubbled through the biodigester. *[1]* (CCEA)

3. The table shows the change in pH of milk during the production of yoghurt.

Time (min)	0	20	40	60	80	100
pH	6.8	6.1	5.6	5.2	5.0	4.9

a) i) On a piece of graph paper, draw a line to show how the pH changes during 100 minutes.
Draw a curve of 'best fit'. *[3]*

ii) What is the pH at 50 minutes ? *[1]*

b) Explain :

i) the change in pH shown by the graph ; *[3]*

ii) why milk is liquid but yoghurt is semi-solid. *[1]*

c) The milk used for yoghurt manufacture is usually at 30 °C. Why is this important for the process to take place most efficiently ? *[2]* (WJEC)

4. Biogas is a useful fuel. It can be made by microbes.
The diagram shows one design for a biogas generator.

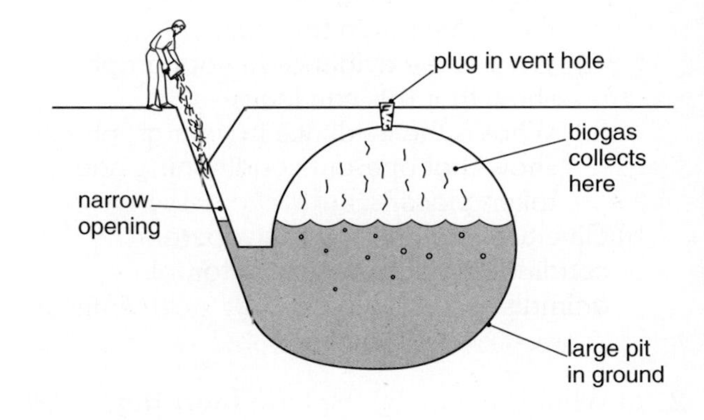

a) Suggest two sources of waste material which could be put into the biogas generator to produce biogas. *[2]*

b) What is the main gas in biogas ? *[1]*

c) Suggest advantages of having a narrow opening to the generator ? *[3]* (AQA)

▷ Behaviour

1. The table gives information about the performance of rats in a maze. The maze had several T junctions at which the rats could either turn left or right. Rats in group A were given food when they completed the maze. Rats in group B were not given food when they completed the maze.

Day	Average number of wrong turns	
	Rats A	Rats B
1	9	10
2	8	9
3	7	10
4	8	9
5	6	9
6	5	10
7	4	9
8	2	8
9	1	9
10	1	10

a) i) Plot a line graph of the data to show the average number of wrong turns made by both groups of rats each day they were put in the maze.
ii) What is the evidence in your graph to show that rats can learn?
iii) What is the evidence in your graph to show that operant conditioning had taken place?
b) Give two examples of how operant conditioning has been used to train animals. (EDEX)

2. a) What is meant by the term **learning**? *[2]*
b) During World War Two the signal to call sailors to battle stations was a bell sounding at 100 rings per minute.
For sailors this signal became associated with the sound of guns and bombs.
15 years after the war ex-sailors and students took part in the following study.
They all listened to a bell **five** times. Each time it was sounded at a different number of rings per minute. On each occasion their heart rates were measured.
The results are displayed below.

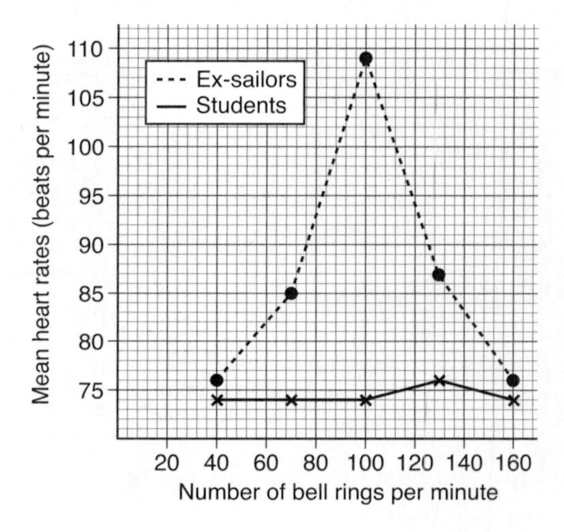

i) Describe the results of the study. *[3]*
ii) How might the theory of **Classical Conditioning** explain the ex-sailors' mean heart rate when there were 100 rings per minute? *[5]* (AQA Psychology)

3. Thousands of years ago farmers used a 'slash and burn' method to grow crops.

A small area of forest was burned and crops planted.
After a few years of growing the same crops, the yield (amount harvested) fell.
The farmers then moved onto another area of forest.
a) Write down two reasons why the drop yield fell after a few years. *[2]*
b) Modern farmers are able to grow crops with high yields without moving to a new area.
Suggest two reasons for this. *[2]* (OCR)

How Science Works

▶ Why we need to know about how science works

Science has helped to shape the world we live in today. Scientists have solved problems, using evidence, and have made modern technologies possible. This has brought great benefits for all of us but has also created problems. Pollution of our environment is one major concern – and scientists are also essential in dealing with this issue.

We all have to make decisions about how we lead our lives. Knowing more about 'how science works' will help you form your own opinions about important issues. These will include decisions about your diet, your transport, your work and your free time.

You will need to question evidence and to weigh up conflicting ideas. For example:

- Will you allow your children to have the MMR jab?
- Will you buy a car? If so, which will be least harmful to our environment?
- Will the latest food scare in the news affect what you eat?
- Will you vote for a party who want to expand nuclear power?

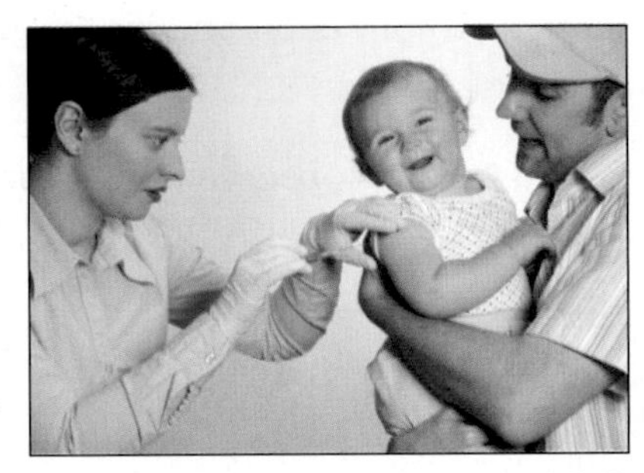

Some people claimed that the MMR jab can cause autism in some babies. However, the evidence used to identify a link was taken from a small sample of cases.

To answer such questions you should consider the evidence available. Then you need to judge if the evidence is based on 'good science'. (You will find some people use evidence that is not scientific at all to answer scientific questions).

- Good scientists make sure their data provides evidence that is **reliable** and **valid**.

Reliable evidence will be repeatable. If you, or someone else, collected the data again it should be the same (or similar). So you can ***trust*** reliable data. It is then valid evidence only if it actually measures what you intended to find out about.

Example
You might want to find out about pollution in a river from a factory. You would need instruments that were sensitive enough to detect small quantities accurately to get reliable evidence.
Then measuring the pollution downstream from the factory will only give you valid evidence if you also have data from the river before it passed the factory. You should also aim to take measurements over a 24 hour period, using a data logger and not just take one 'snap shot' measurement.

So scientists need reliable and valid evidence to draw firm conclusions.

Observing

Observing things is the link between the real world and science.
But observation is not as simple as you might think.
Surely two people looking at the same event will see the same thing, won't they? Sports fans will know that's not true!

But what about something like a well kept hedge?
One person will see it as a pleasant background to the garden that adds privacy.
Another will see it as a wind-break to shelter other plants.

- So what you see depends on what you know already.
- Your prior knowledge also affects the way you **classify** things.

Example
You are given 10 preserved invertebrate specimens.
You have to put them into their correct groups.
Using your previous knowledge of classification, you might use such features as segmentation, number of legs or having a shell, to put each one into its group.

- You need to observe things carefully to see if particular variables are important or not in an investigation.

Example
You are investigating how quickly the enzyme, amylase can breakdown the starch. On observing this reaction, you may decide that the size of the beaker that you use does not matter.
However, you might see that the surface area of different sizes of potato pieces does make a difference. So you will have to use the same sized potato pieces (giving the same surface area in contact with the amylase) – but you can use different beakers to do the tests in.

- Observations can also be the starting point for new investigations.

Example
You are given a selection of leaves to observe.
You notice that the leaves have different surface areas.
This might prompt you to ask a question such as:
Do leaves on plants that grow in the shade have larger surface areas than the leaves of plants that grow in full sunlight?

Making measurements

Scientists must also think about the measurements they make when judging how strong their evidence is. Are they reliable (are they repeatable) and valid (do they measure what you intended)?

- There will usually be slight differences in measurements when you repeat them. This is because it is hard to measure the value of a variable under exactly the same conditions every time.

Example

You measure the volume of a gas given off in a reaction using a gas syringe.
You repeat the experiment, but the temperature of the room might have changed slightly.
This will affect the volume of gas collected.
If the temperature gets higher, how will this affect your volume reading?

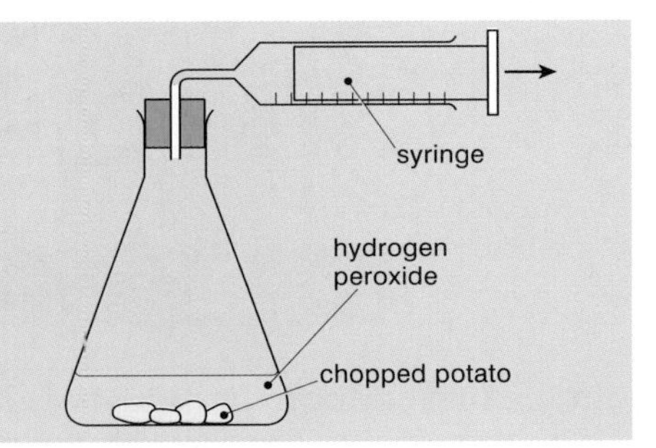

- You should also consider the **accuracy** of your measuring instrument. Accuracy tells us how near the ***true reading*** your measurement is.

Example

An expensive pH meter will probably give readings nearer the true value than a cheaper model. They would also both depend on you following the manufacturer's instructions on using and storing the pH probes. If you don't follow the instructions, the readings won't be reliable and valid.

The more expensive pH meter is also likely to be more ***sensitive***. It will respond to smaller changes in pH. This may not matter in some experiments. But it could be significant in, for example, enzyme investigations.

*If the pH of a solution is tested in different labs, and all the results are similar, we call the pH **reproducible**.*

- The **precision** of a measuring instrument is also important. A precise instrument will give the same reading again and again under exactly the same conditions

Example

You use a balance A to weigh a single leaf.
You remove it and re-weigh the same leaf four times.
Here are your readings: 2.51 g, 2.54 g, 2.51 g, 2.52 g, 2.53 g.
The **range** (difference between the highest and lowest readings) is 2.54 − 2.51 = 0.03 g

You take the same leaf to balance B and repeat the tests.
You get : 2.36 g, 2.41 g, 2.22 g, 2.35g, 2.49 g.
The range is 2.49 − 2.22 = 0.27 g.
Balance A has the ***greater precision***. Its readings are grouped closer together than those taken with balance B. The range is smaller.

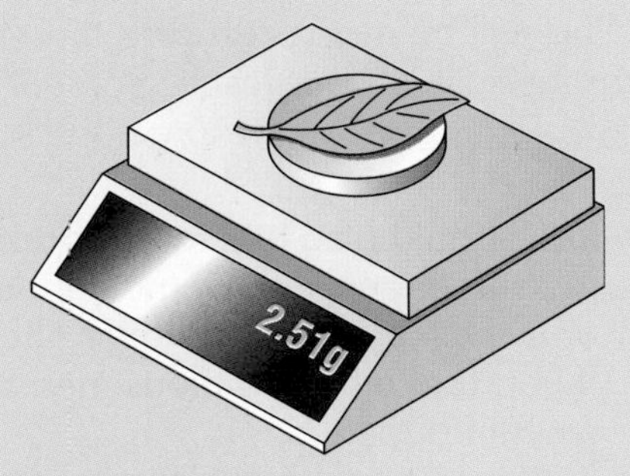

- Then we also have **human error** in measurements.

Example

In the first cartoon the student is just careless. If he repeats his experiment, the results could be spread randomly, all over the place.

In the second cartoon, his partner is more careful. However, she is not reading the volume in the burette correctly.

You should read to the bottom of the **meniscus** (curve in the surface of the solution).
So her repeat readings will be consistently incorrect.
Will all her readings be too high or too low?

- In some investigations you should **repeat** your measurements. This is especially important when measurements are tricky to make. The number of repeats will depend on the accuracy you need.

Example

You are looking at how quickly a reaction is taking place.
In the reaction, protease breaks down milk protein causing the blue dye to decolourise. So you decide to time how long it takes for the blue colour to disappear.
Timing this exactly is very difficult so repeating the test will improve the reliability of the data collected.
You should add up the repeat times and divide by the number of times taken.
This gives you the **mean** (or average) time.
This will be ***more reliable*** than just doing it once. You can place more trust in your result. Someone doing the same experiment would be more likely to get the same result as you.

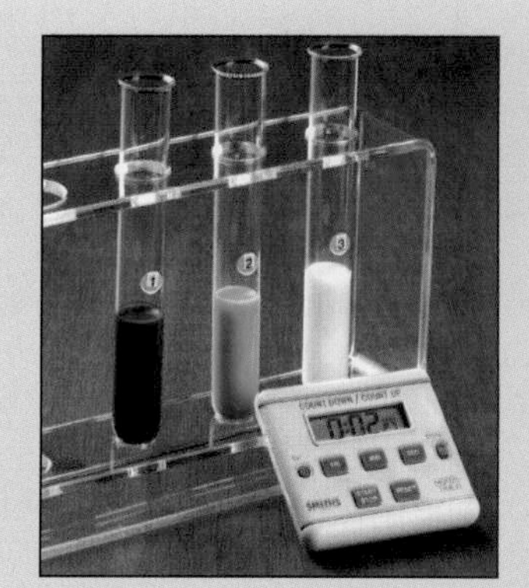

The effect of different pH values on the action of protease

- You should also look out for **anomalous** results. These measurements do not match the general pattern found or lie well outside the range of other repeat measurements. If you find an anomalous measurement, try to work out why it happened. If it was caused by poor measurement in the first place you can just ignore it. (See first cartoon above).

Designing an investigation

The best way to answer some scientific questions is to design a fair test.

Example

You are looking at the reaction between yeast powder and glucose solution. The reaction produces carbon dioxide gas.

You might want to investigate this question:
'What might affect how quickly the reaction takes place?'

You can start by making a list of the variables that might affect the rate of the chemical reaction:
e.g. temperature, yeast concentration, glucose concentration, volume of glucose solution, pH.

You can select any one of these variables to investigate.
Imagine you choose to vary ***the temperature of the reaction*** you use.
This will be your **independent variable**.

But how will you judge how quickly the reaction takes place?
There are different ways to judge this.
Imagine you decide to measure ***the time it takes to give off a certain volume of carbon dioxide gas***.
The time it takes is called the **dependent variable**.

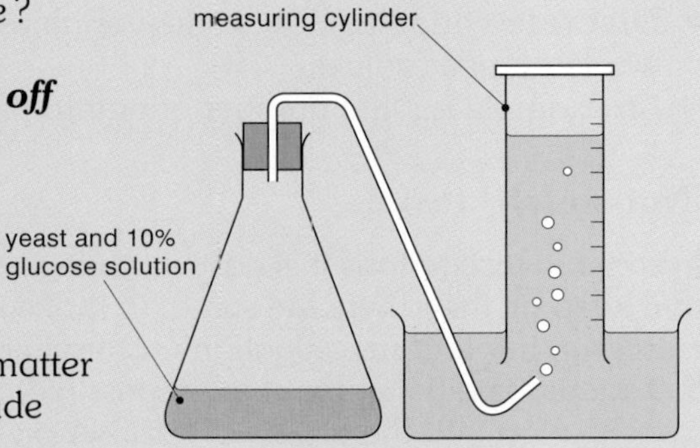

To make this a **fair test** we should only vary one thing at a time (in this case it will be the temperature of the reaction).
So we should try to keep all the other variables that might matter the same. These are the **control variables**. They will include yeast concentration, pH and concentration and volume of glucose solution.

Choosing values of variables

You would have to carry out a few **trial experiments** to decide on how much carbon dioxide to collect each time. These might show that for reasonable temperatures, 20 cm^3 would give sensible times – not too long and not too short.

You could also choose your range of temperatures to use. For instance a temperature range of 20°C, 30°C, 40°C, 50°C and 60°C would produce more useful data than say, a range of 25°, 30°C, 38°C, 45°C and 53°C. Why do you think this would be the case?

Five different temperatures would be needed to draw a decent line graph of the results. These should be well spaced out. If there are any interesting parts on your graph, you can choose to test more temperatures. These might be repeats to test possible anomalous results. Or they might be grouped around an area where the graph looks like it changes e.g. where the slope gets much steeper or levels off.

It's important to get your range right!

Different types of variable

In the investigation on the previous page, you saw different variables listed.
We can classify variables into the following types:

- **Categoric** variables: These are variables that we can describe using words.
  Examples are: 'type of sugar', e.g. glucose,
- **Ordered** variables: These are a type of categoric variable that we can put into an order.
  Examples are: 'large pieces / medium pieces / small pieces' as a way of describing the 'surface area' of potato pieces in the experiment on page 374.
- **Continuous** variables: These are variables that we can describe by any number, as you use measurements to get their values.
  Examples are: 'temperature' or 'concentration'
- **Discrete** variables: These are variables that can only have whole number values.
  An example is: 'the number of potato pieces'.

'Not-so-fair' tests!

In some investigations it is easy to change one variable at a time, and keep all the others the same, to make a fair test.
However, in other investigations controlling all the variables that matter is difficult (or even impossible). An example is an investigation into the effects of fertiliser on plant growth.

If this investigation takes place **'in the field'**, there are factors such as the weather conditions that you can't control. But you should make sure all the plants tested experience the same weather.

You would also use a large sample of the plants to test.
It's no good picking just one plant to test with the fertiliser and one without it. There could be genetic differences between the two plants which might affect the result.
Using a large **sample size** will help to overcome the Problems of setting up a fair test involving living things.

Evaluate your data

Remember that the data you collect must be **reliable** (see page 376). You should also design your investigation so that the data will answer the question posed.
Consider the investigation on the previous page:
Is it **valid** to judge the rate by timing how long it takes to collect 20 cm^3 of gas? After all, as soon as the reaction starts the concentration of glucose will start to decrease!

Presenting your data

As you carry out an investigation, you can record your data in a results table. Scientists arrange their tables so that the independent variable (the one you change deliberately, step by step) goes in the first column.

The dependent variable (used to judge the effect of varying the independent variable) goes in the second column.
For example, if you were doing an investigation like the one on page 377, varying temperature, the table would have these headings:

Independent variable: Temperature (°C)	**Dependent variable:** Time to collect 20 cm^3 of gas (min)

If you decide to repeat your tests at each temperature to get more reliable data, you can split the second column up:

Temperature (°C)	Time to collect 20 cm^3 of gas (min)			
	1st test	2nd test	3rd test	Mean (average)

Then you can show the relationship (link) between the two variables by drawing a graph.

The independent variable goes along the horizontal axis.
The dependent variable goes up the vertical axis.
Look at the axes opposite:

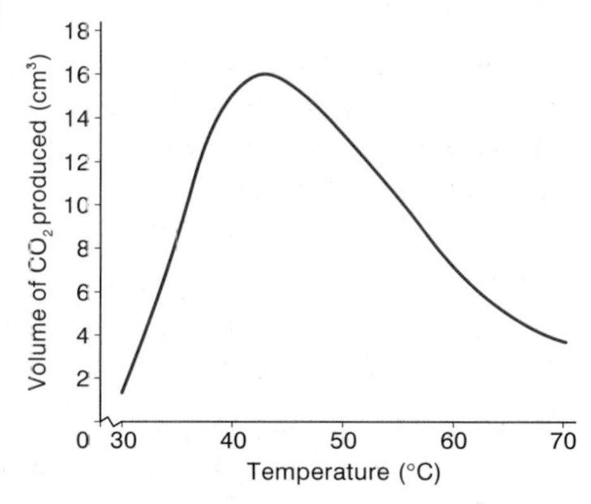

The graph you draw depends on the type of independent variable you investigated (see page 378).

If it is a continuous variable – you can display your results on a **line graph**.
That's because the independent variable is measured in numbers. You might choose to do the tests at 30, 40, 50, 60 and 70 °C. However, you could equally have chosen any points in between. That's why we can join the points with a continuous line.

Look at the graph opposite:
If it is a categoric variable – you have to display your results on a **bar chart**.
That's because there are no values between each bar. (Remember that categoric variables are described by words).

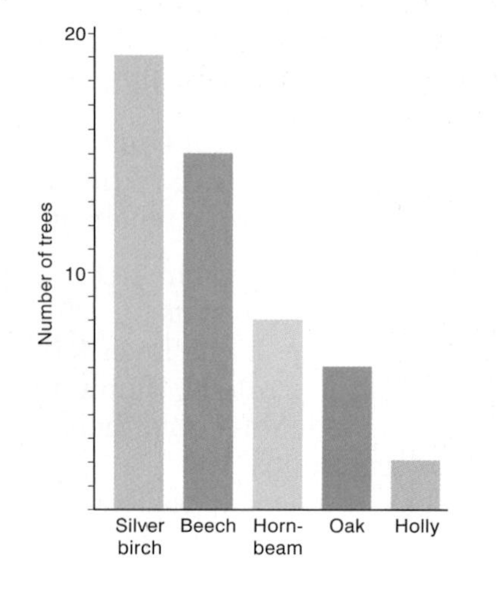

Of course, the dependent variable (up the side) has to be continuous (measured) otherwise we can't draw any type of graph!

Spotting patterns in data

Once you have your graph to refer to, you can see what the relationship is between the two variables.

Examples you will find in biology include:

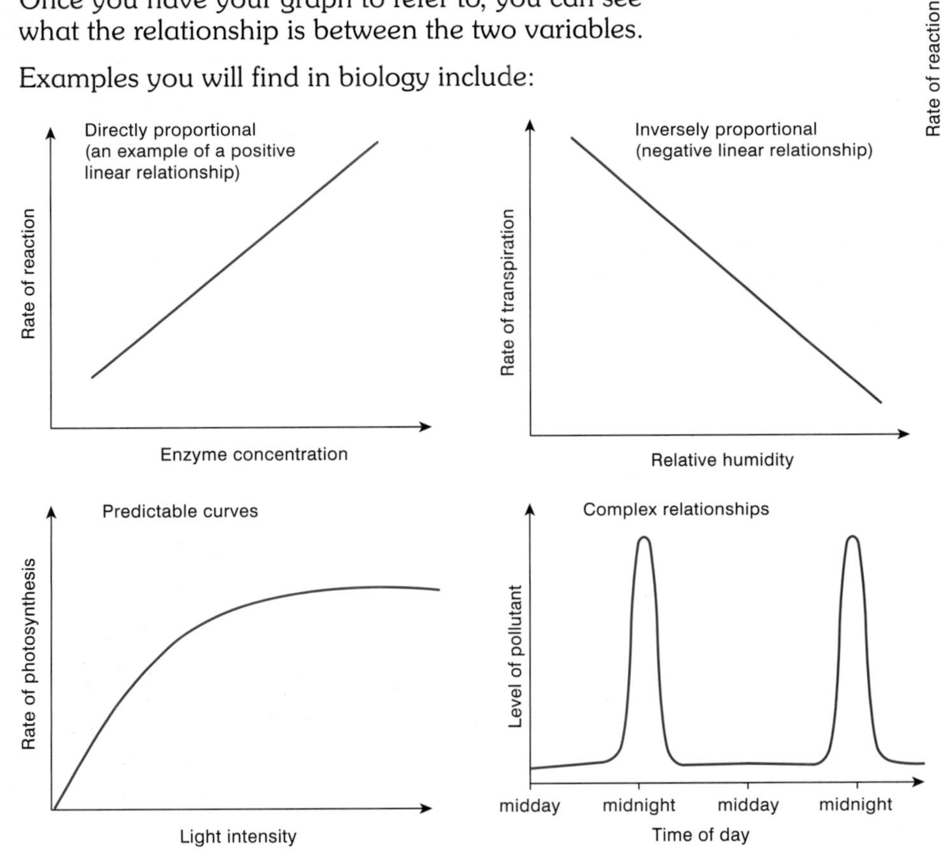

Notice the use of **lines of best fit** to give 'average' lines.
You can also plot all your data to show the range within sets of repeat measurements. This shows the precision and reliability of your data. The larger the spread of repeat readings the less precise your data is. Also the less likely other people are to get exactly the same results as you.

Evaluating your whole investigation

You should consider the reliability and validity of the measurements you make (see pages 373 and 376).
You can also improve reliability and validity by:

- looking up data from secondary sources, e.g. on the internet.
- checking your results by using an alternative method.
  For example, in the investigation on page 375, you might measure the rate by monitoring the loss in mass as the reaction progressed. You could then plot initial rate against different concentrations.
- seeing if other people following your method get the same results i.e. are your results reproducible?

Society's influence on evidence

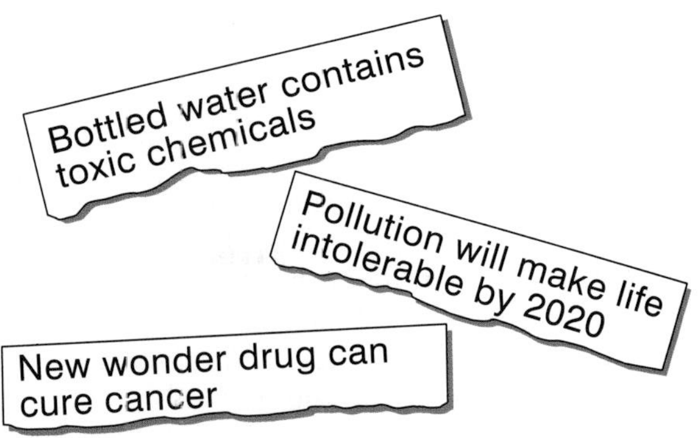

Some scientific studies are of interest to society in general – not just to the scientific community. For example, investigations into:

- pollution from cars and industry
- the safety of food additives
- the properties of new materials
- the purity of drinking water.

These will affect us all. But how do we hear about the evidence these studies produce? Often it is through the media – TV, radio, the internet and newspapers.
So how reliable are the reports we get? Can we trust them?

Tabloid newspapers are likely to 'play up' scare stories. Sensational headlines will sell their newspapers. So often scientists will find their research reported badly in the media. Dangers can be exaggerated. The very small chances of harmful effects may not be mentioned.

On the other hand, successful breakthroughs on a small scale may be reported as findings that will change the world – now! These make great headlines but are often unrealistic.

There are lots of factors that influence the way evidence is presented to us. If it is going to be unpopular with the public, evidence might be 'watered down' or hidden in publications. This might also happen if the research results show a problem that will be expensive to put right.

The reputation of the scientist doing the research can also influence people's response to research findings. Famous, eminent scientists are likely to get their ideas listened to more favourably than less well known scientists.

When we look at evidence for a certain viewpoint we should also consider any bias. For example, do we know who paid for the research? For example, if a food company produce data that a colouring is safe, should we trust that as much as data from a government 'watch-dog'? Or what about an independent consumer group? Are they unbiased?

These protesters believe that genetically modified crops are a danger to the environment

The ideas we have looked at in this section should help you to consider evidence critically. You might want to know about the sensitivity and accuracy of instruments used in tests. The sample size might be important. How scientists chose sites to test and how many times did they repeat their tests could affect the trust we have in their evidence.

▶ Questions

1. Copy and complete:
   a) The ..... of a measurement tells us how near the true value it is.
   b) The .... of an instrument tells us its ability to measure small changes in a variable.
   c) We can improve the .... of data by repeating measurements.
   d) Measurements that do not match the general pattern found can give you .... results.
   e) To make an investigation a .... you should only vary one thing at a time.
   f) Variables that we can describe using words are called ..... variables.
   g) Continuous variables are ones that we can describe by .....
   h) Using a large sample .... will make your results more .....

2. Observation helps us to form hypotheses and make predictions.

Some caterpillars are brightly coloured which makes them highly visible to predators such as insect-eating birds.It has also been observed that potential predators usually avoid them. These caterpillars are often found in groups.

Other caterpillars use camouflage to disguise their appearance.

The caterpillar opposite is difficult to distinguish from a small twig.
Such caterpillars are usually found alone.

   a) Produce a hypothesis to explain the observation that some caterpillars are brightly coloured and conspicuous,whilst others are camouflaged and blend in with their surroundings.
   b) Describe one of the assumptions being made in your hypothesis.

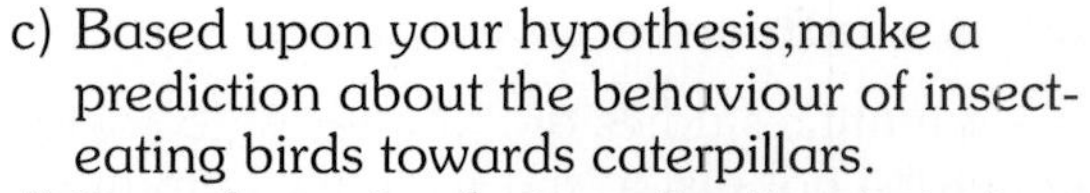

   c) Based upon your hypothesis,make a prediction about the behaviour of insect-eating birds towards caterpillars.
   d) Describe a simple investigation to test your hypothesis and its prediction.

3. a) Using the information on page 378, classify the following examples as categoric, ordered,continuous or discrete variables :
   i) leaf shape ii) lumps of calcium carbonate iii) number of piglets in a litter iv) fish length.
   b) Explain why it is better to collect quantitative data in biological investigations.
   c) Give an example of data that could not be collected in a quantitative manner.

4. You are required to set up an investigation into the effect of different concentrations of fertiliser on plant growth.Explain the importance of each of the following in order to achieve reliable results :
   a) choosing a sensible range of fertilizer concentrations
   b) controlling such variables as soil type
   c) choosing a suitable sample size
   d) repeating your investigation.

5. Foxglove fruits were collected from a mixed hedgerow and their lengths measured in millimeters and recorded as follows :

18 13 16 15 16 13 17
14 18 14 16 15 16 19
14 15 11 19 12 19 15 19
16 19 14 21 19 18 15 16
18 17 15 13 19 20 18 20
15 15 14 12 16 15 15 20
19 17 16 15 13 19 18 15

   a) Place the data into a table showing the frequency of each length.
   b) Display the data in a suitable graph.
   c) What environmental factors could have brought about the range of fruit lengths ?

Doing your coursework

'Practical skills are important'

Your coursework or practical assessment is important.
It is an important part of becoming good at Science. And it counts as a significant part of your GCSE or IGCSE grade.
Doing good coursework can be one of the best ways to boost your final grade.

The different examination boards vary in the ways in which they assess your coursework. There is a short summary lower down this page.
Your teacher will give you full details of what you need to do for your practical assessment. You can also research the details yourself on the exam board's web-site, see below.

Different examination boards allocate different percentages of marks for coursework or practical assessment.
They may also call it by different names.

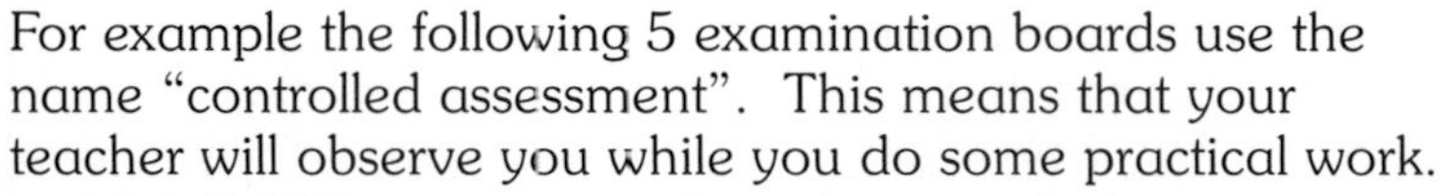

For example the following 5 examination boards use the name "controlled assessment". This means that your teacher will observe you while you do some practical work.

- AQA GCSE examination board : controlled assessment = 25%
- Edexcel GCSE examination board : controlled assessment = 25%
- OCR GCSE examination board : controlled assessment = 25%
- WJEC GCSE examination board : controlled assessment = 25%
- CCEA GCSE examination board : controlled assessment = 25%

Other (IGCSE) exam boards use different methods:

- Edexcel IGCSE examination board has an 'assessment of practical skills' within the written papers (see page 385) = 20%
- Cambridge Cam IGCSE examination board has 3 alternative ways: 'Coursework' (assessed by your teacher); or a 'Practical Test'; or an 'Alternative to Practical' written paper (see page 385). You do only one of these alternatives =20%

Your teacher will give you more details, or you can find more details by visiting the correct web-site in the list below.
Some of these sites have revision materials to help you.

www.aqa.org.uk
www.edexcel.com
www.ocr.org.uk
www.wjec.co.uk
www.rewardinglearning.org.uk (CCEA)
www.cie.org.uk

▶ Helping you to do your practical work

When you are doing your practical work, use the questions in this checklist to help you:

Planning

Before you collect your evidence, think about:

- What is the best way to tackle this particular problem?
- How can you make your tests as ***fair*** as possible?
- Have you identified the independent, dependent, and control ***variables***? (See pages 377–378.)
- How can you make you tests ***safe***? Do you need to carry out a ***'risk assessment'***?
- Can you make a ***prediction***? If so, can you explain it?

- How many observations or measurements will you make? What ***range*** of values will give suitable results?
- Will you need to repeat results to make them more ***reliable***?
- Which apparatus will you choose to get accurate results? Will datalogging equipment help you to get greater accuracy?
- Can you use other (***secondary***) sources of information to help you plan?
- Should you do a ***trial run*** to check your ideas before you start?
- How will you ***record*** your results clearly and accurately?

Finding a Pattern, Drawing a Conclusion

After you have collected your results, think about:

- Can your results be shown on a ***bar-chart*** or a ***line-graph***?
- Can you see a ***pattern*** in your results?
- Are there any ***anomalous results*** which do not fit the general pattern?
- Do your results support your prediction (if you made one)?
- Can you ***explain*** your results using the work that you have done in Science?

Evaluating

When you have decided your conclusion, think about:

- Can you suggest any ***improvements*** you could make to
  - the way you carried out your tests?
  - the accuracy of your readings?
  - the reliability and validity of your results?
- Are your results good enough to draw a ***firm conclusion***? Do you have enough evidence to be sure? How could you gain ***further evidence***?

▶ Further Questions

1. A protein is used to hold other chemicals onto the clear plastic backing of photographic film, as shown in the diagram.

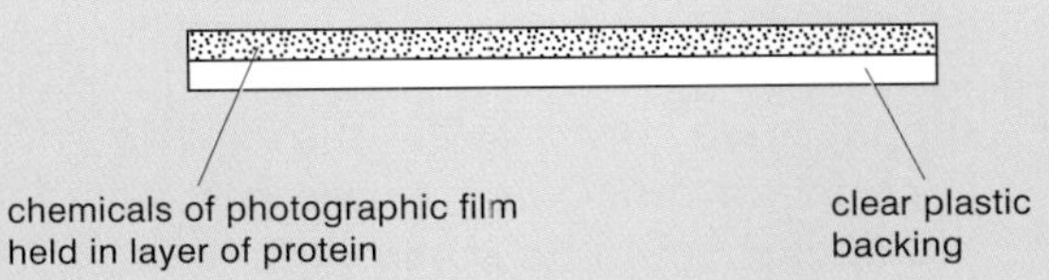

Trypsin is an enzyme which will digest the protein so that the coating on the photographic film is removed and the film becomes clear.
The table shows the results obtained by two students who investigated the effect of pH on the activity of this enzyme. They made up the solutions, set up the experiment and timed how long the enzyme took to digest the protein and clear the film.

pH	time for the protein to be digested / mins	
	student 1	student 2
2	12.0	14.0
4	8.0	9.0
6	2.0	3.0
8	0.5	1.0
10	8.0	9.0

(a) (i) Plot the results obtained by **student 2** in the form of a suitable graph. *[5]*
(ii) Describe and explain the effect of pH on the activity of the enzyme. *[5]*
(b) (i) Suggest reasons for the difference in the results for the two students. *[3]*
(ii) If you were to carry out this investigation, describe what steps you would take to ensure that your results were as reliable and valid as possible. *[5]*
[Total: 18] (Cam IGCSE)

2. Rakesh had three different species of water plant (A, B and C).
He carried out an investigation to find out which of the three species of water plant had the fastest rate of photosynthesis.
(a) He counted the number of bubbles coming from each plant in 10 seconds. The diagrams represent what he saw.

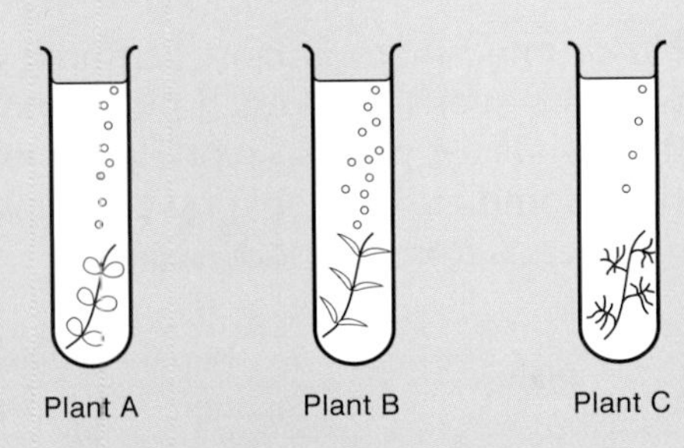

(i) Count the number of bubbles of gas coming from each plant in 10 seconds. Complete the tally chart below.
Plant A has been done for you.

Plant	Tally	Number of bubbles
A		8
B		
C		

[2]

(ii) In Plant A, each bubble has a volume of 4 mm^3. Calculate the volume of oxygen given off by plant A in one minute, assuming that the rate remains constant. Show your working. *[2]*
(b) Rakesh concluded that plant B had the fastest rate of photosynthesis. Explain why he may not be justified in reaching this conclusion. *[3]*
[Total 7 marks] (Edex IGCSE)

3. A gardener collected 25 seeds from each of three pea plants that he had grown. He noticed that the pea seeds were either smooth or wrinkled. These are shown in the diagram below.

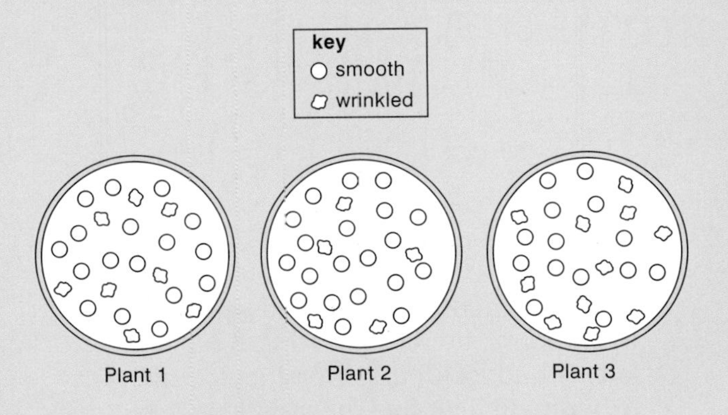

(a) He counted the number of smooth and wrinkled seeds from each plant and recorded the results for plants 1 and 2 in a table.

(i) Complete the table by counting the seeds from plant 3.

Plant	Number of seeds	
	Smooth	Wrinkled
1	17	8
2	20	5
3		

[2]

(ii) Use your results to draw a bar chart to show the number of each type of seeds produced by each pea plant.

(b) The gardener thought that the appearance of the seeds was controlled by a gene. Two plants grown from smooth seeds were crossed and produced some seeds that were smooth and some seeds that were wrinkled. Explain how this could happen. *[3]*

[Total 10 marks] (Edex IGCSE)

4. For his IGCSE coursework, Kieran wanted to look at the effect of different conditions on the rate of water loss from leaves.
He decided to measure the change in mass of the leaves after three hours in a warm laboratory.
He took five leaves of about the same size. He measured the mass of each leaf and attached them to a line hung between two stands, as shown in the diagram.

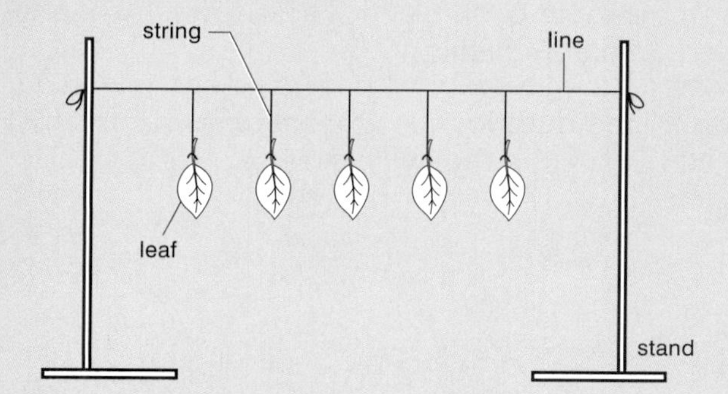

When he measured their masses again after three hours, he discovered that all of the leaves had lost mass. He repeated his experiment with five different leaves but this time he turned off heaters to reduce the temperature in the room.

(a) What apparatus would Kieran use to measure the mass of the leaves? *[1]*

(b) Why did Kieran use fives leaves rather than just one? *[1]*

(c) Give **two** key factors (variables) that Kieran should have controlled in his experiment. For **each** factor that you give, suggest how far that factor could be controlled. *[4]*

(d) Predict what would happen to the change in the mass of the leaves when the temperature in the laboratory was reduced. Give a reason for your answer. *[2]*

(e) Kieran's teacher suggested that there might be a difference between the loss of water from the upper and from the lower surfaces of leaves. Describe how Kieran could modify his experiment to find out if there is a difference. *[3]*

[Total 11 marks] (Edex IGCSE)

5. Alison noticed that the same species of plant was found on the sunny side and on the shady side of a hill. She decided to compare the population size of this plant on each side of the hill. The plan she wrote is shown below.

I will go to a field on the sunny side of the hill and walk into the middle. I will then put a $1m^2$ quadrat on the ground and count how many of the plants I can see in the quadrat. I will do the same thing on the shady side of the hill.

(a) Suggest **two** ways in which Alison could change her plan to improve it. *[2]*

(b) When Alison counted the plants she found more in the quadrat on the sunny side of the hill than on the shady side. She also thought that they looked different in size. She concluded that plant growth might be affected by light intensity.
Describe an investigation you could carry out in the laboratory to find the effect of light intensity on the growth of plants. You should include full experimental details in your account. *[6]*

[Total 8 marks] (Edex IGCSE)

Suggestions for a revision programme

1. Read the summary at the end of the chapter to gain some idea of the contents.
Then read through the chapter looking at particular points in more detail, before reading the summary again.

2. Covering up the summary, check yourself against the fill-in-the-missing-word sentences at the end of the chapter.

Remember to ***re-read*** the summary and to ***review*** each chapter after the correct revision intervals of 10 minutes, then 1 day, then 1 week (as explained on page 389).
Continue in this way with all the other chapters in the book.

3. While reading through the summaries and chapters like this, it is useful to collect together all the statements in red and yellow boxes on a single sheet of paper. At this stage you will also find the checklists and revision quizzes from the Support Pack useful.

4. While you are going right through the book, do this for every chapter:
a) Attempt the questions on the 'Further Questions' pages. These are all GCSE questions from previous years. Your teacher will be able to tell you which are the most important ones for your specification.
You can check against your own particular specification on www.biologyforyou.co.uk.
b) If there are multiple-choice questions in your examination, read the comments about them on page 391.

5. Read the section on 'Examination technique' on page 390, and check the dates of your exams. Have you enough time to complete your revision before then?

6. Several weeks before the examination, ask your teacher for copies of the examination papers from previous years. These 'past papers' will help you to see:
– the particular style and timing of your examination
– the way the questions are asked, and the amount of detail needed
– which topics and questions are asked most often and which suit you personally.

When doing these past papers, try to get used to doing the questions ***in the specified time*** – just like it will be in the examination.

It may be possible for your teacher to read out to you the reports of examiners who have marked these papers in previous years.

The Support Pack contains some extra past paper questions with guidance given on how to answer them. It also contains the answers at all the past paper 'Further questions' included in this book.

Revision techniques

Why should you revise?
You cannot expect to remember all the Biology that you have studied unless you revise. It is important to review all your course, so that you can answer the examination questions.

Where should you revise?
In a quiet room (perhaps a bedroom), with a table and a clock.
The room should be comfortably warm and brightly lit.
A reading lamp on the table helps you to concentrate on your work and reduces eye-strain.

When should you revise?
Start your revision early each evening, before your brain gets tired.

How should you revise?
If you sit down to revise without thinking of a definite finishing time, you will find that your learning efficiency falls lower and lower and lower.
If you sit down to revise, saying to yourself that you will definitely stop work after 2 hours, then your learning efficiency falls at the beginning but ***rises towards the end*** as your brain realises it is coming to the end of the session (see the first graph).

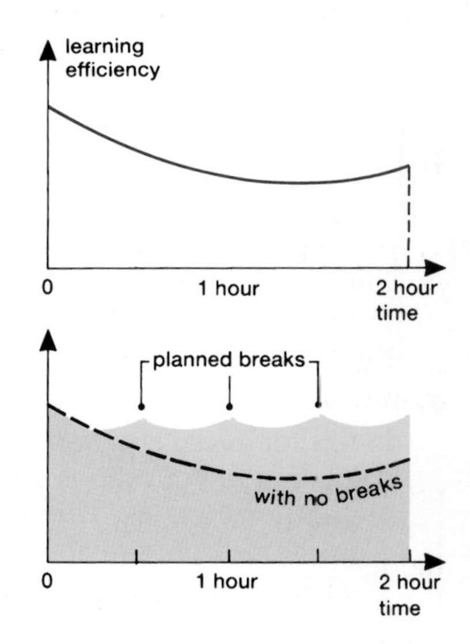

We can use this U-shaped curve to help us work more efficiently by splitting a 2 hour session into four shorter sessions, each of about 25 minutes with a short, ***planned*** break between them.
The breaks ***must*** be planned beforehand so that the graph rises near the end of each short session.
The coloured area on the graph shows how much you gain:

For example, if you start your revision at 6.00 p.m., you should look at your clock or watch and say to yourself, 'I will work until 6.25 p.m. and then stop – not earlier and not later.'
At 6.25 p.m. you should leave the table for a relaxation break of 10 minutes (or less), returning by 6.35 p.m. when you should say to yourself, 'I will work until 7.00 p.m. and then stop – not earlier and not later.'

Continuing in this way is more efficient ***and*** causes less strain on you.

You get through more work ***and*** you feel less tired.

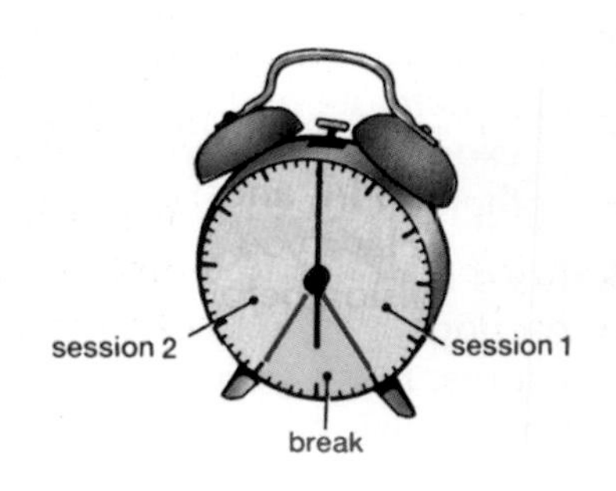

How often should you revise?

The diagram shows a graph of the amount of information that your memory can recall at different times after you have finished a revision session:

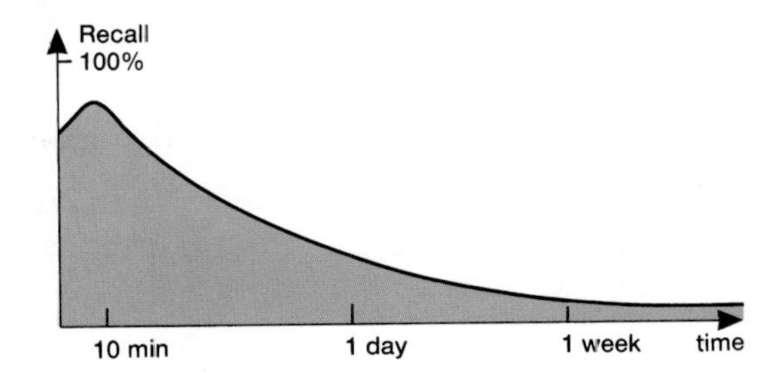

Surprisingly, the graph rises at the beginning. This is because your brain is still sorting out the information that you have been learning.
The graph soon falls rapidly so that after 1 day you may remember only about a quarter of what you had learned.

There are two ways of improving your recall and raising this graph.

• 1. If you briefly ***revise the same work again after 10 minutes*** (at the high point of the graph) then the graph falls much more slowly.
This fits in with your 10-minute break between revision sessions.
Using the example on the opposite page, when you return to your table at 6.35 p.m., the first thing you should do is ***review***, briefly, the work you learned before 6.25 p.m.

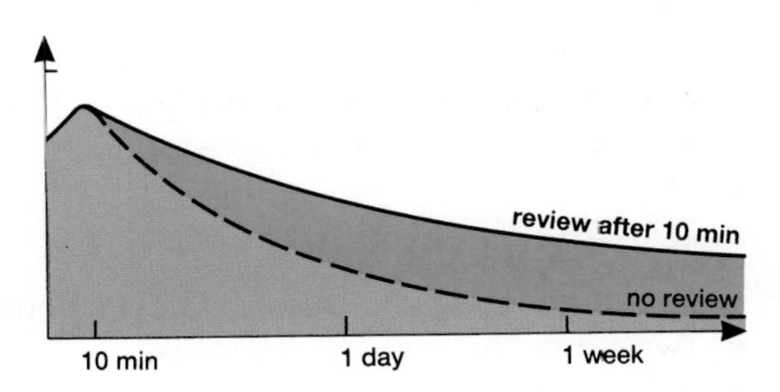

The graph can be lifted again by briefly reviewing the work ***after 1 day*** and then again ***after 1 week***. That is, on Tuesday night you should look through the work you learned on Monday night and the work you learned on the previous Tuesday night, so that it is fixed quite firmly in your long-term memory.

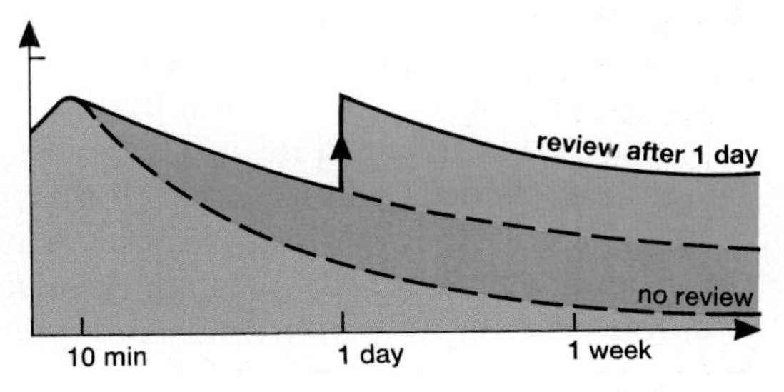

• 2. Another method of improving your memory is by taking care to try to ***understand*** all parts of your work. This makes all the graphs higher.
If you learn your work in a parrot-fashion (as you have to do with telephone numbers), all these graphs will be lower. On the occasions when you have to learn facts by heart, try to picture them as exaggerated, colourful images in your mind.

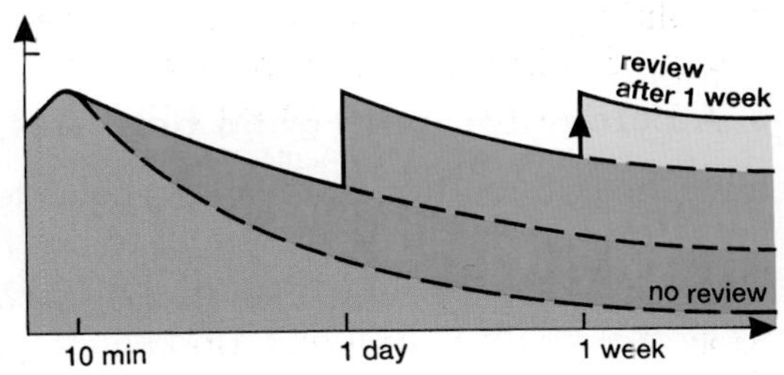

	Mon	Tues	Wed	Thur	Fri
Biology	chap 3	chap 4	p25-9		
Chemistry	p 24-9	chap 5	p67		
Physics	p36-42				
History	chap 3				

Remember: ***the most important points about revision are that it must occur often and be repeated at the right intervals.***

Examination technique

In the weeks before the examinations :

Attempt as many 'past papers' as you can so that you get used to the style of the questions and the timing of them.

Note which topics occur most often and revise them thoroughly, using the techniques explained on previous pages.

Read through the statements in the red and yellow boxes and the chapter summaries.

Just before the examinations :

Collect together the equipment you will need :

- Two pens, in case one dries up.
- At least one sharpened pencil for drawing diagrams.
- A rubber and a ruler for diagrams.
  Diagrams usually look best if they are drawn in pencil and labelled in ink.
  Coloured pencils can be useful for making part of a diagram clearer, for instance, using red for oxygenated blood and blue for deoxygenated blood or colouring chloroplasts in green
- A watch for pacing yourself during the examination. The clock in the examination room may be difficult to see.
- **A calculator (with good batteries).**

It will help if you have previously collected all the information about the length and style of the examination papers (for ***all*** your subjects) as shown below :

Date, time and room	Subject, paper number and tier	Length (hours)	Types of question : – structured ? – single word answers ? – longer answers ? – essays ?	Sections ?	Details of choice (if any)	Approximate time per page (minutes)
3rd June 9.30 Hall	Science (Double Award) Paper 1 (Biology) Foundation Tier	$1\frac{1}{2}$	Structured questions (with single-word answers and longer answers)	1	no choice	4–5 min.

In the examination room :

Read the front of the examination paper carefully. It gives you important information.

> **NATIONAL EXAMINING BOARD**
> **Science : Biology**
> Foundation Tier
> 3rd June
> 9.30 a.m.
>
> Time : 1 hour 30 minutes
>
> Answer **all** the questions.
>
> In calculations, show clearly how you work out your answer.
>
> Calculators may be used.
>
> Mark allocations are shown in the right-hand margin.

In what ways is your examination paper different from this one ?

Answering 'structured' questions :

- Read the information at the start of each question carefully. Make sure you understand what the question is about, and what you are expected to do.
- Pace yourself with a watch so you don't run out of time. If you have spare time at the end, use it wisely to check over your answers.

How much detail do you need to give ?

- The question gives you clues :
  - Give short answers to questions which start : '**State** . . .' or '**List** . . .' or '**Name** . . .'.
  - Give longer answers if you are asked to '**Explain** . . .' or '**Describe** . . .' or asked '**Why does** . . ?'.
- Look for the marks awarded for each part of the question. It is usually given in brackets, e.g. [2]. This tells you how many points the examiner is looking for in your answer.
- The number of lines of space is also a guide to how much you are expected to write.
- Always show the steps in your working out of calculations. This way, you can gain marks for the way you tackle the problem, even if your final answer is wrong.
- Try to write something for every part of each question.
- Don't explain something just because you know how to ! You only earn marks for explaining exactly what the question asks.
- Follow the instructions given in the question. If it asks for one answer, give only one answer. Sometimes you are given a list of alternatives to choose from. If you include more answers than asked for, any wrong answers will cancel out your right ones !

If your exam includes 'multiple-choice' questions :

- Read the instructions very carefully.
- If there is a separate answer sheet, mark it exactly as you are instructed, and take care to mark your answer opposite the correct question number.
- Even if the answer looks obvious, you should look at all the alternatives before making a decision.
- If you do not know the correct answer and have to guess, then you can improve your chances by first eliminating as many wrong answers as possible.
- Ensure you give an answer to every question.

▷ Key skills

Key skills are important in all jobs!

As you study Science or Biology, you will need to use some general skills along the way.
These general learning skills are very important whatever subjects you take or job you go on to do.

The Government has recognised just how important the skills are by introducing a new qualification.
It is called the **Key Skills Qualification**.
There are six key skills :

- **Communication**
- **Application of number**
- **Information Technology (IT)**
- **Working with others**
- **Problem solving**
- **Improving your own learning**

The first three of these key skills will be assessed by exams and by evidence put together in a portfolio.
You can see what you have to do to get this qualification in the criteria below.
You will probably be aiming for Level 2 at GCSE.
If you go for Level 2, you will cover the Level 1 criteria as well.

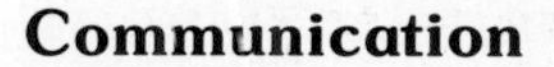

Communication

In this key skill you will be expected to :

- **Hold discussions.**
- **Give presentations.**
- **Read and summarise information.**
- **Write documents.**

You will do these as you go through your course and producing your course work will help.
Look at the criteria below :

What you must do	Evidence
Contribute to a discussion	Make clear, relevant contributions : listen and respond to what others say ; help to move the discussion forward
Give a short talk, using an image	Speak clearly ; structure your talk ; use an image to make your main points clear
Read and summarise information from two extended documents (which include at least one image)	Select and read relevant material ; identify accurately main points and lines of reasoning ; summarise information to suit your purpose
Write two different types of document (one piece of writing should be an extended document and include at least one image)	Present information in an appropriate form ; use a structure and style of writing to suit your task ; make sure your text is legible and that spelling, punctuation and grammar are accurate, so that your meaning is clear

Application of number

In this key skill you will be expected to :

- **Obtain and interpret information.**
- **Carry out calculations.**
- **Interpret and present the results of calculations.**

What you must do	Evidence
Interpret information from two different sources (including material containing a graph)	Choose how to obtain the information, selecting appropriate methods to get the results you need ; obtain the relevant information
Carry out calculations to do with : • amount and sizes • scales and proportions • handling statistics • using formulae	Carry out your calculations, clearly showing your methods and level of accuracy ; check your methods and correct any errors, and make sure that your results make sense
Interpret the results of your calculations and present your findings. You must use at least one diagram, one chart (table) and one graph	Select the best ways to present your findings ; present your findings clearly and describe your methods ; explain how the results of your calculations answer your enquiry

Information Technology

In this key skill you will be expected to :

- **Use the internet and CD ROMs to collect information.**
- **Use IT to produce documents to best effect.**

What you must do	Evidence
Search for and select information for two different purposes	Identify the information you need and where to get it ; carry out effective searches ; select information that is relevant to your enquiry
Explore and develop information, and derive new information, and derive new information, for two different purposes	Enter and bring together information using formats, such as tables, that help development ; explore information (for example, by changing information in a spread sheet model) ; develop information and derive new information (for example by modelling a process on a computer)
Present combined information for two different purposes This work must include at least one example of text, one example of images and one example of numbers	Select and use appropriate layouts for presenting combined information in a consistent way (for example by use of margins, headings, borders, font size, etc.) ; develop the presentation to suit your purpose and types of information ; make sure your work is accurate, clear and saved appropriately

Careers

Have you thought what you want to do when you leave school?
Biology can open the door to many careers.
It is often a good 'link subject' between science and arts subjets.
So if you are looking to 'keep your options open' at A-level, then Biology will fit in well with many non-science subjects.
But hopefully you will want to learn more about Biology because you enjoy it!
Here are some careers in which further study in Biology will be an advantage, if not a requirement:

agricultural biologist
animal technician
bacteriologist
biochemist
biotechnologist
botanist
brewer
Civil Service scientific officer
conservationist
dental technician
dentist
doctor
ecologist
environmental biologist
environmental health officer
farming and agriculture
farm manager
fish farming
food scientist
forensic scientist
forestry
freshwater biologist
geneticist
health scientist
horticulturalist
information scientist
journalist (science)
laboratory technician
lecturer in science
manager in industry
marine biologist
marketing
medical laboratory scientist
microbiologist
nurse
oceanographer
optician
pathologist
pharmacist
pharmacologist
physiologist
pollution controller
research biologist
soil scientist
sport scientist
teacher of science
veterinary surgeon/assistant
waste disposal scientist
water technologist
zoologist

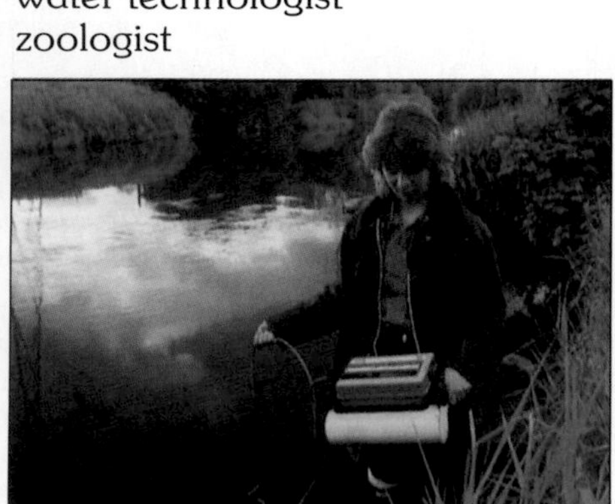
An environmental scientist testing water

A pharmacist

a vet

an arctic ecologist

a biochemist

a farmer

a marine biologist

a botanist

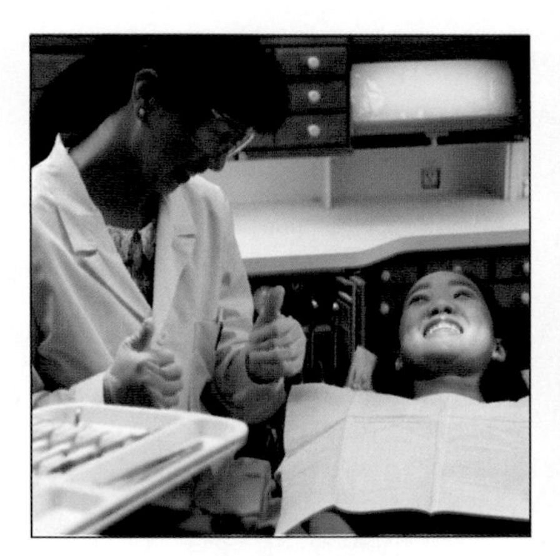

a dentist

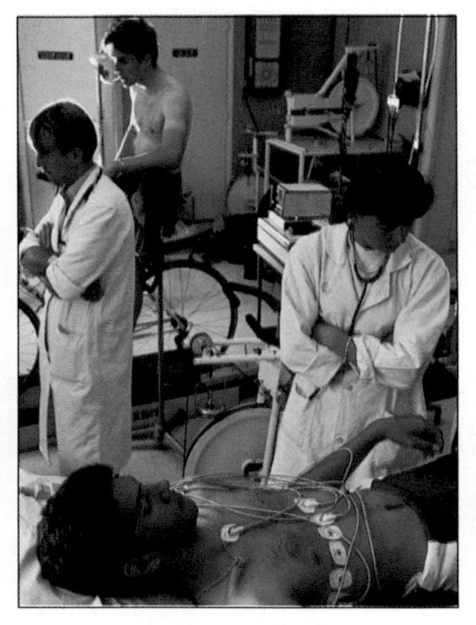

a sports scientist

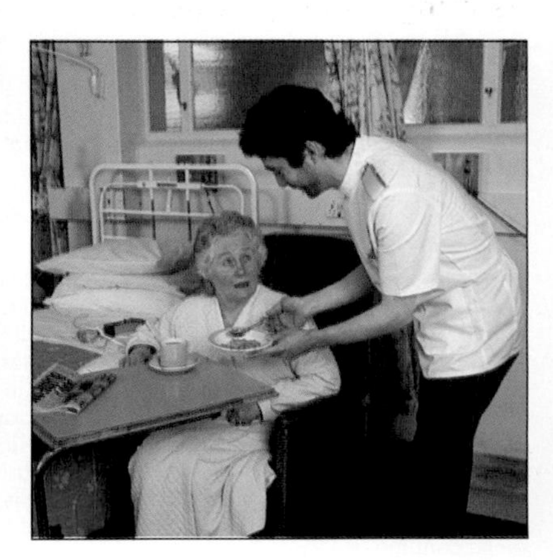

a nurse

Index

Q

R

S

T

U

V

W

X

Y

Z

Acknowledgements

I would like to thank Bob Wakefield and Margaret Bramwell for reviewing and improving the manuscript. I am particularly indebted to Bob for the many original ideas that he has selflessly given to the book and for his realism and sense of humour.

Thanks are also due to Nick Paul, Sue Adamson and Lawrie Ryan for their interest and encouragement during the writing of the manuscript.

Particular thanks to Keith Johnson for his invaluable advice and his insight into the ways in which we learn and what makes a good textbook.

Acknowledgement is made to the following Examining Bodies for permission to reprint questions from their examination papers:

AQA	Assessment and Qualifications Alliance
OCR	Oxford, Cambridge and RSA Examinations
Cam IGCSE	University of Cambridge Local Examinations Syndicate (Cambridge IGCSE Biology Paper 6 Oct/Nov 07 Q1)
Edex IGCSE	Edexcel IGCSE Examinations
EDEX	Edexcel Foundation
WJEC	Welsh Joint Education Committee
CCEA	Council for the Curriculum, Examinations and Assessment.
Website:	www.biologyforyou.co.uk

Other books by Gareth Williams

Spotlight Science 7, 8, 9 with Keith Johnson and Sue Adamson

Science: On Target with Keith Johnson and Sue Adamson

Advanced Biology for You

Top Biology Grades for You

Photo acknowledgements

Actionplus: 121B, 168B, 258T Richard Francis; **Ardea:** 286 J.P. Ferrero, 290BL J.M. Labat, 297T S. Meyers; **Art Directors & TRIP:** 352M; **Astra Zeneca:** 285B, 337B; **Bruce Coleman:** 191 Dr Frieder Sauer, 230TR, 234TR, 253T, 291BL J. Burton, 264B, 282T G. Zeisler, 269 Kim Taylor, 270B H. Lange, 283T E.B. Jurstrom, 284T J. Van de Kain, 284UM, 295T Hans Reinhard, 297LM F. Lanting; **BST (NT):** 122B Banana Stock E; **Bubbles Photolibrary:** 162T H. Robinson; **Chelsea Physic Garden:** 356A, 356B, 356C; **Collections:** 161T; **Colorsport:** 168M; **Corbis:** 152B Richard Wayman/Sygma, 299B Ashley Cooper; **Corbis (NT):** 164B V198; **Corel (NT):** 96B Corel 401, 165 Corel 164, 187B Corel 660, 230BL Corel 103, 322B C603, 328M Corel 588, 335T Corel 312, 349T Corel 765, 367B, 395BL; **Department of Health:** 166B; **Diamar (NT):** 209 D7; **Digital Vision (NT):** 4B Steven Frink, 42B DV10, 50B DV17, 186B DVJA Gerry Ellis, 231BR Michael Durham, 232BL Gerry Ellis, 258M DVAA, 273UM DVLU, 285M Karl Ammann, 324T, 329T DV15, 325T DV NASA, 334B DVWT, 334LM Jeremy Woodhouse; **Ecoscene:** 322M Quarry, 332B Amanda Grazidis, 334T John Farmer; **Fotolia:** 63T, 72B, 121T, 151B, 231BL, 233BR, 235BL, 265M, 267T, 290T, 293M, 296M, 312, 326; **Frank Lane Picture Agency:** 230BR H. Schrempp, 235BR D. Hosking, 273T H. Clarke, 290ML R. Hosking, 364TL, 364TR, 366M Frans Lanting/Minden Pictures, 366T Peter Davey, 382B Brian Turner; **Garden Matters:** 193; **Gareth Williams:** 288, 306; **Gene Cox:** 21A, 204B, 236TL, 236TR; **Getty Images:** 74M G. Mortimore, 75T Simon Bruty, 108 D. Cannon, 114B, 163B, 168T C. Mason, 135T D. Rogers, 152T Prakash Singh/Stringer/AFP, 223B M. Hewitt, 100BL J. Silverman; **Getty Stone:** 42T T. Henshaw, 84T B. Ayres, 100T Arnulf Husmo, 101BR, 116B Nick de Vore, 270M H. Grey, 316T D. Paterson, 325LM P. Tweedie, 351B M. McQueen, 395TC; **Holt Studios International:** 156, 194T, 195T, 196B, 261B, 316B; **Horticulture Research International:** 189A; **Hulton Getty:** 150T Chris Ware/Keystone; **Hypoxico Inc:** 75B; **Image State:** 101T; **iStockphoto:** 29, 43, 48B, 49T, 67T, 74B, 74T, 92, 96T, 97, 98T, 100B, 109T, 115, 116M, 116T, 119, 122T, 126B, 129, 143T, 140,144, 145B, 145T, 153T, 161M, 162M, 166T, 185T, 186T, 187T, 188T, 194B, 196T, 198, 199, 202, 222L, 222R, 223T, 228TR, 233BL, 233TL, 233TR, 224B, 224T, 228BR, 228TR, 229TL, 230TL, 231TL, 232TL, 234BR, 235TR, 237BR, 240T, 251, 258M, 264M, 264TL, 265B, 265TR, 271B, 270T, 271T, 273LM, 282B, 282LM, 282UM, 283B, 284B, 285T, 291M, 293B, 293T, 294B, 295B, 296B, 302, 309, 320, 323B, 324B, 328T, 330B, 330T, 334UM, 346M, 347M, 354B, 357B, 362T, 364M, 365M, 369M, 395ML, 395MR, 395TL, 395TR; **John Bailey:** 299T, 299M; **Martyn Chillmaid:** 16T, 16B, 17T, 19, 24, 28, 32, 34B, 35, 44, 45, 48T, 52, 53T, 62, 67B, 72T, 73T, 87B, 99T, 114T, 155T, 155B, 157T, 157B, 161B, 163T, 199T, 203B, 223M, 336, 346T, 347B, 350B, 352B, 355T, 358B, 375, 376; **Mary Evans Picture Library:** 139M, 145M, 247; **Natural History Museum:** 273B; **Natural Visions:** 78B, 216B, 216M, 216TL, 228BC, 228BL, 229BL, 229TR, 232TR, 233ML, 234BL, 237TC, 237TR, 284LM, 287B, 290MR, 296T, 297MR, 307, 333UML, 333UMR; **Nick Cobbing:** 261T, 381; **Panos Pictures:** 321 J. Hartley; **Parke Davis & Co:** 80; **PhotoDisc (NT):** 143B PD46, 188B PD19, 190 PD29, 235TL PD6, 323T PD31, 368B PD69, 369B PD38A; **Photolibrary:** 368T; **Photolibrary/Oxford Scientific Films:** 22A, 217 P. Parks, 232BR, 265TL, 265B, 274T, 274B T.C. Middleton, 283M C. Monteith, 289 Scott Camazine, 290BR R. Milkins, 292T V. & M. Gibson, 294T W. Johnson, 327M R. & J. Kemp, 327T M. Leach, 333BR Colin Milkins, 350M Peter O'Toole, 351T Manfred P. Kage, 267B, 333BL; **RBM online:** 220A; **Reuters:** 153B Eric de Castro, 253B, 259, 287T; **Rex Features:** 148 B. Bailey; **Robert Harding Picture Library:** 292B; **Sally & Richard Greenhill:** 50T; **Science Photo Library:** 6, 7, 8B, 11B, 20R, 20L, 63B, 73B, 85, 91, 98B, 110T, 110B, 181, 185B, 206BL, 206BR, 208B, 229BR, 231TR, 234TL, 236BL, 237TL, 237BL, 244B, 295M, 297B, 358T Biophoto Associates, 11T, 78T, 89 Michael Abbey, 22B, 88, 255L Dr Gopal Murti, 26 J.C. Revy, 31 Leonard Lessin, 34T James Holmes/Celltech Ltd, 59 Alain Pol, 79 Prof. P. Motta/Dept of Anatomy/University 'La Sapienza', Rome, 84B Lunagrafix, 87T 317B, 331, 394R Simon Fraser, 90 Power and Syred, 93T, 93B Jerry Mason, 99B Mark Clarke, 105 BSIP, Beranger, 109B Manfred Kage, 130 Andy Harmer, 133TL Dept of Clinical Radiology, Salisbury District Hospital, 133B Alfred Pasieka, 135B Chris Bjornberg, 139B A.B. Dowsett, 141BR Linda Stannard/UCT, 147 Adam Hart-Davis, 150B Charlotte Raymond, 154T NIBSC, 154B David Parker, 160, 183B, 354T, 355B, 362B Cordelia Molloy, 162B George Bernard, 182 John Clegg, 195B Sinclair Stammers, 197 Jerome Wexler, 199M David Thurber/Agstock, 206T, 235BC, 315, 382T Dr Jeremy Burgess, 216TR, 245, 373B Pascal Goetgheluck, 218 Rosenfeld Images Ltd, 233MR Tom Bledsoe, 236BR Alex Rakosy, Custom Medical Stock Photo, 240B CNRI, 243T Div. of Computer Research & Technology, National Institute of Health, 243B A. Barrington Brown, 244T M.I. Walker, 254 Simon Fraser/RVI, Newcastle-Upon-Tyne, 255R Omikron, 256, 353 Maximilian Stock Ltd, 257T, 395BC Philippe Plailly/Eurelios, 257B Hank Morgan, 261M. 317T Martin Bond, 266T National Library of Medicine, 291TR Art Wolfe, 291TL Andrew J. Martinez, 293B Annie Haycock, 322T Skyscan, 325B Harris Barnes Jr/Agstock USA, 327B Claude Nuridsany & Marie Perennou, 333LML John Walsh, 333LMR David Spears, 337T Vanessa Vick, 350T Dr Tony Brain, 352T Rosenfeld Images Ltd, 363 Michael Donne, 364B Darwin Dale, 365T A.J. Photo, 366B Peter Chadwick, 369T George Roos/Peter Arnold Inc., 373T Samuel Ashfield, 395BR St Bartholomews Hospital, 395MC Alexis Rosenfeld, 4T, 133TR, 133M, 139T, 149, 243M 266B, 333T; **Still Pictures:** 291BR John Newby, 335B; **StockByte (NT):** 164T SB9, 349B SB 34; **Topfoto:** 49B Collection Roger-Viollet, 126T IMW, 151T The ArenaPAL Picture Library, 329B Mark Antman, 351M The Image Works, 357T.